A History of Street Networks

from Grids to Sprawl and Beyond

A History of Street Networks

from Grids to Sprawl and Beyond

LAURENCE AURBACH

Pedshed Press
Hyattsville, Maryland

Pedshed Press
P.O. Box 8313
Hyattsville, MD 20787-8313
http://pedshedpress.com

Library of Congress Control Number: 2019919789
ISBN: 978-1-7343458-7-2

Publisher's Cataloging-In-Publication Data

Names: Aurbach, Laurence, Jr., 1963- author.
Title: A history of street networks : from grids to sprawl and beyond / Laurence Aurbach.
Description: First Pedshed Press edition. | Hyattsville, Maryland : Pedshed Press, 2020. |
    Includes bibliographical references and index.
Identifiers: ISBN 9781734345872
Subjects: LCSH: Traffic engineering--History. | Grid plans (City planning)--History. | Roads-
    -History. | Cities and towns--Growth--History. | BISAC: ARCHITECTURE / Urban
    & Land Use Planning. | TECHNOLOGY & ENGINEERING / History. | ARCHITEC-
    TURE / History / General.
Classification: LCC HE341 .A97 2020 (print) | LCC HE341 (ebook) | DDC 388.1--dc23

Visit the author's blog at http://pedshed.net

Table of Contents

INTRODUCTION 1

GLOSSARY 7

CHAPTER 1. VERTICAL TRAFFIC SEPARATION: EARLY SCHEMES 11
    Leonardo da Vinci 12
    Invention and Ferment in the 1830s–1840s 14
    Great Victorian Way 23
    Holborn Viaduct 27
    New York Elevated Railway Visions 30
    The Decades of Invention 34
    John Jacob Astor IV 36
    Technological Utopianism 37
    West Street and Chelsea Piers 41
    Chapter 1 Summary 46

CHAPTER 2. VERTICAL TRAFFIC SEPARATION: 1900s–1930s 47
    Meik and Beer's Main Avenues 47
    Visionary Illustrators 51
    William Wilgus and Grand Central Terminal 61
    Freight Subways 68
    Plan of Chicago, Michigan Avenue, and Wacker Drive 74
    Hudson River Crossing Complex 77
    Popular Hyperurbanism of the 1920s 83
    Skyscraper-Bridge Urbanism 83
    Harvey Wiley Corbett 86
    Hugh Ferriss 88
    Le Corbusier 91
    John Harriss 94
    Chapter 2 Summary 97

CHAPTER 3. HORIZONTAL TRAFFIC SEPARATION: DIVIDED ROADWAYS 99
    Early Promenades and Boulevards 100
    Etienne Cabet, *Travels in Icaria* 103
    Avenue de l'Imperatrice and Other European Avenues and Boulevards . . . 106
    Olmsted and Vaux: Central Park 109
    Olmsted and Vaux: Parkways 113
    Chapter 3 Summary 119

CHAPTER 4. HORIZONTAL TRAFFIC SEPARATION:
INSULAR ROADWAYS TO 1910S...................................... **121**
    Early History of Traffic-Restricted Streets and Districts............... 122
    Regent's Park.. 123
    London's Estates... 125
    Private Suburbs.. 127
    Olmsted's Disconnected Subdivisions................................ 131
    St. Louis's Private Places 134
    German Planning and Early Zoning................................. 138
    Charles Mulford Robinson 140
    Unwin, Letchworth, and Hampstead Garden Suburb.................. 143
    Forest Hills Gardens... 150
    Plan of Chicago 152
    Quarter Section Competition....................................... 153
    Chapter 4 Summary... 155

CHAPTER 5. HORIZONTAL TRAFFIC SEPARATION:
INSULAR ROADWAYS 1910S–1930S.................................. **157**
    German Planning 1910s-1930s and American Continuance 157
    Clarence Perry and the Neighborhood Unit......................... 173
    Radburn.. 176
    The Federal Government Steps In................................... 181
    Chapter 5 Summary... 190

CHAPTER 6. HORIZONTAL TRAFFIC SEPARATION: FAST ROADWAYS **192**
    Speed Driving and Speedways 192
    Introduction of the Motorcar 199
    Vanderbilt and the Long Island Motor Parkway...................... 201
    Bronx River Parkway 205
    Westchester County Parkways 210
    Robert Moses... 213
    Edward Bassett and Freeways 217
    Thomas MacDonald and Roosevelt's Interstates 218
    Chapter 6 Summary... 226

CHAPTER 7. BLENDING AND WINNOWING **228**
    Regional Plan of New York 228
    Paul Hoffman and Miller McClintock............................... 231
    1939 World's Fair and Futurama 245
    H. Alker Tripp.. 252
    Guidebooks of the 1940s... 255
    Chapter 7 Summary... 261

CHAPTER 8. ESTABLISHMENT OF FUNCTIONAL CLASSIFICATION **263**
    Automotive Safety Foundation...................................... 263
    Detroit and Chicago Studies....................................... 266
    National Committee on Urban Transportation 268
    Guidebooks of the 1960s... 271
    US Federal-Aid Roadways, 1968 and Afterward...................... 274
    Chapter 8 Summary... 282

CHAPTER 9. MID-TWENTIETH CENTURY TO EARLY TWENTY-FIRST 284
    Buchanan Report: *Traffic In Towns* 284
    Donald Appleyard and Cellular-Layout Ethics 287
    Neotraditionalism and New Urbanism............................. 290
    Jane Jacobs 291
    Christopher Alexander... 295
    St. Lawrence Neighborhood 295
    Léon Krier and Rob Krier 299
    New York City's Urban Design Group............................. 308
    Battery Park City.. 308
    Andrés Duany, Elizabeth Plater-Zyberk, and Seaside 312
    New Urbanism and Traffic Planning................................ 317
    British Street Design Manuals 322
    Cellularity in Neotraditionalism and New Urbanism................... 323
    Other Trends 324
    Gated Communities in Recent Decades 324
    Dedicated Rail and Bus Lanes 326
    Carfree and Car-Limited Districts.................................. 328
    Chapter 9 Summary... 330

CHAPTER 10. CONCLUSION: EVALUATING TRAFFIC SEPARATION.............. 333
    Justifications of Functional Traffic Separation 333
    Economic Effects of Congestion.................................... 337
    Traffic-Safety Effects of Roadway Layouts 339
    Questionable Assumptions 341
    Future Trends 342
    Recommendations 346

NOTES 349

IMAGE SOURCES 395

ACKNOWLEDGEMENTS 399

INDEX... 401

Introduction

Traffic has a powerful effect on our quality of life. If you live in a metropolitan area, you probably think the roadways have too much traffic at least some of the time, and perhaps all the time. Excessive traffic interferes with our ability to go where we want, when we want. It makes urban roadways ugly, noisy, and polluted, and the adjoining spaces inhospitable. The quality of urban life is also affected by speeding traffic. Speeding makes roadways more dangerous and distressful, and discourages walking and bicycling. Excessive traffic volume and velocity make communities less livable.

The problem of excessive city traffic has been with humankind for a long time. It vexed the poets and emperors of ancient Rome. It became widespread during and after the Industrial Revolution, as large urban agglomerations grew in Europe and America. It has been with us so long that it might qualify as one of life's certainties, along with death and taxes. Reckless drivers speeding in cities were also a chronic annoyance. When automobiles became common in cities, the annoyance escalated into an urgent problem.

Excessive traffic volume and velocity conflicted with livable roadways, and the conflict was fundamental. It motivated a perennial effort to invent new urban forms as solutions. City visionaries, architects, engineers, and officials consistently used one basic idea to guide that effort. The idea was *functional traffic separation.*

Functional traffic separation is the separation of different types of traffic according to their functions; that is, their roles or purposes in the transportation realm. Certain varieties of functional traffic separation have been most common in urban history. For instance, slow traffic was separated from fast traffic. Local traffic was separated from longer-distance traffic. Business traffic was separated from pleasure traffic. Walkers were separated from drivers.

A History of Street Networks is a survey history of that concept: the many visions, projects, and policies that separated city traffic in myriad ways. It is a story of far-reaching reform, as dreamers, designers, engineers, and business interests sought to remold urban environments into new and radically different patterns. And it is a story of countermovement, as critics attacked some of the most extreme types of traffic separation and sought a more moderate balance of old and new.

The idea was contentious because the consequences were substantial. Functional traffic separation was a powerful shaper of the built environment in cities. It helped determine the configuration of roadways and the layout of roadway networks. It helped determine whether an area developed as a well-connected, continuous fabric or an atomized scatter of insular pods. It affected many aspects of urban life including convenience, efficiency, prosperity, comfort, health, pollution, and safety. It had important implications for urban sustainability, long-term adaptability, and other quality-of-life issues.

The effects of traffic separation promised to be long-lasting because roadway layouts were the most permanent built elements of cities. They commonly lasted for centuries, and in some places, for millennia. Even as monarchs, empires, and nation-states rose and fell, roadway layouts endured and continued to affect the way cities functioned.

Since the early twentieth century, traffic separation has been fundamental to urban planning and engineering. It underlies the beliefs and visions that continue to shape built environments today—often without our conscious awareness. The more we can be aware of its influences, the better we can exercise self-determination and agency when imagining and building new urban places.

Book Overview

A History of Street Networks explores the origins and institutionalization of modern urban roadway configurations and networks, particularly those of suburban sprawl. The narrative covers the most important ideas and how they were modified and incorporated into new schemes. It is global in scope, but focuses on the places and periods of greatest innovation or influence: Western Europe, Britain, and America from the early nineteenth century to the present. The metropolises of Paris, London, New York, and Chicago have dominant roles in this history.

Chapter 1 is about traffic separation in the vertical dimension, and covers that history through the nineteenth century. Proposals to separate traffic vertically began to appear in earnest around the 1840s, as the Industrial Revolution reached maturity. The aim was to bring railroad speed to city streets. Advocates felt that speed was progress, and that layering rail transit and streets would improve city convenience and business activity. Toward the end of the century, a few visionaries created surprisingly precocious multilevel schemes for road vehicles.

Chapter 2 continues the vertical-separation theme through the early twentieth century. The proposals of the early 1900s responded to the accelerating pace of technological change, which included skyscrapers, automobiles, and mechanization in general. Now the advocates wanted to add automobile speed to city streets. They believed that vertically separated roadways would accelerate traffic, improve city environments, and promote prosperity. These projects and visions helped lay the foundations of urban futurism, and were sometimes inspired by a utopian urge.

Chapters 3 through 6 are about traffic separation in the horizontal dimension. Chapter 3 covers divided roadways, which have separate lanes for different traffic types. These were originally created as recreational facilities for aristocrats and nobility. Through the early twentieth century, they retained their associations with higher social status, aesthetic quality, and recreation. They were often intended to induce genteel, upper-class suburban development.

Chapters 4 and 5 are about insular roadways, which are removed from general traffic circulation. They were prompted by a complicated set of motives. Advocates wished to exclude unwanted population groups, provide protection from traffic and disruptive behavior, or ensure superior social status. By the 1930s, traffic safety had become another primary motive. Although some of the leading advocates were inspired by anarchist-socialist political movements, in the United States the concept of insular roadway layouts was ultimately enshrined by big business and big government.

Chapter 6 is about fast roadways, which originated in road racing for recreation and social status. Around World War I, new justifications for fast roadways were asserted, such as congestion reduction, economic development, and safety. Advocates wanted whole regions to be structured by higher-speed parkways and expressways, which would usher in the automobile-commuter lifestyle.

Chapter 7 covers the phase from the 1920s to 1950s when traffic-separation concepts began to be blended and condensed. Advocates proposed visions, principles, and systems that were standardized for use at regional and national scales. The era of the singular visionary designer or planner was fading, to be replaced by professional organizations, government agencies, and powerful corporate coalitions.

Chapter 8 covers the emergence in the United States of the standardized system known as functional classification. It was codified and propelled by the automobile industry and highway engineers, and their allies. After years of coordinated lobbying, it was mandated nationwide. It helped shape the roadway patterns of American sprawl, and helped establish thousands of square miles of suburbs as utterly auto-dependent environments.

Chapter 9 covers various traffic-separation trends of the mid-twentieth to early-twenty-first centuries. During that period, the status-quo development practices that resulted in total automobile dependence were challenged by countermovements that sought to create more livable built environments. Roadway layouts were a significant part of those debates. A diverse range of traffic-separation methods contended for influence, each claiming to improve quality of life. Some were compatible with each other and some were not.

Chapter 10 concludes the history by evaluating the performance of traffic-separation practices. Specifically, it compares sprawling, disconnected roadway patterns to compact, connected roadway patterns. The former were originally justified by intuition and anecdote, and have not lived up to the promises made on their behalf. Historical knowledge can help avoid mistakes of this nature.

Timeline

Traffic-separation history has a discernable shape and arc through time. It goes from separate strands of visioning and experimentation, to consolidation and triumph, to criticism and countermovement, and finally to the present situation of diverse contending practices. The structure of *A History of Street Networks* reflects that timeline.

A History of Street Networks is generally arranged chronologically, but gives priority as needed to thematic cohesiveness. The first six chapters focus on similar time

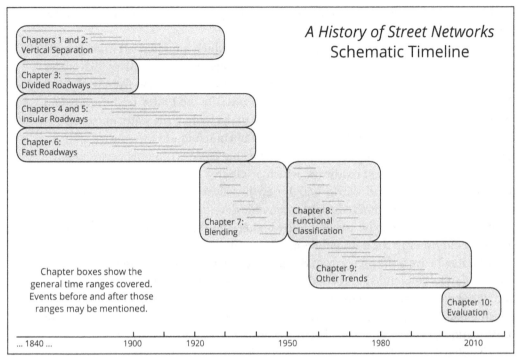

Figure 0.1: Schematic timeline of *A History of Street Networks*

periods, from the early nineteenth century to the early or mid-twentieth century. Chapters 7 and 8 follow a more linear path through the mid- and late twentieth century. Chapter 9 overlaps much of chapter 8. Indeed, all the chapters overlap in time to some degree. Within each chapter, the profiles of people, projects, and initiatives are roughly chronological, and they too overlap in time.

Thus, the book recounts the early history of traffic separation several times. Each pass adds a new perspective and builds a more complete understanding. The overall narrative is like an oil painting whose image is built up from multiple layers of paint. Some topics are briefly sketched early in the book and are treated in greater detail in later chapters.

Filtered and Omitted Topics

Traffic planning is a mature field that encompasses centuries of writing and thought; a truly comprehensive narrative could fill a set of encyclopedias. *A History of Street Networks* purposely filters and omits many aspects of that voluminous history. It is concerned with cities and suburbs. It covers only the most innovative or influential visions, built projects, individuals, and ideas. It focuses primarily on spatial forms, dimensions, and patterns.

A History of Street Networks is mainly about vehicular facilities, and gives only a small amount of attention to bicycle and pedestrian facilities. The latter had little effect on the shaping of roadway networks. Even so, the decision to omit pedestrian facilities was difficult because the histories of vehicular and pedestrian facilities are often interlinked, and one cannot fully understand the history of one without the other. The omission was necessary to keep the book to a reasonable length and centered on its main topic: the origins and institutionalization of modern roadway patterns.

Conventional bridges, tunnels, and viaducts are generally omitted from the discussions of vertical traffic separation that constitute chapters 1 and 2. Instead, those chapters focus on multilevel facilities that had the potential to engage their surroundings more fully and become active parts of a city's civic life.

The topic of geometric traffic separation is omitted. Geometric traffic separation divides traffic into different streams regardless of role or purpose. Some examples are medians, one-way streets, and channeling by means of painted lines, barriers, and traffic islands. Geometric separation may supplement functional separation, but is not a focus of this book by itself. Its influence on urban form was minor compared to the copious and comprehensive effects of functional traffic separation.

Author's Background and Aims

My interest in street networks began when I was a boy and my family moved from a suburban neighborhood to Washington, DC. A new world opened as I walked and biked the streets of DC. I learned how street networks could directly affect my independence and social life, and how street designs affected my sense of safety and civic engagement. I discovered that streets could be beautiful, comfortable, delightful spaces to be in.

In 1998 I joined the new urbanism movement, which is a reform movement in the fields of urban design, planning, and development. As a new urbanist, I advocated town and neighborhood layouts that were similar to urban places built before the 1930s—layouts that supported walking, bicycling, and transit, as well as accommodating cars. That orientation had a thorough influence on *A History of Street Networks*. It influenced the book's organization, selected topics, and highlighted themes.

Although the book is critical of the most extreme forms of traffic separation, it strives for an evenhanded treatment of the historical figures and their ideas. My hope is that readers will find *A History of Street Networks* informative and useful no matter what planning philosophy they favor.

A History of Street Networks was motivated by idealism and an urge to educate. I believe that a knowledge of traffic-separation history can help create better roadway layouts, which will improve the quality of urban life. The ultimate goal is roadway layouts, transportation infrastructure, and built environments that are more humane, enjoyable, and environmentally and socially responsible.

How can historical knowledge contribute to better roadway layouts? One, understanding the ways that roadway patterns were envisioned and instituted in the past increases awareness of similar processes operating in the present. Historical knowledge thus can provide a strategic advantage to reformers. Two, understanding past debates—the arguments for and against different types of traffic separation—helps inform participation in current debates, because many of the issues and arguments are similar. Three, the outcomes of past practices were subpar in many cases, and understanding why helps practitioners avoid similar mistakes in the present. Four, past experiments and visions may inspire the designers of future urban forms and roadway patterns.

Traffic-separation history helps demystify the physical patterns of contemporary built environments. Those patterns did not spontaneously generate from a baffling fog. They were neither accidental nor predetermined. They were the result of many dedicated people working to realize definite visions through purposeful actions, often strongly influenced by earlier visions. Our present-day built environments were, in many respects, intentional. Traffic-separation history is one key to understanding those intentions, which are embodied in every street and highway of the modern city.

Glossary

Abutter: Owner or inhabitant of a property that adjoins a roadway.

Abutter access: The ability of an abutter to move directly from a roadway to his or her property, and vice versa. The ability of all visitors, customers, employees, etc., to move similarly is included in this definition. The functional classification system refers to this concept simply as *access*.

Accessibility: The ability to reach destinations. *Regional accessibility* is the ability of all inhabitants of a region to reach destinations in the region. An example of a regional accessibility metric is the number of jobs can be reached in a given time span.

Arterial: A major roadway designed to carry large volumes of traffic at relatively high speeds. An arterial may or may not have limited access and grade separation.

Cellular layout: A pattern of land development. A network of fast, high-capacity arterials forms the boundaries of *cells*. Inside the cells, slow roadways or pedestrian facilities provide abutter access. The internal roadway layouts discourage or bar through traffic, and the number of connections between internal roadways and bordering arterials is minimized. Closely related terms that describe cells are *neighborhood unit* and *precinct*.

Cellularity: The characteristic of having a cellular layout.

Connectivity: Roadway connectivity is the directness of routes and the degree of route choice provided by roadways that connect a set of locations.

Deconcentration: To reduce the crowding of population and buildings, and increase open space.

Decentralization: To move people and construction activity away from central areas to the outskirts of a city. It is often a means of deconcentration.

Dendritic: Describes a tree-like pattern of trunk and branches. The branches successively subdivide into smaller branches, and finally terminate at the extremities.

Dendritic roadway layout: A tree-like roadway layout that typically consists of arterials, which branch into collector streets, which branch into cul-de-sacs.

Frontage: On roadways, the frontage is the space between the building facade and the vehicular way. Frontages in pedestrian-oriented areas may include sidewalks, benches, tables, kiosks, landscaping, and so on. A related term, *roadside*, refers to land immediately adjacent to vehicular ways.

Functional classification: A system that classifies roadways into a few types to guide roadway design and administration. The types are defined by mobility and access, and in the system overall, mobility and access are inversely related. Functional classification generally supports the concentration of traffic on large, fast roadways, as well as cellular layouts. See also *mobility* and *abutter access*.

Horsecar: A horse-powered mass-transit vehicle on rails; a horse streetcar. See also *omnibus*.

Hyperurbanism: A configuration of urban space in which public travelways are integrated with inhabited spaces on multiple levels. In the full-fledged form, vehicular ways or railways are stacked vertically, and each level has inhabited facades and abutter access.

Limited access: Relating to the prohibition of abutter access. On limited-access roadways, direct access to adjoining buildings and properties is prohibited.

Mobility: The term *mobility*, as used in the US functional classification system, generally refers to the combination of vehicular speed and traffic volume. Synonym: *movement*. See also *access*.

Multimodal: Relating to travel by a variety of modes, especially walking, bicycling, and mass transit.

Neotraditional: Relating to traditional forms and practices that are modified in response to contemporary needs and conditions. When applied to land development, synonyms include *traditional neighborhood development* (TND) and *new urbanism*.

Omnibus: A horse-powered mass-transit vehicle on wheels; a horse bus. See also *horsecar*.

Right of way: A strip of land that contains a travelway and is owned by a government entity.

Roadway: Any facility for travel by animal- or motor-powered passenger or freight vehicles (e.g. carriages, wagons, automobiles, and trucks). Includes all alleys, streets, avenues, boulevards, roads, highways, freeways, motorways, and so on.

Roadway configuration, roadway layout, roadway network: In common usage, these can be synonyms. In this book, each term is generally associated with scale. *Roadway configuration* refers to the design of individual roadways (e.g. width, number of lanes, and lanes dedicated to certain vehicle types or travel purposes). *Roadway layout* refers to a pattern of any size that is formed by multiple roadways. *Roadway network* refers to the roadway pattern at neighborhood scale (15–160 acres or 6–65 ha) or larger scales.

Skywalk: A pedestrian facility elevated above ground level. It may traverse streets and blocks, and public and private properties, and link various indoor spaces such as corridors, courts, concourses, atriums, and malls. Synonym: *skyway*. An individual link that crosses a street is a *skybridge*. An extensive system that covers much of a downtown or district is a *skywalk network*.

Thoroughfare: A major roadway that primarily carries through traffic. Thoroughfares are generally located in urban settings and may feature pedestrian-oriented design.

Travelway: Any facility for travel by any mode including pedestrian, horse, carriage, streetcar, bicycle, and motor vehicle. Includes footways, bikeways, and railways as well as vehicular lanes.

Tunnelwalk: A pedestrian facility that is similar to a skywalk but runs underground. An extensive system that covers much of a downtown or district is a *tunnelwalk network*.

Urban fabric: The generally continuous system of roadways, blocks, buildings, and civic spaces that constitutes the physical aspect of traditional and neotraditional urban areas.

CHAPTER 1
Vertical Traffic Separation: Early Schemes

In schemes of vertical traffic separation, infrastructure is arranged so that different traffic types run on different vertical levels. Proposals for vertical traffic separation began to appear in earnest around the 1840s, as the Industrial Revolution reached its mature phase. The visionaries who proposed those schemes were seeking new ways to move increasing numbers of people and vehicles through cities that were growing ever larger and more built-up.

The early history of vertical traffic separation was sporadic and disjointed. During the nineteenth century, the international trend was more a punctuated record than a smooth progression. Ideas and influences moved fitfully between the major cities of Continental Europe, Britain, and America. Much of the activity occurred in Britain through the 1860s, and New York City emerged as a rival later in the century.

Of all the traffic-separation methods, vertical separation inspired the most spectacular and fantastic visions. Transport in three dimension had sublime overtones; it was associated with industrial works like mines, ports, and cross-country railways, and brought a sense of industrial efficiency to urban public realms. It helped define urban rapid transit, and set the stage for urban futurism.

Hyperurbanism

The travelways of vertical-traffic-separation schemes could be elevated above surface roadways, or depressed to a level lower than surface roadways, or buried beneath surface roadways. Innumerable bridges, tunnels, and viaducts were built in cities throughout history, but only a few types had a special relevance to the civic life of urban places. The common types of grade-separated infrastructure did not have abutter access, and so did not fully engage their surroundings. Only the ones that had abutter access could fully engage the adjacent frontages and provide the social and civic functions of ordinary city streets.

Therefore, this history introduces the concept of *hyperurbanism*. In the general category of hyperurbanism, public travelways are integrated with inhabited spaces on multiple levels. In the subcategory of full-fledged hyperurbanism, several features are present.

One, roadways or railways are stacked vertically. The roadways or railways are usually congruent on the vertical axis; that is, they occupy the same space when viewed from directly above. They are usually congruent because they usually occupy the public right-of-ways of traditional corridor-type streets.

Two, direct access to abutting buildings and activities is provided on multiple levels. This differentiates hyperurbanism from other types of grade-separated infrastructure, such as conventional bridges, tunnels, and viaducts.

Three, the travelways that provide abutter access are fully public. Like ordinary streets, they function as public right-of-ways and are open to the public at all times. This differentiates hyperurbanism from other types of vertically stacked circulation facilities, such as private corridors in multistory buildings. This feature is also based on the role of urban thoroughfares throughout most of recorded history. They were fully accessible components of the public realm, where much of the city's public life occurred.

Full-fledged hyperurbanism proposals were more common in the era before motor vehicles came into widespread use. That is the era covered by this chapter.

Leonardo da Vinci

The earliest plans for multilevel urbanism were sketched in the late 1400s by the celebrated polymath Leonardo da Vinci (1452–1519). Over his entire working life, da Vinci filled a series of notebooks with drawings and notes that documented his astoundingly elegant ideas. His first notebook, known as *Manuscript B*, was created between 1487 and 1490, when he was in his mid-thirties. At the time he was serving as an engineer and painter to the Duke of Milan, Ludovico Sforza. Da Vinci explored more than four hundred topics in *Manuscript B*; at least 89 sketches were directly related to his ideas for an ideal city.[1]

His ideal city had a double-level transportation system. The upper-level streets were elevated 13 feet (4 m) above the ground. They were 44 feet (13.4 m) wide—much wider than Milan's existing streets—and gave direct access to public buildings and the *palazzi* of the wealthy. The lower-level system comprised canals open to the sky, canals under streets, and freight streets under streets. The lower level gave access to the city's storerooms and stables.

Da Vinci's system separated functions and reinforced class distinctions:

> . . . those who want to travel through the whole area by the high streets can make suitable use of them, and those who want to travel by the low ones, again the same. On the high streets no wagons or similar things should go; rather, those should be for gentlemen only. On the low ones should go the wagons and other loads for the use and convenience of the people.[2]

A primary motive of his double-level scheme was sanitation. Da Vinci was horrified by the filth, crowding, and chaos of Milan, where a conglomeration of people

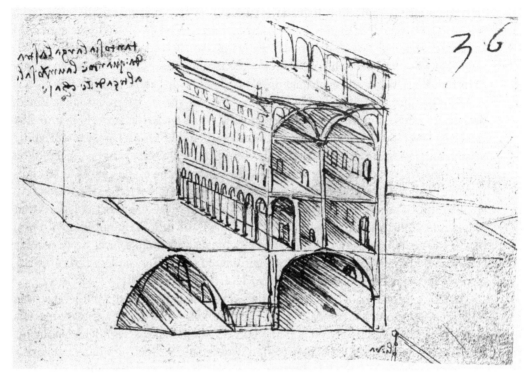

Figure 1.1: Double-level streets and building access, Leonardo da Vinci, ca. 1490.

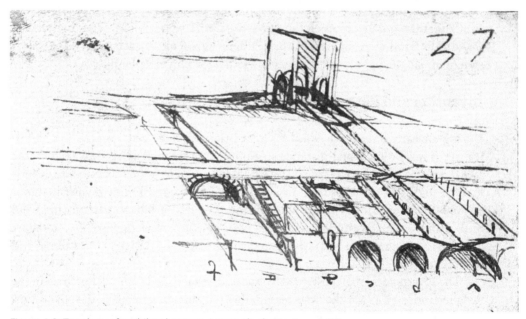

Figure 1.2: Typology of multilevel streets, Leonardo da Vinci, ca. 1490.

lived "like goats, one on top of the other, filling every place with a stench and sowing seeds of pestilence and death." He had survived the Milan plague of 1484–1485 that killed some 50,000 people, which was one-third of the city's population. He was deeply concerned with cleanliness and devised many techniques to clean the Ideal City's buildings and streets. His upper-level streets had a V-shaped profile; narrow slots cut along the centerline drained the surface and provided light to the lower level. Waste and refuse fell to the lower-level streets and from there flowed into sanitation canals. Alternatively, waste dropped directly into canals below the streets. Massimiliano et al. observed that "the real secret of the famous Ideal City is not in the beauty of its buildings, but in the civil 'machines' that kept it functional and clean."[3]

Another purpose of the double-level street system may be inferred from da Vinci's designs for houses and castles. His notebooks at times suggested a world haunted by treachery; even personal servants and houseguests might pose a threat to a sleeping aristocrat. Da Vinci designed fabulously complicated staircases that connected the living quarters of a castle to its ramparts. They allowed the castle guards to be completely separated from the mercenaries, and the mercenaries to be subdivided into small groups. The aim was to prevent betrayal and sabotage. Da Vinci explained that "when one of the mercenaries wants to be wicked, the others cannot join with him on the ramparts." One can speculate that the Ideal City's double-level street scheme served a similar purpose. By separating gentlemen from pack haulers and cart drivers, da Vinci may have hoped to reduce social friction and conflict.[4]

In the early history of functional traffic separation, advocates of multilevel streets tended to support urban centralization. Da Vinci was one of the few exceptions. His dislike of the tumultuous city led him to propose a comprehensive resettlement scheme. Overcrowded slums would be dispersed to new urban districts on Milan's outskirts.[5]

Da Vinci had a tremendous influence on art and engineering while he was alive. His fame grew after his death and his notebooks were highly prized and sought after. But they remained poorly understood for centuries. It was not until the 1870s and 1880s that the notebooks, including *Manuscript B*, were translated and published worldwide. Until then, da Vinci's urban designs were a historical curiosity, an expression of his singular genius rather than an actual force in city planning.[6]

Invention and Ferment in the 1830s–1840s

During the early nineteenth century, Great Britain was the center of the global rail-transport revolution. Long-distance steam railways reached a practical stage in the 1820s and the first intercity routes were established in the 1830s. These were experimental, high-risk ventures that pushed technology to new limits, involving major advances in tunnel and viaduct engineering. The first urban steam railways were built with the same attitude. New types of infrastructure were developed to allow 20-mph (32-kmh) trains to move through cities originally designed for walking and trotting speeds.

The Liverpool & Manchester Railway (1830) established a number of firsts in the fledgling industry. It was the first steam railway to operate scheduled, ticketed trains. It had the first viaduct built for a steam railway, the 600-foot (183-meter) Sankey Viaduct over the Sankey River Valley. And it had the first urban rail tunnel, the Wapping Tunnel, which extended 1.3 miles (2 km) underneath Liverpool. The tunnel allowed trains to access the port district and travel across the city without hindrance. The route's opening drew national attention, in part because of promotional efforts and in part because of the accidental and widely reported death of a local official who was run over by a train. Despite its sobering start, the line was instantly profitable because

Figure 1.3: Bird's-eye view of London & Greenwich Railway, 1836.

Figure 1.4: London & Greenwich Railway, demonstration homes in viaduct arches, detail. Lithograph published 1840–1841. Courtesy of Sammlung Deutscher Drucke, Goethe-Universität Frankfurt.

Liverpool and Manchester were booming at the time. Liverpool was a fast-growing global port and Manchester was the nation's manufacturing center.[7]

 The London & Greenwich Railway was built a few years later, opening in stages between 1836 and 1838. It was the first entirely elevated railway, the first elevated railway built through existing urban development, and the first railway built specifically for commuters. It ran 3.5 miles (5.6 km) from London Bridge, through London's southeastern suburbs, to its terminus in the town of Greenwich. It was elevated on 878 brick arches to avoid interference with existing streets and traffic. About 50 of the arches were rented out as warehouses, stables, workshops, and retail shops, many for short periods. The railway company even built a few demonstration homes in the arches, but abandoned that idea after a few years. The dwellings were expensive to heat, the arches leaked in the rain, and the trains passing overhead were thunderously loud. Nevertheless, the viaduct set an early precedent for city-spanning, multilevel, multi-use transportation facilities.[8]

While many early railways were popular, some had difficulty turning a profit. The London & Greenwich, for example, was not profitable until suburban growth increased the demand for suburban transportation. Businesses and travelers were slow to switch from established travel modes, and investors held back from participating until the railroads could show financial gains. The industry went through a cycle of speculative excitement and drought in the 1830s and early 1840s. Only 50 miles (80 km) of railways were authorized from 1838 to 1843.

Then Britain experienced a railway mania unlike any before. Investment funding seemed bottomless; between 1844 and 1847 Parliament authorized 9,500 miles (15,290 km) of railways. Many schemes were poorly conceived or outright fraudulent. Even so, two-thirds of the routes proposed during the boom were built within a few years; they formed the core of the nation's rail system. Fortunes were made and lost during the 1840s as the transportation system was revolutionized. Similar transformations took place in Europe and America, although at different scales and rates. The urban railway proposals of this era were made in a context of great technological and economic ferment.[9]

Fl. de Kérizouët, Paris

Fl. de Kérizouët was a French civil engineer and railroad administrator who argued during the 1840s and 1850s that Paris required a fast, efficient urban-rail system. He declared that "The most prominent industrial fact of our century is the improvement of locomotion," because it lowered the cost of goods and improved the welfare of the masses. Kérizouët admired the urban circulation improvements made by English and American cities. By comparison, Paris was "still a rudimentary engine" where congestion increased the cost of living. "If we calculate the loss of time occasioned in Paris by locomotion, we should arrive at a fabulous figure," he said. "To perfect this locomotion is to diminish the price of existence."[10]

Kérizouët first publicized his urban-rail scheme in 1845. The system he proposed for Paris ran around the perimeter of the city, connecting existing railway terminals, and extended into the city center, making an inner loop that connected the commercial port (Port de l'Arsenal) and the central market of Les Halles. The railways were entirely grade separated. In city's central areas, they became part of a multilevel arrangement that would aid freight transfers.[11]

Kérizouët had been educated at the School of Mines in St. Etienne in south-central

Fig. 4.

Figure 1.5: Kérizouët's basement-level railway with elevated walkways, detail, 1845.

France, and that perspective showed in his scheme. He proposed to drive the two-track railway through block interiors—through rear courtyards and "unproductive" gardens. The railway ran in a trench and passed under every cross street via a tunnel. The tracks were placed at the same level as shop basements and riverside docks, which allowed freight to be transferred without expensive, cumbersome cranes. The catwalks at the second level ran both parallel and perpendicular to the tracks, providing abutter access and allowing movement between buildings.

Four stories of shops, warehouse space, and apartments stood along both sides of the tracks. In addition, mixed-use buildings lined the cross streets. Kérizouët calculated that one line in the city's central district would accommodate a population of 7,000 in 200 buildings. He also suggested that the footbridges crossing above the tracks could be replaced over time by mixed-use buildings; the railway would run through their basements.[12]

Kérizouët said his concept was different from a railway, even a grade-separated urban railway. It was a "street of iron" and a "true omnibus" that had entirely different implications for urban development and business operations. Unlike a regular railway, partially completed route segments could be functional and profitable. That would allow the system to be built in increments and form new branches according to market demand.[13]

He argued that his scheme would have many benefits. It would diminish traffic congestion, provide inexpensive transportation to the poor and less-prosperous classes, promote business development, and create new housing. He said it combined innovations such as the London Docks at Wapping, London; urban railways such as the subgrade and underground portions of the Liverpool system; and the street-running railways of Baltimore and Philadelphia, where disaggregated freight was delivered with ease and speed.[14]

Kérizouët promoted his scheme over the next several years in articles, pamphlets, and plans sent to city and national officials. He explained that it presented no technical barriers; rather, "the difficulty is purely financial." But his scheme was just one of many that called for an urban rail system, and the government was already struggling to fund the emperor's program of urban renewal and street enlargement in Paris. Neither Kérizouët's scheme nor any other rail-transit system was built in central Paris during this period. However, a circumferential railway to link the outlying railroad stations, known as the Petite Ceinture (Little Belt), began construction in 1852 and was completed by 1867.[15]

James Clephan and William Curtis, London

By the mid-1840s, railway mania was in full swing in the United Kingdom and entrepreneurs were launching thousands of miles of railway across the country. The most conspicuous service gap was in London's center, where high land prices and political opposition made railway development especially risky and difficult. By 1846 all the railways that served London had plans to extend routes into the city's center. The Metropolitan Railway Commission (also known as the Royal Commission on Metropolis Railway Termini) was set up that year to examine various proposals and make recommendations that would protect the public interest.[16]

The commission discussed nineteen proposals. They encompassed a wide variety of technical approaches; the most futuristic was the London Railway by the English architect James Clephan and the engineer William Joseph Curtis. They envisioned multilevel vehicular ways with facades and abutter access on each level—in other words, an early example of hyperurbanism.[17]

Clephan was experienced in the design and construction of large buildings such as workhouses and hospitals, and often practiced in the regions to the northeast and northwest of London. He also had developed a successful niche practice catering to nobles and wealthy clients who wanted to play the role of architect. His clients would design their own mansions, and Clephan would then step in as the executant architect to handle the practical details. William Joseph Curtis was a civil engineer and inventor who had patents on steam boilers and other railroad equipment.[18]

Clephan and Curtis had begun working on their urban-rail concept around 1844–1845. It was a system of double-level streets with atmospheric trains (propelled by pressurized air) on the upper level. The upper level had two tracks, one on either side of the street, and walkways adjacent to the building facades. The designers also envisioned major trunk lines that were completely decked over to accommodate three tracks and wider footways for strolling and window shopping. But the shopkeepers they consulted with objected that the lower street would be gloomy, so that design was abandoned.[19]

The 10-mile (16-km) system would link all the regional rail terminals that encircled the city, and would carry passengers and freight. Stations would be spaced 1 mile (1.6 km) apart; trains would average 20 mph (32 kmh) and would operate on five-minute headways. The designers claimed the system would cut suburban commutes from one hour to about ten minutes. They were confident that it would "relieve the thoroughfares of a large amount of traffic, whereby the public convenience and safety will be greatly increased." And they imagined the rail tracks would be supported by

Figure 1.6: Clephan and Curtis, trunk viaduct for London Union Railway, abandoned concept, ca. 1845. Courtesy of London Metropolitan Archives, City of London.

grand colonnades, similar to those of the Palais Royal in Paris, which would create "objects of the highest architectural beauty."[20]

The commissioners vehemently disagreed and expressed their firm disapproval of Clephan and Curtis's proposal. They sniffed, "As its projectors contemplate occupying two of the bridges over the Thames, and passing through the heart of the metropolis

Figure 1.7:
Clephan and
Curtis, viaduct
for London
Union Railway,
submitted
concept,
ca. 1845.
Courtesy
of London
Metropolitan
Archives, City
of London.

in two directions in a most objectionable way, we consider this scheme altogether inadmissible."[21]

The commissioners decided to ban all railways from central London. Too many residences would be disturbed, they said, and existing buildings were too valuable to demolish. New stations in the city's center would generate too much street traffic. New rail tracks might interfere with proposed street improvements, especially in the Holborn vicinity. Also, they felt that the needs of intra-city travelers and commuters were relatively unimportant.[22]

The established railroad companies were content with the ban. They could avoid the crippling expense of central-city lines, and their competitors would be unable to make incursions. Actually, the commission itself may have been staged merely to justify the status quo. The commissioners did manage to recommend one regional-planning idea: a rail line that would encircle central London and link the peripheral terminals. Years later, that idea motivated London's first subway (1863) and was finally realized as the Circle Line (1884).[23]

John Randel, New York

An elevated railway for Manhattan was first suggested by Colonel John Stevens (1749–1838) in the late 1820s or early 1830s. Stevens was a prolific inventor who started the world's first scheduled steam-ferry service in 1811, operating between Lower Manhattan and Hoboken, New Jersey. In 1825 he built America's first steam railroad on the lawn of his Hoboken estate. In 1829 he built a aerial iron railway on his estate and advertised free rides to the local community. The gravity-powered proto-roller coaster was 400 feet long (122 m), had a drop of 30 feet (9 m), and achieved relatively blazing speeds.

For Manhattan, Stevens proposed an elevated railway that ran from the Battery to the West Village along each side of Washington Street or Greenwich Street. The tracks would be set on pillars 10–12 feet (3.0–3.7 m) above the street curb. Upon reaching Greenwich Village, they would rise to a height of 60–70 feet (18–21 m), cross the Hudson River to Hoboken, and continue on to the Morris Canal west of Newark, a total of 15 miles (24 km). The railway would carry passengers, merchandise, and goods, particularly Pennsylvania coal. Stevens also proposed an elevated railway from the Battery to the Harlem River around the same period.[24]

Aspiring inventors and engineers made similar proposals for New York City over the next several decades. One of them was John Randel Jr. (1787–1865). As a young man, Randel had been the surveyor of the 1811 Commissioner's Plan of New York, which was the map that established Manhattan's famous street grid. Later he surveyed canal and railway routes, and eventually became an engineer of new railways in the eastern United States. In 1846 Randel asked the New York Board of Aldermen for permission to build an elevated railway along Broadway. The board found that Randel's idea had promise and told him to return with a more fully developed plan.

Randel unveiled his detailed concept the following year. He invited the board, the mayor, the press, and every business proprietor on Broadway to view the 31-foot (9.4-meter) all-metal working model that he had built at a cost of $3,000. The purpose of his scheme was to relieve the blockages on Broadway and provide swift transportation that was also reliable, safe, and economical.[25]

The proposed railway ran 3 miles (4.8 km) from the southern tip of Manhattan to Union Park. The trains operated at a constant, continuous speed of 6 mph (10 kmh)—they would never stop. In order to board a train, passengers would first board a tender car. The train would snag the tender car as it passed and the two would proceed in tandem for ninety seconds, allowing passengers to step from the tender car to the train. The trains would be propelled by cables, and power would be furnished by a central steam plant.

Randel proposed elevated tracks running along both sides of Broadway, above the curbs. An upper-level promenade was optional but desirable. It would bridge the space between the tracks and building facades to create an extra level of window shopping, which would attract additional business. The promenade's floor would be made of glass ground with prismatic facets, permitting light to filter down to the lower level.[26]

Randel imagined the upper level as a social space. Second-story rooms in adjoining buildings would serve as weather-protected train stations. Where rooms were not available, upper-level pavilions on the promenade would provide space to rest and meet friends who would be riding in the same car. The scheme also included a

Figure 1.8: Randel's elevated railway with "sofa elevators" and ladies' pavilion, detail, 1848. Courtesy of New York Public Library Digital Collections.

luxury passenger elevator. Randel called the device a "sofa elevator," and depicted a large upholstered bench atop a screw-type lifting column. The sofa was covered by a quaint Victorian parasol.[27]

The proposal was rejected in December 1847 by the Board of Aldermen. Its Committee on Streets said that "should it come into use on Broadway, it would no doubt destroy the appearance of the street, as well as drive the citizens entirely from it." Furthermore, the Committee recommended that no railways of any sort be permitted on Broadway.[28]

Randel continued to promote his scheme. He petitioned the Board of Aldermen again in 1852 and showed it at New York's Crystal Palace exhibition of 1853. He defended the Elevated Railway against four or more competing proposals that he criticized as mere copies of his original idea. But despite years of promotional activity and endorsements from professional organizations and leading citizens, he could not overcome the political barriers.[29] His experience was not exceptional. Numerous entrepreneurs launched similar efforts over the following decades, yet no elevated railway was ever built along Broadway.[30]

In 1849 Randel added the "City Belt Avenue" to his repertoire of proposals. It was a 28-mile (45-km) elevated railway and promenade that would encircle Manhattan along the city's waterfronts. Randal was unsuccessful in convincing city leaders to take action on that idea too. Congestion near the wharves remained chronic, and conflicts between freight movement, ship and ferry passengers, and through and local street traffic vexed the city throughout the late nineteenth and early twentieth centuries. As a result, proposals similar to Randel's appeared repeatedly during that period.[31]

Great Victorian Way

When Joseph Paxton (1803–1865) proposed the Great Victorian Way in 1855, it was the most ambitious megastructure idea that London had seen yet. It was an 11-mile-long (18 km) building that would encircle London and extend into the city center on a spur route. The interior was structured by an atrium 108 feet high (33 m), which was lined with shops and residences to form an arcade. The structure would be framed in iron, sheathed in ceramic tile, and roofed with glass. It would have an internal paved street at ground level and eight rail lines running in the upper stories—four local and four express. The Great Victorian Way was essentially a giant arcade that housed an urban transit system and a population of full-time residents and workers.[32]

Paxton's proposal was an attempt to remedy congested and unhealthy conditions in Victorian London. The city was experiencing explosive population growth, cruelly overcrowded slums, and debilitating pollution. Between 1800 and 1855 the population of the city tripled to about three million, making London the world's largest city. Trains brought great tides of people daily. Omnibuses, carriages, coal carts, and freight wagons clashed with pedestrians. City leaders and reformers described the overfull streets as diseased, likening them to blocked blood vessels or lung tissue. The upper class was particularly aggravated by clogged streets between central London and the western suburbs, where new housing was being developed around Hyde Park and Regent's Park.[33]

To investigate these problems, Parliament formed a Select Committee to review ideas and recommend solutions. Paxton assured the committee that his proposal met the challenge posed by congestion. The Great Victorian Way would travel close to the major railway terminals that encircled London, permitting easier transfers and more efficient connections for intercity travel. Patrons could travel from one end of the system to the other in 15 minutes or less. The rail lines would be entirely grade-separated above the surface streets, and would present no barrier whatsoever to cross traffic.[34]

Paxton had great personal credibility owing to his amazing achievements, expertise, and unflagging work ethic. He was one of Britain's most celebrated horticulturalists and landscapers, a self-taught architect, and the world's leading authority on greenhouses and their construction. His "Great Stove" in Chatsworth, North Derbyshire (1840), was the world's largest greenhouse upon its completion, equal in size to train stations of the time. It had three circulation systems: a carriage road, footpaths, and an underground railway for coal deliveries. Paxton used construction techniques of his own devising to make his grandest and best-known building, the Crystal Palace in London (1851). It was the world's largest glass structure and an internationally renowned engineering marvel.

Although Paxton was no utopian, he was an inveterate optimist and believer in progress. He had started out as a garden laborer and, through a combination of luck, talent, and hard work, rose to a position of wealth and authority. He made a fortune by investing in the fledgling rail industry, served on the boards of several railway companies, and was an advisor on railway route siting and engineering issues. At the time of the commission's hearings, Paxton also was a member of Parliament, having been elected the previous December (of 1854).[35]

Paxton was supremely confident about the Great Victorian Way's profitability and

Figure 1.9: Paxton's Great Victorian Way with pneumatic trains on third level, 1855. Image © Victoria and Albert Museum, London.

ease of operation. The project's £34 million capital cost would be fully repaid by rental income. The interior temperature would be comfortable in all seasons; infirm persons would prefer to live there instead of traveling south for the winter because "it would be almost equal to going to a foreign climate." Passive solar ventilation would ensure air quality superior to most of London's (but admittedly not as good as Hyde Park's).[36]

The trains would be atmospheric, which meant they would be propelled by pressurized air. This technology, combined with double-wall building construction, would eliminate the problems of indoor smoke, noise, and vibration. The trains would be suitable for operation adjacent to businesses and dwellings. Atmospheric trains had proved unreliable in previous applications; the critical problem was the airtight seal between the train piston and the pressurized pipe. When operating outdoors, the leather seal was too stiff in cold weather and too loose in hot weather. But inside the Great Victorian Way, the temperature could be maintained at a constant moderate level for optimal sealing.

The Great Victorian Way was based on several models that lent an aura of utopian aspiration and luxurious consumption. The primary models were the Crystal Palace and its greenhouse precursors, and other experimental greenhouses. They were vectors for technological innovation in the nineteenth century. Precise climate control and heating methods originated in such greenhouses. Paxton's mass-produced components and modular construction system allowed unprecedented volumes of space to be enclosed at a rapid speed. According to the historians Kohlmaier and von Sartory, utopian thinkers of the era were fixated on glass buildings as "a symbol of the Garden of Eden on Earth." The utopians envisioned the glass building as the center of communal life, enhanced by indoor parks and verdant corridors, realizing dreams of domestic comfort.[37]

Another antecedent was shopping arcades, which first appeared in Paris in the early 1800s. They were pedestrian passages; they usually cut through city blocks, and were lined by shops on both sides and roofed by glass. They catered to the growing bourgeoisie, displaying luxury goods in safe, well-appointed surroundings that were removed from the dirt and turmoil of the streets. Shopping arcades served as social gathering spots, places of conspicuous consumption, and entertainment zones.[38]

The Great Victorian Way may have been spurred by a competing entry. Walter Mosley claimed to have been working on his Crystal Way idea since 1851, four years before the commission reviewed it. It was a megastructure 2.4 miles (3.9 km) long that ran from London's western suburbs to the center city. A glass-roofed pedestrian arcade, containing shops and dwellings, was elevated 25 feet (8 m) above street level. Railways ran 12 feet (4 m) below street level. An opening to the lower level was provided at each street crossing, and Mosley believed that those openings would provide adequate light. Nonstop atmospheric trains would run every five minutes. Mosley said his Crystal Way would relieve street congestion at Holborn Hill and on the Strand. He said it would perform better than contemporary proposals for new streets, which would merely shift congestion from one location to another.[39]

The Select Committee was not persuaded by Mosley's idea. And although the committee was enchanted by Paxton's "splendid design," the Great Victorian Way was too vast and novel to receive its full endorsement. Instead, the Select Committee recommended three major infrastructure projects.

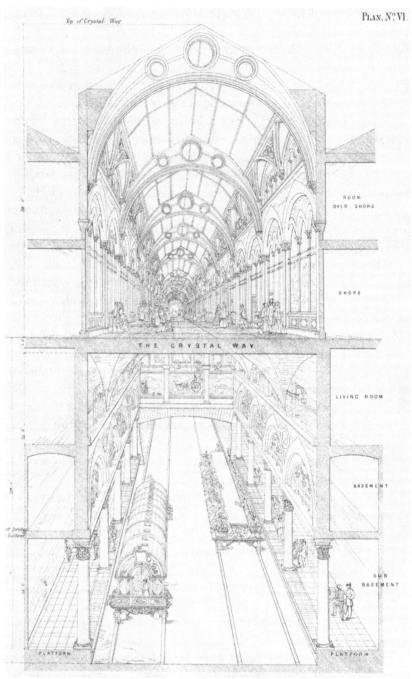

Figure 1.10: Mosley's Crystal Way, 1855. Alfred H. Gumaer book fund, Anne and Jerome Fisher Fine Arts Library, University of Pennsylvania.

One was the metropolitan sewer and Thames Embankment, designed to clean the fetid, stinking River Thames and create roadways along its banks. The second was the Metropolitan Railway, the world's first underground metro, which had already been authorized. It would run from the edge of downtown to the western suburbs and connect several railway terminals. The third was the elevation and widening of thoroughfares in the Holborn Valley area. The Select Committee's report added momentum to these projects; all three started construction within a decade.[40]

Holborn Viaduct

A new subway might speed east-west travel, but city leaders felt that the need to solve surface-street congestion remained acute. That was particularly true for the Holborn Valley, where steep slopes impeded travel between downtown and the growing residential districts to the west. The 1855 Select Committee heard several proposals for major roadway projects at that location. A city official testified about the government's avid interest:

> For 20 years there has been a great desire in the Corporation [the City of London] to carry out the large improvement so much required at Holborn Bridge; that is an improvement which is connected with the whole of the metropolis. No perfect communication with the Bank can be made from a large portion of the West End except by passing through Holborn; the Corporation have desired, beyond anything, to carry that improvement out; they have approved of the plans which have been laid before them, and are very anxious to obtain the means of doing it.[41]

The City of London began to prepare its own plans in 1860. After several failed starts, the city engineer William Haywood was chosen in 1863 to create the preliminary design. New city coal taxes were levied to generate construction funds. Several years of property claims and design misadventures ensued until finally, in 1866, Haywood was appointed as the construction manager. He completed the viaduct three years later, and the reconstruction of the surrounding streets continued through 1871. The project's total cost, including land acquisition, was £2.5 million.[42]

It entailed extensive slum clearance, wiping out 348 dwellings that housed nearly 4,200 people. Haywood described the demolished buildings as "miserable" and said the poor were much better off in new dwellings. The city spent about 1.8 percent of the viaduct's budget to build working-class housing nearby, but probably few, or none, of the displaced residents relocated there.[43]

The Holborn Viaduct was possibly the first elevated roadway built specifically to reduce traffic congestion. It was 80 feet (24 m) wide and extended 1,400 feet (420 m) through the Holborn Valley neighborhood, crossing over two streets and a rail line. The longest crossing was the Farrington Street iron bridge, which was flanked by four office buildings. Staircases inside each building allowed pedestrians to reach the upper and lower street levels. A gently curved access street, Snow Hill, allowed carriages to drive from one level to the other.

Haywood built "subways" (passages) within the viaduct that carried gas and water pipes, telegraph wires, sewer tunnels, and a pneumatic tube for package delivery. Iron rails set in the subways' floors allowed workers to move heavy materials more easily. In addition, one-to-three-story arched vaults honeycombed the space underneath the road, on both sides of the viaduct.

The under-road vaults were connected to the adjacent houses and were generally intended for coal storage. Some were lit by street-facing windows and could be used as office or retail space; others were lit by overhead glassed grates or gaslight. Some

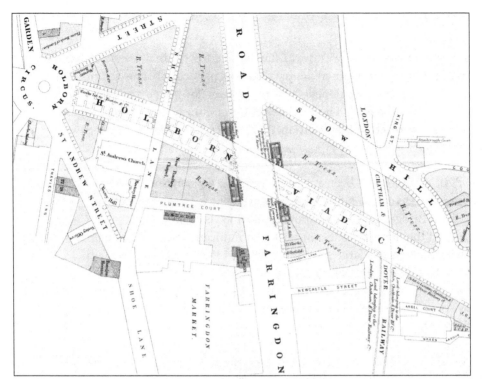

Figure 1.11: Holborn Viaduct street plan showing arrangement of bridges, stairs, and inclined streets, 1872.

Figure 1.12: Holborn Viaduct cross section, showing twin utility vaults, central access vault, and pneumatic freight tube, ca. 1872.

were connected by passages that ran along the viaduct's axis or crossed it perpendicularly, allowing them to be rented individually or in groups. Soon after the viaduct opened, a wine merchant used a block of vaults in the western end as a wine cellar; his freight wagons were able to drive through the subways to load and unload wine. Businesses operated underneath the viaduct for many decades and continue in the present day.[44]

The Holborn Viaduct, together with Blackfriars Bridge over the River Thames, was formally opened by Queen Victoria on 6 November 1869. It was an event of great fanfare and celebration, attended by huge crowds and all the pageantry the city could muster. William Haywood presented the queen with a finely crafted book about the viaduct. The viaduct's subway was open to the public for a week and was toured by thousands of citizens and dignitaries. A contemporary guide described the viaduct as "one of the greatest and most successful works ever undertaken in the city of London . . . which will ever be quoted as a notable example of the energy and public spirit of our time."[45]

Over the following decades, the viaduct continued to be a symbol of modernity in London. Often it was associated with novel technologies and advanced fields of business. The city's first (and short-lived) experiment with electric street lighting was an installation of electric arc lights on the Holborn Viaduct in 1878.

Thomas Edison chose the Holborn Viaduct and its environs for a pilot installation of his electricity generation and distribution system. It was the world's first electric system to operate at a district scale. Service to one thousand lights was inaugurated on 12 January 1882; expansions brought the number up to three thousand. The system illuminated the viaduct and nearby streets, as well as offices, residences, restaurants, a hotel, the post office and its telegraph station, and the City Temple (the first church to be lit by electricity). Edison chose the viaduct because its subway allowed easy installation of wires and access to the area's businesses and public buildings. Only the gas utilities had authority to dig up the streets; therefore Edison used the subway to bypass their "jealously guarded" monopoly.[46]

The viaduct was also one of the first streets in London

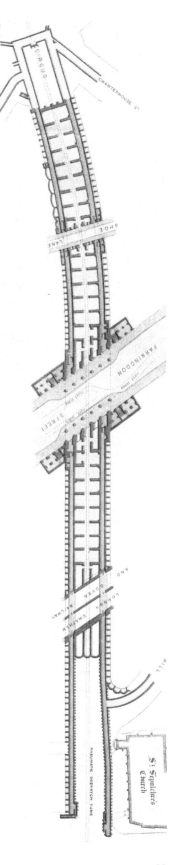

Figure 1.13: Holborn Viaduct plan of lower-level vaults, 1872.

Figure 1.14: Holborn Viaduct street view with imagined future buildings and crowds, 1867.

to be paved with smooth asphalt. In the 1880s it became a favored location for cycle showrooms. By the 1890s some cycle shops were converting to auto sales. Manufacturers of other industrial and commercial products opened their own showrooms, and the viaduct area became a sort of exhibition district. By the start of World War I, most of the major automobile and motorcycle manufacturers had sales offices on or near the viaduct.[47]

New York Elevated Railway Visions

As London moved forward with urban railway experiments, New York City suffered similar problems of clogged, dangerous, and unsanitary streets. The city was America's largest, and its island location constrained growth to one direction: north. That linear form was well suited to rail service. New Yorkers discussed elevated railways for forty years before finally building the first one.

The great interest in elevated railways was stimulated by many conditions. Surface-running steam trains were banned from most streets because of the high risk of collisions and explosions. The existing omnibuses (horse-drawn coaches) and horsecars (horse-drawn trolleys) were slow, overcrowded, uncomfortable, and often got stuck or blocked. Horses were treated barbarically and died by the hundreds in epidemics. Horse excrement that pooled on the streets was a constant source of complaint.[48]

In the 1850s and 1860s, the number of elevated-railway proposals snowballed into a major surge. Every amateur inventor in the city seemed to be dreaming of money and fame; they were possibly inspired by London's activities and the New York Crystal

Figure 1.15: Arcade Railway proposal, detail, ca. 1868. The upper street is linked to abutting facades by ramps and stairs. On the lower level, open-top local trains serve the continuous retail facades.

Palace Exhibition of 1853. But the state legislature zealously protected the incumbent horsecar and omnibus companies, and was reluctant to permit any elevated schemes. It was not until 1868 that the political logjam was broken and the first passengers began riding elevated trains in the city.[49]

Many of the proposals were focused on Broadway, the city's premier business corridor and busiest transit route. Most were focused solely on transport infrastructure, but a few had especially intriguing configurations of civic space and commercial facades.

Arcade Railway

From the 1860s through the 1890s, New York State and the City of New York set up a series of commissions to examine rapid-transit ideas and make recommendations. The first commission of 1866 examined more than 30 concepts for underground, subgrade, and elevated railways.

One of the most complete proposals was the Arcade Railway, created by a team led by the engineer Egbert L. Viele. It appeared to be modeled on Charles Pearson's Arcade Railway proposal for London, which Pearson had promoted in the 1840s and 1850s. The New York team proposed to reconstruct Broadway and other avenues as two-level arcaded streets. They would be excavated to their full width and capped by a street deck made of concrete and iron. Express and local trains would operate on the lower level. The system would span the entire length of Manhattan on two lines, one on Broadway and Ninth Avenue and the other on Fourth Avenue

The Arcade Railway was notable for its double-level travelway frontage. Continuous

Figure 1.16: Arcade Railway proposal, detail, ca. 1868, showing an alternative method of providing light—a grill set in the sidewalk. New York Public Library, Rare Book Collection, Astor, Lenox, Tilden Foundations.

promenades on the underground level gave access to shopping, manufacturing, and warehousing businesses. "Free and ready ingress and egress is afforded to the arcade at all points of the route," said Viele, "thus securing the essential condition, *Convenience*." He envisioned thousands of basement spaces abutting the lower level, each "fronting on a broad, pleasant, and sheltered sidewalk." The underground shop fronts would be "finished in the same or a corresponding style with those above" at no cost to the proprietors. Grilles and glass panels set in the surface sidewalks would provide ventilation and light to the promenades below.

The continuous underground facades and frontages allowed operation that was unique for a subway (although more common for surface transit): local trains would "stop at the will of the passengers" anywhere along the route. Express trains would stop at stations spaced 0.5 mile (0.8 km) apart.

Rent from the new retail spaces would repay the railway's construction costs within four years, and thereafter would generate income for Broadway land owners. The promoters concluded that the Arcade Railway would be "an ornament to the city ... surpassing any other street in the world for the magnificence of its design and the utility of its arrangement."[50]

The state commission endorsed subways in general as the best option, but the underground schemes were mired in political machinations for decades. Broadway business interests opposed the Arcade Railway in the belief that it would disrupt business and damage buildings. The Arcade Railway's promoters continued to campaign for its construction, steadfastly navigating a rocky road of political and legal obstacles until an 1889 court decision ruled its charter unconstitutional.[51]

Speer's Endless Traveling Sidewalk

Alfred Speer (1823–1910) was a energetic businessman and inventor who began his working life as a cabinetmaker's apprentice. He established his own furniture-making business in what is now Passiac, New Jersey, but had his sights set on greater horizons. In 1852 he patented a cylindrical piano; the amazing contraption was featured on the cover of *Scientific American* and a built version won accolades at a New York exhibition. As he peddled his inventions, he took up winemaking as a side hobby and discovered that wine was far more profitable. So he built a business that specialized in sacramental and medicinal wines. That success allowed him to spend more time on hobbies such as improving his town and inventing mechanical devices.[52]

Speer had an office in Manhattan and became absorbed in the city's urban-transit debate. In 1871 he obtained a key patent for a transit system that he called an "endless traveling sidewalk." It was an elevated continuous platform that circulated in a loop. Speer proposed to build the elongated loop on Broadway, which would provide service in both directions. Stations were spaced 660 feet (200 m) apart. Passengers climbed to the second-story level and boarded small transfer cars. Similar to John Randel's system, the transfer cars were snagged by the moving sidewalk, and passengers had a short period of time to disembark while the two moved in tandem. The moving sidewalk maintained a constant speed of around 10–15 mph (16–24 kmh).

A unique aspect of Speer's proposal was the provision of social gathering space on the moving sidewalk itself. He explained, "If you come across a friend, you do not lose any time in stopping to talk with him, for you are going along all the while with the sidewalk." Onboard, passengers would find shaded benches for seated travel, handrails to lean against while watching the passing view, or clear lanes for walking or running. ("Just imagine the spectacle of a man walking along at the rate of nineteen or twenty miles an hour!" exclaimed a promotional pamphlet.) Mixed-sex enclosed rooms provided shelter and were heated in the winter. In addition, the moving sidewalk had smoking rooms for men and drawing rooms for women. The drawing rooms

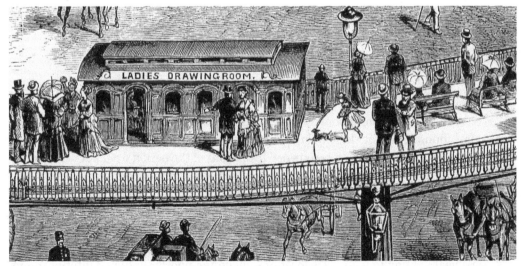

Figure 1.17: Speer's Endless Sidewalk, 1875. Detail shows the moving platform functioning as social space. Below the platform, walkers, wagons, and carriages travel on Broadway's surface.

were staffed by female attendants and were provisioned with couches, drinking water, and supplies for primping.

The moving sidewalk could furnish abutter access on the second story, which Speer believed would expand retail opportunities. He said the second story would be "as good for stores as the ground floor," and furthermore, "in the case of large establishments, the second story could be used as a retail department, while the ground floor below could be used as the wholesale department."[53]

Because the sidewalk moved continuously, passengers never waited for trains and were never delayed by stops en route. Speer claimed that the moving sidewalk was more convenient, spacious, and pleasant than competing proposals; it occupied half the space, and was cheaper to build and more profitable to operate. "It is the solution, and the only true solution, of rapid transit," he asserted. He estimated that one mile of moving sidewalk would cost $225,000 to build; in comparison, one mile of the Arcade Railway would cost $2 million to build.[54]

Speer built a large working model that was viewed by thousands of people. He found committed investors and gained political support. The state legislature, by large majorities, granted a charter for his company to construct the scheme. But the governor vetoed the bill twice, in 1873 and 1874, citing a lack of city-council control and insufficient compensation to the city.[55]

Speer was disappointed, and made pamphlets to defend the practicality of his idea. It was "no dream of an enthusiastic fancy, but the results of nineteen long years of prosaic and profound study." Still, he retained his "ardor and energy" for the concept and for transportation work in general. In 1879 he organized a company to build a 1-mile (1.6 km) moving sidewalk on Coney Island, but nothing came of it. He continued to bring moving-sidewalk schemes before various New York City rapid-transit commissions through the 1880s and 1890s.[56]

The moving-sidewalk concept inspired generations of visionaries and engineers. A moving sidewalk at the 1893 Columbian Exposition in Chicago carried nearly one million riders, and a 3.5-kilometer (2 mi.) elevated moving sidewalk at the 1900 Exposition Universelle in Paris was one of the most popular attractions. By the early 1900s—within Speer's lifetime—moving sidewalks were common in visions of future urban transportation.

The Decades of Invention

A profusion of mechanical inventions and scientific and engineering knowledge was introduced to the world between 1880 and 1900. These developments laid the technical foundations for skyscraper cities, which were city centers tightly packed with extremely tall towers. Many renowned inventions of the period were not wholly new; often the inventors adapted prior scientific breakthroughs for commercial use. Below is a brief summary of some of the transformative trends and technologies.

Electric lighting and electricity distribution. Practical electric light bulbs and electricity distribution systems were introduced from 1880 to 1882. The bulbs were safer, cheaper, easier to install, and eventually brighter than gas lighting. They brought artificial lighting to many new locations, including poorly ventilated interior rooms and underground spaces.

Electric streetcars and railroads. An electric streetcar with reliable motor technology was demonstrated by Frank Sprague in Richmond, Virginia, in 1887. Compared to steam trains or horse-drawn omnibuses, streetcars were swift, clean, quiet, and reliable. They revolutionized urban transportation and spurred a wave of suburban growth tailored to the upper middle class. In addition, electric subways and railways were introduced between 1890 and 1895. They opened new vistas of potential for multilevel travelways and multilevel urbanism.

Automobiles. Karl Benz's gasoline-powered Patent Motorwagen was first sold in Paris in 1888, marking the commercialization of the internal-combustion automobile. The nascent auto industry was established in Europe by 1895 and began to shed its daredevil image a few years later.

Skyscrapers. Skyscraper office buildings began to appear in Chicago and New York in the 1880s. Chicago's Rand McNally Building (1890), designed by Burnham and Root, was the first skyscraper to have an all-steel skeleton frame. The skeleton frame rapidly became the standard technique for skyscraper construction and enabled office buildings to shoot above 18 stories. Nearly all large cities in Europe and America responded by imposing height limits. Partly as a result, New York stood alone in the world in terms of supertall office buildings from the 1890s to the 1910s. Therefore, most hyperurbanism visions and proposals of the period were centered on New York.[57]

Electric elevators. Electric elevators helped make skyscrapers a practical reality. The Otis Brothers commercialized the electric elevator and installed the first models in 1889, in midtown Manhattan. Through the 1890s, the average speed of elevators quadrupled while operation became smoother and more efficient. In 1903 the gearless traction elevator was introduced by Otis Elevator, raising the maximum lifting height from 25–30 stories to 100 stories or more. It was installed in all the tallest skyscrapers.[58]

Germ theory. Through much of the nineteenth century, public health experts believed miasma theory and called for urban deconcentration as a cure. The scientific evidence proving germ theory became irrefutable by the late 1880s to early 1890s, and American health authorities turned their attention to technological methods of disease prevention.[59] Germ theory reduced many of their objections to urban density.[60] Some of the more enthusiastic proponents of skyscraper cities rhapsodized about the benefits for people who would live in sanitary constructs of concrete, steel, and glass, breathing the pure air high above the streets.[61] The skyscraper-city idea could not have taken hold and progressed before miasma theory was made obsolete.

Media. The mass-market scientific and technological press arose from the 1870s to 1900. It consisted of media such as dime novels, pulp magazines, highbrow magazines, and semi-professional journals. It delivered to a mass audience news about inventions and impressive technical and engineering achievements. Millennial fervor around the turn of the century boosted interest in far-future speculations, which sometimes portrayed future lifestyles and built environments as if they were inevitable. Meanwhile, new forms of fiction emerged that had technology as a major theme. In the 1890s the "marvel" genre of exploration adventures became popular, often featuring bizarre and fantastical transportation technologies invented by alien races.[62]

Popular articles and stories expressed some of the cultural ambivalence about skyscraper cities that existed at the turn of the nineteenth century. On one hand, the skyscraper agglomeration was a grand, exceptionally complex setting to showcase humankind's greatest achievements. On the other hand, it was a metaphorical focus for the myriad sins and flaws, real and imagined, of city life. New York City in nineteenth-century fiction was attacked and demolished many times over. The new media reflected and inculcated new attitudes toward technology and the built environment. It expressed both apprehension and excitement about future cities and transportation.[63]

John Jacob Astor IV

The marvel genre attracted the attention of John Jacob Astor IV (1864–1912), an heir to the Astor family fortune and one of the richest men in America. A prim, censorious man, Astor was fascinated by technology, especially transportation. He built a home laboratory and patented several inventions, including a bicycle brake and a mechanical dustblower to clean streets. The latter won a prize at the 1893 World's Fair in Chicago. In 1894 Astor published *A Journey in Other Worlds: A Romance of the Future*, a marvel novel set in the year 2000. It was a grab-bag of popular themes: astounding scientific progress and mechanical inventions, interplanetary exploration, colonialism, and Christian spiritualism. The economic system in Astor's future was little changed from the nineteenth-century status quo. He believed that scientific progress would perfect capitalism and eliminate poverty.[64]

Astor's tale made several forecasts about cities and city streets. The layout of his cities resembled Frederick Law Olmsted's ideal. Main avenues in the suburbs were 200-foot-wide (61 m) parkways that carried different modes in separate lanes, and they connected the city's many parks in a comprehensive network. Astor imagined a blend of vertical and horizontal traffic-separation strategies in the business districts. Heavy freight moved on underground electric railways, while electric cars sped as fast as 40 mph (64 kmh) on smoothly paved surface streets. The surface level was devoted to warehouses and motor vehicles—it had no inhabited spaces—and the streets had eight, ten, or more traffic lanes. The lanes were finely graduated by speed. The slowest traffic traveled in the outermost curb lane and the speed limit increased by 10 mph (16 kmh) in each lane toward the center of the street. The fastest traffic traveled in the center lane, so it was "therefore only in the wide thoroughfares that very high speed can be attained." All traffic was monitored by police, and speed limits were checked by speed cameras.[65]

Pedestrians were completely removed to the second story, where they trod on glass sidewalks:

> The ground floors in the business parts are used for large warehouses, trucks running in to load and unload. Pedestrians therefore have sidewalks level with the second story, consisting of glass floors let into aluminum frames, while all street crossings are made on bridges. Private houses have a front door opening on the sidewalk, and another on the ground level, so that ladies paying visits or leaving cards can do so in carriages. In business streets the second story is used for shops.[66]

A Journey in Other Worlds sold well in the United States, going through several editions, and was republished in Great Britain and translated into French. Although its direct influence is difficult to ascertain, similar traffic-separation ideas were promoted by engineers, architects, and other visionaries for many decades after its publication.[67]

Astor was a prominent automobile enthusiast and was said to own more cars than anyone in America (as many as eighteen). He was an early member and officer of the Automobile Club of America, which was a predecessor of the American Automobile Association. This club of wealthy automobilists was initially headquartered in the Waldorf-Astoria, the famous Manhattan hotel owned by Astor and his brother William. At its first dinner in April 1900, the club resolved to advocate a transcontinental highway system partially funded by the federal government.[68]

Astor took up that advocacy personally and urged a national system. The first phase would be a New York-San Francisco route. It would be modeled on the system in France, where "one can fly along at better than forty miles an hour in a comfortable touring car over roads that are wide, smooth and straight for many miles at a stretch, past beautiful scenery and between rows of trees." He recommended that highways skirt the edges of towns rather than pass through them, "for the right of way costs less and there is then less restriction of speed."[69]

Technological Utopianism

Americans in the late nineteenth century became increasingly fascinated with predictions, glorifications, and warnings about future lifestyles and technologies. The country's obsession with futurist literature reached a crescendo from 1888 to 1900, as seen in a genre that historians have labeled *technological utopianism*. It was a genre that proselytized for social reform (or in some cases, maintenance of the status quo) by describing the ideal society that would eventually result.

More than 160 technological-utopianism books were published in the United States; in its heyday, it was possibly the nation's most popular literary genre. Edward Bellamy's novel *Looking Backward: 2000–1887* (1888) was the preeminent work. It was one of the top sellers of the nineteenth century and launched a reform movement supported by a national magazine and 162 grassroots clubs.[70]

Social reformers of the era believed that cities were horrid environments: crowded, polluted, and unsanitary; harboring the worst extremes of wealth and poverty; breeding injustice and moral deficiency. But the technological utopians did not call for a return to rural living as some earlier reformers had. About one-third envisioned new villages, towns, or cities established in virgin areas. The other two-thirds favored the reconstruction of existing cities. Their visions ranged across a wide gamut of possible urban forms, from small compounds or village-size complexes, to a 44-story pyramid inhabited by tens of thousands of people, to a vast metropolis of towers housing the entire population of the United States.

The utopians expected that advances in transportation technology would make travel nearly instantaneous. Location would be rendered nearly irrelevant. Some writers envisioned mass ownership of fast motor vehicles that drove on exceedingly broad streets. Gleaming high-speed trains or electric airplanes would deliver city residents anywhere in a matter of minutes. City infrastructures would be completely rebuilt as multilevel streets with underground rapid transit, trains elevated on multiple levels, and underground pneumatic tubes for home deliveries. Grand, towering edifices often lined the streets of the future.[71]

Such facilities were conjured up to create an impression of unlimited abundance. Any hint of overcrowding and inconvenience was eliminated from the clean, smooth streets. For example, *The Milltillionaire* (1895) presented a fabulous multilevel scheme with blithe disregard for cost. All of the city's streets were 1,000 feet wide (305 m), including 400 feet (122 m) of landscaped borders on each side. In the center ran a 200-foot-wide (61 m), five-level Canopied Highway. It had a freight-subway level underground and two levels for electric vehicles aboveground. Above that was a pedestrian and cyclist level, "beautifully and smoothly floored with granite and marble," and enclosed by plate glass. The central 100 feet (31 m) were reserved for cyclists. On top was an open-air promenade for pedestrians and cyclists "who desire to enjoy the sunshine and magnificent prospect afforded from this altitude."[72]

The Human Drift

The most elaborate visual documentation of technological utopianism was presented by King Camp Gillette in his book *The Human Drift* (1894). At the time he wrote his book, Gillette was a moderately successful bottle-cap salesman and an inveterate yet unsuccessful inventor. He was in his late thirties, recently married, and had a young son to support. His desire to obtain material security, peace of mind, and spiritual elevation was evident in *The Human Drift*, for those were the benefits he promised to all humanity.[73]

Gillette was spurred by the same economic concerns as his fellow utopians. "We are all like hyenas in a cage," he protested. "Our system of production and distribution is radically wrong." He predicted that corporate power would become ever more concentrated and inimical to human welfare. The best solution, he felt, was a single global public-interest corporation to control the economy. All material needs would be supplied for free; work requirements would be minimal; and money, crime, greed, and other sins would disappear. A centralized and systematic living arrangement was best for efficiency, equality, and opportunity. Therefore a single city, Metropolis, would house the entire population of the United States.[74]

Existing cities were miserable, ignorant, and filthy, said Gillette. They lacked grass and flowers, and their streets were narrow and poorly paved. The city of Metropolis would be clean, orderly, beautiful—a magnificent fairyland. The 1893 World's Fair in Chicago had illustrated the idea in embryonic form.[75]

Metropolis was located in northeastern New York near Niagara Falls, and ran on hydroelectric power. It covered 1,800 square miles (4,660 sq km) and had a population of 60 million. Everyone lived in 25-story apartment towers. Within the inhabited region were 24,000 apartment towers and another 12,000 towers for education, amusement, food preparation, and shopping in the form of huge malls that dispensed free manufactured goods.[76]

Metropolis would require no excavation; all construction was above ground. The whole city was built on a continuous three-level podium. Level A, the lowest level, was for utilities. Level B was for the city's electric transit system and long-distance electric railways that went to other parts of the continent. Level C was for general travel during inclement weather—pedestrians, bicycles and electric cars moved amidst indoor

Figure 1.18: Gillette's utopian city, 1894. Each tower sits on a hexagonal superblock, surrounded by lawns and wide streets. Images on this page from Utopia Collection in Rare Books and Manuscripts, Eberly Family Special Collections Library, Penn State University Libraries.

Figure 1.19: Detail of Gillette's three underground levels. Lowest level for utilities and sewer, middle level for electric transportation, upper level for walking. Pneumatic tubes deliver food to communal dining rooms.

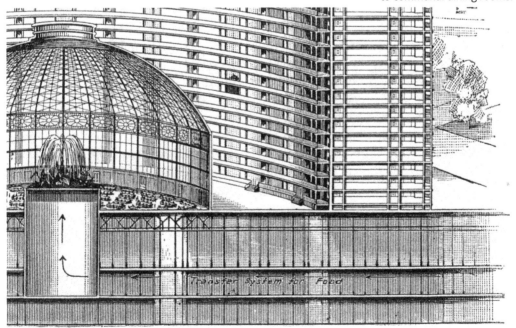

Figure 1.20: Gillette's street layout of hexagonal superblocks. The triangular traffic islands serve as skylights for the three levels below. Utopia Collection in Rare Books and Manuscripts, Eberly Family Special Collections Library, Penn State University Libraries.

flower gardens and lavishly decorated galleries. All three levels had glass ceilings to admit sunshine and would be "light as day."

Surface streets were laid on top of the podium. The surface layout was a grid of hexagonal superblocks, each about 16 acres (6 ha) in area. One tower occupied each block, and each block was edged by lawns 150 feet (46 m) wide. It was an early prototype of the "tower in the park" pattern. All streets on the surface level were 150 feet (46 m) wide and paved with spotless glass and ceramic tile. The only individual vehicles permitted in the city were electric cars and bicycles.[77]

Gillette's vision was audacious even within the body of technological utopian literature. He was one of the most avid believers in the potential of technology to create perfect societies and perfect urban environments. He went on to achieve great success in the razor-blade business, but he never gave up his belief in a global technocracy. His vision of an entire metropolis perched upon a multilevel transportation podium was emulated and reinvented by numerous visionaries, architects, and engineers over the next century.[78]

Discontinuous Leap into a Static Future

The rise and popularity of technological utopianism was spurred by economic and social upheaval in the United States. The prosperity of the Gilded Age was distributed very unequally and the economy was prone to booms and busts. The country went through recessions in the 1870s, 1880s, and 1890s that were more severe, on average, than those of the twentieth century. Labor strikes grew more frequent and more violent. The Panic of 1893, and the ensuing wave of business failures and unemployment, led many Americans to question whether the economic system could survive. Adding to the disruption, the nation's ethnic diversity was increasing rapidly because of migration and immigration. By 1890, 14.8 percent of the US population was foreign born, an all-time high. Many immigrants settled in cities, and social reformers struggled to improve their living conditions. Technological utopians believed that society was at a critical point: either the system would collapse or reforms would bring about a utopian state. A few suggested that collapse was inevitable but that utopia would rise from the ashes.[79]

Utopianism as a worldview called for an abrupt spiritual-cultural leap forward, a revolution of morality and ethics akin to (and sometimes explicitly compared to) being born again in Christ. Having achieved that monumental leap, the utopians implied that society would settle into its perfected state, fixed and unchanging for all time. They glorified progress but longed for stability.[80]

Technological utopianism ebbed after 1900, partly a victim of its own success. Bored critics complained that the genre's production was excessive and repetitive. The market was saturated with books, articles, and clubs. The movement fragmented as various factions squabbled over strategy and goals. Its reform urge was absorbed and co-opted to some extent by reformist politics, particularly the Populist Party.

In addition, the genre's alarming predictions—which were the impetus for its recommended sweeping reforms—failed to materialize. Society did not collapse. The economy returned to a state of relative prosperity. The all-encompassing visions of technological utopianism faded from popularity, to be supplanted by non-utopian reform movements that were more circumscribed. Non-utopian reformers sought "limited, piecemeal improvements in American society" rather than profound, and likely unobtainable, transformation. The historian Howard Segal described their certitude:

> The conservationists, the corporate and government reorganizers, the city and national planners, and the scientific managers and technocrats saw no need for wholesale alterations in the fabric of American society. . . . Yet these reformers were as confident as the technological utopians that their particular panaceas would gradually solve America's fundamental problems, without endangering its basic institutions and values.[81]

West Street and Chelsea Piers

West Street ran along the Hudson River, from the southern tip of Manhattan to the Chelsea District 2.5 miles (4 km) to the north. The street was an integral component of the Port of New York. By the end of the nineteenth century, the port extended up the Hudson River to 70th Street, and also to the East River and Brooklyn waterfronts. West Street was broad, busy, and lined with tightly packed ship terminals and industrial buildings. Through a remarkable convergence of geography, industrial development, and government policy the Port of New York—and West Street in particular—became a critical bottleneck in the United States' international commerce.

The city's waterfront was its business powerhouse, its gateway to the world, its reason for being. Shippers brought the raw materials that enabled the city to become a global manufacturing center, and then carried away the finished goods to national and foreign markets. Vast amounts of goods were consumed by New Yorkers themselves (the city was the second-largest in the world in 1900). Ocean liners and other passenger ships sailed to and from New York in great numbers. Freight shipments from the Midwest arrived via the Erie Canal. Interstate railways and coastal shipping lanes also converged on Manhattan. By 1900 nearly half of the nation's international commerce, both imports and exports, passed through the Port of New York.[82]

No bridges or tunnels crossed the Hudson River into Manhattan in the nineteenth century. Instead, railways to Manhattan terminated in New Jersey. The railcars had to be transferred to barges, floated across the river, and unloaded at the docks. The rail barges competed for the same riverfront dock space as the intercoastal shippers and oceangoing freighters. In addition, New Jersey commuters who traveled by train and ferry arrived at the Manhattan docks daily by the thousands.

Buildings grew denser near the riverfront and business activity grew more intensive. Manufacturing and warehouses strove to be as close as possible to the docks. Compounding the crowding, steamship companies preferred to use the piers along West Street. Even though miles of uncrowded shoreline were available in Midtown to the north, the abundance of infrastructure and support businesses near West Street was a powerful attraction. As a result, West Street was filled with horse-drawn wagons, either parked as they loaded and unloaded freight, or moving slowly as they hauled freight to and from the docks.[83]

The City of Manhattan had granted a franchise to the Hudson River Railroad in 1847 to run steam-powered freight trains on westside streets, including a stretch along West Street. Freight trains traveled on those streets for more than eighty years. Other traffic was brought to a standstill when they passed through. Collisions with pedestrians and vehicles were not uncommon and further tangled traffic. The horse-car route that ran the entire length of West Street was an additional complication.

Consequently, streets near the docks were chaotic and perpetually congested. Manhattan business interests and the public demanded solutions. The removal of freight and passenger trains from the streets of New York had been recommended for many years. In 1867 the first rapid transit commission declared that surface-running trains were "an evil which has already been endured too long, and must speedily be abated." Several proposals to solve riverfront congestion with elevated freight railways were made in the 1870s. West Street was widened in the 1880s but the congestion problems only grew worse.[84]

In 1889 the city authorized two pedestrian bridges across West Street, one at Rector Street for the Central Railroad of New Jersey and the other at Cortlandt Street for the Pennsylvania Railroad. Engineers and designers continued to develop vertical-traffic-separation ideas to solve West Street's problems.[85]

Alfred Thorp

In 1891 New York City formed yet another Rapid Transit Commission, this one charged with selecting a specific technology and designating one or more routes. It heard nineteen proposals by inventors and developers for elevated railways and subways. One was an grand multilevel scheme created by the New York architect Alfred H. Thorp (1843–1917). Trained at the Ecole des Beaux Arts in Paris, Thorpe was known as a dandy and society architect. He had designed several Manhattan skyscrapers in the 1870s and was a co-designer of the Mark Twain House in Hartford, Connecticut (1874). Possibly his most important building was a one-room study perched on a rural hilltop in upstate New York, built as a gift to Twain from his sister-in-law. The small octagonal structure, which had sweeping views of the surrounding valleys, was where Twain wrote many of his most popular books.[86]

The system Thorp proposed in 1891 would encircle Manhattan along the waterfront. A belt of reclaimed land would extend the shoreline 250 feet (76 m) outward into the Hudson and East Rivers. Along the Hudson riverfront a New West Street would be built, as well as new piers and wharves. On the newly created strip between Old and New West Streets, a multilevel transportation viaduct would adjoin midrise buildings. Elevated cross streets would connect Manhattan's inland districts to the encircling viaduct.

Thorp's scheme was possibly the first serious, city-scale, multilevel scheme with an elevated roadway. He envisioned a double-deck structure with a roadway on top, rail tracks on the middle level, and local freight transfers on the surface street. The top level would be a "splendid boulevard" for carriages, bordered on one side by "a promenade between rows of trees" and on the other by "an arcade similar to that of the Rue de Rivoli, in Paris." The middle level would carry six rapid-rail tracks in a "light, well-ventilated and cheerful" gallery. Slow, heavy freight wagons would operate on the surface level, where abundant warehouse space would be available.[87]

Thorp argued that elevated roads crisscrossing Manhattan would be superior to the existing elevated railways because they could offer business access on multiple levels. He wrote that "those stories of the buildings on a level with and opening on to the upper drive-way could easily be altered into retail shops, stores, etc., while the lower stories would still have access to the streets below for wholesale business."[88]

Thorp continued to promote his scheme and refine its details through the 1890s. He enhanced his sales pitch, stating that the scheme could clear a profit of $5 to $10 million per mile. It would eliminate freight congestion from the main arterials. The elevated boulevard could include pneumatic tubes for small freight, and the rail level would use a construction technique that "has proved almost noiseless in Berlin on the Metropolitan Elevated Railway."[89]

The wharves themselves were inefficiently organized and in notoriously bad condition. After decades of planning, and authorization in 1890 by the US Secretary of War, the city's Department of Docks began to extend lower Manhattan's shoreline, reconstruct the piers, and widen West Street. Thorp presented an altered proposal in 1898 that was possibly a response. He wanted to demolish West Street and its buildings, and install all his previous ideas in the vacated space. He added a continuous two-story structure on the river side of the street, which would link the new wharves. The structure would accommodate ferry stations, equipment sheds, storehouses, and wholesale businesses. The middle level would carry two rail lines for freight transfers to and from ships. The roof level "could be arranged as a continuous elevated park or garden, with light bridges connecting at intervals with the elevated boulevard" across

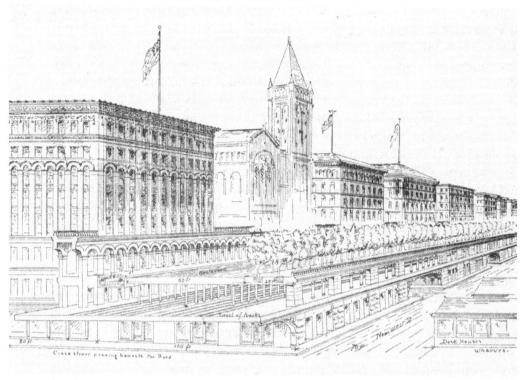

Figure 1.21: Thorp's triple-level boulevard-and-railway structure, 1891. Division of Rare and Manuscript Collections, Cornell University Library.

the street.[90]

Thorp's schemes likely influenced New York's planning over the following several years. In March 1904 the Thoroughfares Committee of the Municipal Art Society of New York (MASNY), headed by Charles R. Lamb, proposed a similar scheme. It had four levels, two for freight and two for passengers. The lowest level was an underground freight subway that carried foreign and domestic freight. Freight carts and wagons operated as usual on the surface. An electric rail system carried passengers on the second-story level. For the top, Lamb suggested an "unobstructed upper deck boulevard adapted for electric vehicles and pedestrians, which would connect with open-air recreation spaces to be placed on the flat roof of each pier shed." The *Engineering Record* noted with approval that this would furnish "a summer resting place for the overcrowded population of lower New York." Lamb also proposed that the freight subways should run across lower Manhattan. They would allow shipments to be transferred between the Hudson and East River riverfronts, and could deliver freight to building basements along the way.[91]

In 1904 Mayor George B. McClellan Jr. appointed an Improvement Commission to meld disparate proposals for civic beautification and improvement into a comprehensive plan. The commission consisted of prominent businessmen and designers including Whitney Warren, one of the architects of Grand Central Terminal. The commission consulted with the Olmsted brothers, and was influenced by Beaux-Arts planning ideals and the MASNY recommendations.[92]

The commission adapted elements of Thorp's scheme in its draft plan. Its

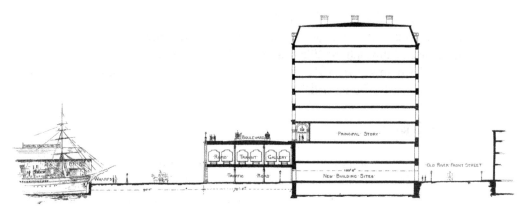

Figure 1.22: Cross section of Thorp's proposal, 1895.

illustrations showed a viaduct with a street on the upper level that connected rebuilt piers. The commission hoped to reduce congestion by elevating pedestrian and carriage traffic. Its illustrations were put on exhibit, covered by newspapers and national magazines, and published in the draft New York City plan of 1904. The elevated street was ultimately rejected by the Improvement Commission in its 1907 final plan because other bridges, tunnels, and street widenings were already being developed.[93]

The rest of the plan to rebuild Chelsea Piers survived and was designed by Whitney Warren's company with classical details, pink granite, and giant iron globes. The Chelsea Piers opened in 1910 and hosted many grand ocean liners of the time, such

Figure 1.23: Lamb's proposal for an elevated boulevard, 1904. The four-level facility occupied the waterfront and connected directly to the piers.

as the *Lusitania*, the *Olympic*, and the *Mauretania*. The *Titanic* was bound for the Chelsea Piers on its first voyage. The riverfront elevated highway concept was continually re-imagined through the 1920s, and was finally realized as the West Side Elevated Highway. The highway opened in 1930, nearly four decades after Thorp had proposed a riverfront elevated boulevard.[94]

Chapter 1 Summary

In the late 1400s, Leonardo da Vinci outlined the first comprehensive scheme for separating traffic vertically according to its function. He was approximately four centuries ahead of his time. During the nineteenth century, proposals for general and full-fledged hyperurbanism proliferated as visionaries responded to exploding urban populations, increasing congestion, and technological innovation. Many were harbingers of twentieth-century ideas, some remarkably so. Alfred Thorp's 1891 scheme was possibly the first serious proposal for a city-scale multilevel roadway system. King Camp Gillette in 1894 envisioned a metropolis built upon a multilevel, multimodal transportation podium. Although no actual hyperurban projects were built during this era, one project in London, the Holborn Viaduct, came close and was highly visible on the national stage.

Through most of the nineteenth century, elevated railways predominated in hyperurban proposals. Those proposals combined the convenience and bustle of railroad speed with the social and civic functions of ordinary streets. By the 1890s, multilevel roadways began to appear in hyperurban proposals. In some schemes, visionaries imagined fast, clean electric automobiles on the roadways. Other schemes were intended as congestion solutions rather than futuristic visions, and depicted elevated roadways occupied by horse-drawn carriages.

Da Vinci was one of the few who stated outright that class stratification was a goal of vertical traffic separation. But most schemes put freight traffic operated by the working class on the lowest level, and several put recreational traffic for the leisure class on the topmost level. Many schemes created noticeably different environments on different levels: the bottom levels were often dark, poorly ventilated, and utilitarian in character, while the top levels had fresh air and sunlight, and often had landscaping and fine views.

Some common themes appeared when justifications were offered for vertical traffic separation. Increased speed and efficiency of travel were the most frequently promised benefits. In the 1840s, Kérizouët linked those qualities to a lower cost of living, increased business activity, and greater prosperity. But most visionaries assumed that rapid urban travel was good in and of itself, and felt little need to explain its general economic benefits. Other reasons commonly given for hyperurban and multilevel schemes included convenience, congestion reduction, physical order, civic pride, and stimulation of business in adjoining spaces.

CHAPTER 2
Vertical Traffic Separation: 1900s–1930s

The trend of multilevel and hyperurban traffic-separation schemes became more continuous and internationally interrelated in the early twentieth century. As international communication and travel grew faster and easier, ideas and schemes were circulated, modified, and recirculated. The practical effects of new technologies—especially mechanized transport—pervaded every aspect of urban culture. It was a time of new organizations, grandiose imaginations, and bold experiments.

The trend was advanced by a variety of groups and movements. The cultural phenomenon of millennialism celebrated the onset of the twentieth century and the unquestioned progress that would bring humankind to a better state by the year 2000. The powerful influences of visionary architects, artists, and engineers were supported by a growing public appetite for futuristic visions. In New York City and Chicago, large-scale transportation projects incorporated some of those futuristic ideas.

New York City was the global center of multilevel transportation schemes and hyperurban visions during this period. It was the world's largest and most intensely built-up city, wealthy and ambitious, and until the late 1920s it had more automobiles than any other city. But Europe and Britain also made notable contributions to the international discourse and took the lead in at least one case.[1]

Meik and Beer's Main Avenues

Sir John Wolfe Barry was one of Britain's leading engineers and famously known as the designer of London's Tower Bridge (1886–1894). In 1898 he addressed the Royal Society of Arts to argue for a new system of high-speed thoroughfares in London. The city needed to think about its streets more systematically, in "a whole and large-minded way," because street traffic was "one of the pressing matters of our time." Trends like suburban growth and commuting meant that congestion was bound to increase. He argued that congestion cost Londoners time and money, and increased the number of crash deaths and injuries.[2]

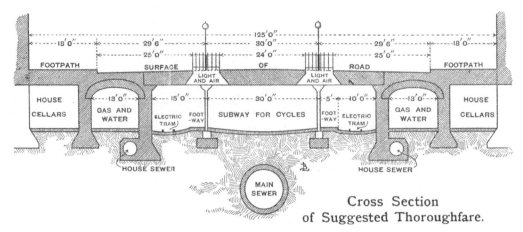

Figure 2.1: Barry, underground bicycle thoroughfare, 1898.

Fast and cheap transportation was vital to London's welfare, he asserted, and the city needed to spend more on streets. Private spending on trains and trams was an order of magnitude larger than public spending on new streets and street widenings. The Holborn Viaduct remained by far the city's largest street-project expenditure. The Holborn Viaduct was "very fine and creditable," but it was a local improvement that only shifted congestion to other spots. Barry repeatedly praised William Haywood's civil works and traffic analyses, saying he was pleased that Haywood's views "entirely coincide with mine."[3]

In the width of its streets, London suffered from a "fatal parsimony." Narrow streets restricted air circulation and were unable to accommodate electric trams. Bicycling was a practical impossibility because the streets were too crowded and dangerous. Bicycles were becoming almost as necessary as a pair of boots, said Barry, and he predicted that the existing bad conditions would soon be seen as absurd.[4]

Barry proposed a system of major thoroughfares traversing London. One ran east-west and another two or three ran north-south; each was 4–5 miles (6.4–8 km) in length. The thoroughfares were approximately 120 feet wide (36 m) and had fully grade-separated, exclusive lanes for both bicycles and electric trams. Barry sketched a two-level street with an underground bicycle road flanked by tram lines. Bicycle parking garages could be provided on the underground level. Elsewhere in the city, major streets would undergo a program of widening, and major intersections would be grade separated to relieve confusion and congestion.

Costs would be high, but the benefits would be multifold. The city would be more convenient and attractive, the stress of life would be lightened, the savings of time would be enormous, and the working class would be able to move to the suburbs and thus be happier.[5]

A year later, Barry observed that his lecture had generated "many notices and criticisms." His scheme was called "utopian," its costs "unwarrantable and extravagant." In response, he strengthened his funding argument and made detailed estimates of congestion costs, which he claimed would justify increased spending on street construction.[6]

Barry's lectures added to the general clamor for traffic improvement. When the Royal Commission on London Traffic was formed in 1903, Barry was appointed to the commission and presided over its advisory board, which evaluated proposals and recommended solutions. Barry's own scheme was a mere outline, and he had said someone else better qualified should make a more systematic proposal. That work was taken up by the team of Charles Sheffield Meik, a harbor engineer, and Walter Beer, a street-tram engineer. They refined and detailed the scheme as a formal submission to the commission.[7]

Meik and Beer proposed two "Main Avenues" traversing London, one east-west, the other north-south, both 24 miles (39 km) long. The centrally located portions, comprising some 31 miles (50 km), were double-decked to carry high-speed traffic. Lesser "first-class roads" branched from those Main Avenues, bringing the total extent to 94 miles (151 km). The system would serve 162 square miles (420 sq km) of the London region and would put 5.2 million people within a 45-minute commuting range of the city center.[8]

When Barry had proposed an underground bicycle roadway, bicycling was in its heyday and bicycles typically were the fastest vehicles on the streets. Motor vehicles were absent from his scheme; fewer than 1,500 motor vehicles existed in Britain at the time. In contrast, when Meik and Beer made their proposal five years later, motor-vehicle ownership was booming. Some 51,000 motor vehicles were registered in Britain in 1904 and 70,000 the following year. Britain had 18 percent fewer motor vehicles than the United States, but having half the population, Britain had 60 percent more motor vehicles per capita. Meik and Beer's scheme ignored bicycles and gave priority to fast motor vehicles. It was perhaps the first serious proposal for exclusive motor-vehicle lanes on grade-separated urban thoroughfares.[9]

Meik and Beer's scheme was complex. Their avenues would accommodate six modes of traffic plus utilities. They developed several different cross sections that were keyed to different urban and suburban surroundings. In the densest areas where intersections were closely spaced, motor vehicles ran in dedicated lanes on the upper level. In less-dense central areas, motor vehicles ran in dedicated lanes on the lower level, rising to the upper level only to cross intersections. The upper level had additional lanes for medium-speed vehicles (such as horse-drawn buses, cabs, and carriages) and the lower level had additional lanes for slow, heavy vehicles. The arrangement of train and tram tracks varied to accommodate the motor-vehicle lanes. In outer suburban areas, all traffic ran on the ground level, including motor vehicles in their exclusive lanes.[10]

The exclusive lanes would allow motor vehicles to "make use of their available high speed" and avoid the 30–60 minute congestion delays that were common in central London. They would improve safety, protect pedestrians, and have high commercial value. Meik and Beer were adamant about the lanes' necessity, stating that "the great importance of combining a special motor road with any new main thoroughfare can hardly be too strongly urged."[11]

The upper deck would be the main level for abutting buildings, where all shop facades and residential entrances would be located. Pedestrians, seeking "the most cheerful road," would walk on the upper level generally, but might use the lower level during rain storms. The lower level would be the basement level of abutting buildings, where freight vehicles could access shop storage, warehouses, and residential cellars. Thus, freight and waste collection would not interfere with traffic or degrade the avenue above. Both levels would be policed.[12]

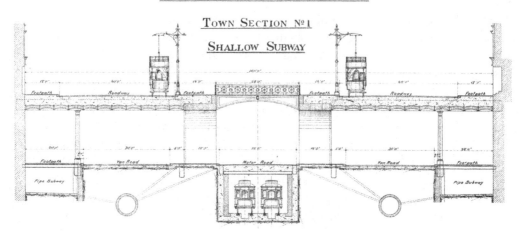

Figure 2.2: Meik and Beer's main avenue, cross section, 1905. Exclusive motor lanes on lower level; subway underneath.

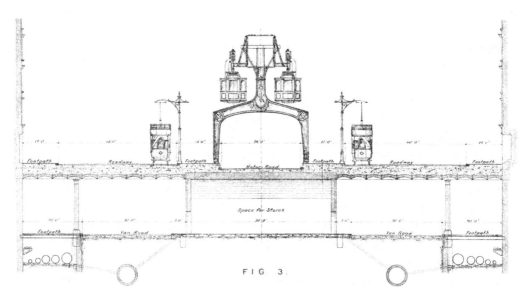

Figure 2.3: Meik and Beer's main avenue, cross section, 1905. Exclusive motor lanes on upper level; storage or shops below. Suspended railway was suitable for areas with a high water table.

The elevated avenues would have a character and effect on surrounding communities just like that of the Holborn Viaduct, said the authors. The property values of the abutting buildings would increase, and that could help fund the scheme. Construction of the Main Avenues would clear out "insanitary" and overcrowded areas and poor-quality properties wherever possible. A large number of working-class households would be displaced and would relocate to the suburbs. Meik and Beer imagined new high-value shopping corridors in the city's center and new working-class residential suburbs at the city's edges.[13]

One critic of the scheme pointed out that functionally divided roads were incapable of accommodating a short-term surge of any particular type of traffic, while in contrast, all-purpose unspecialized lanes were flexible. Another more favorable commenter said, "The scheme of the authors is Napoleonic, and would have gladdened the heart of Baron Haussmann himself . . . I wish the general scheme, heroic as it is, all possible success."[14]

It was not to be. The Commission on London Traffic endorsed a similar scheme of two Main Avenues traversing the city, but without exclusive motor-vehicle lanes or elevated portions. In 1908 two bills were submitted to Parliament for limited access, grade separated, exclusive motor-vehicle roadways in the western suburbs of London, roughly along the path of the present-day M4 motorway. Neither passed out of committee. Other major-arterial plans were put forward, but their high cost and the city's fragmented political structure hindered any action. Instead, the city made street trams the focus of its transportation strategy, and from 1905 to 1914 expanded its tram-track mileage by about 50 percent.[15]

Visionary Illustrators

The popular conception of US cities was undergoing a revolution by 1900. The ferocious pace of technological progress and the wide dissemination of grand utopian schemes altered common ideas about future cities, their form and function, and the experience of living in them. The setting for visual depictions shifted from the horse-and steam-powered 2–6 story city to the electrified, motorized 20–50 story city. The imagining of vertically stacked urban transportation was in full flower.

Many of the most powerful, impressive drawings of this era were created by popular illustrators rather than engineers or architects. Activity was intense in New York City, where newspapers and magazines regularly featured artists who specialized in technology-related illustration. Three artists were especially prolific and influential in the field of city and streetscape visualization: Louis Biedermann, C. McKnight Smith, and Harry M. Pettit.

Louis Biedermann

Louis Biedermann (1874–1957) was born in Brooklyn and at age 13 began working as an apprentice artist at *Leslie's Weekly*. He worked for Joseph Pulitzer's *The World* newspaper for 32 years, and was the art director for King Features Syndicate from 1922 to 1940. Like other news illustrators of the time, Biedermann executed rapid drawings of breaking stories such as court trials and ship disasters. He was known for his draftsmanship and imagination, and was nicknamed "the bird's eye man" for the detail in his aerial views. As his career progressed, he became more devoted to comic and fantastic themes.[16]

In December 1900, Biedermann executed a double-page spread for *The World's* special supplement in honor of the new century. *The World* was one of the most popular newspapers in New York City and the special supplement was sure to draw extra attention. His drawing was a spectacular panorama of Manhattan in 1999, its buildings grown to elephantine proportions, each covering many city blocks. Skybridges at multiple levels proliferated throughout the city, and large blimp transports floated across the sky.

A detailed inset panel contrasted Madison Square in 1900 with the Madison

THE MADISON SQUARE OF A CENTURY HENCE — 1999.

Figure 2.4: Biedermann's vision of Madison Square in 1999 (1900). Over the next several decades, hundreds of future-city illustrations used a similar perspective.

Square of 1999. Bulky skyscrapers crowded the streetscape, connected by a profusion of skybridges at many levels. At the base of the buildings, multilevel arcades or stepped terraces tripled the amount of pedestrian frontage. The surface streets had a mix of pedestrian, motorcar, and streetcar traffic, but no horses. Automobile congestion seemed not to be a concern in the future world of 1999. Finally, a cutaway showed an expansive subway concourse below the surface.

The drawing was a prototype of many future-city visions that appeared over the following thirty years. The medium-height perspective, combined with the below-surface

Figure 2.5: Biedermann's fanciful vision of railways and highways snaking over rooftops like vast roller coasters, 1916. Reproduced in *Famous Fantastic Mysteries*, May-June 1940. Image copyright © Steeger Properties, LLC. All rights reserved.

cutaway and cross-section, revealed multiple transportation levels in a clear, encompassing manner. Despite its quasi-comic style, the drawing was accompanied by endorsements from city leaders. Andrew H. Green, identified as the "father of Greater New York," said the drawing gave "a conservative idea of how the city will look," and H. H. Vreeland, president of the Metropolitan Traction Company, said that "while prophetic, it is based on reasonable imagination."[17]

Biedermann was one of the few illustrators of the early twentieth century who easily crossed the stylistic boundary between comic-fantasy drawing and sober rendering. Those styles tended to represent different attitudes toward future cities. Comic styles were associated with satires of overdevelopment and daredevil transportation schemes; sober styles with serious forecasts. Biedermann's 1916 aerial view of a future transportation network was closer to the comic end of the spectrum. It showed railway and motor-vehicle bridges and viaducts snaking through and over a city of towers in an impossibly complicated Piranesian knotwork.[18]

In 1921 Biedermann illustrated John A. Harriss's elevated-street proposal for *Popular Science* magazine (figure 2.39). The image was more like a serious architectural rendering and seemed to use realistic dimensions and other details. The next year, Biedermann depicted an urban elevated highway for an article in *Collier's* magazine by Charles Clifton, president of the National Automobile Chamber of Commerce. Clifton predicted that cities would inevitably resort to "complete two-level streets" in response to congestion. Beidermann's visualization was the most accurate yet in terms

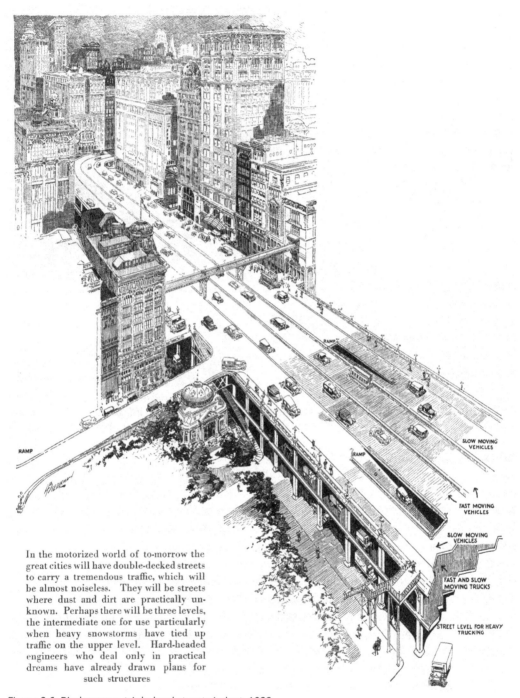

In the motorized world of to-morrow the great cities will have double-decked streets to carry a tremendous traffic, which will be almost noiseless. They will be streets where dust and dirt are practically unknown. Perhaps there will be three levels, the intermediate one for use particularly when heavy snowstorms have tied up traffic on the upper level. Hard-headed engineers who deal only in practical dreams have already drawn plans for such structures

SLOW MOVING VEHICLES

FAST MOVING VEHICLES

SLOW MOVING VEHICLES

FAST AND SLOW MOVING TRUCKS

STREET LEVEL FOR HEAVY TRUCKING

RAMP

RAMP

RAMP

Figure 2.6: Biedermann, triple-level street viaduct, 1922.

of forecasting actual appearance; his boxy, utilitarian structure formed three levels and the effect of shading was not avoided. The surface level was for heavy trucks, the second level carried fast and slow trucks in separate lanes, and the top level carried fast and slow general traffic in separate lanes. Notably, the top level had broad sidewalks and pedestrian-oriented building facades. Those features would soon disappear from elevated-roadway portrayals as the concept of limited access became prevalent.[19]

C. McKnight Smith

Charles McKnight Smith (1865-1933) was born and lived in the New Jersey suburbs of New York City. In the 1880s he began working for *The Daily Graphic*, which was the first American newspaper to have daily illustrations. In the 1890s he specialized in fine-art paintings of ships and boats and became widely known as a naval artist. When he started working for *Scientific American* in 1894, his signed paintings graced the magazine's front covers almost immediately. Smith had an impressive talent for melding intricate detail and a sense of great solidity and mass. His paintings were serene, polished, and remarkably comprehensible.[20]

Smith gradually learned the house style at *Scientific American*. The magazine's artists often tried to convey a feeling of awe through techniques like complex cutaways, deep perspectives, and surreal juxtapositions. By 1900 Smith was illustrating marine structures in addition to ships. Meanwhile, the magazine covered the construction of the Williamsburg Bridge over the East River and New York's first subway line. The stories and images about the city's fabulous civic works proved popular, and soon Smith was

Figure 2.7: Traffic separation on the Williamsburg Bridge by McKnight Smith, 1903.

Figure 2.8: Stacked travelways at Sixth Avenue by McKnight Smith, 1906.

drawing multilevel bridge decks, multilevel streets, and other urban infrastructure. He illustrated existing projects at first; by 1905 he was illustrating speculative ideas too. From 1902 to 1907 Smith was possibly the most prolific mass-market illustrator of advanced urban transportation concepts.

Several of his cover images were especially notable and influential. In 1903 he drew the multilevel approach to the Williamsburg Bridge. Its carrying capacity, which was greater than any other bridge in the world, was provided by five types of travelways on three levels. In 1906 he drew the intersection of Sixth Avenue and 32nd Street in Manhattan, where five railways were stacked vertically below and above the surface. The stack was topped by a pedestrian footbridge on a sixth level. A modified version of the image was published by Werner Hegemann in his 1913 book *Der Städtebau*, which in turn was studied by Le Corbusier and reprinted in his 1925 book *Urbanisme*. In 1907 Smith illustrated a speculative proposal for a three-level street that included an underground truck level with access to abutting shops and warehouses. Although the idea dated back to Leonardo da Vinci, this design was a response to the congestion caused by 20-story buildings and their freight deliveries. In 1905 Smith drew a cross

Figure 2.9: Multilevel street with underground freight level by McKnight Smith, 1907.

section of a Cunard ocean liner, and in 1909 a similar cross section of a White Star ocean liner. Le Corbusier presented a revised version of those drawings in his 1935 book *La ville radieuse*, suggesting that the "floating apartment house" was a model for vertically stacked cities.[21]

After 1908 Smith shifted back to drawing ships primarily, and after the early 1910s he spent more time on paintings commissioned by boat owners and shipbuilding companies. Although his work was exhibited at several world's fairs and was widely reproduced in textbooks and international magazines, he remained obscure. Today he is virtually unknown in the history of commercial art.

Harry M. Pettit

Harry McEwen Pettit (1867–1941) was born in Rock Island, Illinois, and began his career as a staff artist for his hometown newspaper. He moved to New York City around 1890 and, after a sojourn as an interior designer, became a successful commercial artist. Pettit specialized in architectural paintings and was published in a wide variety of

Figure 2.10: Elevated roadway network along waterfront and cross streets by Pettit, 1905.

newspapers and magazines. Although his brushwork could be somewhat loose and casual, his compositions were exceedingly detailed and accurate.[22]

In 1905 Pettit made a double-page spread for *Harper's Weekly* that illustrated elements of the 1904 draft New York City plan. The spread presented several views of elevated and multilevel streets, including a network of elevated roadways over West Street and adjacent streets. It also showed a redeveloped Hudson River frontage along Riverside Drive (figure 6.11).[23]

The importance of this era's popular illustrations was never acknowledged by contemporary architects, engineers, or officials. Yet the illustrations likely influenced a generation of city builders. For instance, Robert Moses was a high school student when Pettit's Riverside Drive vision was published. A decade later, Moses described his vision of a future Hudson riverfront in terms that closely matched Pettit's painting. In the 1930s Moses built the Henry Hudson Parkway with features similar to Pettit's painting, and even included a rotunda feature as Pettit had. Apparently the illustrator's minor amusement became an administrator's conceit.[24]

One of Pettit's jobs during the 1900s was contributing illustrator for Moses King's series of New York City guidebooks. He illustrated existing buildings for several years; then in 1908, he painted a "Cosmopolis of the Future" that was crowded with towers

Figure 2.11:
"King's Dream"
by Pettit, 1908.

and lumbering blimps. The company was so enamored with Pettit's illustration that it dressed up the image as an alternate cover and titled it "King's Dream of New York." In terms of transportation facilities, it duplicated Biedermann's 1900 vision and added elevated, double-deck, bullet-shaped trains. Automobiles and streetcars shared the surface-street space; the surface streets were busy but not gridlocked.[25]

In 1910 the *New York Tribune* presented a future-street concept by a mechanical engineer named Henry Suplee. By 1935, said Suplee, the streets of Manhattan's business section would have traffic divided on multiple levels. Freight and passenger subways would move below ground, ordinary vehicles on the surface, and pedestrians and

Figure 2.12: Five-level street, *Scientific American* cover, 1913. Most likely by Harry M. Pettit.

moving sidewalks on elevated levels. The automobile was too valuable to be checked by speed limits, so all driving restrictions would be removed and "if a man walked at the street level it would be at his own risk." The concept's full-page illustration was most likely made by Pettit. It was a compelling perspective-and-cutaway view of a street with five main levels, and skybridges and rooftop airports above. A modified version of the image appeared on the cover of *Scientific American* in 1913. The main alteration in the later version was to jam the surface street with swarms of vehicles, probably a reflection of Manhattan's rapidly swelling traffic streams.[26]

Other Pettit paintings that appeared in *Scientific American* during the early 1910s depicted extremely complicated multilevel transportation arrangements, such as Grand Central Terminal's many tunnels and passageways. His images fired the imaginations of contemporary architects. (The most obvious example was Harvey Wiley Corbett, who in 1925 proposed an updated version of the five-story street.) Reproductions and revisions of Pettit's five-story-street and Grand Central Terminal images traveled swiftly across the Atlantic and were reprinted in European magazines. The images had an immediate impact on young radical designers—for instance, the Italian Futurists Antonio Sant'Elia and Mario Chiattone—and were studied by proto-modernist architects across Europe.[27]

Later in his career, Pettit devoted more attention to works commissioned by business and industrial concerns, educational institutions, and civic organizations. He created large-format bird's-eye views of factories, railyards, campuses, and so on. He painted the official map of the 1933 Chicago World's Fair, and one of his last commissions was a map of the 1939 New York World's Fair. The detailed yet expansive aerial view appeared in the Fair's official guidebook and capped Pettit's forty years of imaginative urban depictions.[28]

The popular illustrators of the early 1900s exhibited a degree of imagination and humor that architects and engineers of the time generally eschewed. The purpose of their urban illustrations ranged from satire, comedic fantasy, and earnest speculation to factual reportage that was solidly grounded in engineering reality. The architecture historian Carol Willis argued that the popular future-city images of the early 1900s reflected the laissez-faire spirit of the era. They showed future cities made by private interests, without zoning, aesthetic controls, or overall plans. Many of the images certainly did that. But others, particularly the visions of multilevel streets, would have required coordinating authorities that were every bit as powerful as those required by the more ordered, authoritarian visions of later generations.[29]

William Wilgus and Grand Central Terminal

William J. Wilgus (1865–1949) created the formidable and exceptionally influential scheme to build Grand Central Terminal and remake its surrounding area. He was an ambitious, self-made railroad executive who enjoyed working on grand projects at the largest scales. He was meticulous and reserved in his professional relations, and was sometimes described as cold and aloof, but in private he was prone to outbursts of anger. As a self-taught engineer he was sensitive to any criticism of his engineering abilities. He prized recognition and praise from his professional peers, and endeavored to correct the record when his accomplishments were ignored or forgotten (which seemed to happen with some frequency).[30]

Wilgus began his career as an apprentice surveyor. In a series of positions with small Midwestern railroads, he learned railroad engineering and handled management and business responsibilities. He was an energetic employee and acquired a wide breadth of experience, from drawing plans for electric trolleys to bushwhacking a rail route through the Minnesota wilderness for iron-ore shipments. He joined the New York Central Railroad—the Vanderbilt railroad empire—in 1893 and quickly worked his way up the ranks to become chief engineer of the entire system in 1899.[31]

By that point in time the railroad's Manhattan passenger terminal, Grand Central Depot, was badly overcrowded and functionally obsolete. Inspired by a visit from Frank Sprague, Wilgus began to think about electrifying the terminal's operations. Clean-running electric trains, without the smoke and heat of steam trains, could freely operate underground and in enclosed spaces. The station's capacity could be expanded by adding a second level of tracks under the existing train yard. Wilgus communicated his ideas to the railroad's board, which gave preliminary approval in 1899. But the railroad did not authorize construction until 1902, when a horrible train crash in the smoke-filled tunnels killed seventeen people. The crash inflamed the city with anger and the railroad was forced to act.

Wilgus took the opportunity to comprehensively rethink the terminal plan and its relationship to the surrounding area. North of the terminal, the track yard was a smoky chasm that disrupted the city's grid of blocks. "The yard tracks on the surface acted as a veritable 'Chinese wall' to separate the city into two parts for fourteen blocks—nearly three quarters of a mile—between 42nd Street and 56th Street," Wilgus observed.[32]

If the entire track yard could be sunk below grade, the street grid could be re-established above it. Revenue-producing buildings could rise over the tracks on pilings. Wilgus envisioned an entire Terminal City, a complex of interconnected buildings elevated over a double-level railyard. The monetary value of these "air-rights" buildings, he calculated, would finance the whole project.[33]

The neighborhood immediately south of the terminal, Murray Hill, demonstrated the increase in land value that could result when tracks were buried and non-steam transport was used. In 1837 an open cut was dug through the solid rock of Murray Hill, allowing long-distance steam trains to run along Fourth Avenue. The open cut

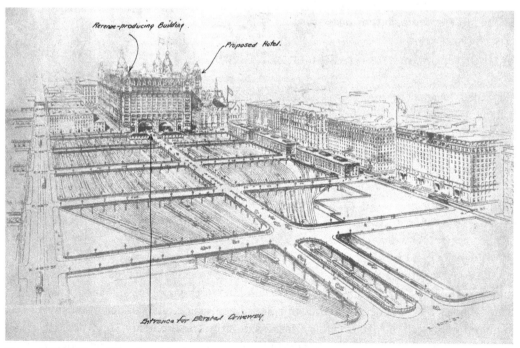

Figure 2.13: William Wilgus's original Terminal City proposal, drawn by Samuel Huckel Jr. in 1902, with annotations by Wilgus. Courtesy of New York Public Library Digital Collections.

was roofed over in 1851 to comply with the city's demands. In the 1860s, 40-foot-wide (12 m) parks were installed in the median of the avenue, inspiring real-estate sellers to rebrand the corridor as Park Avenue. In 1871 the steam trains were discontinued and replaced by horsecars. Around that time—the late 1860s and early 1870s—Park Avenue in Murray Hill became an address for the wealthy elite, and it filled with expensive, elegant mansions.[34]

Wilgus persuaded his skeptical boss of the scheme's merits and won approval from the railroad's fearsomely powerful board of directors, which included William K. Vanderbilt, Cornelius Vanderbilt III, William Rockefeller (uncle of John D. Rockefeller Jr., who developed Rockefeller Center) and J. P. Morgan, the railroad's financier.[35]

As part of the Terminal City, Wilgus proposed a new Park Avenue that would extend over the rail yard to reach the terminal building. The avenue would continue inside the building, make an abrupt turn to the west, and exit onto Madison Avenue. The internal drive would primarily serve baggage deliveries and passengers arriving or departing by carriage.[36]

An architectural competition was arranged to elaborate Wilgus's proposal. One of the entrants was Reed and Stem, an architectural firm co-directed by Wilgus's brother-in-law Charles Reed. Wilgus, being the project manager, was likely responsible for selecting Reed and Stem's plan as the winner. Their plan routed Park Avenue around the perimeter of the terminal building, elevated on a terrace above the surrounding streets. The avenue continued south on a viaduct that crossed over 42nd Street. That arrangement put the elevated avenue on prominent display and created one of the most recognizable features of the new terminal. According to a history that Wilgus probably wrote, Reed and Stem's plan was chosen because of this "novel suggestion."[37]

The scheme pleased the politicians who worried about the congestion that might result from the station area's redevelopment. At the plan's unveiling, Mayor Seth Low said the viaduct would keep a large percentage of carriage and automobile traffic off the congested surface streets. The mayor told Wilgus, "I hesitate to predict how wonderful will be the changes made in New York during the next fifty years. Your comprehensive scheme is proof . . . that the changes which are to come about within a comparatively short time will entirely alter the complexion of the city."[38]

Construction of the Terminal City's foundation was a gargantuan task. The excavation stretched from 42nd Street to 56th Street and reached a depth of 90 feet (27 m). Three million cubic yards (2.3 million cu m) of soil and rock were removed using techniques invented for the Chicago Canal and the Panama Canal. The excavation began in 1903 and continued through 1909.

Burying the infernal rail yard transformed the land north of the terminal into prime Manhattan real estate. Wilgus's scheme opened 40 acres (16 ha) to development between 42nd Street and 52nd Street, including 2 miles (3.2 km) of new streets and the terminal building itself, which was built with structural support for an office tower on top. First-rank hotels, apartments, offices and specialty buildings were built in the Terminal City over the next thirty years, such as the Waldorf-Astoria Hotel, the Biltmore Hotel, and the Yale Club. Wilgus estimated that the reconstruction of the terminal and its rail yard added $500 million (in 1940 dollars) to assessed property values in the area.[39]

The elevated-avenue scheme was subject to internal dispute, and at times its

Figure 2.14: Reed & Stem's painting of terminal facade and viaduct, submitted for the 1903 competition.

survival was in doubt, but Wilgus and Reed fought successfully to keep it in the plan. When the terminal complex had its grand opening in 1913, the elevated avenue was opened along the south and west sides of the terminal building. For the next six years, a ramp at 45th Street was the only way for traffic to ascend to the elevated avenue. In 1919 the long-planned viaduct was constructed over 42nd Street; from there it descended to street level at 40th Street. That allowed through traffic to use the elevated

Figure 2.15: Above: Grand Central trainyards, looking south from 48th Street in 1906. Below: View from the same location showing the Terminal City in 1920.

avenue, but it created a permanent traffic jam at 45th Street.

Almost immediately the Fifth Avenue Association, which represented local businesses, began agitating for a solution. A plan to extend two traffic viaducts over 45th Street was proposed by New York Central Railroad engineers during negotiations with the city in 1921–1922. The eventual agreement required the city to pass enabling legislation, and the railroad company to grant easements for public use.

Construction began in 1926 and the official opening was celebrated in September 1928. Along the east and west sides of the terminal, the ramps were removed and the elevated avenues were extended, crossing over 45th Street on bridges. As they tunneled through the New York Central Building (now Helmsley Building), they swept closer together and descended to street level at 46th Street. The railroad was responsible for all the roadway construction and kept the two underground train-yard levels operating without interruption. The work was actively promoted and expedited by Manhattan borough president Julius Miller and the city's administration, which the *New York Times* praised as a fine example of private and municipal coordination. The Fifth Avenue Association hailed the project as "the first major step toward relieving traffic in Manhattan" and anticipated that it would spur a variety of other traffic projects toward completion, including the West Side Elevated Highway.[40]

Similar to some of New York's subway stations, the new terminal was connected to surrounding buildings via underground passageways. Connections to at least four buildings were in place by 1920. These "inside streets" offered a bewildering variety of goods and services in addition to the usual food and sundries: musical supplies including pianos, electrical appliances including washing machines, a shaving supply shop, a circulating library, a post office, and more.[41]

Figure 2.16: Cutaway of New York Central Building shows Park Avenue routed through the lower floors. Image ca. 1925. Courtesy of New York Public Library Digital Collections.

By 1934, buildings in the area were linked to the terminal by twenty-six underground connections. Many were lined with small shops; some were lavishly decorated to coordinate with the lobbies they debauched into. It was the largest, most intricate network of mixed-use tunnelwalks and building connections in the world. The network shrank over the decades but remained extremely busy. In 1991 the city's planning department found that twenty-one buildings were connected to the terminal. A 2013 report by the Municipal Art Society of New York identified nine active connections and passageways.[42]

The elevated Park Avenue was one of the iconic features of the Grand Central Terminal complex, and its image was broadcast widely. It was surpassingly influential to designers, planners, and others committed to traffic improvement in cities. But the greater achievement in the eyes of developers, financiers, academics, and pubic officials may have been the Terminal City and the great financial success of its air-rights development.

The Terminal City demonstrated for the first time on a large scale the feasibility of multilevel urbanism. Its transportation facilities and buildings were stacked, layered, and interconnected in a unified complex that achieved amazing efficiencies of space and complexities of configuration. It was internationally acclaimed, and for years afterward it informed a broadly shared understanding of the opportunities offered by large-scale hyperurban complexes.

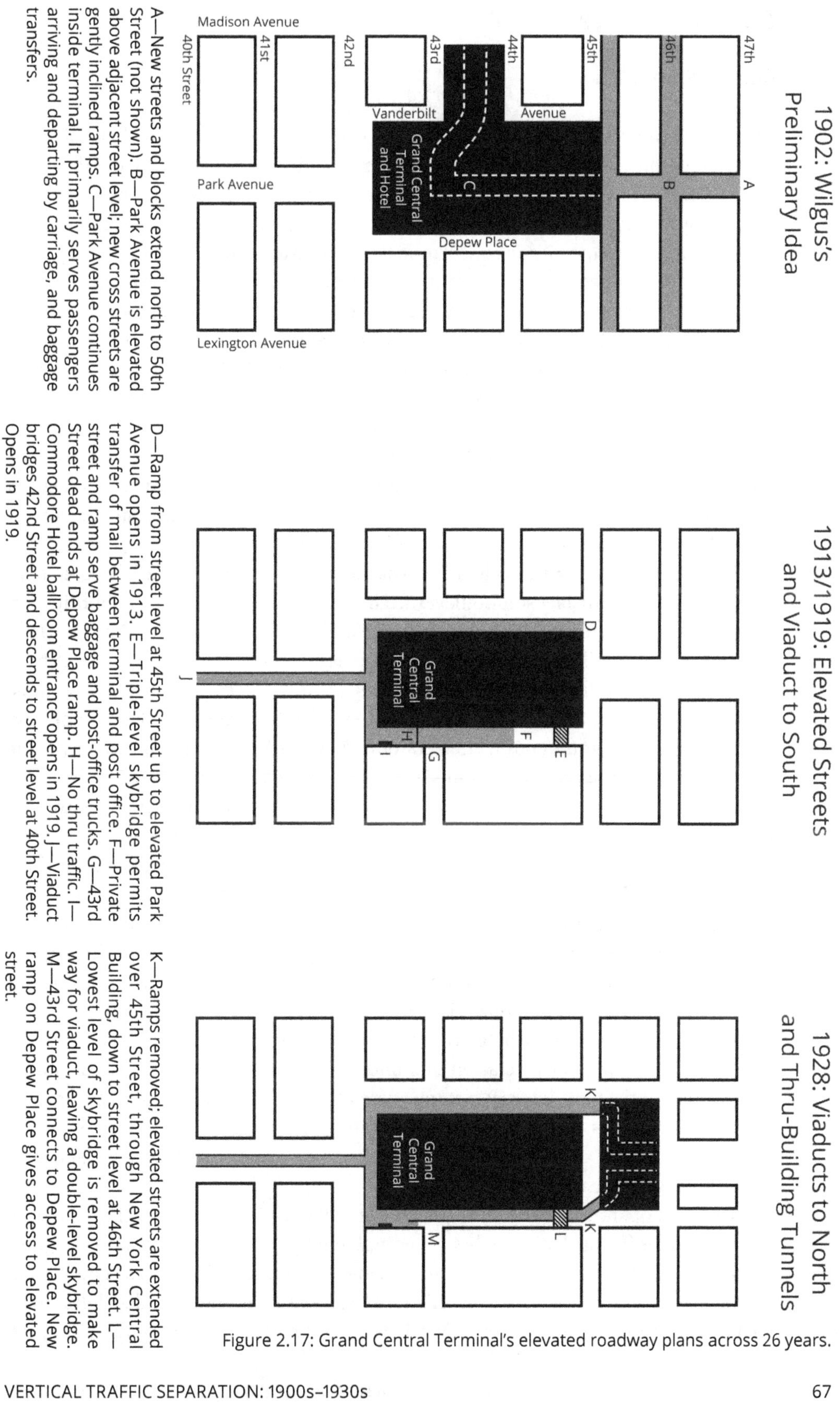
1902: Wilgus's Preliminary Idea
47th
46th
45th
44th
43rd
42nd
41st
40th Street
Madison Avenue
Park Avenue
Lexington Avenue
Vanderbilt
Avenue
Depew Place
Grand Central Terminal and Hotel
A
B
C
A—New streets and blocks extend north to 50th Street (not shown). B—Park Avenue is elevated above adjacent street level; new cross streets are gently inclined ramps. C—Park Avenue continues inside terminal. It primarily serves passengers arriving and departing by carriage, and baggage transfers.
1913/1919: Elevated Streets and Viaduct to South
Grand Central Terminal
D
E
F
G
H
I
J
D—Ramp from street level at 45th Street up to elevated Park Avenue opens in 1913. E—Triple-level skybridge permits transfer of mail between terminal and post office. F—Private street and ramp serve baggage and post-office trucks. G—43rd Street dead ends at Depew Place ramp. H—No thru traffic. I—Commodore Hotel ballroom entrance opens in 1919. J—Viaduct bridges 42nd Street and descends to street level at 40th Street. Opens in 1919.
1928: Viaducts to North and Thru-Building Tunnels
Grand Central Terminal
K
K
L
M
K—Ramps removed; elevated streets are extended over 45th Street, through New York Central Building, down to street level at 46th Street. L—Lowest level of skybridge is removed to make way for viaduct, leaving a double-level skybridge. M—43rd Street connects to Depew Place. New ramp on Depew Place gives access to elevated street.

Figure 2.17: Grand Central Terminal's elevated roadway plans across 26 years.

Freight Subways

Chicago Freight Tunnels

In 1899 the Illinois Telephone and Telegraph Company obtained a franchise to install telephone cables under the streets of downtown Chicago. Between 1901 and 1902 it built 12 miles (19 km) of tunnels and laid narrow-gauge rail tracks in them—which, the company claimed, were necessary to move the telephone-cable drums. During this initial phase of construction, a consortium of Pennsylvania coal magnates took partial control of the company and financed an expansion of the tunnels. The company then revealed, to the consternation of city officials, that it was building an electric railway system. It cheerfully described the tunnels as "literally a new system of streets, only underground." The company renegotiated its franchise with the city and reorganized itself as the Illinois Tunnel Company, establishing the first freight subway to serve an entire downtown.[43]

The company used its newly legitimate status to attract investment from major industrialists, rail executives, and bankers, such as E. H. Harriman and J. Ogden Armour. Money from the mainstream business establishment represented a vote of confidence in the underground freight delivery concept.[44]

The formal opening was celebrated with a grand banquet for 1,200 people held in the tunnel beneath Jackson Boulevard. The tunnels were decorated in bunting, an orchestra played, and speeches were delivered. The business-friendly Chicago Daily Tribune anticipated the start of operations with eagerness. "Chicago people are to have the streets to themselves, and lumbering drays, reeking dirt carts, grimy coal wagons, and pounding hoofs and grinding tires are to vanish from the downtown shopping district," wrote a commentator. "Let London, New York, and Paris put their people underground. Chicago will put its unsightly commerce into subways and welcome to its streets and shops as many healthy, well clad millions as can find home within its broad limits."[45]

Conditions in Chicago seemed promising for an underground freight system. One, the city was the Midwest's premier shipping center. Its rail and port operations were among the biggest in the world. Two, the canal that connected the Great Lakes to the Mississippi River system gave the city its great geographical advantage. Shippers and other businesses wanted to locate near the juncture of canal and lake. As a result, Chicago's freight and commercial districts were extraordinarily concentrated. Three, street congestion was exacerbated by parked and slow-moving freight wagons. Four, there was a widespread expectation that underground freight delivery was a coming trend; pneumatic mail-delivery systems were already well established in several US and European cities, and one was being installed in Chicago. Five, Chicago's subsoil layer was composed of clay, which made the freight tunnels easy to excavate and simplified future expansion.[46]

Revenue operations began in 1906. Meanwhile, the company continued to dig. Some 60 miles (97 km) of tunnels were completed by the early 1910s, accessed by 82 railcar elevators and 26 connections for coal and ash transfer via hoppers, chutes, and bucket conveyors. One hundred and thirty-two electric locomotives hauled 2,400 merchandise cars and 600 hopper cars. Much of the rolling stock was mining equipment,

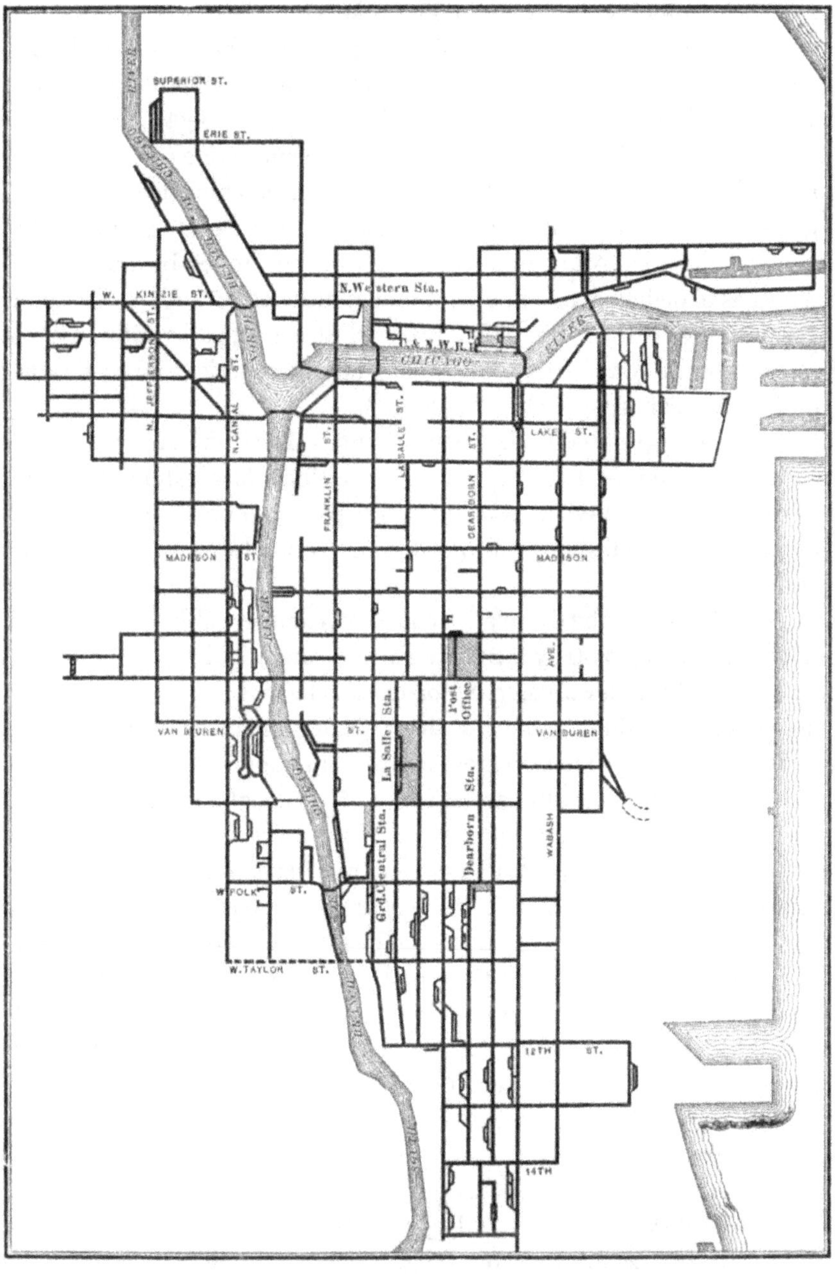

Figure 2.18: Map of Chicago's freight subway system, 1912.

so the cars could be lifted manually and maneuvered easily in close confines.

The tunnels ran beneath almost all streets in the Loop and extended short distances to the north and west under the Chicago River. The company opened four public receiving stations outside the Loop where any shipper could drop off freight and packages for delivery. These operations were responsible for 42 percent of the company's revenues in 1913, its largest single revenue category. The company also transferred freight between railroads, served local industries, delivered coal, and removed ash and subsoil. The company reported that it was moving about 1,700 railcars per day in 1913. It estimated that its operations reduced surface traffic by the equivalent of 1,500 wagons per day.[47]

The layout of the tunnel system was simple: workers burrowed under the center-line of every street in the downtown area, mirroring the grid above. But the layout, while comprehensive, was inefficient in operation. In order to ship a parcel, it first had to be loaded on a small railcar, which was lowered by elevator 40 feet (12 m) under-ground. The railcar was hitched to a passing train and went to one of eleven train-assembly points. There, switching crews disassembled and reassembled ten-car trains. The parcel was sent to its final destination, loaded on another elevator, and lifted to the business's receiving area. All train movements were controlled by a dispatcher "instructing crews as to deliveries and pick-up en route" through 250 telephones in the tunnels. The trains moved in one direction under each street, "thus forming a system of loops." In summary, the system was operated as a miniature freight railroad rather than being optimized as an urban delivery system.[48]

Inefficient operations resulted in slow delivery times. The company lost its mail-delivery contract soon after starting commercial operations. Meanwhile, the Team-sters Union mounted an effective fight against the upstart competitor. The tunnel company's freight tonnage fell short of projections and operating costs were higher than forecast.[49]

Revenues were also limited by the relative paucity of commercial-building connec-tions: 45 in 1910, increasing to 60 by 1924. Businesses usually had to pay the costs of digging shafts and installing elevators, so motor-truck delivery was generally cheaper, faster, and more flexible. In addition, the growth of trucking and highways in the 1920s allowed industries to move to suburban areas far from the congested downtown. The tunnel company struggled financially throughout its 53 years of operation and went through several defaults and reorganizations.[50]

Even so, the tunnel system played an important role in shaping Chicago's center. As new buildings were erected in the Loop, much of the excavated subsoil was trundled away by the underground railcars. They dumped the fill along the lakefront, extend-ing Grant Park and creating most of the Museum Campus in the 1920s. Ash removal remained a reliable source of income until the company went out of business in 1959. The system was a steady workhorse but did not produce benefits at the scale prom-ised by its promoters, neither for its investors nor for Chicago's street congestion.[51]

Wilgus's Freight System

Starting in the early 1890s, the New York Department of Docks had widened West Street from 70 to 200 feet (21 to 61 m). But freight congestion had only grown worse over the ensuing years. Government and civic groups were continually calling for solu-tions. Various railway viaduct and tunnel ideas were publicized, as well as schemes by the Municipal Art Society and the City Improvement Commission that included elevated roadways. Popular journals joined the fray. A 1907 *Scientific American* cover story (see figure 2.9) suggested that underground freight streets could improve con-ditions on the surface:

> The removal of heavy trucking from the streets would do more to
> expedite traffic than any other change that could be made; and the
> most effective way to make this change would be to double-deck the

A HISTORY OF STREET NETWORKS • CHAPTER 2

streets . . . freight could be delivered direct to the basement of the business houses . . . a large amount of handling and elevator service would be eliminated, while the sidewalks would be rid of the intolerable nuisance which is now occasioned by unloading and transferring freight at the street level.[52]

But all of those were limited, local solutions. They ignored the railroad barges that crossed from New Jersey and occupied 30 percent of the Hudson River piers. If the river traffic was not addressed, the traffic chaos on West Street would not be abated.[53]

Some hoped that relief would be delivered by the three twin-tube railway tunnels that were being built under the Hudson River. The tunnels opened for service between 1908 and 1910, carrying passenger trains only. They demonstrated the feasibility of under-river routes between New Jersey and Manhattan, and relieved some of the passenger-ferry demand. But the ferries used only seven percent of the Hudson River piers, so any improvement to waterfront congestion was likely to be minimal and short-lived.[54]

In addition, the chronic danger and deaths caused by surface freight-train collisions enraged the Lower West Side community and sparked political action. In 1906 the state legislature passed the "Saxe Law," which mandated that freight trains be moved off of Manhattan's surface streets and onto safer, less obstructive facilities. It empowered the Rapid Transit Commission to enforce the terms or else take over the rail line. The goal was laudable but no one knew how to achieve it in a practical way. The commission failed to budge the powerful railroad, and its threat of condemnation was revealed as a bluff. It was disbanded and a successor, the Public Service Commission, hired William Wilgus to make a plan.

Wilgus was confident that he could devise a better solution. He had previously created a system for Grand Central Terminal that separated baggage movement from passenger circulation. When a train arrived at the terminal, its baggage was unloaded from the baggage cars and transferred to electric carts. Thirty or more hydraulic elevators, each with a capacity of three tons, moved the carts between the terminal's levels. Most carts were lifted to the giant baggage room that occupied the northern half of the terminal on the ground floor. The carts could also cross under the train platforms via two "subway" corridors, which allowed them to transport mail to the post office next door.[55]

Wilgus proposed a comprehensive solution for freight congestion in the New York region. A freight-subway system would serve all shippers equally. It would permit direct delivery from the railroads' transshipment yards in New Jersey to businesses and warehouses in Manhattan. The 65-mile (105-km) system incorporated 196 miles (315 km) of tracks in a layout that was hierarchical and modular. A high-speed belt line encircled Manhattan along the waterfront, lower-speed trunk and secondary lines extended into industrial and commercial districts, and the slowest local lines served individual streets and buildings. Wilgus made detailed plans for West Street and the surrounding commercial blocks.

He assured readers that "the handicaps of the Chicago freight subways, will all be avoided." The railcars would be reasonably large and powerful, yet nimble and light enough to be lifted by cranes and elevators. The local rail lines would run beneath

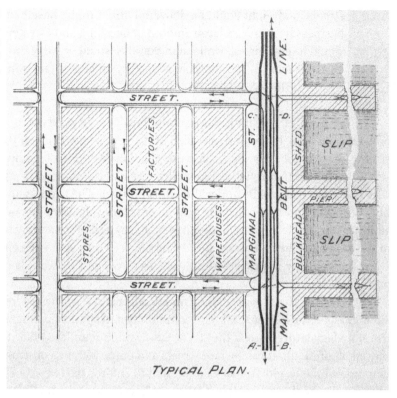

Figure 2.19: Detail of Wilgus's proposal, 1908. Shows main routes and local tracks under every sidewalk.

sidewalks so that railcars could roll directly into store basements. The flaws of the Chicago system would be solved, such as excessive transfers and the need for every recipient to have elevators or deep basements.[56]

Wilgus also developed a containerized-cargo concept to extend the system's reach and flexibility. A railcar could be delivered to one of 24 transfer stations scattered throughout Manhattan. There, the body was detached from the chassis and loaded onto a truck for final delivery via surface streets. He cited England as a model, where intermodal railway containers were beginning to be used in nationwide service. Wilgus also specified standard-gauge tracks so that his railcars could travel on existing railways to suburban sites.

Wilgus's 1908 report surveyed the competition and asserted that the freight subway was less costly, more practical, more comprehensive, and achieved a greater reduction of street crowding, danger, and pollution. But the scheme faced strong opposition from entrenched interests. Several of the private railroad companies refused to participate in cooperative ventures. Dock workers and freight haulers opposed any arrangement that would diminish their business. Wilgus might have overcome that opposition, but another situation made the issue moot: the chairman of the Public Service Commission was corrupt. Communicating through a hired flunky, the chairman demanded shares of stock in Wilgus's company in exchange for approval of the freight subway. Wilgus and his partner flatly refused to pay, and their scheme stopped dead in its tracks.[57]

Over the following years, other groups and individuals put forward ideas to relieve freight congestion, some of which included elevated roadways. A 1912 suggestion by Amos L. Schaeffer, the consulting engineer for the Borough of the Bronx, recalled

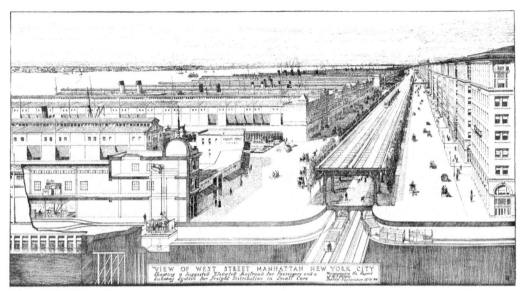

Figure 2.20: Wilgus's vision for freight handling on West Street, 1908. Freight cars could travel throughout the pier structures on additional tracks and elevators.

Figure 2.21: Wilgus's vision for freight handling in office districts, 1908. The system's shallow depth allowed packages to be transferred directly to building elevators.

Alfred Thorpe's concept. Schaeffer imagined six railway tracks on the surface of West Street enclosed by a "subway structure" that had a vehicular roadway on top. Freight could be delivered on both levels. Spur tracks could be laid into any building that needed a direct freight connection, or freight could be delivered by truck or wagon via the upper roadway. Meanwhile, the New York Central Railroad fought the state's track-removal mandate with tenacious determination. The battle moved to the court system and the railroad won temporary victories and years of delays.[58]

Wilgus's experiences in this arena led him to conclude that a port-congestion solution required a stronger authority. It required an authority with interstate scope and the power to compel cooperation from squabbling private interests and territorial public bodies. The Port of London Authority, established in 1908, was his model. From 1909 onward, Wilgus argued for a similar authority for the New York region. In 1911 Woodrow Wilson, as governor of New Jersey, signed legislation written by Wilgus to establish a bi-state port commission. New York did not reciprocate.[59]

New York harbor's freight congestion grew worse, and arrived at a crisis point during World War I. The city's freight system collapsed under the pressure of wartime materiel exports. Trains bound for New York and other Atlantic ports backed up as far west as Chicago and the Mississippi River. To resolve the nationwide freight problem (which had numerous causes), President Woodrow Wilson nationalized the railroads from 1917 to 1920. That episode changed the terms of debate in the New York region. It greatly strengthened the power of government planners in freight and other transportation matters.[60]

The states of New York and New Jersey created a Port and Harbor Development Commission in 1917. Two years later, the commission released a freight-subway plan similar to Wilgus's plan. It had a main trunk line that connected the New Jersey railyards to a number of new freight depots in Manhattan. It had no secondary or local lines, and therefore offered no direct access to abutting businesses. The plan also featured a variant of the intermodal container idea. At the railyards, most freight would be placed in small wheeled carts. The carts would be loaded on railcars, shipped to the depots, and transferred to wagons and trucks for final delivery.[61]

The Port of New York Authority grew directly from the Port and Harbor Development Commission. It was established in 1921; its mission was to build a consolidated rail system to solve the region's freight congestion. In December 1921 the Port Authority announced its plan. It envisioned an extensive regional network of new freight-rail routes and water crossings, and it endorsed the Port and Harbor Development Commission's freight subway plan as a major component. Much of the Port Authority's plan used ideas that Wilgus had advocated since 1908, but once again he received little or no credit.[62]

Plan of Chicago, Michigan Avenue, and Wacker Drive

The Plan of Chicago was organized by a dynamic businessman named Charles D. Norton. He was the secretary of the Merchants Club of Chicago, a social club restricted to men under age 45 that was devoted to business promotion and public-interest initiatives. His ally on the club's executive committee was the engineer and railroad-company president Frederic A. Delano. Both were experienced in finance and management, and both were interested in works that furthered the public good. Delano was the uncle of Franklin Delano Roosevelt, a law student who would soon begin his political career as a New York state senator.

The organizers felt that the illustrious planner Daniel Burnham was the perfect choice for creating Chicago's comprehensive plan. In mid-1906, Norton persuaded Burnham to serve as lead planner, and soon afterward secured funding from the Merchants Club. Norton went to give Burnham the good news but found Burnham in an upset state of mind:

> We raced over to tell Burnham to begin, that we were financed. He was sitting in that beautiful office, high up in the Railway Exchange Building, where for three years thereafter we were to meet so often. He was gazing out over the lake front, and he appeared to be in serious distress. "It is wonderful, Charles," he said, "but I am afraid it is no use. My doctor has just been here to tell me that I have a mortal disease—that I have at most three years to live."
>
> There was an embarrassed and painful silence, and then I blurted out, "But, Mr. Burnham, that is just time enough; it will take only three years."
>
> Burnham looked startled, then he broke into a laugh and said: "You are right. I will do it."[63]

Burnham was well experienced for the job. He had led the design of the nation's first comprehensive city plan, the McMillan plan for Washington, DC (1901), and subsequently completed several more. His major-street plans rationalized circulation by connecting major activity centers and, where possible, by forming regional radial-concentric patterns. His street plans usually had some type of traffic separation. His plan for Manila, Philippines (1905), proposed a 20-mile (32-km) multiway boulevard along the oceanfront. His San Francisco plan (1905) proposed a network of boulevards, several of which were the grand multiway type. Heavy freight traffic would be restricted or banned on all the boulevards. Along the wharves, an elevated pleasure boulevard would run on top of warehouses, which would "add a special charm to the life of the city."[64]

In the *Plan of Chicago* (1909), Burnham designated several types of street networks. Avenues carried through traffic consisting of vehicles and streetcars, which might be separated in dedicated lanes. Boulevards were lavishly planted and ornamented, and might have continuous playgrounds; all heavy traffic was excluded from them. Certain districts had critical problems and their streets received special attention. Michigan Avenue and the adjacent Chicago River frontage was one of those.

The existing river crossing (Rush Street Bridge) was a major connection between downtown and all points north. It was also an aggravating bottleneck: an estimated 50 percent of north-south traffic squeezed through it, causing daily backups. Burnham anticipated that future growth would multiply the traffic pressure. "Michigan Avenue is probably destined to carry the heaviest movement of any street in the world," he warned. Chicagoans had been discussing a multilevel river crossing since the 1880s; Burnham revived the idea of a street with an elevated upper deck.[65]

He proposed that Michigan Avenue's traffic be horizontally separated, with a central lane for through traffic and side lanes for local shopping traffic. It would also be vertically separated, with passenger vehicles on the elevated level and freight vehicles below. The whole structure would be about 250 feet (76 m) wide and one-half mile (0.8 km) long. The lower level would be well lit, ventilated, and weather-protected, providing "ideal conditions" for freight handling.[66]

Some property owners immediately opposed the "boulevard on stilts" for fear that it would harm property values. The plan's boosters responded by forming the semi-public Chicago Plan Commission, led by the businessman Charles Wacker, and launching a vigorous multiyear publicity campaign. The City Council authorized the plan in 1913; the legal battles over condemnation payments ended in 1918; construction began in April 1918; and the structure opened to traffic in May 1920. It was the first built example of full-fledged hyperurbanism—that is, the first to have powered vehicles and continuous abutter access on multiple congruent levels.[67]

The Chicago Plan Commission said the project was a phenomenal success. It increased traffic capacity, raised property values, and generated benefits much greater than its $16 million cost. "The improvement of Michigan Avenue has been successful beyond almost all hopes. It was an object lesson that won many friends to the Chicago Plan," boasted the commission. That was important because the commission wanted to extend the multilevel network according to Burnham's vision. Burnham had been inspired by the waterfronts of certain European and African cities, the Seine riverfront in Paris above all.[68]

Design work on the extension commenced in 1917. It would run 1.25 miles (2 km) along the Chicago River frontage and would complete a circuit that allowed vehicles to bypass the crowded downtown streets. The upper level would be "one of the show places of the city," broad and handsomely ornamented, and would attract high-class enterprises demanding 10–15 story buildings. The lower level would provide warehouse storage and parking. It also could function as freight-transfer facility, because it had river transport on one side and a railroad terminal on the other. The main purpose was to relieve the "appalling congestion" caused by multiple streams of traffic moving in different directions for different purposes.[69]

The commission's public relations team kicked into gear. Impressive illustrations and urgent promotional descriptions appeared in major newspapers and national magazines, playing to Chicago's desire to be a world-class city. The campaign worked well, and the roadway was built from 1924 to 1926. In June 1924, a few months before construction began, the city council voted to name the roadway Wacker Drive in honor

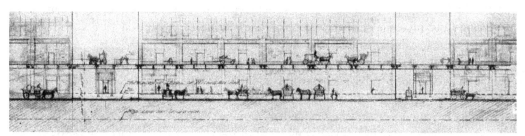

Figure 2.22: Proposed double-level Michigan Avenue, 1912, showing retail entrances on upper level, freight operations on lower level. Staircases were located at each cross street.

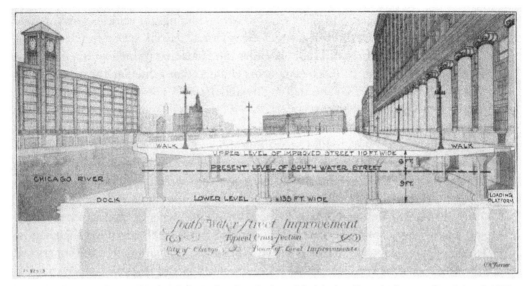

Figure 2.23: Water Street (Wacker Drive), showing dock and freight-loading platform on lower level, 1922.

of the Chicago Plan Commission chairman who administered and promoted the Plan of Chicago for seventeen years.[70]

The Michigan Avenue-Wacker Drive complex was highly influential to planners and engineers who believed that grade-separated expressways were essential to the automobile-centric urban future. It, along with the West Side Elevated Highway in Manhattan, was frequently cited as a precedent of the elevated-expressway proposals of the 1920s and 1930s. In later decades of the twentieth century, segments were added to the Michigan Avenue-Wacker Drive complex and a few portions were made triple-level.[71]

Hudson River Crossing Complex

The Hudson River motor-vehicle crossing complex consisted of the Holland Tunnel (1921–1927), Route 1 Extension in New Jersey (1923–1932), and West Side Elevated Highway in Manhattan (1929–1937). Each project was a pioneer in some way. Combined, they formed the largest, most complicated, most expensive motor-expressway complex yet built. The complex was grade-separated and limited-access along most of its length, and was the first such system to carry both passenger and commercial motor traffic through urban areas.

Holland Tunnel

Before the 1920s, no roadway linked New Jersey to New York. The Albany-Greenbush Bridge (1882), located 130 miles (209 km) north of midtown Manhattan, was the nearest road facility that crossed the Hudson River. All road vehicles traveling directly between New Jersey and New York City used ferries. The ferries contended with the notorious freight congestion that bedeviled the West Side docks and West Street. The problems were well known, and the city had a long history of proposals for vehicular crossings. Traffic separation had been among the solutions from an early date.

The first official group to study Hudson River crossings for vehicles was a bi-state commission formed in 1906. The engineering firm of Jacobs & Davies, which previously had designed three rail tunnels under the Hudson, outlined a tunnel concept for the commission in 1913. The engineers claimed that vehicular-tunnel construction was "perfectly assured and thoroughly understood." They recommended a route from Jersey City to Canal Street in Manhattan that would connect the major traffic centers on both sides of the river. One of their designs, dated 1910, showed two-level tunnels that carried slow traffic (pedestrians, horse-drawn vehicles, motor trucks) on the upper level and fast traffic (passenger autos) on the lower level. The tunnel concept went through several design iterations over the following years. Several of them separated fast and slow traffic on different levels or different lanes.[72]

In 1919, New York and New Jersey authorized a vehicular tunnel across the Hudson. The bi-state commission named William Wilgus as chief consulting engineer; he led the engineering team that established the basic design parameters and supervised the initial construction. The tunnel was an undertaking of firsts and superlatives. It was the longest underwater tunnel in the world and the first designed exclusively for motor vehicles. Wilgus's team commissioned pioneering research on vehicle exhaust and the health effects of carbon monoxide. The ventilation system was novel and added $12 million to the tunnel's cost.

Another task was to determine the tunnel's size and capacity. To do that, Wilgus had to establish the tunnel's role in the greater regional transportation system. He believed that the legislative mandate directed his team to match the tunnel's capacity to the street capacity at the tunnel's entrances. So his team specified twin tubes of two lanes each, and banned horse-drawn vehicles to increase operating speed and capacity. Wilgus commissioned traffic studies that assumed the tunnel would draw no more than 20 percent of the freight traffic that was currently moving across the river on railcar barges. He absolutely did not want the tunnel to be a substitute for a dedicated freight system, and resisted calls to build six lanes. He expected that most freight would be carried on a future consolidated freight-subway system because that was the Port Authority's mission at the time.

Construction began in 1920 and Wilgus's team completed its work in 1922. The lead engineer of the whole project was Clifford M. Holland, who made a heroic effort to finish the tunnel on schedule. He suffered a nervous breakdown and died of a heart attack at age 41. The Holland Tunnel, which was named in his honor, opened in 1927. It was a resounding success: traffic exceeded projections by 70 percent in the first year, and toll revenue eventually repaid all construction costs and generated large surpluses. Initiatives to build more vehicular tunnels and bridges in the region were decisively validated.[73]

Route 1 Extension

New Jersey officials foresaw that local streets would be overwhelmed by Holland Tunnel traffic. They acted quickly to build a through-traffic highway for the expected hordes. In 1921 the state legislature authorized a highway connecting the mouth of the Holland Tunnel to US Route 1, which was the major north-south highway along the eastern seaboard of the United States. The Route 1 Extension would run 13.2

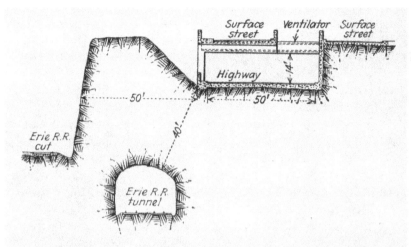

Figure 2.24: Cross section of Hoboken Avenue Viaduct, 1926, illustrating the complicated site conditions.

FIG. 1—SECTION SHOWING HIGHWAY IN RELATION TO RAILROAD TUNNEL AND CUT

miles (21.2 km) through Jersey City, past the Newark Airport, and around the city of Elizabeth, traversing miles of undeveloped marshland and rivers along the way.[74]

Planning began in 1923, and an advisory board was appointed that included Clifford M. Holland and Ernest P. Goodrich as a consulting engineer. The board estimated that 20 percent of all traffic was horse-drawn, and felt confident that it could be ignored. The highway would serve motor vehicles exclusively. The board's recommendation about at-grade intersections was brief: they should be eliminated as much as possible because they slowed traffic and created dangerous conditions.[75]

The board did not need to belabor the principles of limited access and grade separation. Its outlook was dominated by its chairman, William G. Sloan, who was also the newly appointed state engineer. Sloan was especially experienced in railroad engineering and he had definite ideas about the Route 1 Extension. It would be the primary highway link between New York City and all points west and south. It would function like a trunk railroad, and would be designed for high volumes of passenger and heavy-freight traffic. It would have no abutter access, no at-grade intersections, and its route would be as direct and efficient as possible.[76]

Major construction work began in 1924. No construction guidelines existed for such a highway, so the engineers generally used railway design specifications. One element they had to invent was access ramps. Their ramps were relatively steep and two-way, and entered the highway in the center. They probably were the models for the access ramps of the West Side Elevated Highway in Manhattan.[77]

The highway traveled through intensively developed areas of Jersey City on above-grade viaducts and in below-grade structures. In one neighborhood, the highway commission proposed that the roadway be depressed below grade. Local residents objected because that would divide the community and obstruct travel. The solution was the Hoboken Avenue Viaduct, an unusual box-like structure 0.64 mile (1 km) long. It was a double-level roadway that cut through the traditional grid of small blocks. The highway ran on the lower level, below the local streets. Sections of the roof and walls were open to air so that no mechanical ventilation was needed. On the upper level, a new thoroughfare was built on the highway's roof. The local grid of streets intersected

Figure 2.25: Hoboken Avenue Viaduct, 1928. Upper level with urban frontages and central light wells.

the upper thoroughfare and crossed over the highway, thus maintaining the integrity of the grid. Over the following decades, some of the abutting block faces were developed to form new street-oriented frontages, while others languished as parking lots.[78]

The first segment of the Route 1 Extension opened in 1926 and the final segment was completed in 1932. It was the largest individual highway project of its time, and the first limited-access roadway to carry commercial traffic through urban areas. It was extensively covered by the professional press and extremely influential in the engineering and highway-planning fields. In 1932 Thomas H. MacDonald, chief of the federal Bureau of Public Roads, called it "the greatest highway project in the United States today." Many people considered it the first urban superhighway.[79]

West Side Elevated Highway

As construction began on the Holland Tunnel and design work began on the Route 1 extension, civic groups and government officials in New York City called for an elevated expressway to handle the anticipated flood of traffic. By 1922, the roster of supporters included some of the city's most respected leaders and engineers: Frederic A. Delano, chairman of the Regional Plan of New York and Its Environs initiative (RPNY); Nelson P. Lewis, RPNY's director of surveys and engineering; Amos L. Schaeffer, engineer to the Borough of Manhattan; and Richard Enright, New York City police commissioner.[80]

Julius Miller, president of the Borough of Manhattan, decided in summer 1924 to champion the project. He had been elected in 1922 and had made traffic congestion and street planning his signature issues. He was already urging and facilitating a northward extension of the Park Avenue viaduct.

Miller warned that the Holland Tunnel was going to bring traffic from the entire New York region and northeastern United States. Equally important, the New York Central Railroad was still running trains on West Street and Eleventh Avenue. The tracks created such a dangerous environment that Eleventh Avenue was often called

"Death Avenue." Miller announced his solution in February 1925. He proposed a triple-level roadway: regular traffic on the surface, a freight railroad on the second level, and an express motor highway on the third level. It would run about 4.25 miles (6.8 km) along the Hudson riverfront from Canal Street to 72nd Street. Miller claimed to have invented the idea, although proposals such as Amos Schaeffer's likely served as inspirations.[81]

Action was delayed for years by political disagreements. The first major obstacle was raised by the Port Authority. It argued that Miller's scheme would give the railroad a virtual monopoly over freight movement in Manhattan. It said the scheme was piecemeal, neither comprehensive nor efficient, and jeopardized the consolidated freight subway. Miller retorted that the Port Authority was "delaying an immediate solution of New York's traffic congestion problem for the sake of a visionary plan which would take a quarter of a century to complete." Ira A. Place, vice-president of the New York Central, weighed in with the railroad's position. "Joint freight terminals are all bunk," he grumbled. "They are not feasible." As the historian Jamison Doig described it, the railroad was engaged in a long-term game of cat-and-mouse with the Port Authority to defeat the consolidated freight subway.[82]

Miller resolved the disagreement by splitting his scheme. The elevated expressway would run along the riverfront. The railroad would have its own viaduct (which it had been proposing since 1911) located 1–2 blocks inland. Because the timing of the railroad viaduct's construction was uncertain, the elevated highway would be tall enough that trains could continue to travel underneath it. The Port Authority gave its approval and Governor Al Smith signed the authorizing bill in spring 1926.[83]

The second major obstacle was raised by Mayor Jimmy Walker, who "insisted that the Miller plan was inextricably interwoven with the negotiations to remove the New York Central tracks." Walker would not permit the elevated highway to proceed until track removal was assured. Miller doggedly pressed his case before the Board of Estimate, which was the government body that controlled the city's budget, land use, and contracts. Tempers began to fray. One Board of Estimate member scolded Miller for the selfish, unceasing pursuit of his "pet project."[84]

Mayor Walker finally gave his support and the Board of Estimate voted its approval in January 1929. In total, the project had been on the Board of Estimate's agenda 152 times. When construction began in May with great fanfare, the mayor paid tribute to Miller. "I never knew a man to be so vitally interested in anything as Mr. Miller has been in this project," said Walker. "Sometimes he has even been annoying."[85]

Miller never abandoned his vision of a double-deck facility and made sure that a second roadway level could be added if capacity was needed in the future. Strengthening the foundations and steel structure for that purpose added $7 million, or 64 percent, to the highway's cost. The first segment opened in 1930 and the final segment was finished in 1937. Walker officially named it the Miller Elevated Highway in 1931, after Miller had joined the state supreme court and was out of local politics.[86]

When Miller first proposed his elevated highway, RPNY suggested attaching it to the adjacent facades so it could provide access to the abutting buildings. RPNY wanted the highway to be well-integrated with its surroundings, just like the Grand Central Terminal's viaduct. City authorities rejected the idea, saying that costs would be excessive and local access would interfere with express traffic. Miller himself promised

Figure 2.26: West Side Elevated Highway at 54th Street, 1938, showing center ramps, relationship to piers, and urban context. Courtesy of New York State Archives.

that the upper highway level would have sidewalks and access to the transatlantic piers. Apparently the city's policy wavered, because city engineers in the early 1930s were prepared to add upper-level pier connections for passenger pickup and dropoff. Regardless, the connections were not built and the highway's upper level served express motor traffic only.[87]

RPNY and other civic groups were deeply disappointed in the highway's design and criticized it harshly. RPNY declared that it "destroys the beauty of the facade of the Chelsea Piers," that it "does injury to property," and "in appearance and effect on surroundings it is quite similar to the much criticized elevated railroad." The critique was prophetic. Elevated urban freeways built later in the United States and around the world were similarly intrusive and destructive, if not more so.[88]

The West Side elevated highway was intensively used and perennially congested during rush hours. In the late 1930s, it was extended northward to complete a limited-access express route to Westchester County. But its narrow lanes, steep ramps, and sharp corners made it obsolete within a few decades. Lack of maintenance hastened its decline. A section of the highway collapsed in 1973 and the entire structure south of 59th Street was demolished from 1977 to 1989.[89]

From the late 1920s through the 1940s, the West Side highway was a preeminent example of an elevated expressway operating in the most intense of commercial-industrial environments. It taught the lesson that waterfront land was the cheapest and easiest for expressway construction. Also, it was generally congruent with existing streets, unlike many other urban viaducts, and therefore minimized the costs of land acquisition and demolition. It spurred proposals for similar elevated highways elsewhere in New York City; in big cities like Boston and Chicago; in California; and in federal reports advocating a national freeway system.

Popular Hyperurbanism of the 1920s

A new round of hyperurbanism visioning occurred during the 1920s and, to a less prodigious degree, the 1930s. Those decades were a golden age for urban futurism. Public interest had never been higher and new visions were proliferating in the professional and popular realms. In many of the visions, the configuration of the roadways exhibited a notable shift. Previous visions had often shown abutters having access to roadways on multiple levels. The visionaries had assumed that each level would function more or less like a traditional street. With the advent of mass auto ownership, and the construction of motor parkways and viaducts, more people became aware of the risks and demands of high-speed motor traffic. The popular visions began to feature a more thorough isolation of urban arterials from their immediate surroundings. Full-fledged hyperurbanism was gradually abandoned in favor of elevated and below-grade limited-access highways.

The following survey covers only a selection of the more famous or influential visions, and is by no means an exhaustive review.

Skyscraper-Bridge Urbanism

The works of the eminent bridge engineer Gustav Lindenthal (1850–1935) may have sparked an extravagant subgenre of urban futurism: skyscraper-bridge urbanism. His Queensboro Bridge (1909) marched across the New York City landscape like a colossus, supremely unruffled by the bustle and congestion below. But where it touched down in Manhattan and on Blackwell's Island (now Roosevelt's Island) in the East River, it engaged with the surrounding urbanism. One area below the bridge deck was fitted out as a farmer's market and roofed in glorious basket-weave tilework by the Guastavino company. On Blackwell's Island, passenger elevators traveled within the bridge's support towers, connecting the bridge's deck to the land below.

The need for convenient vehicular access to Blackwell's Island became apparent as motor vehicle traffic increased. To accomplish that, an "Elevator Storehouse" was put into operation in 1919. The nine-story building was sited next to the bridge and connected by a short ramp. Delivery trucks and emergency vehicles could drive from the bridge's deck onto the roof of the building. From there, vehicles could ride elevators to the building's warehouse levels or to the street-level exit. The building thus functioned as a vertical thoroughfare for motor vehicles.[90]

The Elevator Storehouse demonstrated that urban highways elevated to extreme heights could be technically feasible. Visionaries began to depict a new form of urban design, in which skyscrapers served as support pylons for high-speed bridges. Motor vehicles could ride swift elevators inside the supporting buildings to virtually any height, allowing high-speed roadways to be elevated hundreds of feet in the air. Proposals in the skyscraper-bridge subgenre were made by Robert Charles Lafferty (1923), Raymond Hood (1925), and numerous other designers.

Lindenthal himself publicized a Hudson River bridge design in 1921. He had begun working in 1885 on a mighty bridge to carry rail tracks over the Hudson River, and he had revived the idea periodically over the succeeding decades. Over the years, his proposals for the Hudson span had grown bigger and more elaborate, with more

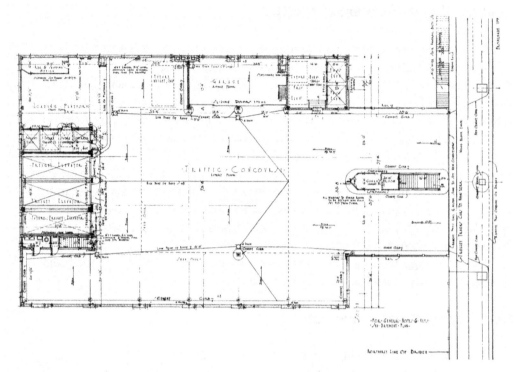

Figure 2.27: Elevator Storehouse top deck showing ramp to bridge, guardhouse in center of ramp, and vehicular elevators on left side.

Figure 2.28: Elevator Storehouse under construction, ca. 1919.

Figure 2.29: Lindenthal's vision of the world's mightiest bridge, with an office building perched over the access ramp, 1921.

Figure 2.30: George Washington Bridge Apartments in 1973.

lanes for more traffic types. His 1921 proposal would be the world's longest bridge and tallest structure. Twenty-two-story office buildings sat atop the bridge's anchor piers; they were positioned over the bridge's decks and travelways, and loomed above the surrounding neighborhoods.[91]

None of the skyscraper-bridge proposals were built. Their main effect was to instill the idea that urban highways could be exceedingly flexible—elevated to any height, placed near any inhabited space, incorporated into any multilevel structure. The proposals helped make the elevated urban expressway a symbol of progress and futurity, and magnified people's excitement about future construction.

Perhaps the Port Authority retained a memory of Lindenthal's vision when it added a second deck to the George Washington Bridge in the early 1960s (the consulting engineer was Lindenthal's former assistant, Othmar Ammann). The city, working with the Authority, sold its air rights so that the Washington Bridge Apartments could be built directly over the bridge's approach highway. Protestors decried the impacts on residents even before construction began, but no one addressed their concerns. From the opening day to the present, residents have struggled with the noise, vibration, and pollution emanating from the constant heavy stream of traffic below.[92]

Harvey Wiley Corbett

In early 1921 the Russell Sage Foundation launched the largest city planning effort yet attempted: the Regional Plan of New York and Its Environs (RPNY). It aimed to make a comprehensive plan for the entire New York region. Charles Norton, who had organized the Chicago Plan initiative fifteen years earlier, led RPNY in its initial phase. He recruited several teams of prestigious architects to work *pro bono* on ideas for specific areas. One team, chaired by the New York architect Harvey Wiley Corbett, focused on congested 59th Street and the topic of traffic. Corbett had previously designed the Bush Tower (1918), a neo-Gothic skyscraper noted for its stylistic elegance.[93]

At a March 1923 meeting in his office, Corbett declared that double- and triple-level streets were the only feasible way to increase traffic capacity in Manhattan. He predicted that by 2023, most of Manhattan would be raised above ground level on platforms, allowing traffic to flow underneath. RPNY's staff engineers were skeptical and opined that such ideas were "entirely impractical and would not stand the light of day." So Corbett and his colleagues developed a more modest and incremental scheme based on historical ideas and models.[94]

Corbett was familiar with earlier ideas about vertical pedestrian separation. He cited as precedents Leonardo da Vinci, historic European cities, and Chicago's Michigan Avenue. In addition, he was likely familiar with schemes by the designer Charles R. Lamb. Lamb had proposed elevated pedestrian arcades in 1898, and in 1902 made a more detailed proposal for street-level arcades along 59th Street in Manhattan. Lamb's arcades were formed by condemning the lower floors of buildings, moving the sidewalks into the newly created space, and converting the former sidewalks to vehicular traffic lanes. Lamb became president of the Municipal Art Society of New York in 1906; Corbett was participating in the Society's exhibitions by that time.

Unlike most previous hyperurbanization schemes, Corbett's paid attention to the implementation process, possibly to anticipate critics who might deem the plan

Present conditions—one moving lane.

With elevation of sidewalks—three moving lanes.

With arcades for standing vehicles—six moving lanes.

Deeper arcades provided in permanent construction—eight moving lanes.

Figure 2.31: RPNY's four-part progression to elevated pedestrian arcades is shown in cross sections, 1923.

infeasible. The elevated arcades would be built in three stages. The first stage consisted of simple cantilevered metal structures that supported upper-level sidewalks, similar to a 1911 scheme by the engineer Ernest P. Goodrich. In the second stage, ground-level frontages were converted to parking and truck-loading space, and the roadway was widened. In the third stage, buildings were rebuilt with elevated pedestrian arcades and the roadway was widened yet again. The process of street widening could continue until the entire ground surface beneath the buildings was consumed by traffic uses.

Corbett said the elevated-arcade scheme was an ideal blend of civic art and efficient planning. He reassured skeptics by evoking the beauty of historical urbanism, describing streetscapes whose "whole aspect becomes that of a very modernized Venice." Walking and shopping would be a joy, and the "overwrought nerves" of New Yorkers would be restored. Not least, the problem of insufficient street capacity would be solved "for all time."[95]

Corbett worked with several illustrators to portray the arcade scheme. His collaboration with Hugh Ferris was the most significant, and Ferriss was credited as a contributing architect on the team. The scheme was submitted to the RPNY committee in 1923 and appeared in popular and professional publications throughout the 1920s. Heightened by Ferriss's dramatic, painterly drawings, it generated public discussion and was both praised and condemned.

The arcade scheme was a recommended element of the 1931 RPNY final report. The report proposed an elevated network more than 5 miles (8 km) in length, which would link major destinations in midtown Manhattan. But the report gave several caveats. First, any effort to build such arcades would encounter daunting obstacles. The cooperation of all affected property owners would be required, and the cost would be prohibitive in all but the most densely developed districts. Second, the elevated-arcade idea was incomplete. A more sound and proper system would also have separate levels for slow and fast auto traffic, which were essential for rapid through movement.[96]

After working on the arcade scheme, Corbett emerged as a leading and energetic advocate of urban concentration. Through the 1920s, he wrote articles, gave presentations, and engaged in debates to defend and promote skyscraper cities and multilevel streets. He freely borrowed any vertical-separation idea that appealed to him. A 1925 *Popular Science* article about Corbett's vision of a four-level street featured an illustration nearly identical to a 1913 *Scientific American* cover image (figure 2.12). The 1925 illustration was so intensively multilayered that the notion of a ground plane became meaningless. Even so, pedestrians were given the prime space: the level open to the sky. "Pedestrians have more need of light and air than motorists," Corbett noted. "Otherwise they would not be pedestrians."[97]

Hugh Ferriss

Hugh Ferriss (1889–1962) was trained as an architect, and at a young age achieved success as an architectural illustrator. By the late 1910s his work was appearing regularly in major magazines; he drew shipyards for the US Army, industrial infrastructure for US Chambers of Commerce, and advertisements for Wall Street firms. In 1922 Corbett and Ferris collaborated on series of illustrations of New York's skyscraper zoning rules. The illustrations became iconic in the architecture field and catapulted Ferris into national prominence. He wrote about the potential of the future city with an extravagant, millennial fervor and apparently inspired Corbett to adopt a more expansive, opinionated style of advocacy.[98]

Ferriss's highly expressionistic drawing style was instantly recognizable. His painterly use of charcoal, carbon, and crayon—the soft focus, deep shadows, and coronas of light—gave the skyscaper city and its vertically separated travelways a monumental, otherworldly aspect. His illustrations used stagecraft to conjure cityscapes of immanent mystery and moment.

For the 1923 elevated-arcade project, Ferriss made several dynamic perspective views to supplement the cross sections. His elevated travelways had a neo-Gothic character: harmonious and dignified, yet filled with Manhattan's busy rush. Through the 1920s, Ferris collaborated with Corbett and other designers such as Raymond Hood to illustrate future-city schemes with vertically separated travelways. He adopted vertical traffic separation as a central concern in his own visionary work.

Ferriss's style and vision were tremendously successful. By the mid-1920s he was America's best-known illustrator of the contemporary and future city. His striking vistas "became the look of the future in the popular imagination," according to the historians Corn and Horrigan. His work was published in professional journals and exhibited internationally; he was in great demand as a teacher and lectured on design and rendering at leading universities. He began to advise city planners and consult for city-planning groups in several cities.[99]

Ferriss's first book, *The Metropolis of Tomorrow* (1929), collected his thoughts on city and transportation planning. The modern city was "a little like Dante's descent into Hades" because of noise, pollution, jostling crowds, and chaotic appearance. Unchecked skyscraper construction led to increasing traffic congestion, which was

Typical conditions in a commercial district.

First step—an elevated sidewalk of temporary construction.

Second step—arcades on the ground level for standing vehicles.

Third step—pedestrian arcades provided on the upper level as a feature of permanent construction.

Figure 2.32: Ferriss's series illustrating RPNY's four-part arcade progression, 1923. Ferriss used lighting and composition to sell the goal of a "modern Venice."

"rapidly approaching the point of public danger." Urban decentralization was no panacea either. It was an attractive fantasy, but no evidence for it could be found in contemporary trends, and so it "must be dismissed as a mere dream." The multilevel street seemed "in the long run inevitable."[100]

Ferriss had a very specific ideal in mind. He rejected the type of unrelieved density

Figure 2.33: A multilevel roadway in Ferriss's ideal metropolis, 1930. The adjacent ground level is entirely dedicated to vehicles.

that Corbett favored, as well as roadways on high-elevation building terraces. Such facilities put auto noise and pollution at the windows of tower inhabitants and shadowed the city below. He was likely familiar with Eliel Saarinen's 1923 Chicago Lake Front project that integrated an elevated pedestrian level, below-grade expressway, and gigantic underground garage into a City Beautiful plan. He wrote that Saarinen's "decided point of view may, before long, influence our larger civic projects." Ferriss's imaginary city was intensively multilevel yet orderly, with towers widely spaced to provide light and air. The entire ground level was devoted to local motor traffic; express motor traffic and subways ran on underground levels, and pedestrians used elevated walkways along the streets or through the centers of blocks.[101]

Ferriss's work during the 1920s was an outgrowth and expression of the era's cultural and financial exuberance. It proved too flamboyant and impractical for the Great Depression years. Furthermore, his vision of the city as an omni-coordinated megaconstruct implied a level of technocratic control that society increasingly viewed with disfavor. His second book was tentatively titled *Remold the Metropolis* and had the separation of pedestrian and vehicular traffic as a central focus, but it was canceled. He ceased making ideal-city visions by the mid-1930s and quit the role of futurist. Yet he retained his passion for drawing constructs of great scale and ambition, such as airports, dams, bridges, and important buildings. Meanwhile, his 1920s vision and brio were emulated by others. The sublime, expressionistic future city became a touchstone of science fiction, and filtered into pulp magazines, advertisements, comic strips, and technology periodicals.[102]

Le Corbusier

During the first decade of his career, the Swiss architect Charles-Édouard Jeanneret (1887–1965) was a garden-city enthusiast and devotee of Camillo Sitte. As an assistant to Peter Behrens in 1910, he made a careful study of the Hampstead Garden Suburb plan. Before and during World War I, he designed two garden suburbs, one with a curvilinear layout, the other similar to an Unwin-style cul-de-sac. He wrote that city streets should be designed for the movement and delight of pedestrians, and that vehicles should travel on a separate yet interlaced network.[103]

Jeanneret moved to Paris in 1917 and over the next several years made drastic changes to his inner life and professional outlook. He invented an alter ego named Le Corbusier, one that would always be strong and brave, never subject to doubt or discouragement. Le Corbusier attacked Jeanneret's earlier positions on urban design. Sitte's lessons on visual beauty became "insidious pleas." Irregular, winding street layouts were now morally suspect, "the result of happy-go-lucky heedlessness, of looseness, lack of concentration and animality." Such layouts could not survive the unceasing press of motor vehicles. Fast traffic demanded new urban forms, and the lively, picturesque qualities of traditional streetscapes had to be sacrificed.[104]

Four Traffic Schemes

Throughout the 1920s and 1930s, Le Corbusier generated a variety of large-scale city-planning models that glorified fast auto traffic. His favorite techniques of traffic separation were vertically layered traffic levels, multilevel roadways, and superblocks.

Le Corbusier published his *pilotis*-city (city on stilts) scheme in a 1921 issue of his magazine *L'esprit nouveau*. It had four transportation levels: subway tubes underground, a freight level on the surface, a raised podium for rapid traffic and pedestrians, and pedestrian terraces and skybridges at roof level. The concept resembled several previous schemes. In the 1860s the French engineer Henri-Jules Borie proposed that giant complexes of megastructures be inserted into central Paris. Each building could be as long as 366 meters (1,200 feet) and ten to eleven stories tall—taller than any inhabited building in the world at that time. Broad terraces and skybridges at the fifth story formed a continuous upper-level pedestrian network. Borie claimed that his scheme would triple the amount of circulation space, and Le Corbusier made exactly the same claim about his pilotis city.

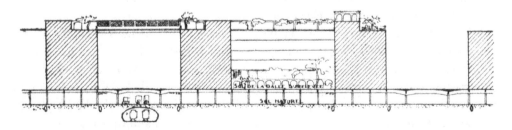

Figure 2.34: Le Corbusier's Pilotis City, 1921. Many of his later ideal-city plans had multiple transportation levels in some variation of this scheme. © F.L.C. / ADAGP, Paris / Artists Rights Society (ARS), New York 2019.

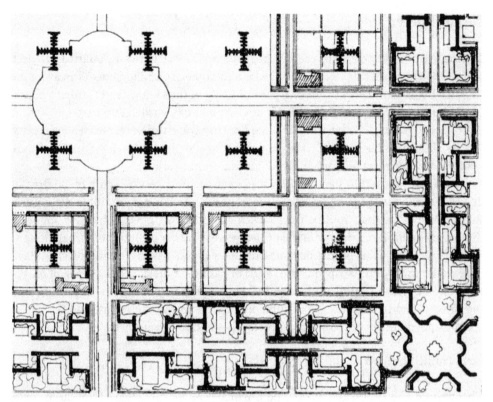

Figure 2.35: Le Corbusier's City for Three Million, 1923. Plan detail shows cruciform business towers surrounded by residential superblocks. Elevated highways run along the major axes, and residential slabs cross over surface roads. © F.L.C. / ADAGP, Paris / Artists Rights Society (ARS), New York 2019.

The pilotis-city's multilevel transportation base resembled King Camp Gillette's utopian Metropolis scheme (figure 1.19), as well as a 1910 scheme by the French architect Eugène Henard (which was based on popular illustrations of the time). Another influence was a 1906 *Scientific American* cover by C. McKnight Smith that showed transportation facilities stacked on six levels (figure 2.8).[105]

Le Corbusier made a splash with his "Contemporary City for Three Million Inhabitants," presented at the 1922 Salon d'Automne art exhibition in Paris. It was a general model intended to replace existing historic cities, which would be summarily demolished. The thoroughly rationalized and regimented plan was structured by extremely broad arterials and expressways. They were typically spaced 400 meters (1,300 feet) apart and formed a grid of superblocks as large as 29 hectares (72 acres) in area. The vertical traffic configuration was similar to that of the pilotis city, with the addition of multiple mass-transit levels belowground.[106]

In 1925, Le Corbusier exhibited his Immeubles Villas scheme at L'Esprit Nouveau pavilion at the Exposition Internationale des Arts Decoratifs in Paris. The scheme's apartment district was a grid of perimeter blocks, each approximately 6 hectares (14 acres) in size. The vertical traffic separation was similar to that of the pilotis city, but only the streets were multilevel, not the whole city. The scheme also had multistory skybridges and under-street tunnels that allowed residents to walk from one superblock to another.[107]

The pilotis-city scheme was republished in Le Corbusier's book *Vers une architecture*

(1923), which was translated in 1927 as *Towards a New Architecture*. His 1922 and 1925 schemes appeared in his book *Urbanisme* (1925), which was translated in 1929 as *The City of To-morrow and Its Planning*. These early books were bestsellers and caused a great stir in the architecture and planning fields. Le Corbusier's urban plans conveyed a sense of grand scale, strict order, and perfect function, like an intricate clockwork. His audacious visual presentations were amplified by his aggressive, peremptory rhetoric, which projected revolutionary fervor and brooked no dissent. Architecture students in particular were ardent admirers.

Le Corbusier began working on his book *The Radiant City* in 1930; it was published in 1935 but not translated into English until 1967. The Radiant City was yet another large-scale model for new cities. It drew on his earlier planning models, but the layout was more strictly cellular and confining for walkers and bicyclists. Each superblock was bordered by a vertical stack of freight arterials and high-speed expressways. Walkers could only move from one superblock to another via a few tunnels that crossed underneath the highways, or via the corridors in a few buildings that crossed over the highways.[108]

Themes

Le Corbusier was frequently inconsistent and self-contradictory in his writings and principles, but the bulk of his work made his positions clear. The most important traffic-planning goals were separating the pedestrian from the auto and allowing autos to zoom across the city without interruption. He was zealously opposed to the "corridor street," the traditional form of urban streets that had existed in most cultures since the dawn of cities. According to Le Corbusier, the corridor street was monotonous and depressing. It lacked light, air, and broad vistas; it was crowded, congested, dangerous, and polluted. "The present idea of the street must be abolished: DEATH OF THE STREET! DEATH OF THE STREET!" he ranted.[109]

When traditional streets and other traditional forms like city squares were eliminated, traditional street life would disappear too. All outdoor social interaction would take place on lawns, terraces, rooftops, and the like. Le Corbusier's urban designs were simply not intended to foster active street life along roadways.

Le Corbusier said that cities must tear down and remake their centers. He demanded increased density in the form of regimented towers set within grids of superblocks, and claimed that was necessary to achieve prosperity and a high quality of life. Le Corbusier was very much a centralizer, but while his plans centralized the city and its population, his urban designs aimed to deconcentrate the spaces that surrounded buildings. He idolized wide-open spaces within the city, no matter whether they were lawns, plazas, or broad highways.

Le Corbusier was not opposed to suburbs *per se*. Indeed, his Contemporary City for Three Million housed two million in garden suburbs. But his ideal cities were high-density and compact, approximately 13 kilometers (8 mi.) in diameter. Upon encountering the sprawling metropolises of America in 1935, he quipped, "Yes, the cancer is in good health." He vehemently criticized distended agglomerations 100 kilometers (60 mi.) in diameter as "the great evil of the USA"; they wasted resources on a massive scale and forced workers into an exhausting routine of long daily commutes. He blamed long commutes for depleting civic spirit, dividing families, and emasculating the American male.[110]

Influences

Le Corbusier's early books attracted global attention and controversy. In America, his planning ideas inspired some urban designers like Harvey Wiley Corbett, Raymond Hood, and Hugh Ferriss. But most American planners, engineers, businessmen, and journalists of the 1920s and 1930s dismissed Le Corbusier's large-scale visions as overly mechanical, fantastical, insensitive, and foreign to American values. They could be implemented only under the most authoritarian political regimes imaginable. It was no coincidence that Le Corbusier dedicated *The Radiant City* "to authority."[111]

However, few depictions of expressway-dominated downtowns were as compelling or well known. During the 1940s and 1950s, the Corbusian planning vision filtered into the professions and colored the default recommendations for downtowns, urban renewal, and high-density suburbs. The consensus vision for downtowns featured superblocks with towers and expansive lawns or plazas; the superblocks were bordered by broad arterials and linked by skybridges or pedestrian tunnels. Cities around the world adopted those prescriptions. American city leaders believed that the prescriptions would help downtowns, but instead they made downtowns less attractive and livable. That, in turn, hastened the suburbanization trend.

One problem was that Le Corbusier badly underestimated the amount of parking and roadway space that his schemes would require. As James Dunnett pointed out, the schemes could work as envisioned only if auto use was radically limited. But Le Corbusier paid little attention to alternative travel modes. His paramount transportation concern was fast auto traffic. As a result, the "tower in the park" model, when translated into reality, became the "tower in the parking lot."[112]

In the final analysis, Le Corbusier and his modernist-architect followers had a powerful influence on the architecture profession, a relatively small influence on urban planning, and a negligible influence on traffic engineering. In the traffic field, they augmented certain trends that were already well underway. They helped diminish the role of traditional streets and squares as civic space; encourage superblocks; and promote the urban freeway as a harbinger of dynamism, progress, and sublime futurity. Perhaps their strongest influence in the traffic field, especially during the second half of the twentieth century, was the promotion of pedestrian separation. They designed and inspired numerous skywalks and tunnelwalks (which were popular in the large cities of North America and East Asia); pedestrian malls (which were briefly popular in North America); and carfree suburban centers (which were popular in Europe).[113]

John Harriss

John A. Harriss (1875–1938) combined two very different vocations in his career: multimillionaire businessman and traffic planner. Although he was educated as a physician, he gave up medicine for business, and was president of a variety of firms. He launched and ran a large munitions manufacturing firm during World War I, which likely boosted him into the ranks of the superwealthy. His personal wealth was reported to be forty million dollars.[114]

From his office overlooking Fifth Avenue in Manhattan, Harriss watched the traffic jams and became obsessed with traffic planning. He toured European cities to learn all he could about the topic. His reform ideas came to the attention of Police Commissioner Richard Enright and Mayor John Hylan, and in 1918 they asked him to work for the city. According to the mayor, "after some persuasion he was induced to accept the position of deputy police commissioner in charge of the regulation of traffic in the greatest city in America." The position was unpaid.[115]

Harriss took his position along with a dozen or more "multimillionaire commissioners" who worked with the police department during the Hylan administration (the three wealthiest being Rodman Wanamaker, Edmond Guggenheim, and T. Coleman DuPont). Harriss donated two of his Riverside Drive townhouses to be a police clubhouse, fully equipped with a dormitory, gym, library, and offices. One of his duties was to supervise the clubhouse. Harriss had a cheerful personality, full of humor and song; he was very sociable and equally at ease in the company of beat policemen and fellow millionaires. He was generous to his friends and the causes he supported, and hosted numerous parties and dinners for policemen and servicemen.[116]

Harriss carried out relatively prosaic actions to speed traffic, like creating more one-way streets and widening streets by ripping out sidewalks. In addition, in autumn 1918 he introduced a traffic-separation program that designated 12 of Manhattan's north-south roadways to be exclusively for business vehicles and 10 exclusively for passenger vehicles. Many of the affected businesses protested, and in early 1919 the restrictions were lifted from some of the roadways. On the other roadways, the restrictions were changed to apply only during daytime hours. Harriss said the program was "eminently effective" at relieving congestion, and noted that similar restrictions had been applied to two Brooklyn thoroughfares.[117]

In 1919 Harris spent $20,000 of his own money to erect traffic-signal towers along Fifth Avenue. It was one of the earliest coordinated traffic-signal systems in America. Mayor Hylan reported that "traffic has been speeded up, so that the real value of the motor vehicle could be realized." He gushed that Harriss had "revolutionized our ideas on the evolution of traffic efficiency." Journalists began calling Harriss a leading traffic expert.[118]

Harriss also advocated ambitious and increasingly extravagant traffic visions, similar to the more grandiose ideas of the 1890–1913 period. He was a skilled promoter and understood that the more extreme and fantastic the proposal, the more likely it was to cause a sensation in the popular press. His proposals were featured with spectacular illustrations in the pages of *Popular Science*, *Collier's*, *The American City*, and even *Science and Invention*, which was the prototype of science-fiction pulp magazines.

Harriss started playing the role of visionary in 1918 by proposing an elevated roadway on Sixth Avenue. The upper roadway would carry through traffic and would have sidewalks that accessed upper-level retail in the abutting buildings. Louis Biedermann, the artist who had envisioned a street of many skybridges two decades earlier, illustrated Harriss's concept for *Popular Science* in 1921.[119]

Harriss's proposals became more improbable and outré. In 1922 he outlined his vision for large cities fifty years in the future. Major roadways would be double-decked, forming "vast arcades, tunneling through massive business blocks." The upper level

Figure 2.36: Harriss's concept for elevated auto roads flanking elevated railways, 1921. Illustration by Louis Biedermann.

would carry high-speed automobiles. Commuters would park in 25-story garages and take elevators to rooftop airports.[120]

In 1924 Harriss proposed to drain the East River and build in its place a multi-level transportation structure 5 miles (8 km) long and 500 feet (150 m) wide. The lower level would accommodate heavy truck traffic, garages, and subway lines. The upper level would carry local and express auto traffic in separate lanes, and have a central pedestrian promenade. High schools and playgrounds would be built on the edges of the vast highway.[121]

In 1927 Harriss proposed a system of six-level highways laced through Manhattan and extending to the suburbs. Each level would be dedicated to a different type of traffic as follows: ground level for local mixed traffic; second level for truck traffic; third and fourth levels for bus traffic and bus stations; fifth level for autos, promenade walks, rest rooms, and gasoline stations; top level for high-speed auto traffic. "It will segregate all types of vehicles," Harriss explained. "I trust it will lift us out of the tedium of present-day conditions." He said the multilevel highway system would solve Manhattan's traffic problems for the next one hundred years.[122]

During the latter years of his government service, Harriss traveled and lectured internationally, consulting with municipalities and helping set up traffic signals. He exited city government in 1925, at the end of Mayor Hylan's term, yet continued to be recognized as an international expert. In 1928, the *New York Times* identified Harriss as the leader of the multilevel-street philosophy in Manhattan.[123]

Harriss became president of the Broadway Association in 1929 and head of the Citizens Street Traffic Committee in 1930. The latter was sponsored by the Automobile Club of America and lobbied for congestion-relief measures in New York City.

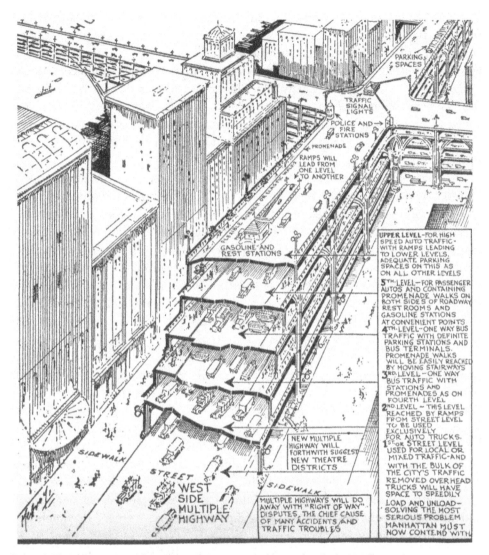

Within the illustration the following labels appear:

PARKING SPACES

TRAFFIC SIGNAL LIGHTS

POLICE AND → FIRE STATIONS

PROMENADE

RAMPS WILL LEAD FROM ONE LEVEL TO ANOTHER

GASOLINE AND REST STATIONS

UPPER LEVEL–FOR HIGH SPEED AUTO TRAFFIC– WITH RAMPS LEADING TO LOWER LEVELS. ADEQUATE PARKING SPACES ON THIS AS ON ALL OTHER LEVELS

5TH. LEVEL–FOR PASSENGER AUTOS AND CONTAINING PROMENADE WALKS ON BOTH SIDES OF ROADWAY REST ROOMS AND GASOLINE STATIONS AT CONVENIENT POINTS

4TH. LEVEL–ONE WAY BUS TRAFFIC WITH DEFINITE PARKING STATIONS AND BUS TERMINALS. PROMENADE WALKS WILL BE EASILY REACHED BY MOVING STAIRWAYS

3RD. LEVEL–ONE WAY BUS TRAFFIC WITH STATIONS AND PROMENADES AS ON FOURTH LEVEL

2ND. LEVEL – THIS LEVEL REACHED BY RAMPS FROM STREET LEVEL TO BE USED EXCLUSIVELY FOR AUTO TRUCKS.

1ST. OR STREET LEVEL USED FOR LOCAL OR MIXED TRAFFIC–AND WITH THE BULK OF THE CITY'S TRAFFIC REMOVED OVERHEAD TRUCKS WILL HAVE SPACE TO SPEEDILY LOAD AND UNLOAD– SOLVING THE MOST SERIOUS PROBLEM MANHATTAN MUST NOW CONTEND WITH

NEW MULTIPLE HIGHWAY WILL FORTHWITH SUGGEST NEW THEATRE DISTRICTS

SIDEWALK

STREET

WEST SIDE MULTIPLE HIGHWAY

SIDEWALK

MULTIPLE HIGHWAYS WILL DO AWAY WITH "RIGHT OF WAY" DISPUTES, THE CHIEF CAUSE OF MANY ACCIDENTS AND TRAFFIC TROUBLES

Figure 2.37: Harriss's citywide system of six-story roadways, detail of 1927 illustration.

Harriss continued to advocate a system of multilevel streets, but in structures even more gigantic—up to twelve roadway levels high. The structures' roadways could access the abutting buildings on multiple levels; each level could have shops that catered to the particular class of traffic on that level.[124]

Harriss lost his fortune in the economic crash of the Great Depression and thereafter lived on the goodwill and donations of his friends. His reputation never dimmed. When he died in 1938, his pallbearers included Governor Lehman, former governor Al Smith, Mayor La Guardia, and Walter P. Chrysler, founder of the Chrysler Corporation.[125]

Chapter 2 Summary

During the early decades of the twentieth century, New York City raced ahead of other cities in its bid to become supertall and superdense. It was the global locus of vertical-traffic-separation schemes and visions; only a few other cities were near rivals, particularly Chicago. The New York-New Jersey Hudson River complex was a pioneering urban highway system that had numerous vertical-separation elements. It was the first limited-access highway system to carry both passenger and commercial traffic through urban areas. Meanwhile, Chicago was the first city to build stacked roadways with abutter access on all levels. And Chicago's freight-subway system was a unique model that ultimately failed to compete against trucking. It helped inspire freight-subway plans in the New York region but, by the late 1920s, those too were superseded by trucking.

From the turn of the century through the late 1920s, vertical-traffic-separation visions exhibited definite changes in response to expanding automobility. Abutter access on multiple levels faded from the visions as designers accepted the principle of limited access. As abutter access disappeared, so did the possibility for multilevel roadways to function on all levels as social and civic spaces, like ordinary streets. In most schemes through the mid-1920s, pedestrians were given the prime space—the uppermost level open to the sky. After the mid-1920s, schemes like the West Side Elevated Highway and John A. Harriss's six-level highway pointed toward a different configuration, in which automobiles occupied the top level while walkers were relegated to lower or underground levels.

As was the case in the previous century, common themes appeared when reasons were given for vertical traffic separation and multilevel streets. Above all, visionaries claimed that their schemes would speed motor vehicles, reduce or eliminate congestion, and increase business activity and property values. Some also promised improved safety (a claim that appeared more frequently as the 1920s progressed); greater civic beauty and order; improved environmental qualities such as sunlight, fresh air, and quiet; and more pleasurable walking and shopping. Some of the claims were marketing fluff, not based on evidence or experience. Nevertheless, during the boom years of the 1920s and the depression years of the 1930s, a cadre of designers, engineers, and automakers believed that grade-separated expressways were the inevitable and rational path to city prosperity.

A noteworthy aspect of hyperurbanism until the 1930s was that no individuals stood out as enablers of a broad movement. Hyperurban proposals appeared and faded from view over the decades, often repeating, but never developing a large body of experience or community of practitioners. Hyperurbanism was mostly a paper movement that lacked a true continuity of ideas. Many who seriously investigated the concept found critical disadvantages and impracticalities that stopped further development. But its influence should not be discounted as frivolous or irrelevant. By the 1930s it had enlarged the public's awareness of urban futures, and excited many designers by the vigor and ambition of its dreams.

CHAPTER 3
Horizontal Traffic Separation: Divided Roadways

Divided roadways are physically marked or divided along their lengths to form separate lanes or travelways. The lanes or travelways are reserved for different types of traffic that have different functions and purposes. The divisions can be as minimal as a painted line or railing, or as elaborate as a landscaped park within a wide median.

Roadways with designated walkways date back at least to Kanesh, an Old Assyrian merchant town that flourished circa 1900 BC (located in modern Kültepe, Turkey). Sidewalks were built in the cities of Etruscan Italy and the Roman Republic, and arcades (roofed sidewalks) were built in Rome by the first century BC. After large parts of Rome were destroyed by fire, Emperor Nero encouraged arcades in the rebuilt areas, and by the second century AD they were customary in Rome, the towns of central Italy, and Roman colonial settlements. The famous porticoes of Bologna, Italy, began to appear around AD 1100, and the form spread throughout Europe during the Middle Ages.[1]

The Chinese city of Chang'an, capital of the Western Han dynasty, was built in the second and first centuries BC. Its main avenues were divided into three lanes by drainage ditches; the central lane was 20 meters (66 feet) wide and reserved for imperial use. Luoyang, a later imperial capital, had a similar arrangement except that the lanes were divided by walls. The pattern of a main avenue with a separated central lane persisted in Chinese society for centuries. Typically the central lane was reserved for walkers and palanquins, and the outer lanes for wagons and carriages.[2]

In European cities, the traffic-separation idea was eventually applied to animal and wheeled traffic. During the 1600s different types of animal and wheeled traffic began to be sorted into the lanes of divided roadways. Later, in the nineteenth century, a few projects and visions elaborated that concept by differentiating more traffic types and sorting each into its own lane or travelway.

Early Promenades and Boulevards

Early European boulevards evolved from the tastes and recreational pursuits of the aristocracy. European culture become more cosmopolitan and socially intertwined during the 1500s because of more frequent wars between nations, peacetime travel, and aristocratic intermarriage. Landscape forms and their associated traditions were transmitted across borders and between cultures, leading to new inventions and hybrids.

One aristocratic pursuit was the promenade. Promenades developed from a variety of traditions including the semi-public gardens and parks of the Italian Renaissance and Northern European hunting grounds. As the scale of landscaped grounds expanded to match the ostentation and egos of landowners, the *alleé*, a long outdoor corridor formed by straight rows of planted trees, became prevalent. Nobles and aristocrats used alleés for recreation and sport, wealth display, socializing, and the pursuit of romance within exclusive domains. On occasion, these garden forms were imported into urban settings. In 1536 Charles V, the Holy Roman Emperor, had the Lange Voorhout in The Hague planted with a double row of trees. Expensive residences and prominent institutions were built along the landscaped path, and by the end of the century it was the most fashionable promenade in the region. By the early 1600s, wooden railings had been installed to separate the everyday traffic on the side lanes from the more recreational traffic and activities in the center.[3]

A promenade in Berlin was inspired by the Lange Voorhout. Following the terrible destruction of the Thirty Years War, Prince-Elector Friedrich Wilhelm sought to rebuild the city in a grand and enlightened manner. In 1647 he built a promenade from the royal palace west to the royal hunting park; the promenade and park were

Figure 3.1: View of Lange Voorhout by Jan van Call, ca. 1690. Courtesy of Haags Gemeentearchief.

A HISTORY OF STREET NETWORKS • CHAPTER 3

opened to the public. The landscaped portion of the promenade was about 2,850 feet (870 m) long, 200 feet (61 m) wide, and lined with double rows of nut and linden trees. The roadway became known as the Unter den Linden. It eventually developed as an exclusive, high-status address boasting grand mansions and the finest hotels, academies, and museums. By the nineteenth century its wheeled traffic was separated from its other traffic: carts and carriages ran in the side lanes, while the center mall had a bridle path, shaded walkways, and park benches. As the main ceremonial thoroughfare in a capital city, the Unter den Linden was prominent and well admired. It was the model for similar promenades in Northern Germany and Poland that used allées and railings to separate utilitarian and recreational traffic.[4]

During the 1600s, the wealthy and upper-middle classes of Europe were growing and seeking new ways to enjoy and publicly display their leisure. The game known in French as *palemail* or *paille maille* (*pall mall* in English) fit that purpose well. The game used wooden mallets, balls, and hoops, like croquet, but was played over longer distances, like golf. Commoners played on a dry, bare field or wide road, but the lords played on a purpose-built course called a *mail*. A mail was a straight corridor 0.5 mile (0.8 km) or more in length bordered by low walls.

Figure 3.2: Palemail player, 1717. Overhead swings could drive the ball long distances.

Palemail originated in Italy and was imported to Paris in 1597. A few years later, King Henry IV had a mail built along the Seine River (just inside the city wall near the Bastille) that became the city's most popular recreation ground. Palemail was enthusiastically adopted by the leisure class and spread to cities throughout France. It spread to the Netherlands and England, where grounds such as the Maliebann in Utrecht and the Pall Mall in London were well known.[5]

When the game fell out of fashion in the mid-1600s, most of the grounds were converted to tree-lined pedestrian promenades. New malls were built for the sole purpose of promenading. The words *mail* and *mall* came to signify promenades without gaming activities.

Another very popular leisure activity was a manner of carriage promenading that also originated in Italy. Members of high society would gather at a certain time each day to drive carriages and socialize. The first roadway made specially for that purpose was the cours la Reine in Paris. It was built in 1616 by Queen Marie de Médicis in a bid to supersede the memory of her rival, the well-liked former queen Margeurite de

Valois. Queen Marguerite had created a very successful allée for walking in the royal Tuileries garden that was open to all classes of people. After Margeurite's death, Marie built the cours la Reine to have a very different character.

It was a triple allée of planted trees extending about 1,340 meters (4,400 feet) along the banks of the Seine, west of the Tuileries garden. It could accommodate four carriages abreast in the center lane and two abreast in each of the side lanes. The cours was gated and guarded, and only the wealthy (or those who could pass as wealthy) were allowed to enter. It was one of the most exclusive social venues in the city, very popular and often crowded with carriages, especially on summer evenings. It was a place to announce oneself, ostentatiously display wealth, socialize, and engage in courting and romance.

The pastime of daily carriage promenading spread across France and to other European towns and cities. Although the gates and guards of the cours la Reine were not generally imitated, in some cities class distinctions continued to be an important part of the promenade experience. The historian Henry Lawrence wrote that in Aix-en-Provence, informal rules "dictated that people of different classes use separate sides of the promenade at different hours of the day. The classes were not to mix, and social inferiors were chased away with derisive laughter."[6]

The *boulevard* was a type of carriage promenade that originated from military considerations. In the 1670s King Louis XIV decided that Paris was no longer at risk of foreign attack. As a demonstration of his own glory and beneficence, he ordered that the city's defensive walls be converted to the *Grands Boulevards* for pleasure riding and strolling. The project took more than thirty years to complete. The walls—actually broad earthen ramparts—were planted with rows of trees that defined three lanes. The center allée was reserved for promenading carriages, and the side lanes for promenaders on foot. Commercial traffic was banned. The circumferential route was elevated as it traveled on top of the ramparts, but descended to ground level to cross the major streets radiating from the city's center.

The Grands Boulevards were little used until the 1750s, when the land nearby

Figure 3.3: Palemail grounds, after an illustration by N. Guérard, ca. early 1700s.

A HISTORY OF STREET NETWORKS • CHAPTER 3

was developed as fashionable housing and entertainment districts. Images from this period show that pedestrians sometimes strolled and chatted in the central vehicular ways and that, on occasion, the central ways were used for lively, crowded street fairs. By the 1760s, commercial traffic was permitted. It was regulated to control speed and parking, and to keep pedestrians and pushcarts on the side lanes. City-wall boulevards soon gained currency throughout Europe. Many cities converted their defensive walls, or built alongside their walls, or demolished their walls and built in the cleared space. The Napoleonic regime and its aftermath accelerated the demolition of city walls across Europe.[7]

By the mid-1800s, promenades, boulevards, and other types of divided streets that separated and allocated traffic according to function were prevalent throughout urban Europe. Over a period of centuries, they had developed cultural associations with elite society and the status markers of wealth and leisure. By the mid-1800s, many were open to commercial and freight traffic, but still retained connotations of affluence.

Etienne Cabet, *Travels in Icaria*

Etienne Cabet was a French lawyer, writer, and radical leftist who became prominent during the 1830s as a critic of the repressive Louis-Philippe regime. His fiery tracts and political activities landed him in trouble, and in 1834 he was convicted of writing documents that were "an affront to the king." Given a choice of imprisonment or five years of exile, he moved to London. He spent much of his exile in the British Museum's library writing books. One was the utopian novel *Travels in Icaria*, which was published widely in 1840.

The book explored the imaginary country of Icaria: its history, culture, politics, economics, and physical planning. Icaria's sociopolitical system was based on brotherly love, labor-saving machinery, and near-total state control. By putting his proto-communist program in the form of a speculative novel, Cabet was able to avoid further legal charges in France.

Cabet could draw upon more than seventy years of utopian and reformist thought on the topic of Paris's reconstruction. Among his many influences, one may have been the reform architect Pierre Patte, whose pioneering treatise on urban design was published in 1769. In Patte's view, an ideal city had a comprehensive street plan, easy circulation, wide streets (40–60 feet or 12–18 meters wide in temperate climates), and awning-covered sidewalks. Another was Louis-Sébastien Mercier, author of the very popular utopian novel *L'an 2440, rêve s'il en fut jamais* (1770). Mercier described a far-future Paris in which most wheeled traffic was banned, congestion was eliminated, and the few remaining coaches obeyed a speed limit and kept to the right side of the street.[8]

Another likely influence was an 1829 article by John Claudius Loudon, the world-renowned landscaper and gardening expert. Loudon was interested in housing and planning reform, and believed that the urban masses should live in healthful, convenient suburbs. His article described an ideal city plan and street layout. The city occupied a circular area 8.5 miles (14 km) in diameter and was arranged like a target. Concentric bands of residential "town" space alternated with nonresidential "country" space, and the central circle contained national and municipal government buildings. The city's streets were laid out in a radial-concentric pattern. In the town zones, heavy freight traffic and cattle herds were limited to every alternate street, while the remaining streets could be used by light freight traffic such as mail carriers. Freight traffic in the country zones was also limited to certain streets. All streets had public transit, which could be horse-drawn buses, mechanized buses, or even steam carriages on rails. The latter could move people from zone to zone "with inconceivable rapidity."[9]

Cabet's book was mainly concerned with Icaria's capital city, the city of Icara. It was circular, bisected by a river, and centered on a circular island. The shape obviously resembled Paris. The city's street system was generally laid out as a grid and used traffic separation to an unusual degree. While some streets had specialized lanes, the more important characteristic was that most streets were specialized by mode and function.

The system had five street types. *Railroad streets* (with four rail tracks) and *canal streets* were intended for heavy freight movement and served industrial and warehouse areas. Merchandise wagons were permitted to travel only on those streets. *Grooved streets* had four lanes cut with deep grooves that guided the wheels of vehicles. Only passenger-carrying omnibuses were permitted on the grooved streets. The double-decker, air-conditioned omnibuses were the sole means of passenger transportation, because the city had no private carriages or taxicabs. *Tree-lined streets* were similar to Parisian boulevards and linked the city's public squares. The remaining streets were *dog-cart streets* where household goods were delivered by carts pulled by large dogs. Omnibus and wagon traffic were prohibited on those streets.

Cabet's characters used a multicolored map to discuss the city's street system. The map designated each street type by a different color: railroad streets in red, canal streets in blue, grooved streets in yellow, and tree-lined streets in black. The main goals of the transportation system were safety, cleanliness, and convenience. The grooves in the omnibus streets would keep vehicles in their lanes and prevent vehicular collisions. Segregating freight traffic from passenger traffic would also reduce collisions. Icara's mass-transit system would be faster than any private carriage; the omnibuses' two-minute headways ensured that "all the citizens were transported everywhere more conveniently than if each had a separate rig."

In addition to its roadway network, the city had a separate pathway system. Every residential block had park or garden space in its interior, which was traversed by two perpendicular mid-block pathways. That allowed continuous pedestrian travel throughout the city on a separate system. When using the streets, pedestrians found numerous safety features including crosswalks marked by columns, mid-crossing refuge zones, and pedestrian bridges and tunnels across some streets. All sidewalks and street intersections were covered by glass canopies, and the freight streets that connected the city's large depots were completely roofed by glass canopies.[10]

Travels in Icaria was an immediate bestseller, going through five printings in nine years. Cabet's timing was fortuitous and his book was well fitted to the era's popular tastes. Maxime du Camp, who was a teenager in the 1830s, recalled that "from 1830 to 1840 social, philosophical and religious innovation became a mania." Numerous utopian movements were springing into existence, each preaching its own system of world reform. Middle-class professionals and skilled artisans were particularly responsive

Icara: Typical Streets and Blocks

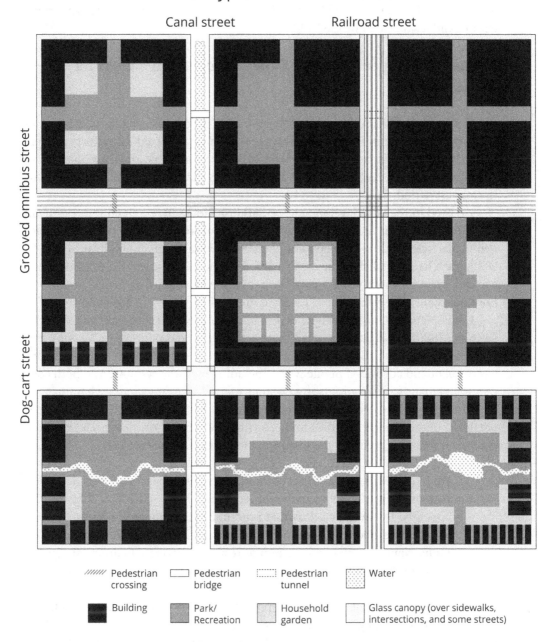

Figure 3.4: A visualization of Icara showing streets specialized for vehicle modes, and the continuous through-block pedestrian system.

to Cabet's message of nonviolent revolution. *Travels in Icaria* was a common sight in French homes throughout the 1840s, and was published and reviewed internationally. Together with Cabet's successful newspaper *Le Populaire*, it launched an international utopian movement some 100,000 persons strong, known as the Icarians.[11]

Cabet and his followers emigrated to the United States from 1847 to 1848. Over the subsequent decades the Icarians created the longest-lived nonreligious utopian community movement in America. Seven Icarian colonies were established across the Midwest and in Texas and California. The colonies gradually merged into American culture and disappeared by the 1890s.[12]

Avenue de l'Imperatrice and Other European Avenues and Boulevards

Charles Louis Napoléon Bonaparte (Napoléon III) began pressing his claim as successor to Napoléon I in 1832, when he was twenty-four years old. His efforts to overthrow the French regime got him arrested, exiled for four years, and then imprisoned for six years. He traveled to several countries during his exile but lived in London for the longest period, from 1838 to 1840.

He lived in the new development of Carleton House Terrace and loved to stroll the adjacent gardens and newly redesigned St. James Park. Those places were elements of a large-scale redevelopment planned by John Nash and built from 1811 to 1832. Nash had demolished the area's existing blocks to make way for Regent Street, a grand street that completed a corridor between two large parks. Louis-Napoleon's London sojourn likely influenced his ideas about city building in a general sense.[13]

Louis-Napoléon visited fellow exile Etienne Cabet seven or eight times in the spring of 1839. Cabet later reported that they spoke about political philosophy and universal suffrage; whether they discussed city planning is unknown. However, both wrote about and advocated public works including roadway systems. And both conceived city maps with idealized street layouts marked in multicolored schemes.[14]

When the ruler of France was overthrown in 1848, Louis-Napoléon was elected president of the French Republic and returned to France triumphant. He carried a document in his luggage that the historian Michel Carmona described:

> One long roll of parchment seemed especially precious: it was a map of Paris, with zebra stripes of red, green, blue, and yellow that appeared to have been drawn at random. In fact, there was nothing random about the composition of that document; for years Louis-Napoléon had had the aim of restoring Paris to its imperial splendor.[15]

Five years later, Louis-Napoléon appointed Baron Haussmann to carry out his program for modernizing Paris. On Haussmann's first day on the job, Louis-Napoléon showed him the multicolored street plan. The map indicated new avenues and boulevards that Louis-Napoléon wished to carve through the medieval fabric of Paris, and the colors corresponded to the urgency of construction.[16]

The emperor felt that a new thoroughfare system was urgent for numerous reasons such as congestion relief, travel convenience, health, civic beauty, and the suppression of revolutionary violence. Most of his proposals were related to deconcentration, in that they involved opening up and clearing out the existing urban fabric of blocks and buildings. The program was neither unusual nor unwelcome. Even before he took office, French reformers were agreed that Paris needed a new arterial network, and from the late 1840s to early 1850s, several had proposed grand schemes for a citywide

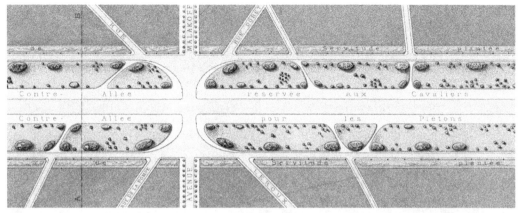

Figure 3.5: Avenue de l'Imperatrice, plan detail, 1873, with lanes reserved for equestrians and walkers, iron fences lining the sidewalks, and required landscaped setbacks. Courtesy of Universitäts- und Landesbibliothek Düsseldorf, urn.

network. Louis-Napoléon's vision, in its broad outlines, reflected the contemporary consensus of the French intelligentsia.[17]

One street long desired by Louis-Napoléon was the Avenue de l'Imperatrice. It was only 1.2 kilometers (0.75 mile) long, but it was the widest and grandest of all of Haussmann's boulevards—indeed, the widest in the world. It linked the Arc de Triomphe and its monumental traffic circle to the new Bois de Boulogne city park.[18]

Jacques-Ignace Hittorff, who had been a distinguished city architect for several decades, was the avenue's first designer. He initially proposed a thoroughfare 40 meters (131 feet) wide, but Haussman felt that was a "banal and petty-minded scheme." Haussmann improvised a counter-design on the spot, declaring: "Forty meters? But *monsieur*, we need something twice, three times wider; yes, three times: 120 meters!"[19]

Hittorf had designed the central roadway in the manner of a traditional boulevard, with a double row of trees separating each lane. Haussman, following the emperor's wishes, removed the trees from the central roadway, which created an unprecedented 40-meter-wide (131-foot-wide) expanse of road surface. It was divided into three lanes: one for general traffic, one reserved for equestrians, and one reserved for pedestrians. At first the lanes were separated by railings; by the late 1860s the railings had been removed and the divisions were marked by low curbs.[20]

Haussmann added landscaped malls to both sides of the central roadway. Each was 31 meters (102 feet) wide, which gave the avenue a park-like ambiance. Flanking the malls were service roads with sidewalks. Haussmann specified tall iron fences along the sidewalks that barred vehicular access to the abutting properties. He believed that such fences would abolish traffic congestion on the adjacent roadways. The fences fronted the large, fashionable residences of the wealthy, which were subject to a strict imperial decree. All commercial activities, public gatherings, and industrial uses were prohibited on the properties. Also, the decree mandated a front yard that was 10 meters (33 feet) deep and landscaped as a formal pleasure garden.[21]

The Avenue de l'Imperatrice opened in 1854 and was a most desirable address for the city's wealthy and well-connected elite. It also became an integral part of an enduring social custom: a daily promenade of carriages conveying the upper class and haute bourgeoisie, who eagerly displayed the wealth and status that connoted

Figure 3.6: Avenue de l'Imperatrice, photo by Charles Marville, ca. 1858–1860. Railings separated different traffic types in the central roadway. Courtesy of Bibliothèque Nationale de France.

their place in the social hierarchy. Thus, the avenue's separated and restricted traffic lanes were prominent symbols of class stratification. At four o'clock each afternoon, the swanky promenade moved into the Bois de Bologne for a *tour des lacs* (tour of the lakes). Contemporary observers described kilometers-long lines of carriages threading through the 845-hectare (2,090-acre) park and circling the lakes. The emperor himself often put in an appearance.[22]

As Haussmann explained, his widening of the Avenue de l'Imperatrice was a "continuation of the promenade of the Bois de Boulogne . . . a promenade in rapport with the park embellishments." The social stratification suggested by avenue's separated lanes was formalized in the park's private clubs and facilities built for parties and play. For example, when visiting the racetrack, the general public traveled on a public-access driveway to the public stands. Members of the exclusive Jockey Club took a private driveway to the emperor's iron-gated pavilion.[23]

In part because of these venues and social displays, the Avenue de l'Imperatrice and Bois de Boulogne became internationally famous. They were settings for public theater performed on a grand scale, a daily pageant on wheels. The promenade of carriages was an almost-compulsory social activity that affirmed the social structure of Parisian high society.

Haussmann's most trusted lieutenant was the engineer Jean Charles Adolphe Alphand, who became the director of public works and continued Louis-Napoleon's building program after the emperor was deposed in 1870. Plans of the Avenue de l'Imperatrice appeared in Alphand's book *Les promenades de Paris* (1867, 1873). The two-volume "elephant folio" book was lavishly illustrated with hundreds of drawings of boulevards, avenues, street furnishings, and parks constructed in Paris during the Second Empire. It was extremely popular and influential around the world. The historian David Jordan said it was "the most widely read treatise on urban art in the nineteenth century and influenced the design of cities as diverse as Berlin, Barcelona, Vienna, and Washington."[24]

Olmsted and Vaux: Central Park

Frederick Law Olmsted (1822–1903) was a towering figure in the history of traffic separation and suburbanization. He and Calvert Vaux (1824–1895) invented the term *landscape architecture*, which in their view encompassed public parks and memorials, private subdivisions and residential yards, and associated boulevards, streets, and paths. In their plans for Central Park in Manhattan, Brooklyn, Buffalo, Chicago, and other cities they advanced the theory and practice of horizontal traffic separation and divided streets.

Vaux was an architect whose path to the landscape-architecture profession was fairly straightforward. He was born in London, began his architectural career there, and was well versed in English park design. He was a schoolboy when John Nash's plan for Regent's Park was completed, and his familiarity with Regent's Park had a direct influence on the paths and roadways of Central Park.

Vaux came to America in 1850 to work for the horticulturist Andrew Jackson Downing. Downing was an international celebrity—a leading advocate of rural villas and cottages, landscaping, and urban parks. Vaux's most prestigious project with Downing was a plan for the National Mall in Washington, DC (1851). Their plan was romantic and mostly informal, following contemporary trends in English park design. It had a system of paths, curvilinear carriage drives, and broad, straight transverse roads that continued the L'Enfant grid.

Olmsted's career took a more circuitous route. For most of his twenties, he was a self-taught farmer with a strong interest in land improvement and scientific management. In his thirties, he was an author and publisher. He wrote popular-travel books and articles, was a correspondent for the *New York Times*, and was an editor and managing partner of *Putnam's Monthly Magazine*, a literary magazine. Olmsted's travel writing took him to the American South, and as a result he became an anti-slavery writer. He was known as a public intellectual who would argue for an ethical cause on the national stage.

Olmsted made two major trips to Europe in 1850 and 1856, visiting England, Ireland, Scotland, the Netherlands, Belgium, Germany, Italy and other countries. Even at those early dates, he was especially drawn to landscape design, and saw many parks and country villas that excited his admiration. Later, after he had embarked on a career as a landscape architect, Olmsted looked to European precedents as he designed parks, roadways, and residential projects.[25]

The company that published *Putnam's* foundered in spite of Olmsted's efforts. His brother died in 1857 and he took responsibility for his brother's family. By chance later that year, he met his friend Charles Elliot, who was on the Board of Commissioners of Central Park in New York City. Elliot suggested that Olmsted apply for the job of park superintendent, and Olmsted did so. He overcame political infighting and skeptics who said he was not sufficiently "practical," and obtained the position on September 11, 1857. On the same day, Elliot submitted a report outlining a competition to redesign the park.

Vaux approached Olmsted and asked him to partner on a competition entry, thinking that Olmsted's new position would bolster their effort. Although Olmsted felt that winning was a "forlorn hope," he had debts to pay and wanted to take his mind off his brother's death. Olmsted and Vaux worked for months to prepare their plan and won the competition in April 1858.[26]

The design brief was complex and specified many features and structures. Olmsted and Vaux wanted to tie together those elements with roads that were peaceful, winding, and rustic, but the brief also required four transverse roads to carry city traffic across the park. Olmsted and Vaux's description of the transverse roads reflected their perception of Manhattan's commercial streets as zones of agonizing sensory impact.

> Inevitably they will be crowded thoroughfares, having nothing in common with the park proper . . . constantly open to all the legitimate traffic of the city, to coal carts and butchers' carts, dust carts and dung carts; engine companies will use them, those on one side of the park rushing their machines across it, with frantic zeal at every alarm from the other; ladies and invalids will need special police escort for crossing them, as they do in lower Broadway.[27]

Their solution was to sink the roads below grade, line them with sheer masonry walls for security, and conceal them with thick vegetative plantings. The grade-separated roads were crossed by ten bridges in total. The plan also had three transverse roads at surface level, which the designers said should be limited to "proper" vehicles such as hackney coaches (taxis) and private carriages. Apart from the ten bridges, the footpaths would cross the carriage roads at surface level.[28]

As Olmsted and Vaux prepared to start construction, the commissioners threw a major complication into the process. They asked for an equestrian-path system in addition to the other travelways. One solution would have been to group all the travelways together in parallel, but the designers felt that would ruin the plan's most important feature, which was open, far-ranging pastoral views. They rejected that option as they revised the plan during the summer of 1858. The revised plan was much more intricate, adding miles of paths and 19 bridges to achieve more complete functional and visual traffic separation.[29]

Olmsted and Vaux identified several models and precedents for the Central Park travelway plan. One was European boulevards. Some of them were crossed by streets "made in the form of causeways and carried over on high arches" to eliminate interruptions. Olmsted and Vaux wanted to retain the convenience of such causeways while avoiding structures that obstructed the scenic views. Another precedent was a certain tunnel in the Regent's Park Zoological Gardens in London. Olmsted said it was Vaux's contribution: "He seized, I remember, upon my tentative suggestion with the greater eagerness because of his familiarity with some construction partially serving a similar purpose in the zoological garden in Regent's Park." The spot in the zoo where the Outer Circle roadway and a pedestrian path were routed together over a pedestrian tunnel became a model for grade separation throughout Central Park.[30]

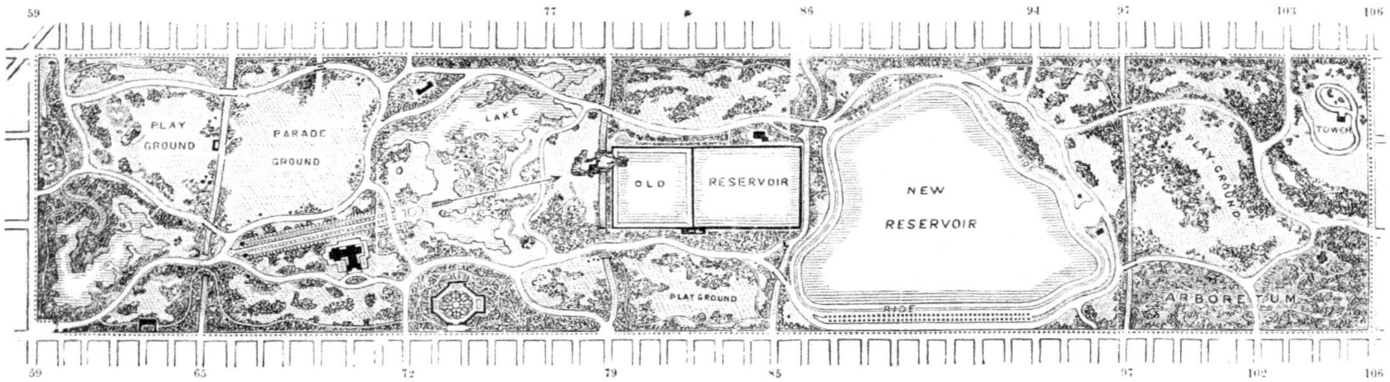

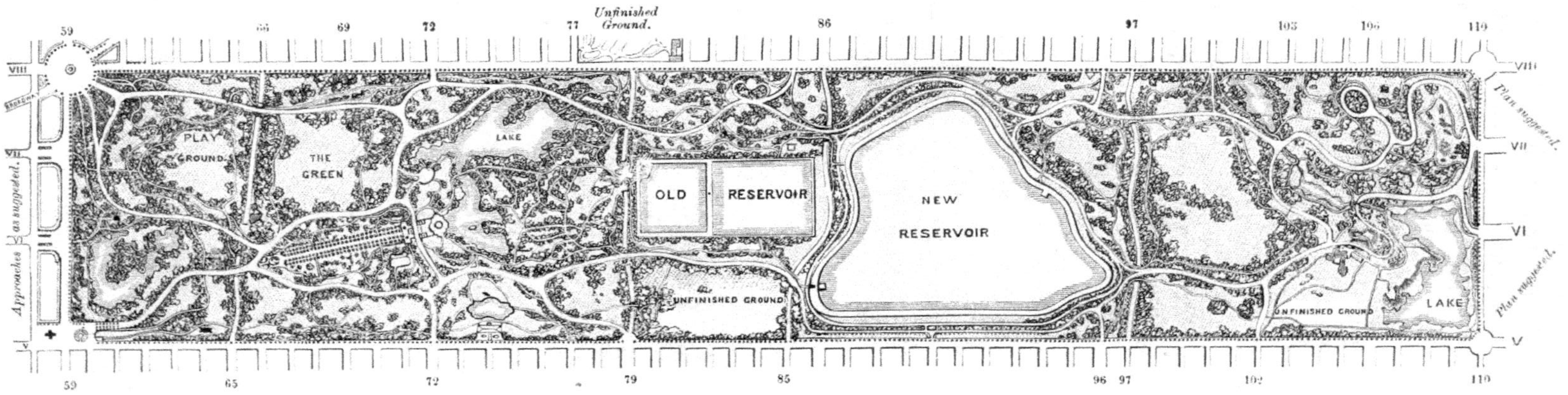

Figure 3.7: Above: Olmsted and Vaux's original competition plan, 1858. Below: map of park in 1868, showing added trail system, bridges, and tunnels.

Figure 3.8:
Regent's Park
Zoo, map
detail, 1852,
showing
pedestrian
tunnel with
roadway
and walkway
overhead.

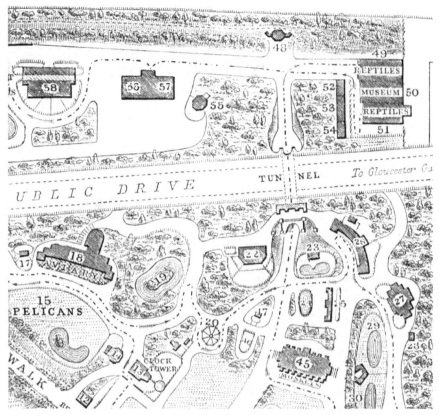

Although Olmsted wrote repeatedly of his boundless admiration for Birkenhead Park (designed by Joseph Paxton from 1843 to 1845), he never cited it as a precedent for the traffic separation in Central Park. His biographers have made the connection, however. George Chadwick wrote, "Olmstead does not comment particularly on the circulation after his visit to Birkenhead . . . but it must have made a deep impression in him," and "at Central Park Olmsted developed the principle still further and provided completely separate systems."[31]

Olmsted argued that traffic separation had psychological benefits. He had fond memories of country pleasure drives taken with his father, either in wagons or on horseback. And he was extremely concerned about the disturbing stress that city dwellers experienced daily. He believed that pleasure rides in rustic surroundings could ameliorate that stress—even cure debilitating medical conditions—but only if the driving was smooth, easy, and uninterrupted. "The mere consciousness that one's path may be crossed by a horse or carriage, causes a feeling of anxiety. The sunken and tunnelled street-thoroughfares across the Park were planned to remove what would have otherwise been a ceaseless annoyance," he wrote. He wanted to make driving so easy that it became an almost unconscious activity, requiring the "least possible anxiety or exercise of skill in regard to collisions or interruptions."[32]

That was an antecedent of freeway-design principles and the "forgiving" design philosophy that dominated roadway engineering thought in the 1960s and afterward. The subtle difference was that Olmsted was preoccupied with recreation and relaxation, while twentieth-century engineers wanted to protect drivers from the dangers of their own inattention and errors.[33]

Olmsted took another trip to Europe in the fall of 1859. For the first time, he was traveling as a professional landscape designer, on an educational and research trip funded by the Central Park commission. It was a much-needed vacation, because Olmsted had heroically guided Central Park's southern half to completion in a little over one year. In Europe he visited many favorite sites, including Birkenhead Park, the Crystal Palace, and Regent's Park zoo. He made eight visits to the Bois de Boulogne in Paris and met with its designer, Adolphe Alphand, who was Baron Haussmann's chief engineer.[34]

Olmsted and Vaux: Parkways

Olmsted suffered several personal tragedies in 1860, one of which was a carriage crash that left him with a permanent leg injury. For the rest of his life he used a cane and was unable to walk long distances. Animal-powered and wheeled transportation were now necessities in his everyday activities; the cross-country rambles he had so enjoyed in his youth were out of the question.[35]

Meanwhile, he was involved in disputes with the Central Park commissioners that gradually became intolerable. He resigned and set off on unrelated career directions. He was head of the US Sanitary Commission, which gave volunteer medical aid and relief assistance to Civil War soldiers. He became intimately familiar with the over-crowding, disease, and stress disorders found in military hospital camps. After that, he managed one of the biggest gold mines in California for two years.

In early 1865, Calvert Vaux negotiated a chance to win a big job. Brooklyn, New York, which at the time was the third-largest city in the United States, wanted a park to rival Central Park. The Brooklyn park commissioners wanted Olmsted and Vaux to design and build it.

Vaux was determined not to lose the opportunity. He sent to Olmsted a cross-country barrage of letters, promising a handsome fee and the possibility of fun times and professional satisfaction. He needed Olmsted on his team. The most important consideration was the "republican art idea"—the values of freedom, equality, and civic virtue—and no one could translate that into spatial form better than the two of them together. Vaux himself wanted to elevate the landscape-architecture profession to a level equal to that of the architecture profession. These were expansive, consequential goals. In fall 1865, Olmsted decided to return to New York and form a business partnership with Vaux.[36]

As that was happening, Olmsted began to pursue design work in California. He proposed landscaped travelways in city districts and yet-to-be-developed suburbs, seeking to extend the restorative influence of parks to inhabited areas. He won a commission to create a park plan for San Francisco, which was completed in spring 1866. It proposed a system of promenades that would start at a large central park and extend throughout San Francisco.

The promenades were 280 feet (85 m) wide and sunk 20 feet (6 m) below street level to provide wind shelter and conserve water. At periodic intervals, cross streets were carried over the promenade on timber bridges. Olmsted believed that arrangement would eliminate the anxiety and risk of mixed traffic and provide tranquil enjoyment, similar to Central Park.

Separate equestrian and carriage lanes occupied 108 feet (33 m) of the promenade's width. A central mall 24 feet (7 m) wide was filled with ornamental plantings, art installations, and zoo and aquarium exhibits for the edification and entertainment of strollers. Olmsted planned 9 miles (14.5 km) of promenades and suggested the system could be "extended indefinitely into the country" toward neighboring towns. Although the idea was not implemented, it was a precedent for Olmsted and Vaux's later parkway concepts.[37]

In early 1866 Olmsted and Vaux issued a preliminary plan for Brooklyn's Prospect Park. They re-used many of Central Park's design strategies, including the comprehensive separation of travel modes. The partners proposed to extend the park's influence by means of a "shaded pleasure drive" that stretched from the ocean beaches, past Prospect Park, into Manhattan, and onward to Central Park. North of Central Park, the route would follow one of the "sylvan roads" being planned by the Central Park commissioners. Olmsted and Vaux's extravagant plan would create a "grand municipal promenade, hardly surpassed in the world either for extent or continuity of interest."[38]

In their 1868 report to the Brooklyn park commissioners, Olmsted and Vaux invented the word *parkway* to describe this new type of roadway. It was modeled on the separated-traffic programs of European boulevards, which both partners were well familiar with. For example, in an 1861 encyclopedia article, Olmsted described a boulevard in Brussels with five different travelways: a graveled pedestrian walk, a macadamized carriage road, a soft graveled horseback road, a paved business road, and another pedestrian walk paved with flagstones.[39]

Olmsted and Vaux recounted a global history of roadway design that climaxed with the parkway type as the inevitable, highest expression of civilized transport. The first stage was "carelessly formed" cattle trails between the rude huts of barbarian tribes. Later, those were paved to become the "serviceable footways" of medieval towns. The second stage was the overcrowded, unsanitary wagon streets of the early Industrial Revolution. In the third stage, streets were widened and straightened, and space was set aside for sidewalks. The fourth stage was avenues having different types of traffic in separate lanes and abundant plantings in wide median strips. Avenue de l'Imperatrice in Paris and Unter den Linden in Berlin were examples.

The fifth stage—the pinnacle of roadway evolution—was Olmsted and Vaux's concept: the suburban multiway parkway. It was as wide as the Unter den Linden (200 feet or 61 meters) and it had twin pedestrian malls like the Avenue d'Imperatrice. Additional design details were similar to the Champs Élysées and other Parisian thoroughfares. The center roadway was reserved for fast carriages and equestrians, the side roads for freight wagons, and the two landscaped medians had pedestrian paths. The designers said that new types of "light, elegant, easy carriages" needed new types of roadways reserved for their use. According to Olmsted's nephew, horse-drawn streetcars were rigorously excluded from parkways because they were inconvenient, ugly, and used for utilitarian travel. Steam-powered rapid transit was excluded because it was deafeningly loud and polluting. Both were entirely incompatible with peaceful pleasure riding.[40]

Olmsted and Vaux envisioned a parkway system of enormous scope. It covered

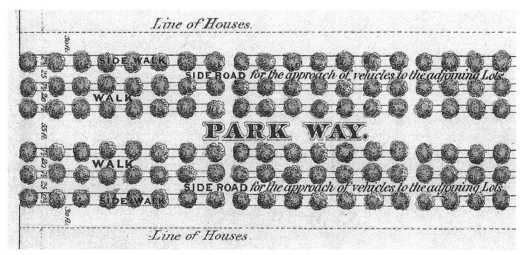

Figure 3.9: Eastern Parkway in Brooklyn, detail of proposed plan, 1868.

more than 80 square miles (207 sq km) and could serve a population of 500,000 within a ten-minute walk of the parkways. Large setback requirements would ensure low-density residential construction. The parkways would be the spines of linear neighborhoods that contained elegant, healthy detached villas, each surrounded by a garden. The designers believed the parkways would guide and greatly improve suburbs; they would introduce light and air, provide restful recreation, separate home from work, and boost property values.[41]

A portion of Olmsted and Vaux's plan was built in the form of two parkways that started at Prospect Park. Eastern Parkway (built 1871–1874) ran 2.5 miles (4 km) east to the Brooklyn city limit. Ocean Parkway (built 1873–1876) ran 5.5 miles (9 km) south to Coney Island. To the disappointment of officials and landowners, the parkways did not immediately stimulate new housing, and the adjoining lands remained mostly undeveloped for a quarter century. But Ocean Parkway was immediately busy and popular as a recreational-driving route to the beach and a freight route for local farmers and businesses. Freight wagons usually kept to the side lanes, but they sometimes used the center roadways when the side lanes were too muddy.[42]

Concurrent with the Brooklyn effort, from 1868 to 1871, Olmsted made park and parkway plans for Buffalo and Chicago. In Buffalo the preliminary plan was completed by 1870, construction began in 1871, and portions of the 6-mile (9.7-km) system opened in summer 1873. Almost immediately, fast driving and heavy traffic on the exclusive carriage lanes necessitated the appointment of a small police force to keep order. The Buffalo plan was a point of pride for Olmsted. He exhibited it at the 1876 Centennial Exposition in Philadelphia, and it won an honorable mention at the 1878 Paris Exposition.[43]

In the Chicago region, Olmsted's first parkway plan was made in 1868 for the private suburb of Riverside. He proposed a grand multiway thoroughfare, 150 feet (46 m) wide and 6 miles (9.7 km) long, to connect Riverside to the outskirts of Chicago. It had four separate travelways for pleasure driving, horse riding, walking, and freight movement. The parkway widened to 300 feet (91 m) at intervals to accommodate rest stops with small parks, sheltered seating, and horse watering. It would transform the

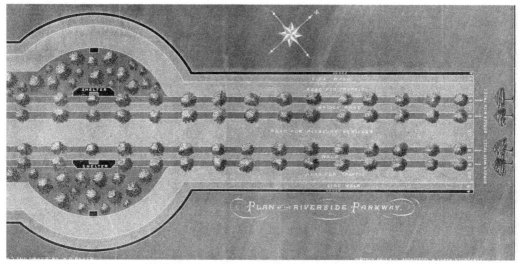

Figure 3.10: Olmsted's Riverside Parkway, as interpreted by *The Land Owner* magazine, 1869.

one-hour driving commute to central Chicago, which Olmsted described as rough and tedious. The trip would become "gay and interesting"; the commuter would encounter cheerful, well-dressed people socializing with each other. "The ride should adjoin the drive, so that equestrians can at pleasure turn from it to converse with friends in carriages," Olmsted advised.[44]

In April 1869 the governor of Illinois authorized the parkway as a toll road, and by October three miles (4.8 km) had been graded. The local communities and abutting landowners were in favor of the project, but the Riverside developer had to cancel it for lack of funds.[45]

It was only a temporary setback for Chicago's parkways—or boulevards, as Chicagoans usually called them. The city's leaders had been advocating a regional park and boulevard system since the mid-1850s, and the concept they found most compelling was a giant greenbelt encircling the city. They were inspired by Paris's redevelopment and Olmsted's work. In fact, Olmsted was a friend or colleague of many of the civic boosters who helped realize the park system. It was authorized in 1869 as a 26-mile (42-km) greenbelt composed of a series of parks linked by boulevards.[46]

Olmsted and Vaux were hired in 1869 to plan one portion of the system: the parks and boulevards of the South Park district, in what is now Chicago's South Side. In the report to the South Park commissioners, Olmsted praised the effect of inefficient street layouts, which had been a consistent theme of his since 1860. Describing the park's effect on the surrounding street network, he noted with approval that "the interpolation of the large closed spaces of the Park, turning transportation out of direct channels, will be obstructive to business." Discouraging business development would, in Olmsted's opinion, permanently ensure a stately character and higher property values for the surrounding neighborhood.[47]

In support of that goal, the city of Chicago in 1873 enacted a comprehensive ban on commercial traffic in parks and on boulevards. At the time, the city's boundaries encompassed the West Park district but not the South Park district, so the South Park commissioners enacted a similar ban in 1875. Nearby residents apparently had few objections. The boulevards were located in the city's sparsely developed outskirts and

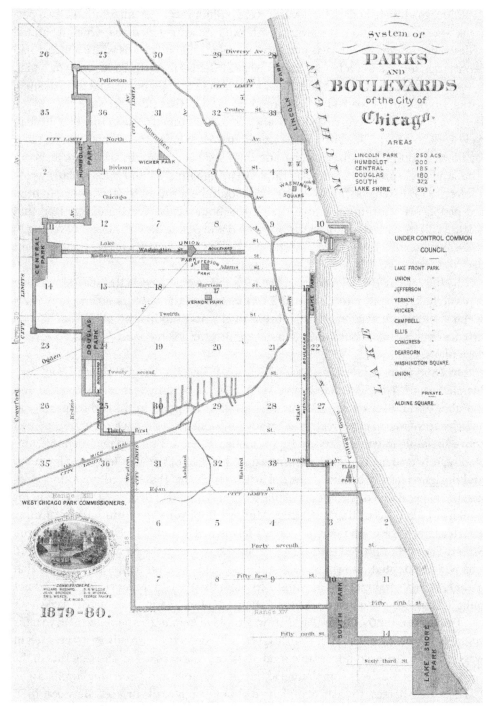

Figure 3.11: Chicago parks and boulevards system, 1880. Courtesy of Norman B. Leventhal Map & Education Center, Boston Public Library.

were of little importance to commercial drivers. Also, the boulevards were generally created in existing street grids, so parallel routes were usually available for business development and commercial traffic. The bans have remained in force to the present day.[48]

Chicago's nineteen park boulevards were built in varying configurations. Two patterns were most common: boulevards with two landscaped medians, which separated pedestrian, equestrian, carriage, and service traffic; and boulevards with a single broad central median. All but a few segments were 200–250 feet (61–76 m) wide or wider. Several West Side boulevards had 400-foot-wide (122 m) segments that formed small parks, similar to the roadside stops proposed for the Riverside parkway.[49]

The boulevards were exceedingly popular and assumed a social role like those in New York and Paris. The city's elite came in droves to enjoy the riding and spectacular floral displays, socialize, and parade their wealth and status. Horace Cleveland (the landscape architect who was implementing Olmsted and Vaux's plan) wrote a letter to Olmsted, saying that Olmsted would be amused to "see how delighted our people are with the new toy—the park & boulevards." Cleveland reported that 4,600 vehicles used the boulevards between 6 and 8 p.m. on one summer evening in 1874. "In short the jam is such that stringent police regulation is necessary to prevent disorder," he wrote.[50]

By the early 1870s, Olmsted and Vaux felt they would have better success working separately. They split amicably in 1872. Olmsted led the nation's preeminent landscape architecture firm, executing dozens of city and subdivision plans that shaped urban street layouts. Vaux continued his architectural career and worked on several park plans.

In 1886 Olmsted designed the widening of Beacon Street through Brookline, Massachusetts. His client was Henry M. Whitney, a wealthy real-estate investor and member of the Brookline park commission. By that point in time, the diversity of vehicles traveling on city streets had greatly multiplied. Cable-powered streetcars had proved reliable in winter service. Bicycling had become a mass phenomenon. Olmsted readily recognized the urban context and his client's goal of land development, and designed a fully urban boulevard with travelways that served new functional needs. He approved of swift, quiet cable cars, and included dedicated rail beds in his boulevard plan. According to Charles Mulford Robinson, the technique of running streetcar tracks through manicured grass lawns was invented by Olmsted for Beacon Street. The turf improved the railbed's appearance and reduced noise and dust, and was widely adopted elsewhere. Olmsted also made several boulevard designs that included single or double cycle paths. Although the Beacon Street cycle path was not built, it was one of the first dedicated cycle-path plans made for an urban parkway.[51]

During the 1880s, Ocean Parkway in Brooklyn began to experience heavy traffic volumes, a growing diversity of vehicle types, and conflicts over roadway usage. Freight wagons, trying to avoid impassable mud, used the center roadway and dug ruts in the surface. Carriage drivers complained about slow wagons and "scorching" cyclists who startled their horses. Cyclists complained about rough road surfaces. Between 1885 and 1897 the park commissioners enacted increasingly stringent regulations, trying to resolve conflicts by separating traffic types with ever-greater specificity. Commercial vehicles were restricted to the side lanes, cycles were restricted to the medians, and pedestrians were shifted to new sidewalks. Automobiles were informally restricted to one of the side lanes from about 1900 to 1910. But as auto traffic boomed, autos came to dominate the road space while equestrian and carriage traffic dwindled and vanished. By 1930 Ocean Parkway's center roadway was given to fast through traffic,

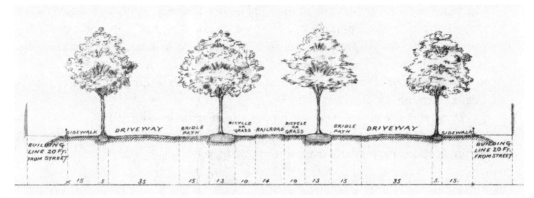

Figure 3.12: Olmsted and Olmsted, proposed Beacon Street with dedicated space for five travel modes. Illustrated by Aspinwall & Lincoln, ca. 1886. Courtesy of Norman B. Leventhal Map & Education Center, Boston Public Library.

its side lanes to slow local traffic, and its medians to bicycles and pedestrians.[52]

Chapter 3 Summary

Dedicated lanes for different types of animal-powered traffic first appeared in European cities. The divided roadways of the 1500s separated recreational traffic from ordinary traffic; by the 1600s, divided roadways were also used to separate commercial traffic. Divided roadways frequently separated social classes and were associated with exclusivity and the leisure pursuits of the elite. Etienne Cabet's Icara City was an exception. His proto-communist utopia was based on perfect equality, and its roadway system was designed to maximize efficiency, safety, and cleanliness.

Multiway boulevards were often associated with new affluent development in European cities. In the United States, Olmsted and Vaux created a variant called the parkway to activate and structure new suburban development. Their goals were urban deconcentration, elegant low-density residential suburbs, and the mental repose provided by carefree driving.

The parkway idea acquired a certain cachet, and many US cities built them to stimulate affluent suburbs. By 1916 approximately 430 miles (690 km) of parkways located outside of parks had been built in at least 33 US cities. But only a few had multiple travelways in the European or Olmstedian manner. Most cities were satisfied with a single broad road surface or a roadway with one median.[53]

The segregation of traffic types on multiway thoroughfares was one response to the chaotic urban street scene of the late nineteenth and early twentieth centuries. The city streets of that era were plied by carriages, carts, wagons, omnibuses, electric streetcars, pedestrians, equestrians, bicycles, motorcycles, autos, trucks, and more. Different interest groups contended for road space, compatible road surfaces, and legally assured priority of use. From the early 1910s to the mid-1920s, motor vehicles supplanted the competition and came to dominate urban roadways.

The skyrocketing growth of automobile traffic shifted the objective of multiway thoroughfares from pleasure riding to express travel. The few that were built in the United States and abroad during the early twentieth century served fast autos, and some of the old multiway parkways were rebuilt for express traffic. The multiway-expressway idea reached an apogee of sorts in the 1924 "super-highway" system proposed by the Detroit Rapid Transit Commission. The commission designed a divided expressway with four rapid-transit tracks, four express motor-vehicle lanes, four local lanes for motor traffic and parking, two sidewalks, and access to abutting properties. But by that time multiway thoroughfares were out of favor with traffic engineers, who considered them unsafe and inefficient.[54]

Divided roadways receded during the mid-twentieth century. In the 1960s and 1970s, they began to regain favor as cities sought to accommodate a more diverse mix of travel modes, particularly mass transit and bicycles.

CHAPTER 4
Horizontal Traffic Separation: Insular Roadways to 1910s

Insular roadways are those that are partially or totally withdrawn from general traffic circulation. They were often intended to provide refuge or protection to their inhabitants. Another common motive was to achieve higher social status by excluding people considered to be inferior or undesirable in some way.

Roadways can be made insular by a number of methods. One, they can be very indirect and inconvenient to use. Two, they can be gated or otherwise restricted. Three, they can be located inside developments, neighborhoods, or districts that are themselves gated or traffic-restricted. Four, they can be configured as loops or dead ends, which eliminate through traffic. The loops and dead ends can be located inside superblocks; or, in an extreme pattern, they can be part of a large-scale dendritic system that makes an entire community function as a gigantic cul-de-sac. Finally, any combination of the above can achieve insular layouts.

Superblocks deserve extra discussion because their effect on roadway networks can be obscure. The larger the superblock, the more internal area is withdrawn from general traffic circulation. The internal roadways may be publicly owned loops and dead ends, or they may be private driveways and parking lots. Superblocks may form roadway networks that are well connected in the technical sense; for example, they may form gridirons. But because superblocks are large, the through streets are spaced far apart. The practical impact is similar to poorly connected roadway networks: superblocks concentrate traffic onto a relative few arterials. Those arterials, as a result, tend to become oversize, noisy, dangerous, and polluted.

The discussion of blocks in this book uses the following general dimensions. Traditional-size blocks are up to 5 acres (2 ha) in area; oversize blocks are 5–15 acres (2–6 ha); superblocks are 10 acres (4 ha) or larger. The categories are imprecise and may overlap.

Early History of Traffic-Restricted Streets and Districts

The formal distinction between through- and local-traffic roadways has historical roots that stretch back to the dawn of urbanism. One source of that distinction was roadway layouts. Mohenjo Daro was one of the first grid-plan cities in history (built circa 2500 BC); its main thoroughfares were clearly differentiated from its narrow local lanes. In some of the ancient Mediterranean cities, through traffic and heavy vehicles were directed to specialized roadways. For example, in Rhodes and Alexandria, wide streets for harbor-freight traffic bypassed the city centers. In Pompeii, wheeled traffic, which was mostly freight carts, was channeled into designated routes by bollards, barriers, and raised sidewalks.[1]

The distinction between through and local streets was legally defined in Islamic Mediterranean cities. Laws regarding city streets, which were based on older Arab practices, were formulated after the seventh century AD and were an established corpus by the tenth century AD. They categorized streets as either thoroughfares, which were continuous public right-of-ways, or "no-exit streets," which were private dead-end streets. The dead-end streets were owned and controlled in common by the abutting residents. Islamic dead-end streets were short; in historic Tunis, Algeria, a sample of twenty had an average length of 40 meters (131 feet). Islamic building laws were promulgated throughout the Islamic Mediterranean and remained in force for extraordinary lengths of time. For instance, Tunis adopted the laws in the twelfth century and used them through the early twentieth century, a span of 750 years.[2]

Another source of the through-local distinction was insular cities and city districts. Walls that enclosed cities, towns, and villages were built from ancient times until the eighteenth century. Although city walls were not universal, they were widely prevalent, existing in ancient and medieval Africa, North America, South America, East Asia, South Asia, Europe, and the Mediterranean. Their primary purpose was to defend against marauders and armies.[3]

In medieval Europe, city walls served various purposes in addition to defense. City walls marked political boundaries and allowed the authorities to charge entry tolls and control the flow of trade goods. Walls and gates were a means of display, announcing the city as a protected locale where residents enjoyed special status. City walls enabled the exclusion of disfavored groups, activities, and land uses, and were sometimes used to exclude traffic types. For example, during the 1600s most Dutch towns banned wagons and carriages inside their walls, preferring canals for major transport.[4]

In general, city walls were not made to restrict movement inside cities, but numerous exceptions existed. Sometimes internal walls were built to contain and pacify strife, which could arise from ethnic-religious differences, political struggles, or the aftermath of war. Antioch, Syria, which was established in 300 BC, had walled districts to separate the conquering Greeks from the native Syrians. Valencia, Spain, built a walled city extension for Muslims after James I of Aragon conquered the city in AD 1238. Other examples were the Jewish ghettoes of medieval Europe, the Manchu districts of Chinese Qing dynasty cities, and early-medieval Pamplona.[5]

Sometimes internal walls were built to reinforce class distinctions, control behavior, and facilitate administration. Most of the Asian imperial capitals that rose and fell between 200 BC and AD 900, such as Chang'an and Luoyang in China, and

Heijo-kyo in Japan, were built according to the ward system. They had strict grids of thoroughfares that bounded wards. The wards varied in size, but 30–80 hectares (70–200 acres) was typical. Each ward was walled and gated; at night the gates were closed and non-residents were forbidden. Many of the wards contained palaces or religious complexes.[6]

Major Islamic cities from the eighth to nineteenth centuries AD had a nested system of spaces. Within the city walls were distinct residential quarters, and within the quarters were dead-end streets that were customarily gated. The residents of each quarter shared some common identity, which could be familial, ethnic, religious, occupational, or a combination. From time to time in various cities, gates were erected between the quarters to maintain security. During periods of rampant crime, feuds between quarters, civil war, or external attack, the gates were sealed day and night. The dead-end streets were usually gated for privacy, and functioned as courtyards for abutting residents' exclusive use.[7]

Another historical source of insular roadways and networks was the suburban and rural estates of the landed aristocracy. Large private estates existed in many parts of Europe and the Mediterranean from antiquity onward. They often were surrounded by fences or walls to bar trespassers. The wealthiest villas had an entrance distinguished by a gatehouse (also called a lodge) that sometimes did double duty as the gatekeeper's residence.

Regent's Park

John Nash (1752–1835) was a small man of average appearance who possessed a quick wit, assured design skill, and ready enthusiasm for new building projects. By his middle age he had established himself in London as a well-connected society architect of country villas. In 1806 he was appointed as architect of the royal Office of Woods and Forests. It was a minor position under ordinary circumstances, but it had major consequences for Nash a few years later.

As early as 1793, one of the king's officers, John Fordyce, had proposed the development of a royal property on the northwest outskirts of London. The land was leased to tenant farmers at the time. In 1809, shortly before the leases expired, Fordyce outlined a program for the property. He described a conventional yet high-quality town extension that would attract "the highest orders of society," and a great avenue connecting the property to Charing Cross, near the Houses of Parliament. The following year, Nash was asked by his commissioners to submit a plan for the area. The commissioners instructed him to emphasize profitability, beauty, health, and convenience; to pay attention to Fordyce's program; to address the relationship to adjacent properties; and to consider Edinburgh and Bath as models.[8]

Nash's March 1811 plan for Regent's Park encompassed 510 acres (206 ha), about half of which were designated for residential villas. The layout did indeed resemble eighteenth-century Edinburgh and Bath. The villas edged superblocks as large as 50 acres (20 ha); inside the superblocks were landscaped parks. Upon seeing this draft, the head of the royal treasury called Nash in for a review. He used to live near the property and ride through it, and he told Nash to drastically reduce the built portion. The revised plan of August 1811 was closer in character to a country estate. Fifty villas

Figure 4.1: Regent's Park East Gate, 1827.

were scattered in a picturesque, ruralized landscape, and residential terraces lined the park's perimeter and enclosed a double circus at its center. Nash was ebullient about his revised plan.[9]

Nash pictured an exclusive enclave "composed of the great and the opulent" that was insulated from its lesser-class neighbors. It would attract the wealthy "by making it select, by shutting out all connection with the inferior streets." The park was to be entirely fenced and guarded and, similar to other royal parks, access would be granted only to individuals deemed suitable. "To realize the effects described," Nash wrote, "it will be necessary to form the roads and plant the parks; they would then immediately become rides and drives to those of the public to whom it should be thought proper to give keys."[10]

Nash touted additional reasons why the park villas would attract wealthy buyers. Villa residents would enjoy scenic beauty; opportunities for exercise on foot, horseback, and in carriages; freedom from traffic noise; and privacy (the villas were to be screened by trees). Residents would enjoy convenient delivery via canal of all necessary goods. They would have a brisk travel route to Charing Cross by way of Regent's Street, which Nash was planning as a complement to the park.

During its early years Regent's Park was private, as Nash had suggested. Its roads were open during the day to allow public access to institutions within the park. The park's gates were closed at ten o'clock every night to all except residents and their visitors. But attitudes about public access changed within a few decades. A portion of the park was opened to the public in 1835, and most of the park was made public by 1841. Its streets were still closed after dark except to residents and their visitors—a policy that continues to the present day.[11]

The park established a notably different model for suburban development. Rather than extending London's street-network pattern as previous developments had, it stood apart. Like an insular aristocratic country estate, it used prominent gates and fences to connote social status and exclude undesirable classes and activities. The ensemble of

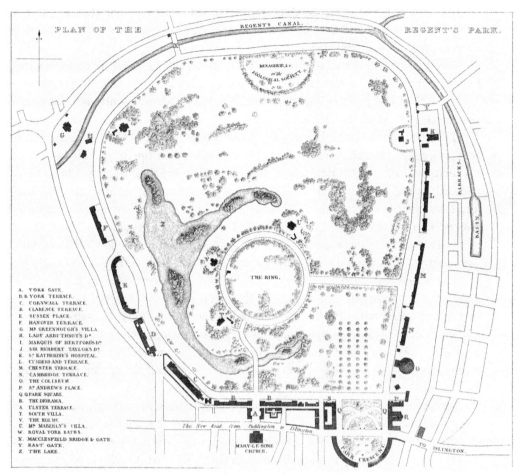

Figure 4.2: Regent's Park in 1827, showing gates at perimeter entrances. Residential development ceased shortly after this map was drawn.

Regent's Park and its grand approach, Regent's Street, became an internationally recognized exemplar of the art of town improvement. It influenced the field of park design and inspired a number of gated suburban developments both directly and indirectly.

London's Estates

London and a few other British towns had a unique landownership model: the leasehold. A handful of noblemen owned large estates in and around the city. When they developed their properties, they did not sell the land under the buildings, but instead sold long-term leases. They thus retained control of their estates. The arrangement encouraged neighborhood-scale planning and management that aimed to maintain value over long time periods. Heads of the landed estates commissioned most of the city's residential squares.

London was, in effect, a confederation of small fiefdoms. Some three hundred authorities controlled the city in 1855; their jurisdictions were uncoordinated and overlapping, and their governing bodies were often ineffective or corrupt. Before the Metropolitan Board of Works was created in 1855, the city had little capacity to plan or coordinate large projects. By default, the landed estates were at the vanguard of planning in the city, and they used their land-control powers and political connections to protect the character and value of their properties.[12]

Street barriers were one of the tactics that the estates used. They built gates, fences, and guard houses on their residential streets to restrict vehicular traffic and "undesirables." The practice began in earnest in the 1820s and continued as a widely used strategy through the 1890s.

The historian Donald Olsen's study of the Bedford estate explored the conditions that gave rise to street barriers in that part of London. The opening of the New Road turnpike in 1756 brought new traffic to the northern fringe of the city. The Duke of Bedford wanted to connect his Bedford House mansion to the turnpike, but the Bedford estate lay between the turnpike and the city's center. Any new connection would naturally attract through traffic, which the Duke wanted to avoid. The solution was to build a road and place a guarded gate at the New Road intersection. Only residents were permitted through the gate, and no one at all was allowed through at night.[13]

Potential threats to the character of the Bedford estate multiplied during the 1820s and 1830s. As urban extensions engulfed the estate, it lost the cachet of a bucolic location on the urban outskirts. The Euston railway terminal brought streams of traffic to the adjacent roads, especially hackney carriages (taxicabs). Nearby Regent's Park was both a competitor and a model of planned development that purposely restricted traffic. It was slow to develop because of a national economic slump, but by the 1820s its plan and character were attracting widespread praise.[14]

Although the Bedford estate felt compelled to permit some through traffic (or else risk a backlash from Parliament), it wanted to prohibit the noisiest and most offensive types. In addition, the new adjoining districts were inhabited by lesser classes, and the estate wanted to insulate itself from them. By 1831 it had placed numerous gates across its streets that were, as Olsen wrote, "intended to reduce the traffic on the estate to a minimum and to impede communications with adjacent and unfashionable neighborhoods." The gates prohibited omnibuses, empty taxis, freight vehicles, and herds of animals. One street, which had an especially convenient location, prohibited all taxis, even those carrying residents. All the gates were closed to all traffic at night.[15]

In summary, during the 1820s and 1830s gated streets emerged as a means of protection from a variety of forces perceived as inimical to neighborhood quality. The Bedford estate's actions were not atypical; street barriers pervaded London until the late nineteenth century. In 1893 the London County Council found more than 187 barriers throughout the city. Some areas were undercounted, so as many as 300 barriers may have existed at any given time. They took a variety of forms: swing bars, drop bars, wood or iron gates, bollards, fences, and masonry walls. Guards in some neighborhoods, such as the Bedford estate, had a reputation for unyielding strictness. Violent disputes between guards and drivers happened frequently.[16]

Estate tenants liked the tranquility and privacy afforded by the barriers. The steward of the Bedford estate said gated streets were "much sought after by professional men, to whom quiet at night is an important element in the choice of a residence." But many other city residents objected to the inefficiency of the gated zones. They complained that the barriers were a huge inconvenience that created lengthy and annoying detours. Also, the symbolism of elitist exclusion aggravated Londoners at a time when political reforms were expanding suffrage and reducing aristocratic power. In 1826 the *Sunday Times* inveighed against "the great landed proprietors" who assumed the "aristocratic privilege of shutting out the public from the [New Road], by the erection of barriers at the end of any new street." A squib in an 1882 issue of *Punch* magazine wrote of "the great Metropolitan Mudlords" who kept "important streets blocked by insolent gatekeepers, the right of thoroughfare refused where most needed."[17]

The city's vestries (civil-ecclesiastical neighborhood governments) led a prolonged effort to remove the barriers. Agitation increased over the decades and reached a crescendo in the 1880s and early 1890s. There was little official response until the London County Council was formed in 1889; after that, action was swift. In 1890 Parliament passed a bill removing four gates on or near the Bedford estate. An 1893 bill removed 59 additional barriers (the remaining barriers were allowed by default). Finally, the London Building Act of 1894 prohibited the erection of any new street barriers. In the future, the qualities of neighborhood quiet and seclusion in London would have to be secured by other means.[18]

Private Suburbs

As suburban subdivisions became popular in the mid-nineteenth century, a number deployed walls, fences, entry gates, and gatehouses to enclose the land and bar public access to internal streets. The goals were various. Gates were installed for protection from crime, pollution, traffic, and other unwanted activities. In some cases residents desired seclusion; gates were often meant to exclude certain unwanted populations and ensure class or ethnic-religious segregation. Gates sometimes helped enforce an internal homogeneity of lifestyle, thought, or belief. Elaborate gates and gatehouses with guards signified status by connoting a privileged zone set apart from quotidian urban space.

Gated developments ranged in size from a single street to hundreds of acres, and their exclusionary perimeters were enforced with varying degrees of strictness. The following brief review covers only a selection of notable or influential examples.

Calverley Park in Tunbridge Wells

In 1828 John Ward, one of the Regent's Park investors, hired Decimus Burton to design Calverley Park. It was a private gated development located in the fashionable spa resort town of Tunbridge Wells in Kent. It was clearly based on the Regent's Park model of exclusive in-park living. In keeping with its vacation-oriented location, it catered to wealthy buyers seeking retreat and restoration, residential privacy, lush landscaping, and splendid views. The layout put twenty-four villas on a curved road that was guarded by three substantial gate lodges. The villas overlooked 20 private acres (8 ha) of meadow and ornamental gardens, as well as a mansion that Burton expanded into a hotel. Calverley Park was widely praised for its peaceful beauty and was recommended by tourist guidebooks. In 1920 the open meadow was purchased by the town and converted to a public park, but the roadway has remained private.[19]

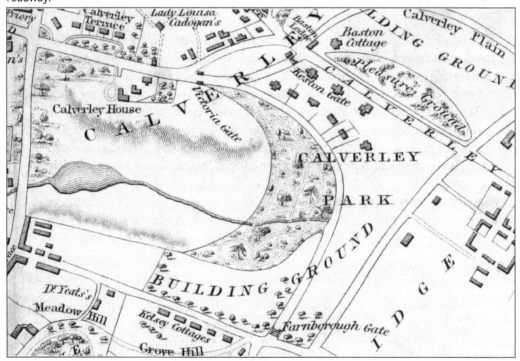

Figure 4.3: Victoria Gate, Calverley Park, 1832.

Figure 4.4: Calverley Park and environs, 1832, including the three gates that barred entrance to the exclusive roadway.

Parc de Montretout in Saint-Cloud

In the western suburbs of Paris, the Château de Saint-Cloud sat on a bluff overlooking the Seine River. The palace had long been a favorite residence of French rulers and aristocrats such as Marie Antoinette and Napoléon Bonaparte. Its large estate was enclosed by massive walls and iron gates, and housed a crew of royal officers and guards. In 1832 an 8-hectare (20-acre) fragment of the estate was sold to a private developer and subdivided into 37 properties. Parc de Montretout, as it was named, developed as an enclave of country homes for Paris's wealthy elite. Although the palace was destroyed in 1870 during the Franco-Prussian War, Parc de Montretout survived intact. Today the development has a population of about 400 and remains a private enclave.

Several other private enclaves in the Paris region were also located on properties that had been fenced previously. For example, the 6-hectare (15-acre) Villa Montmorency, a gated community in the Auteuil quarter, was built in 1853 on the site of an aristocrat's gated estate.[20]

Victoria Park in Manchester

Manchester had an explosion of suburban development in the 1830s and 1840s. Several of its suburbs were private and gated, a trend that was partly motivated by economic and social inequality. The political theorist Friedrich Engels used Manchester of this era as a case study of capitalist exploitation, chronicling the horrendous living conditions of the poor. For its part, the bourgeoisie made every effort to separate and distinguish itself from the lower classes. The desire for social status, and the dangers of labor strife, motivated the bourgeoisie to build gated suburbs that provided class separation and physical security.[21]

The suburb of Victoria Park was founded by leaders of the Anti-Corn Law League (an anti-aristocratic political movement), and catered to middle-class businessmen. Thus, its residents were likely to find a certain homogeneity of political thought and household wealth. The design of Victoria Park was influenced by Regent's Park; it was 146 acres (59 ha) in area, located 2 miles (3.2 km) south of Manchester's center, enclosed by walls, and gated. Design work started in 1836 and construction began in 1837.[22]

In 1845 the trustees of Victoria Park expanded and strengthened the development's exclusionary policies. The rules prevented "the entrance of any carriage or carts improperly seeking to pass through the gates" and authorized day and night guards to "take away any trespassers or persons refusing to leave the park upon being challenged to do so." The trustees also began charging tolls around this time. They wanted the gates to prohibit through traffic while giving "every facility of access" to any house or property inside the development. According to the historian Robert Fishman, Victoria Park became a symbol of bourgeois suburbia and was recommended in tourist guidebooks.[23]

Rock Park in Birkenhead

Rock Park (1837) in Birkenhead was a small gated enclave on the banks of the River Mersey. Liverpool was a short steam-ferry ride across the river, and the enclave catered to middle-class merchants, ship owners, and professionals. The author Nathaniel Hawthorne lived in Rock Park for two years during his tenure as US consul in Liverpool. Upon settling in his new home in 1853, he remarked approvingly, "It is the quietest place imaginable there being a police station at the entrance and the officer on duty admits no ragged or ill looking to pass. There being a toll, it precludes all unnecessary passage of carriages; and never were there more noiseless streets than those that give access to these pretty residences."[24]

Prince's Park in Liverpool

Prince's Park near Liverpool (1842–1843) was Joseph Paxton's first residential-park design. Prince's Park was a private development modeled on Regent's Park, but because it was created during a period of changing social ideals, it attempted to serve competing demands of exclusion and access.

During the 1830s and 1840s in Britain, public and governmental attitudes toward park access underwent a thorough transformation. Crowding and disease conditions were becoming dire in the poorer districts of Britain's major cities. Public access to park space came to be seen as a public health issue. It was needed to clean the air, facilitate exercise, refresh the spirit, and inculcate moral behavior.[25]

In Prince's Park, villas on the perimeter surrounded a central park space. The villas and their adjacent gardens were private, while the central park was public (except for an island planted with beautiful gardens for the villa residents' exclusive use). The villas were accessed by the park's internal carriage drive, and the drive was protected by gates at the park's boundaries. That arrangement suggested the character of a private enclave.

Paxton was dedicated to the principle of open access for the common people, and he designed his next park differently. Birkenhead Park in Liverpool opened four years later as the nation's first municipal public park. Its houses were accessed from the bordering streets rather than the internal carriageway, which gave it a more public character.[26]

St. Margaret's Estate in Twickenham

The St. Margaret's Estate (1854) was a 75-acre (30 ha) residential development located about 10 miles (16 km) southwest of London, near the railroad suburb of Richmond. The property was developed by a mutual-assistance cooperative named the Conservative Land Society, and its housing was intended for artisans, businessmen, and other professionals. Its streets were not gated, but its blocks were oversize (up to 17 acres or 7 hectares) and several had secluded internal parks and trails. The trails ran through the park spaces and were aligned at street crossings to form a neighborhood-wide footpath system. The internal parks and footpaths were owned and maintained by the community. The pattern of oversize blocks with internal parks and separated footpath networks reappeared in some twentieth-century residential developments, notably those inspired by the garden-city movement.[27]

Lewellyn Park in West Orange

Llewellyn Haskell was the owner of a Manhattan pharmaceutical-import firm who, at age 37, suffered from rheumatism, stress from overwork, and health worries. In 1853, on the advice of the architect Alexander Jackson Davis, he began acquiring land in West Orange, New Jersey, 12 miles (19 km) west of New York City. It was a hilly property near the former site of a health spa, with picturesque ravines, brooks, and forests. Haskell felt the air was invigorating. Over the following years he expanded his holdings and set about creating an ideal suburb called Llewellyn Park. In 1857 he published a promotional plan for 350 acres (142 ha). The minimum lot size was 1 acre (0.4 ha) and the average was 6 acres (2.4 ha).[28]

One of the architects who contributed to the design was Howard Daniels. In the mid-1850s Daniels had toured the parks, estates, and residential suburbs of England and had written a series of articles describing the ones he found most admirable and attractive. Among them were Victoria Park, Prince's Park, and Birkenhead Park. The first was entirely gated and private; the second had gated private residential and garden areas; the third had eight stone gate lodges and an enclosing iron fence, and was public.[29]

Llewellyn Park was demarcated by a rustic wooden fence and its main entrance was guarded by a substantial gate lodge, which was designed by Davis and built in 1857 or 1858. The development's exclusionary policies may have been informal during the initial years. The first record of exclusionary rules dates from 1865; they stipulated that only residents, their friends and visitors, and "respectable strangers from abroad" were permitted to enter.[30]

The fences and gateways signified a private lifestyle of pastoral recreation and contemplation. Advertisements for Llewellyn Park said it was for New York businessmen who sought refuge from the city in "accessible, healthful, retired homes in the country." Haskell said his development was "a retreat for a man to exercise his own rights and privileges."[31]

An 1859 edition of Andrew Jackson Downing's treatise on landscape gardening contrasted conventional suburban properties to Llewellyn Park, and presented the latter as an exemplar. In regard to conventional suburban properties, it said that "High boundary fences, and a separate gate-lodge for each place, seem necessary for protection from marauders—while the idea of even a respectable drive over your own ground, secure from the disagreeable objects of the public highway, is rarely entertained." In Llewellyn Park, by contrast, the "fine entrance and approach road can be secured," which permitted "extensive drives and walks for the exclusive use of the proprietors." But the exclusionary policies seem to have conflicted with lot sales. In 1873, a year after Haskell's death, Llewellyn Park was opened to public access and the managers ran a newspaper announcement that rejected any "apparent exclusiveness."[32]

About 45 families lived in Llewellyn Park by that time. Although small in population, it was well known and admired for its idyllic, romantic landscape design. It had a special influence on Calvert Vaux and Frederick Law Olmsted. Vaux had been friends with Haskell and designed Llewellyn Park's first house in 1857. In 1865 Olmsted said his College of California project was one "which I propose to lay out on the Llewellyn plan." Llewellyn Park was a fundamental inspiration to both designers.[33]

Olmsted's Disconnected Subdivisions

In addition to parks and parkways, Frederick Law Olmsted designed large, low-density residential projects. Such projects furthered the cause of decentralization and proper suburban development, which to Olmsted was akin to a moral crusade. He viciously criticized the ethical foundations of "old-fashioned compact towns": they were often created for purposes of killing and plunder; they were ruled by military despots who suppressed personal independence; their residents were habituated to tyranny and feared change. They were racked by plague, pestilence, and fire, and caused illness and shortened life spans. Olmsted believed that decentralization had improved living conditions in recent decades, and he recommended much more of it. In particular, he called for suburban houses with large yards, extensive parkland, and the separation of commercial and residential land uses.

A important part of Olmsted's neighborhood design philosophy was the deliberate creation of poorly connected street networks. He, like many of his contemporaries, was deeply concerned about land-use change. He worried that elegant, fashionable neighborhoods would degrade under the pressure of new shops, taverns, factories, boarding houses, funeral parlors—in other words, business in general. He lamented the destruction of historic homes and fine woodlands. He lambasted the greedy or ignorant developers who destroyed all that was gracious and attractive.[34]

If the street layout could somehow discourage traffic and business growth, the process of unwanted change could be stopped before it could even begin. So, Olmsted deliberately made street networks that were less convenient, less accessible, and less integrated with adjacent districts. He would solve the problem of excess traffic by placing houses on streets that were relatively difficult to reach.

Olmsted had been thinking along these lines for some years. In 1860 he wrote to Henry Elliott, a member of the commission that was planning Manhattan's street layout north of 155th Street. Olmsted outlined the principles necessary to secure a tranquil and secluded environment for villa neighborhoods. To prevent residential roads from becoming heavily traveled, the conventional rules of easy access must be inverted. Routes from within the neighborhood to downtown must be indirect. Few, if any, roads should enter the neighborhood, and those that do must be short. Roads from more distant outer suburbs must not connect to the neighborhood; bypass roads must provide more direct routes to downtown. Neighborhoods designed according to these principles would "permanently stand absolutely against competition" from commercial and industrial uses that caused disturbance and turmoil.[35]

Olmsted used the principles in his Berkeley, California, plan of 1865–1866. He designed a residential neighborhood adjacent to the campus that was composed of 2–5 acre (0.8–2 ha) lots. A primary goal was to avoid attracting "a noisy, disturbing commerce, or anything calculated to destroy the general tranquility of the neighborhood." Olmsted saw the curvilinear, inconvenient street layout as integral to that goal.

> While the roads are so laid out as to afford moderately direct routes of communication between the different parts of the neighborhood, they would be inconvenient to be followed for any purpose of business beyond the mere supplying of the wants of the neighborhood itself—that is to say, it would be easier for any man wishing to convey merchandise from any point a short distance on the other side, to go around it rather than go through it.

If the street layout alone was not enough to discourage through traffic, more forceful methods could be employed. "As a further protection, when it shall be found necessary, the property may be enclosed and gates established at the entrances, so as to exclude from the lanes whatever it may be thought undesirable to admit," he wrote.[36]

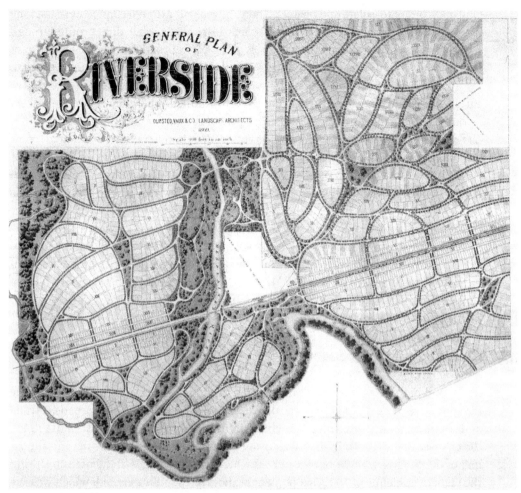

Figure 4.5: Olmsted and Vaux's plan of Riverside, Illinois, 1869, showing 13 street connections to the existing grid on the east side, and a total of 6 connections on all other sides.

Olmsted's next project to use those principles was Riverside, Illinois. In 1868 Olmsted and Calvert Vaux were hired to plan a 1,600-acre (650-ha) railroad suburb located 9 miles (14 km) west of downtown Chicago. The project gave Olmsted his first chance to implement his street-layout principles at such a large scale. Most suburban planning of the era simply extended the existing urban streets, "thus giving a town value to the lots" that lay along those streets. Riverside should aim for the opposite, said Olmsted. Its indirect, curvilinear street layout would reinforce its tranquil, non-commercial character.[37]

Another technique to reinforce the desired character was insularity. On the plan's east side, which faced downtown, external connections were spaced an average of 660 feet (200 m) apart. That was the same measurement as the standard block length in Chicago's grid. On the plan's other sides, external connections were spaced an average of 1 mile (1.6 km) apart—one-eighth as frequently. The Des Plains River formed natural barriers on portions of the south and west boundaries, and the cost of bridges would have been a common reason to limit external connections there. But other parts of the west and north boundaries, which had no natural barriers, clearly demonstrated

Olmsted's desire to isolate and protect. There, infrequent external connections and long blocks created partial barriers to the adjacent districts. The only direct route through Riverside was the main commercial street along the railroad. Thus, the whole street layout would function as a large filtering obstruction in the regional roadway system.

Riverside was not a great financial success, and its construction proceeded slowly. But its street layout achieved what Olmsted had aimed for. Today Riverside's street layout is a distinct island of curvilinearity within the surrounding street grid, and it has resisted rampant commercialization. Instead, commercial strips and apartment buildings developed on the bordering streets, which carried high volumes of traffic.

Olmsted was the foremost proponent of the theory that an indirect, insular street layout would permanently ensure a noncommercial neighborhood character. His residential subdivision projects demonstrated the efficacy of that theory, as did later projects that emulated his style. By the 1940s, the theory was so widely accepted as to be axiomatic. Some of Olmsted's design elements were pervasive in American suburbs after World War II, such as indirect routes within the development, few connections to adjacent neighborhoods, and large-curvature intersections more suited to fast vehicles than safe pedestrian use. The ideas underlying Riverside were precursors to the neighborhood-unit concept.

St. Louis's Private Places

Social and political factions exist in all cities, but in nineteenth-century St. Louis the factions were more divided than most. The city was a continental crossroads, a trade and shipping boomtown, and a launching point for Western settlement. In the 1840s the city was flooded with Irish and German refugees; by the end of the decade almost half of the city was foreign-born, one of the highest percentages in the nation. During the cholera epidemic of 1849, six percent of the city's population died, which was the highest reported death rate worldwide. Native-born residents blamed immigrants and displaced or quarantined many of them.[38]

Relations between immigrants and other ethnic groups were often fractious and occasionally broke into predatory violence or riots. The Dred Scott decision of 1857 further polarized feelings. As an anti-slavery city in a pro-slavery state, St. Louis was viewed by the state legislature with perpetual suspicion if not outright hostility. The state legislature had control of the city's finances, and kept expenditures low and infrastructure underfunded. Compounding those problems, the city's government was riddled with incompetence and corruption. St. Louis won limited control over its finances in 1876, but many governmental functions remained fragmented and the old habits resisted reform.

The city's divided social and political life was reflected in its disconnected street patterns. The streets in poor neighborhoods were badly maintained, which kept them separated from the main streams of circulation. The city's elites developed their own form of geographic withdrawal: private restricted-traffic streets, which were called *private places*. Wealthy families living in private places could avoid the dysfunctional public system and create high-quality blocks under their own control. They could remove themselves from the disease, pollution, crime, and disfavored populations (such as recent immigrants and Blacks) of the poorer districts. Private places also conferred enhanced status and exclusivity. As a result, private places were more prevalent in St. Louis than in any other city.[39]

Lucas Place, developed by James H. Lucas in 1851, was the city's first deed-restricted private street. Lucas's sister had built a residential block (Summit Square, 1828) only to see it overrun by business development. That was a recurring experience for the city's elites. They repeatedly built fancy homes in the city's outlying areas, which were then overwhelmed by growth. After a period of years or decades, they felt compelled to move because business development, traffic, or crowds had deteriorated the neighborhood. Developers attached deed restrictions to individual lots, and later put restrictive covenants on entire developments, in an attempt to halt the process. Another tactic was to develop private streets in tandem with squares or parks, creating developments similar to London's residential squares.[40]

Lucas used both tactics. Business activities and commercial traffic were banned from the three-block length of Lucas Place. Only private passenger vehicles were allowed. An adjacent city block was dedicated as a landscaped square to help maintain a genteel atmosphere. Lucas was following the advice of his architect, George I. Barnett (1815–1898), who created the plan and designed five of its houses. Barnett was the only formally trained architect in St. Louis before the Civil War, and was known as the city's dean of architecture. He had apprenticed with a builder of residential terraces in Nottingham and completed his education with a London-trained architect before emigrating to the United States in 1839. He returned to Europe in 1850 for a professional study tour that included a stay in London. That background suggests that Lucas Place was an emulation of London's traffic-restricted leasehold estates. However, Lucas Place was not demarcated or gated, unlike London's estates.[41]

The deed restrictions had minimal protective power and Lucas Place was subsumed by commercial development. Meanwhile, the area around Lafayette Park, 1.5 miles (2.4 km) to the south, became a favored address. Benton Place (1868), the city's second private-street development, was adjacent to the park. It was platted by Julius Pitzman (1837–1923), a German-born civil engineer in private practice who was also the elected surveyor of St. Louis. Pitzman was familiar with Parisian boulevards and wanted to create a street that rivaled the best streets in the United States. Although Benton Place was only one block long, he gave it a landscaped median 50 feet (15 m) wide. Commercial traffic was banned and rear alleys provided service access. The plan had a street stub for future through traffic, but the connection was never made, so Benton Place remained a cul-de-sac. The plan, design, and legal policies of Benton Place established the template for subsequent private places.[42]

Pitzman may have consulted with Barnett on the layout of Benton Place; the two knew each other and worked on several of the same projects. Barnett designed houses in Benton Place and in Vandeventer Place (1870), another private place laid out by Pitzman. Vandeventer Place was three blocks long and had gates at both ends that barred through traffic. A fountain at one end of the central median served as an entry feature. In spite of its gates and restrictive covenant, Vandeventer Place was completely overwhelmed by commercial development by the early twentieth century. It was demolished from the 1940s to 1950s.[43]

The period from the 1880s to the early 1900s was the peak of private-place development in St. Louis. More than 90 were planned through 1915 and several dozen were

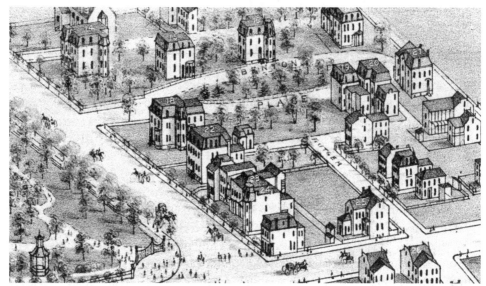

Figure 4.6: Benton Place, St. Louis, 1875, showing rear service lanes and Lafayette Park across Park Avenue.

built, almost all laid out by Pitzman. He was by far the most influential and respected individual laying out the city's private places. And as the elected chief surveyor—a position he held for nearly sixty years—he was also responsible for laying out public streets. An 1899 biography estimated that Pitzman's office had made more than half of all the surveys and subdivisions in St. Louis.[44]

A few private places were located on the South Side, but most were located on the more affluent West Side. The city's elites were moving westward in an attempt to keep ahead of intensive urban growth. The most prestigious addresses were found

Figure 4.7: Vandeventer Place, ca. 1902, showing entryway and central mall. Masonry gate structure was added in 1894, replacing a more modest iron gate. Courtesy of Missouri Historical Society.

Figure 4.8: Westmoreland Place gate structure, ca. 1900. Courtesy of Missouri Historical Society.

along the central corridor near Forest Park. Starting in 1888, private-place developers began to include elaborate gatehouses to signify the special quality of the zones within, and to more effectively restrict ingress. The rest of St. Louis's citizenry looked on from a remove, perhaps with envy or resentment, at a deeply inequitable system that seemed entrenched in the streets themselves.[45]

The early private places demonstrated that control of individual street environments, no matter how strict, was not sufficient to ensure long-term stability. The city's elites came to realize they would have to be even more proactive and exert influence over larger areas. They used their social and business connections to control the character of growth on streets surrounding the private places. They bought up properties; developed high-class buildings like luxury hotels, apartments, and expensive houses; and removed or restricted offensive land uses like retail, manufacturing, and railways.[46]

Soon after the turn of the century, the lack of coordinated planning in St. Louis provoked a group of leading citizens to organize the Civic League and campaign for improvements based on City Beautiful principles. At the League's request, the city formed the Kingshighway Commission to plan a parks and parkway system modeled on Boston's system. Julius Pitzman was the secretary, the respected landscape architect George Kessler was the lead planner, and a newly graduated architect named Henry Wright (1878–1936) was Kessler's assistant.[47]

Kessler and Wright worked together on the 1904 St. Louis World's Fair. After that signal success, Pitzman, Kessler, and Wright served on the League's city plan committee. Their 1907 *City Plan for St. Louis* described the city's fragmentation:

> [In the beautiful residential sections] . . . the choicest paved streets
> have become main thoroughfares for heavy hauling; and only the
> "Places" are protected from the encroachment of street cars, switch
> tracks and objectionable buildings. The average citizen, who is seek-
> ing a quiet home away from the noise and discomfort of traffic, is

helpless in the face of this riot of conflicting and selfish interests—the direct results of a lack of plan and insufficient regulations.[48]

However, the goal of the planners was not to reduce street and land-use fragmentation, but to systematize it and make its benefits—quiet streets especially—available to all St. Louis citizens.[49]

Wright worked for Kessler through 1909. The firm's major work during that period was the famed Kansas City park and boulevard plan. From 1909 to 1917 Wright was independent and worked on subdivision planning, mostly in the St. Louis suburb of Clayton. He designed several private places that barred commercial traffic with signage rather than gates. They included Brentmoor Park (1910) and Forest Ridge (1911), both of which followed Pitzman's private-street template. The houses turned away from the bordering streets and faced a central landscaped median. Service lanes at the rear of the lots gave access for delivery vehicles.[50]

In 1915 Wright was at a planning conference in Detroit when he learned that a project he had been working on, the Central Traffic Parkway, had been rejected by St. Louis voters. He commiserated with a young civil engineer named Harland Bartholomew, whom he had met at the conference. Probably as a result of that meeting, Bartholomew moved to St. Louis and became the City Plan Commission's engineer. Bartholomew said the *Major Street Plan for St. Louis* (1917) was his proudest accomplishment. It guided an extensive program of street construction and widening, reinforced the distinction between traffic streets and residential streets, and launched his career as a maker of comprehensive plans for cities across the nation.[51]

German Planning and Early Zoning

The quarreling German states unified into a single nation in 1871, and over the following years the population boomed. The growth rate was very high—higher than the American growth rate—and nearly all the growth was in the largest cities. Between 1871 and 1914 the population of the largest cities increased 500 percent. Planning for that extraordinary growth became a central concern of many cities.[52]

Land-use zoning emerged in Germany in the 1870s, and street-planning rules were issued around the same period. The Prussian Law of 1875 classified streets into three categories, which Josef Stübben (the preeminent German planner of the 1890s-1900s) described as main traffic streets, medium-rank traffic streets, and side streets. The law specified minimum widths for each category. According to Stübben, the standards were appropriate for "the busy districts of great cities" but were inflexible and excessive for other contexts.[53]

The standards reflected the planning philosophy of the time. During the 1880s, spaciousness was ranked supreme in large German cities. The prevailing wisdom was that arterials should cut through existing city districts in radial-concentric patterns, and new urban extensions should be laid out as gridirons with wide streets. German planners believed that wide streets furnished many benefits. They would make cities healthier and more sanitary by increasing ventilation and sunlight. They would encourage detached single-family housing. They would create more beautiful vistas in line with the "Haussmannesque," or baroque, aesthetic of uniform, well-ordered streetscapes. Above all, planners believed that long, straight streets ensured the free flow of traffic across the city and between major intersections, thus aiding business operations and promoting economic growth.[54]

But the policy of universally wide, straight streets yielded disappointing results: high building costs, speculation, overbuilding, and new high-density slums. Reform-minded planners and housing advocates criticized the "widespread obsession with traffic" and the "dogma of the wide street." City officials agreed with the criticisms. The result was a sea change in German urban design philosophy and policies in the 1890s.[55]

The momentum was boosted by the Viennese architect Camillo Sitte, whose book *City Planning According to Artistic Principles* was published in 1889. Sitte charged that city planning based primarily on traffic considerations erased the character of built places and made them ugly and impractical. He argued against banal repetition and called instead for variety in street layouts. His criticism applied to interminable arrow-straight boulevards and mechanical gridirons as well as casual suburban layouts. "Even the free arrangement of residential suburbs becomes tedious when repeated over too great an area," he said.[56]

Sitte felt that the ideas he promoted were already "in the air" at the time his book was published. The changes that occurred subsequently could have happened only "when everyone is already thinking more or less along the same line." Even so, the overwhelming success and uptake of his philosophy drove the cultural shift much further. Many plans, laws, and recommendations issued during the 1890s reflected that trend.[57]

By the end of the decade, the dualistic conception of through-traffic streets and local residential streets had progressed toward broad acceptance and codification in German law. The Kingdom of Saxony's General Building Law of 1900 stated that "the width of the streets and footways is determined according to the needs of local traffic and must be graduated according to whether the streets are main, side, or merely residential streets. In streets where the houses are detached and there is no through traffic proper, the width of the traffic area may be reduced."[58]

German planners agreed that good city planning established locations for through traffic (in commercial zones and on busy thoroughfares) and local traffic (in quiet residential zones). Furthermore, all those zones and corridors should be planned and enforced by the government to promote the overall community well-being. The spread of those ideas across Europe was assisted by the *Städtebau* planning movement established by Sitte and his followers, and by Stubben's writings and international planning work.

Germany became a popular travel destination for urban reformers seeking models of good city governance. The most enthusiastic admirers came from Great Britain and the United States. Visitors praised the strong civic spirit of German cities—the willingness to put the interests of the whole community before individual interests, and the needs of future generations before unwise short-term gains. They admired the organization and power of German city governments and their honest, competent bureaucracies. The Progressive reformer Frederic C. Howe reported that, in Germany, "no municipal problem receives more attention than the building of streets." He praised the way that main thoroughfares were designed to be "commanding and spacious" while residential streets were designed for "coziness and retirement." The German model of planning and zoning also made a powerful impression on American planners such as Frederick Law Olmsted Jr. and Edward M. Bassett.[59]

Charles Mulford Robinson

Charles Mulford Robinson (1869–1917) was a journalist and author who became well-known as the leading popularizer of the City Beautiful movement in the early twentieth century. His books were bestsellers, and as his fame spread, cities began to ask his advice on planning matters. His celebrity, urban-design knowledge, and personable temperament aided a career shift. He became a planning consultant and, eventually, a professor of civic design.

The City Beautiful was the idea that buildings, streets, and civic spaces should be planned and designed in concert to achieve sensory beauty. In Robinson's view, street layouts were an essential component of civic art, and he discussed them at length in his books. He consolidated and restated Frederick Law Olmsted's street-layout principles, and to a lesser degree he built upon and extended those principles.

More than Olmsted, Robinson had a teleological view of urban change. Historical cities were crowded, miserable, and unhealthy. Their streets were confined and chaotic, and their street layouts were inefficient. Innovations such as rapid transit, street lighting, and sewers allowed the population to disperse to healthful districts with lushly landscaped streets. There, the beauty of civic art could blossom. "Cities begin to bud and flower in beauty only when learning, culture, and art are flowering around them," Robinson proclaimed. That flowering "is the ultimate, the highest, step. It is the phase toward which all the other urban changes tend. . . . That it is the inevitable goal of the progress, the final triumph of municipal development, is shown by the history of the empires of many times."[60]

Robinson had grown up in the Third Ward of Rochester, New York. It was a neighborhood of abundant trees, lawns, and large Greek Revival and Victorian Gothic houses. He often recalled it with fondness and advocated similar "village-like" residential areas. But it had a gridiron layout, and by the early twentieth century it was under pressure from commercial development. The disruption of tranquility in neighborhoods like the Third Ward led Robinson to advocate street layouts that were more resistant to change.[61]

In *Modern Civic Art* (1903), Robinson outlined the ideal city street plan. The citywide network of through-traffic arterials had a radial-concentric (spider web) pattern. The arterials were wide, straight, and uniform; they carried heavy volumes of traffic and connected focal points in the city plan. As the city grew, business districts would extend along the arterials. The interstitial spaces between arterials were residential, and had minor streets that served local traffic.[62]

Robinson proposed different layouts for poor and wealthier residential areas. In poor areas, the local street network had diagonals that shortened walking time. The diagonals did not make important connections outside the neighborhood, but instead converged on local centers such as neighborhood greens and squares. Therefore the diagonals would not attract the business and traffic that made sidewalks crowded, destroyed street trees, and displaced dwellings. His idea of local diagonals was possibly derived from the model industrial towns of Britain, Germany, and the United States, which he wrote about.[63]

In wealthier areas (where presumably everyone drove a vehicle), streets were curving and indirect, and carried no through traffic. Individual privacy and communal beauty were maximized. The streets would feel welcoming, like private homes and gardens. Robinson verged on rapture as he described the streets' civic beauty: it refreshed the spirit, delighted the eye, strengthened children's souls, and furthered the progress of the human race.[64]

On the issue of slum improvement, Robinson held conventional moralistic attitudes and believed that large arterials would cure urban ills:

> It has been found that often there is no better way to redeem a slum district than by cutting into it a great highway that will be filled with the through travel of a city's industry. Like a stream of pure water cleansing what it touches, this tide of traffic, pulsing with the joyousness of the city's life of toil and purpose, when flowing through an idle or suffering district wakes it to larger interests and higher purpose.[65]

By the time Robinson wrote *The Width and Arrangement of Streets* in 1911, much had changed in the traffic-planning realm. He mentioned trends such as garden-city-inspired developments (including Hampstead Garden Suburb in London and Forest Hills Gardens in Queens, New York) and middle-class automobile ownership. Great daily tides of commuter traffic were traveling from suburbs to downtown business districts. City planning was obligated to respond "with an urgency unknown before."[66]

He criticized the contemporary practice of roadway classification. Roadways were classified by traffic volume, and standards for width and design were fixed to those classifications. The system was arbitrary, wasteful, and poorly matched to actual needs. It was unsatisfactory because traffic volumes were certain to change over time. As a result, Robinson worried, "if there be nothing to fix and hold the character of a street, it tends to change." Writing before land-use zoning became common in America, he wanted a classification scheme that would discourage such change.

Robinson's classification scheme had just two classes: the busy major traffic thoroughfare and the quiet minor residential street. He called this a functional classification, as opposed to a classification based on traffic volume. His use of the term *functional classification* in reference to the service characteristics of roadways was possibly the earliest on record.[67]

As a general rule, minor residential streets should carry a minimal amount of through traffic—less than the total amount of traffic generated by the residents themselves. Desirable streets might carry no through traffic at all, becoming like "private entrance ways to the few houses gathered upon them." He described the St. Louis private places that often were "closed to general traffic," and noted with approval "the exclusiveness and privacy of the arrangement." He suggested that many streets simply could be eliminated and replaced by footpaths.[68]

The latter idea had been thriving in Louisville, Kentucky, for twenty years. The city's first pedestrian court, Belgravia Court, was built in 1891 by William H. Slaughter as part of the St. James development. Slaughter was inspired by the posh London estates and dreamed of a subdivision designed "in the English manner." Belgravia Court was two blocks long; its houses faced a wide landscaped mall with sidewalks,

Figure 4.9: Venice, California, center walk, 1909. The center walks escaped the city's widespread demolitions during the 1960s, and currently exist in nineteen blocks.

and rear service alleys gave the only vehicular access. About 20 pedestrian courts were built in Louisville through the 1920s.[69]

A more comprehensive example of the same idea was the oceanfront blocks of Venice, California. The houses in Venice faced "center walks" that were 10–15 feet (3–4.5 m) wide and surfaced with wood or colored concrete. Rear service alleys 20 feet (6 m) wide gave access for vehicles and tradesmen. By unanimous consent of the residents, all of Venice's oceanfront blocks adopted the pattern by 1909, except the frontages on major thoroughfares. The benefits were said to be protection from noise and dust clouds caused by vehicles, "the safety and comfort with which mother and the babies may enjoy the open air before their own door-steps," safe play areas for older children, and space for ornamental landscaping.[70]

Robinson died in the influenza epidemic of 1918 at the relatively young age of forty-three. He was eulogized as a leading authority on city planning. One of his many influences was increased attention to functional roadway classification. Architects and engineers were shifting away from undifferentiated grid layouts, and toward plans that discouraged through traffic on minor residential streets. Robinson's contribution to that trend was early and compelling.

The Third Ward in Rochester, Robinson's fondly remembered childhood home and idealized residential model, survived in a much compromised form. Through the first half of the twentieth century, the area experienced waves of immigration, over-crowding, decay, and White flight to the suburbs. The I-490 freeway (part of the city's "Inner Loop") was built in the 1960s, destroying a large portion of the neighborhood. The destruction was ironic, given Robinson's calls for wide, uniform, high-volume arterials to be driven through low-income areas as a desirable goal of city planning.

Unwin, Letchworth, and Hampstead Garden Suburb

Although Raymond Unwin (1863–1940) began his career as an engineer, social reform was his passion. He was an active socialist as a young man, and throughout his life, socialism was the "surrogate gospel" that underlay his design and planning work. He was a follower of John Ruskin and William Morris, who advocated the reorganization of society through communal ownership of property, the welfare state, workers' guilds, and the revival of traditional decorative arts. Those ideas informed the design movement known as Arts and Crafts.[71]

During the 1890s, Unwin worked on a series of coal-worker villages for his employer, the Staveley Coal and Iron Company. In general they were conventional bye-law developments that had rigid rows of attached housing in gridiron layouts. But Unwin wanted to break free of conventional strictures. He admired the beauty of college quadrangles and believed that residential development could benefit from similar communal designs. For the workers' village of Warsop Vale, he designed a double quadrangle at the heart of the development.[72]

Unwin married in 1893 and left Staveley Coal three years later to form a partnership with his brother-in-law Barry Parker. Unwin was the planner and engineer, Parker was the interior designer and illustrator, and both were architects. Unwin's activism focused increasingly on housing reform, and with Parker he began to publish articles about architecture and design. In his professional and family lives, he adopted Arts and Crafts ideals such as plain living, practicality, and comfort without ostentation. He and his family wore "Ruskin flannel"; their rooms were unadorned yet finely designed.[73]

Unwin expanded his palette of residential block configurations during these years. A block with an informal village green was illustrated in Parker and Unwin's book *The Art of Building a Home* (1901). Houses ringed the green and turned away from the streets that bordered the block. The design also featured shared facilities such as stables, communal laundries and kitchens, and a meeting hall, reflecting Unwin's interest in cooperative living.[74]

Unwin began to publicly criticize conventional terrace (attached) housing. His hero William Morris had fulminated in an 1883 lecture that "every little market-town seizes the opportunity to imitate, as far as it can, the majesty of the hell of London and Manchester. Need I speak to you of the wretched suburbs that sprawl around our fairest and most ancient cities?" Unwin reiterated those complaints in *The Art of Building a Home* and in his lectures and activism. He criticized Britain's bye laws in particular.[75]

The Health Act of 1875 had enabled local governments to control the form of streets and houses to ensure sanitary conditions. Model bye laws were issued in 1877 and by the 1880s were adopted in urban districts throughout Britain. A characteristic form emerged in most cities: the bye-law development of terrace housing. The model bye laws specified minimum road widths and building setbacks, and required sidewalks. The intent was to ban the extremely dense, overcrowded, unhealthy slum dwellings prevalent in Britain's cities.

Slum dwellings were often built around miserable, filthy internal courts, thus giving the cul-de-sac a reputation as home to impoverished, sickly inhabitants. The model bye laws did not ban cul-de-sacs *per se* but did favor the "construction of cross streets at frequent intervals." Bye laws and other laws passed by city governments

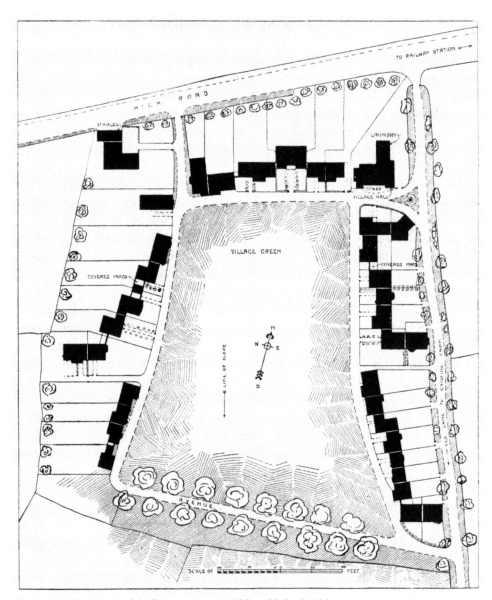

Figure 4.10: Unwin's model village green, ca. 1899, published 1902.

made internal courts prohibitively expensive. In addition, the market for communal courts was dwindling because of cultural changes that put more emphasis on family life inside the home. As a result, developers used simple gridiron layouts almost universally. Bye laws that banned cul-de-sacs outright were less prevalent than the model bye laws, but according to Unwin they were not uncommon.[76]

As a critic of conventional development, it was only natural that Unwin should join forces with the garden-city movement, which he did in 1901. The movement's leader was Ebenezer Howard, who in his book *To-Morrow: A Peaceful Path to Real Reform* (1898) crystallized a number of themes fermenting in British society.[77] The movement took its inspiration from British charitable housing trusts and model industrial villages such as Port Sunlight, Saltaire, and Bournville, as well as German town-extension planning. It sought to reform many aspects of city-making, including the unrelieved rigidity and ugliness of bye-law housing.

Howard wanted to disperse urban populations into new, self-sufficient settlements called garden cities. In the garden city, land ownership would be cooperative, low- or medium-density housing would be surrounded by gardens and parks, and different land uses would be neatly segregated in specialized zones. The roadways were laid out in a radial-concentric pattern that featured "magnificent boulevards" 120 feet (37 m) wide.[78]

Unwin attended the Garden City Association's first conference at Bournville in 1901, which led to a commission to design New Earswick. It was a model industrial village near York, developed by Joseph Rowntree of the Rowntree chocolate company. The 1903 plan by Unwin and Parker hinted at the creation of a cul-de-sac inside a block by suggesting that three or four houses might share a driveway "if found desirable." Also in the plan were blocks with internal playgrounds, allotment gardens, or greens. Unwin would use that pattern in most of his later projects.[79]

Unwin was rising into the public spotlight. Through his lectures, publications, and projects he became known as a leading reform-minded town planner. In 1903 Unwin and Parker were selected to design the first garden city, Letchworth, which was 38 miles (61 km) north of London in North Hertfordshire. Having 1,300 acres (526 ha) of planned town development and 2,500 acres (1,012 ha) of rural land, Letchworth was easily the largest garden-city development in the United Kingdom. It was intended to house up to 35,000 residents and have a density of 23 people per acre (57 per ha) in the town section.[80]

Letchworth was located in a rural district, so it was not required to adhere to bye-laws. Unwin and Parker's 1903 plan included several inner-block cul-de-sacs. Although those particular roadways were not built, Unwin's first cul-de-sac was built in 1906 in the Birds Hill section of Letchworth. Cul-de-sacs in Letchworth were more cost-effective than standard streets because they could be narrow, lightly paved, and built without sidewalks. The Birds Hill and Pixmore Hill sections of Letchworth, both designed by Unwin, had oversize blocks 8–9 acres (3.2–3.6 ha) in area.[81]

One of Unwin's colleagues during this period was Letchworth's estate manager, Thomas Adams. Known as a hard-working and capable organizer, Adams had served as secretary of the Garden Cities Association and was largely responsible for building its national reputation. He oversaw Letchworth's construction and used the project to proselytize for garden-city principles through visits, conferences, and publications. By such means, Adams and his fellow devotees integrated the garden-city ideal into the nation's social-reform mainstream.[82]

In 1905 Unwin and Parker began working on Hampstead Garden Suburb. It was a 243-acre (98-ha) property located near a new extension of the London Underground in the city's northwest suburbs. Unwin's first sketch plan used a few cul-de-sacs, but he encountered a legal obstacle. Strict local bye laws discouraged the kind of narrow, lightly paved cul-de-sacs that Unwin and his client wanted to build. Legislative action would be required to move the plan forward. Fortunately for the designers, the developer Henry Vivian was a member of the Hampstead Garden Suburb Trust Council and had just been elected to Parliament. Unwin and Vivian probably had met when they worked together on Birds Hill in Letchworth, which was one of Vivian's "co-partnership" developments. They both were interested in social reform and dedicated to

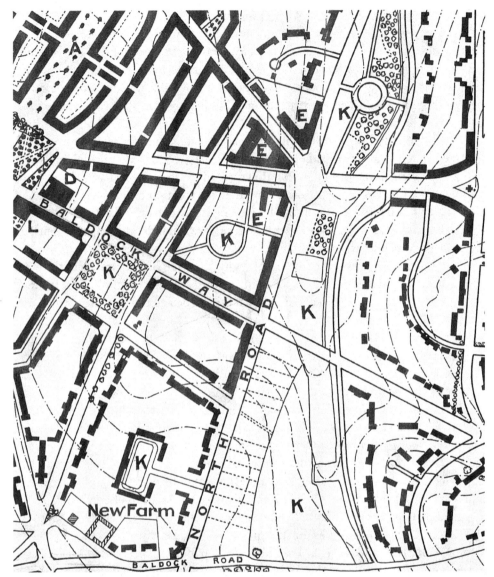

Figure 4.11: Letchworth master plan, detail, 1903. Unwin's first systematic use of inner-block cul-de-sacs. Courtesy of Garden City Collection, gardencitymuseum.org.

well-designed housing surrounded by gardens and open space.[83]

Unwin probably convinced Vivian that Hampstead Garden Suburb needed legal relief. Vivian introduced legislation to Parliament in February 1906. It was approved in August as the Hampstead Garden Suburb Act 1906, and it applied only to Hampstead Garden Suburb. It was the first town-planning law in the United Kingdom.[84]

Unwin wrote most of the Act himself. It classified roadways by drawing a legal distinction between through streets and local streets, the latter "not exceeding five hundred feet in length, constructed primarily for the purpose of giving access to a group of houses in the Garden Suburb." The Act permitted local streets to be as narrow as 20 feet (6 m), exempted them from paving and drainage standards, and made sidewalks, riding tracks, and grass margins optional.[85]

Hampstead Garden Suburb added acreage over the next five years, and Unwin

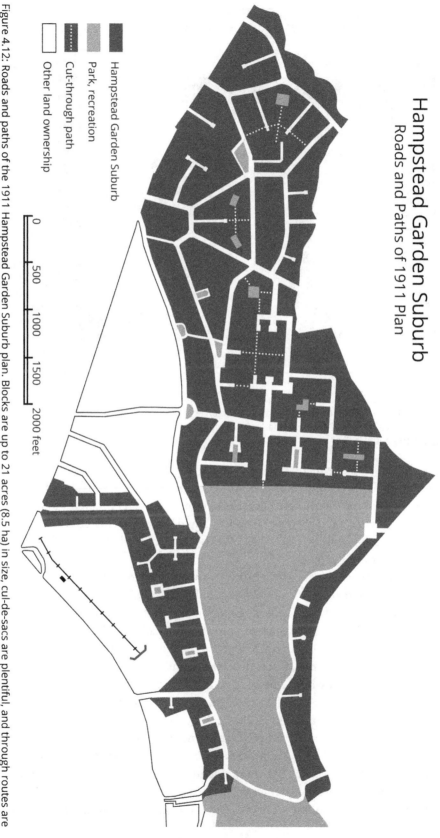

Hampstead Garden Suburb
Roads and Paths of 1911 Plan

Legend:
- Hampstead Garden Suburb
- Cut-through path
- Park, recreation
- Other land ownership

Scale: 0 — 500 — 1000 — 1500 — 2000 feet

Figure 4.12: Roads and paths of the 1911 Hampstead Garden Suburb plan. Blocks are up to 21 acres (8.5 ha) in size, cul-de-sacs are plentiful, and through routes are angular or sinuous.

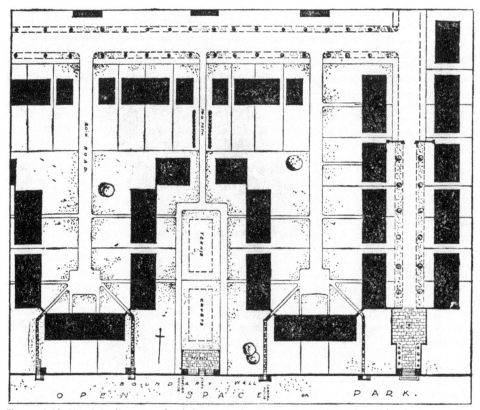

Figure 4.13: Unwin's diagram of cul-de-sac types in Hampstead Garden Suburb (not built as pictured), ca. 1906-1908. All had pedestrian paths connecting to the adjacent park. Some houses faced the paths, a likely inspiration for Radburn.

refined the plan. He increased the number of cul-de-sacs and made them a defining feature of the development. Many were arrayed around a central park (Hampstead Heath Extension). Some had footpaths so that people could walk from the street ends to the parks beyond. Whereas Letchworth had tentatively introduced the cul-de-sac to garden-city planning, Hampstead Garden Suburb made the cul-de-sac a signature element of the movement.[86]

During the first years of the 1900s, Unwin had cited only aesthetics as the justification for his street loops and cul-de-sacs. By 1909 he had added automobiles. "Particularly since the development of the motor car," he said, cul-de-sacs were "especially to be desired for those who like quiet for their dwellings." He recommended cul-de-sac designs that incorporated small greens or recreational spaces. He felt that such communal spaces promoted social order and intimacy.[87]

By the 1910s Unwin had become an international celebrity in the planning field. He visited the United States for three weeks in 1911 and reported that "the zeal of the Americans for 'city planning,' as they call it, and especially for the Garden Suburb side of it, has converted our journey into something like a triumphal procession!" He returned to England with a manifest admiration for American parkways, especially Chicago's parkway system. "You may ride in a motor hour after hour round Chicago and the whole of the time be traveling along its park-ways and through the parks and hardly leave them," he said. "This Green Girdle is indeed, a wonderful creation."[88]

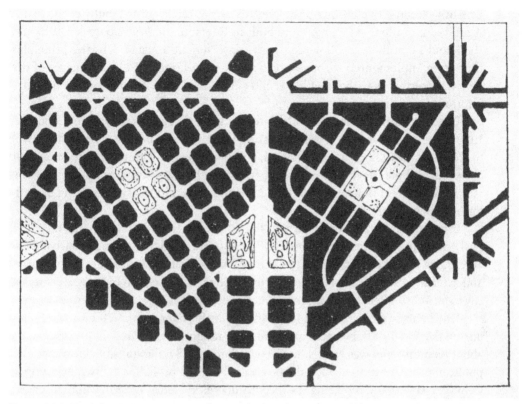

Figure 4.14: Unwin's 1914 comparison of a standard gridiron to a "rightly" arranged layout that reduced the number of intersections on thoroughfares. The diagram likely was a model for Clarence Perry's neighborhood-unit diagram (figure 5.12) and H. Alker Tripp's precinct diagram (figure 7.10).

As the impact of automobiles on urban environments grew, Unwin honed his roadway-hierarchy concepts into consistent principles that he advocated for the rest of his career. Main arterials should carry all through traffic. Increases in traffic volume should be accommodated by widening the arterials. Conversely, minor streets in the interstitial residential areas should carry no through traffic at all. Secondary roads should "gather up" the local traffic and deliver it to the arterials. That would limit the frequency of intersections on arterials, reduce the chance of collisions, and allow traffic on arterials to flow without delay. Unwin offered a conception of street layouts that was literally treelike: "We may take the analogy of the tree; first the trunk, then the main branches split up into minor branches, and finally the twigs. We do not want our twigs growing direct out of the trunk!"[89]

Around 1915, Unwin transitioned from private practice into the UK government. He was a natural diplomat and had an exceptional talent for mediating groups and disputes. Furthermore, he was widely regarded as an elder statesman of planning. He worked on wartime housing and became the chief housing architect of the Ministry of Health. From 1919 to 1933, British laws encouraged local governments to prepare working-class housing schemes and submit them to the Ministry of Health for approval. The government would then pay a share of the costs to the developer (which could be local government, a public-interest organization, or a private firm). The national government issued several reports and design manuals that reflected

Unwin's garden-city planning principles; those materials guided many of the plans. A total of 2.1 million dwellings were built in England and Wales between 1919 and 1933, and 1.2 million, or 56 percent, were government-assisted. Unwin's principles thus were implemented throughout the nation. In large UK developments of the period, superblocks with street loops and cul-de-sacs were standard, while ordinary gridirons were almost entirely absent.[90]

Unwin's relationships and collaborations with Americans grew throughout the 1920s. The Regional Plan of New York and Its Environs committee brought Unwin to New York in 1922 for a consultation, and his colleague Thomas Adams was later chosen to lead the effort. Unwin became friends with Lewis Mumford, Clarence Stein, and Henry Wright in the early 1920s, and participated in the site planning of Radburn, New Jersey, in 1928.

From the late 1920s to the early 1930s, Unwin was engaged in regional planning for London and laid the groundwork for London's future greenbelt and suburban New Towns. He imported ideas from the United States, such as limited-access parkways and extensive use of grade-separated intersections. He expanded his roadway hierarchy to include limited-access thoroughfares and highways with parallel service roads.[91]

Unwin made many international visits during his later years. In the United States during the mid-1930s, he participated in wide-ranging lecture and fact-finding tours about planning, and was closely involved in shaping US policy on slum clearance and public housing. In 1936 he took the position of visiting professor in town planning at Columbia University, replacing the recently deceased Henry Wright, whom he called a "valued and respected friend." Unwin taught at Columbia until his death in 1940. In his lectures he fondly described Radburn as a model of good planning, emphasizing the benefits to children that the separate pedestrian network provided. He expressed his wholehearted support for "the Radburn principle," and visited Radburn often.[92]

Forest Hills Gardens

The tasteful urban designs of Unwin and Parker were an inspiration for the Forest Hills Gardens project in Queens, New York. Funded by the philanthropic Russell Sage Foundation, it was intended to be a model middle-class suburb that would also generate revenue for the foundation.[93]

The Borough of Queens was rapidly transforming from a rural district to a residential suburb because of new rail and bridge connections, which cut commuting time by half or three-quarters. Real estate advertisements promised that areas near Forest Hills Gardens were just fifteen minutes from Penn Station in Manhattan.

Forest Hills Gardens' planning and architectural design were executed in 1909 by Frederick Law Olmsted Jr. and Grosvenor Atterbury. Olmsted Jr. was carrying on the legacy of his eminent father and was a distinguished planner in his own right; Atterbury was a successful society architect with a longstanding interest in housing reform.

The Sage Foundation strove to make the 142-acre (57-ha) site a demonstration of comprehensive planning. The designers oriented the plan to the town square and transit station at the northern edge. They created an overall gradation of spatial character that ran from the built-up, hard-paved commercial area to the leafy, detached-housing areas. Forest Hills Gardens had smaller blocks, higher density, more housing

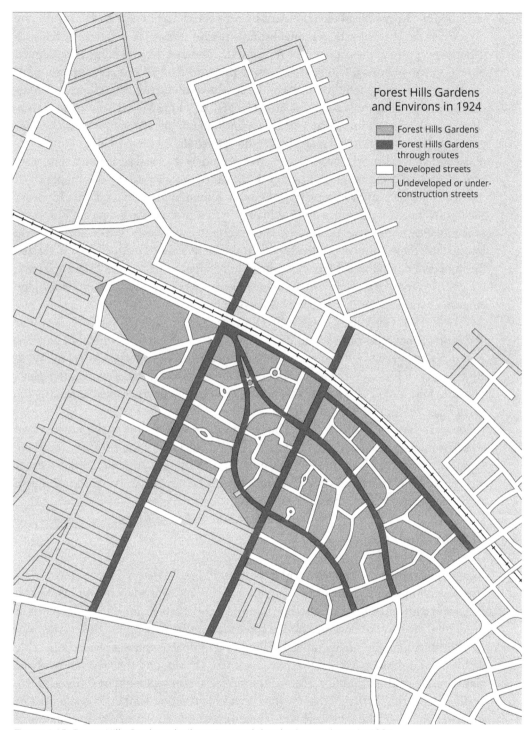

Figure 4.15: Forest Hills Gardens, built project and developing environs in 1924.

diversity, and more mixed use than Olmsted Sr.'s suburbs of the 1870s–1890s. It gave more attention to ensembles of buildings that formed architecturally attractive spaces.

During the initial planning sessions, the designers discussed a Riverside-style curvilinear street layout and an irregular, medieval European layout. Olmsted Jr. was intrigued by the medieval idea but Atterbury rejected it as "a very bad example." He preferred a design that was "reasonable and straightforward" to better serve the educational purposes of the project. The final layout combined several influences: Camillo Sitte, German planning, Olmsted Sr.'s residential layouts, and Beaux Arts planning.[94]

Olmsted Jr. matched the widths of the streets to their traffic functions and adjacent land uses. They ranged from 40 to 80 feet (12 to 24 m) wide. The narrowest were short and usually terminated at T-intersections to moderate through traffic. The widest were also the longest and most direct, and carried the heaviest traffic volumes. The plan created five through routes. Two were required by the local government and were extensions of the surrounding street grid; the other three led to the central plaza.[95]

A few months after completing the plan, Olmsted Jr. delivered an address to the first National Conference on City Planning that praised the emerging European practice of comprehensive planning. He enumerated the flaws of standardized grid layouts and their uniform-width streets. In the standardized grid, all streets carried through traffic. That was a "distinct injury" to residents who wanted to "escape from the disturbance of traffic," as well as to business owners who wanted to maximize the amount of traffic moving past their businesses.[96]

Forest Hills Gardens opened in 1911 and received much attention in the popular and professional press until World War I. It was a short distance from Manhattan, but America's first garden suburb was sometimes described by reporters as belonging to another world. It caught the public's imagination as an exemplar of cooperative planning and harmonious good taste. It was also criticized as overdesigned and artificial, like a stage set for an operetta.[97]

At first the area had little traffic, but traffic volumes mounted as the surrounding blocks were developed and the West Side Tennis Club (site of the US Open for many years) was built next door. In 1916, one critic argued that Forest Hills Gardens' street plan should have used cul-de-sacs to provide traffic refuges, and cited the English garden suburbs as better models.[98]

Plan of Chicago

In regard to roadways, Daniel Burnham's 1909 *Plan of Chicago* directed most of its attention and passion to major thoroughfares, especially the grand downtown boulevards and associated civic spaces. Burnham did not create visions or model plans of residential streets. His coverage of that topic was minimal.

But Burnham did not completely ignore the topic. His thinking was compatible with that of designers like Olmsted Sr., Pitzman, Unwin, and the German roadway planners. He said that traffic streets and residential streets should be differentiated. Traffic streets should divide the city into "great blocks" that contained residential or service streets. Because they were wide and direct, traffic streets would draw the surging "tides of traffic" away from residential streets.[99]

Residential streets could be narrower and cheaper. Traffic control on residential streets was "highly important" to reduce costs, improve efficiency, and maintain property values. Burnham suggested that particular types of traffic, such as heavy freight, should be banned on residential streets. The city should be able to institute such restrictions without having to designate the streets as park facilities (as the existing parkways had been), and Burnham said that the state legislature should grant that authority. Also, banning streetcars on residential streets would prevent their gradual conversion into business streets and the associated loss of property value. "With good planning these ruinous transformations become unnecessary, and the purchase of a home then becomes a stable investment and not a gambling hazard," he advised.[100]

Quarter Section Competition

The City Club of Chicago, established in 1903, was a social club and city-reform organization whose members were concerned with municipal efficiency and public welfare. In 1908, partly in reaction to the Burnham plan, the club formed a city-planning committee. Most Chicago reformers of the time believed that the Burnham plan attended to decorative frills instead of seriously answering the city's needs for housing, jobs, and recreation. City Club members thought the Burnham plan lacked a necessary attention to the design of residential areas.[101]

In 1910, at the second National Conference on City Planning, the City Club proposed an exposition of model plans tailored to the needs of a yet-unspecified city. But before it endorsed specific principles, the Club gathered information from leading experts. It hosted lectures by garden-city advocates and housing reformers from around the world. Raymond Unwin spoke in May 1911, and told the Club that overcrowded, unhealthy cities with congested streets represented a failure of civilization. He used a plan by Camillo Sitte to illustrate traffic-separation principles; it showed a framework of straight traffic thoroughfares in "true relation" to a system of minor streets. He said that many minor streets in Hampstead Garden Suburb were removed from main traffic flows "to avoid the dust and smell from automobiles and other vehicles."[102]

British, European, and American garden suburbs were admirable, but few had been designed for a gridiron context like Chicago's. So the City Club organized an international design competition, which ran from December 1912 to March 1913. The brief was to design a model residential tract for suburban Chicago. Because the tract was a quarter section (a square 160 acres or 65 hectares in area), the contest was popularly known as the Quarter Section Competition. The organizers wanted to exhibit the best of residential neighborhood planning and hoped that some of the plans would be used to develop actual suburban tracts. The competition's reading list consisted entirely of garden-city literature, covering topics such as model company towns and garden suburbs in Britain, city planning in Germany, and Forest Hills Gardens.[103]

Thirty-nine entries were reviewed. The competition brief stated that the tract was bounded on all sides by thoroughfares with streetcar lines, while the interior layout was unspecified. Most entries abandoned the standard Chicago gridiron for layouts that were more curvilinear or circuitous. The winning plans were similar to Forest Hills Gardens, but more radical ideas were also submitted.[104]

The plans by Edgar Lawrence, Charles Tirrell, and Alfred Yeomans featured large blocks or superblocks with interior play fields, playgrounds, or tennis courts. Robert Pope's plan had superblocks up to 17 acres (6.9 ha) and a continuous system of off-street walkways throughout the tract. Albert Sturr's plan was a hybrid: a grid of 16 blocks, ten of which had internal cul-de-sacs "for those who prefer a more secluded environment and freedom for the frolics of young children."[105]

Figure 4.16: Selected
entries in the Quarter
Section Competition,
1913. Top: Sturr's
gridiron of oversize
blocks, each with
an internal cul-de-
sac. Bottom: Tirrell's
curvilinear layout of
oversize blocks with
internal greens.

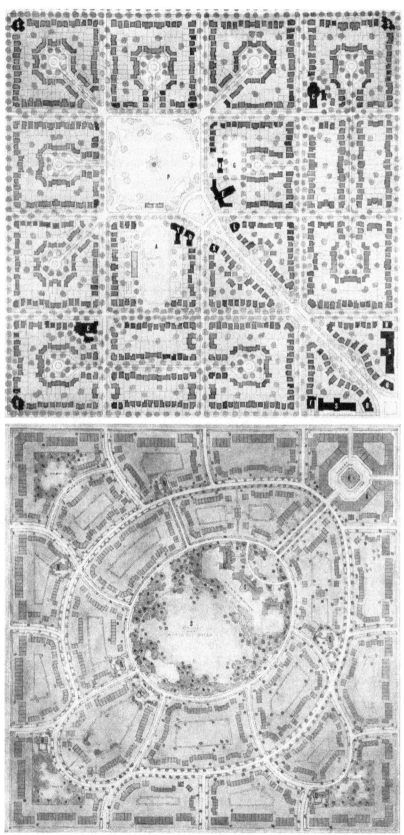

Frank Lloyd Wright and the prairie style of architectural design had a notable influence on the competition. Wright was member of the City Club and submitted a "non-competitive" entry. Several other competitors had worked in Wright's studio; one of them was the architect William Drummond.

Drummond's entry was not a specific design, but a more abstract concept that he labeled the *neighborhood unit*. Neighborhood units were demarcated by major thoroughfares. Business uses were clustered at the corners of each unit so that internal streets would not suffer the noise and danger of business traffic. The internal street layout was generally gridlike, but narrow streets and strategic disconnections would ensure that the "better class of residences" was protected from noise and traffic.

Each neighborhood unit had civic, educational, and recreational uses located at the center. Drummond drew his neighborhood units as quarter-sections, but said the actual size might be larger or smaller—whatever was needed to establish a permanent neighborhood social grouping. He endorsed the goals of the community-center movement, such as volunteerism, adult learning, and recreation. Achieving those goals, he contended, required the reorganization of the city as a fabric of neighborhood units. The overall aim was order. Orderly neighborhoods would inculcate systematic and harmonious city politics. In the absence of order, neighborhoods fell prey to the "sinister machinations of exploiters."[106]

The Quarter Section Competition had a moderate influence within the city-planning field. In May 1913, international attendees of the fifth National Conference on City Planning saw the entries on exhibit. In 1916, the competition was published as a lavish book that featured Frank Lloyd Wright's entry in full color. The City Club apparently wanted to equal the *Plan of Chicago* book in terms of production quality and professional importance. The two books had identical dimensions; the City Club's book may have been intended to complement *Plan of Chicago* on book-owners' shelves.

The Quarter Section Competition fell out of the public's awareness because of World War I, according to Lewis Mumford. But superblock planning continued to gain adherents, and Drummond's neighborhood-unit concept was re-used in a form that became exceedingly popular indeed.[107]

Chapter 4 Summary

The roots of insular roadways date to ancient times, and include walled towns and cities, fenced aristocratic estates, ghettoes, dead-end passages, and other patterns. The first speculative gated suburb was probably Regent's Park (1811), and a number of others were built over the next fifty years in Britain, France, and America. Gated streets were prevalent in London throughout the nineteenth century. Exclusion, status, and protection from undesired people, activities, and traffic were the typical goals of those developments.

Frederick Law Olmsted was a leading advocate of indirect, inconvenient roadway layouts. Such layouts, he believed, insured that middle- and upper-class residential neighborhoods would never change or support any business activity. Private gated streets with proto-suburban features developed in St. Louis in the late nineteenth century. Official planning policies that separated through from local traffic appeared in Germany in the 1890s, augmented by Camillo Sitte and his followers. In America,

Charles Mulford Robinson used the term *functional classification* to describe similar policies, and was a powerful advocate for them.

Raymond Unwin, the leading planner of the garden-city movement, was central to the early development of suburban cul-de-sacs, superblocks, and cellular roadway layouts. He exerted a primary influence on British urban-design policy. He traveled often, had numerous contacts and followers abroad, and was a key transmitter of insular-roadway ideas. In the first decade of the 1900s, insular-roadway ideas were propagated internationally by a number of leading planners such as Unwin, Daniel Burnham, and Frederick Law Olmsted Jr. In the 1910s those ideas started to percolate into the rank and file of the architecture and planning fields. An example of that dissemination was the Quarter Section Competition; its guidelines drew on Unwin's work, and at least one entry helped define the insular-roadway principles of subsequent decades.

CHAPTER 5
Horizontal Traffic Separation:
Insular Roadways 1910s–1930s

Well-connected layouts of small blocks dominated city roadway-network planning in the early twentieth century because walking and mass transit were still the primary means of travel. Meanwhile, in the smaller field of insular roadway design, the trend had moved away from gated streets and districts. More permanent and determinative methods were gaining favor. Designers experimented more frequently with cul-de-sacs and superblocks, and policymakers applied those methods to ever-larger areas. Insularity was becoming more intrinsic to the layouts themselves.

In Germany after World War I, those processes developed under conditions of economic instability and political strife. Housing shortages were widespread and city planners struggled to respond. In several noteworthy situations, garden-city idealism was refashioned by the demands of postwar scarcity. German city planning reassumed its prewar role, for a brief period, as an important international influence.

German Planning 1910s-1930s and American Continuance

The garden city idea was very popular in Germany. The German Garden City Society (Deutsche Gartenstadtgellschaft, or DGG) was founded in 1902, only three years after Ebenezer Howard had founded the Garden Cities Association in Britain. At its peak in 1915, DGG had ten thousand members. They were mainly young leftists, artistic intelligentsia, and bohemian bourgeoisie who responded positively to the socialist and social-reformist thrust of Howard's vision. DGG and its British counterpart were closely linked by personal contacts, professional visits, and joint conferences.[1]

The German garden-city advocates developed projects that melded housing, health, recreational, and environmental concerns. German projects generally had higher densities than British ones, reflecting the government's tighter control of land and the greater prevalence of apartment lifestyles. Narrow, winding residential streets and cul-de-sacs were intended to lower housing costs and exclude the noise and pollution of through traffic.

Martin Wagner

As a young architect, Martin Wagner (1885–1957) was deeply influenced by the British garden-city idea. He took a tour of British garden cities that was organized by DGG in the summer of 1910. He designed a small garden suburb in Rüstringen, Germany, where he was head of the city building department. Also in Rüstringen, he organized an exhibition of British and American parks in autumn 1912. Wagner admired the "American model" of park design (probably a reference to Olmsted's Boston park system), meaning that parks should serve hygienic and recreational purposes. Another influence was the Greater Berlin Competition of 1910. Prize-winning entries by Hermann Jansen and the Möhring-Eberstadt-Petersen team proposed citywide green corridors of park and recreational space, and a system of major traffic arteries that separated different land uses.[2]

Wagner served briefly at the battlefront during World War I, where he experienced firsthand the disease and landscape devastation of trench warfare. He returned to Berlin to earn a planning doctorate, and his dissertation *Das sanitäre Grün der Städte* (The sanitary green in cities) was published in 1915. It presented a regional development model in which "green sprouts," or strips of parkland, were laced throughout new districts. A model suburb had superblocks traversed by those green corridors. Within the superblocks, rows of cul-de-sacs terminated at pavilions, which gave entry to the green corridors. The comb-like arrangement of cul-de-sacs within superblocks was created by Wagner more than a decade before Radburn, New Jersey, was planned. It clearly was an antecedent, but Radburn was far better known and was always identified as the progenitor of the pattern.[3]

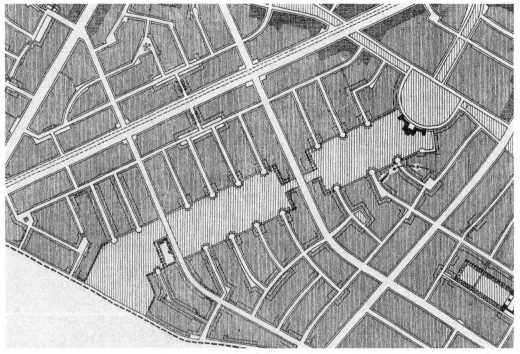

Figure 5.1: Wagner's model plan for a Berlin suburb, detail, 1915. Superblocks contain rows of cul-de-sacs that terminate at greenery corridors. Courtesy of Avery Architectural & Fine Arts Library, Columbia University.

Access to green space was an overriding concern in Wagner's ideal model. He said residents should be able reach playgrounds within 10–15 minutes, parks within 20 minutes, and sports fields and city forests within 30 minutes. Green space was depicted as a fecund river of vegetation, and neighborhood civic buildings were placed within or adjacent to it. Wagner believed that the expansion of health-promoting park and playground space would be urban planners' primary task in the coming years.[4]

During the 1910s and early 1920s, Wagner worked for various cities and organizations involved in regional planning and social housing. His plans continued to reflect the influence of Unwin and the German garden city projects. For example, Lindenhof (1918–1921) was located in an industrial district of suburban Berlin. It was a 13-hectare (33-acre) development that had 5–6 hectare (14–15 acre) superblocks, two cul-de-sacs, pedestrian paths, and long apartment rows that bridged a cross street. Because of its location, design, and mix of land uses, Lindenhof was unusually self-sufficient, and was one of the best-known developments in Berlin in the early 1920s.[5]

Superblocks were starting to enter the mainstream of German planning. Hermann Jansen had achieved instant fame when he won the Greater Berlin Competition in 1910. As a planning professor and creator of more than seventy urban plans, he was highly influential during the Weimar period. In his plans for Cassel (1921) and Hieligensee, Berlin (1922), superblocks were bordered by through-traffic streets and traversed by green corridors. Narrow cul-de-sacs terminated at the green corridors, much like those in Wagner's dissertation. Safety was a primary concern for Jansen. He considered cars to be a hazard because of crash risk and pollution.[6]

Architectural modernism was developing during the same period. Its adherents called for "rationalized" planning, which meant mass production, standardization, uniformity, and efficiency in all aspects of design, including street layouts. Their reasons were several. One, in the aftermath of World War I, housing shortages and tenement overcrowding escalated to crisis levels. The modernists demanded the rapid production of affordable housing on a mass scale, using assembly-line methods. Two, modernism expressed a new attitude toward life and a firm rejection of nineteenth-century mores and aesthetics. The modernist architects spoke, to varying degrees, of renunciation and sacrifice. Traditional craftsmanship, historical knowledge and expertise, and bourgeois luxury were considered obsolete. Three, austere and orderly built environments were a relief from distraction and nervous dissipation. They allowed an increased degree of concentration, mental work, and inner awareness. Four, the aesthetic of repetition expressed an ideal of egalitarianism. The uniform arrangement of buildings and blocks with the same orientation gave all people equal access to sunshine and natural ventilation.[7]

Around 1923–1924, a group of ten architects, most of whom were radically modernist, began meeting regularly in Ludwig Mies van der Rohe's office in Berlin. Although small, the group was conspicuous and persuasive. Group members exchanged ideas, wrote articles, organized exhibitions, and exerted a significant political influence. In May 1926 the group formally organized as *Der Ring* and expanded to 27 members. The roster included Martin Wagner; Ernst May from Frankfurt; Walter Gropius, head of the Bauhaus school in Dessau; and Ludwig Hilberseimer, a planning theorist and art critic. *Der Ring* won outsized victories: it installed Gropius as a director of the Association of German Architects, and in 1926 successfully lobbied to appoint Martin

Wagner as Berlin's chief of planning and construction.[8]

More than 140,000 subsidized dwellings were built in Berlin between 1924 and 1931, the product of a national rental tax instituted in 1924. And in 1926, *Der Ring* members Gropius and May helped obtain a subsidy for those housing settlements that tested rationalization methods. No city built more public housing during the late 1920s than Berlin. The majority was delivered in more traditional urban forms such as infill and perimeter blocks; less than ten percent was designed by modernists. Even so, the amount of experimentation was notable. Seventeen *Großsiedlungen* (large-scale social-housing schemes) were built on the city's periphery, linked to the center by rail-transit extensions.[9]

With each passing year, the pressure grew to house more people at a lower cost. Large modernist settlement projects became more standardized and regimented. Streets were omitted wherever possible and superblocks became more common. Modernist settlement projects were increasingly disconnected from surrounding local and regional road networks—not only in Berlin, but elsewhere in Germany and in other European cities.

Ernst May

Ernst May (1886–1970) was born to an upper-class family in Frankfurt am Main. His father ran a leather factory; his grandfather was a local politician. In 1907 he went to London to study architecture at University College, and lived in Hampstead as construction of Hampstead Garden Suburb was beginning. He finished a compulsory year of military service in late 1908, then studied architecture in Munich. One of his important teachers was Theodor Fischer (a follower of Camillo Sitte), and he developed friendships with Bruno Taut, Hugo Häring, and other students who later became prominent modernists.[10]

Some German architects visited English garden cities, but May had a stronger commitment. He returned to England to study with Raymond Unwin from summer 1910 to early 1911. The studio was working on Hampstead Garden Suburb at the time, and May also contributed to the German translation of Unwin's book *Town Planning in Practice*. The experience only increased May's admiration for Unwin's planning work and principles. He later said his time in Unwin's office was "the foundation on which the whole of my work is based" and that he "took over the idea of neighborhood units in most of my town planning work in Germany and elsewhere." May maintained a lifelong friendship with Unwin and his family.[11]

May was a large, solidly built man with a dominating physical presence and personality. One employee described him as a "massive and inconsiderate giant" on first impression; some critics said he was dictatorial. He tended to make promises that he did not deliver on. But he also inspired loyalty and admiration, and from the 1910s through the early 1930s, he directed ever-larger planning efforts.[12]

May served in the military again during World War I. He designed and built cemeteries, managing as many as 30 artisans and 100 prison laborers. From 1919 to 1925 he was the technical and artistic director of a housing welfare association in Silesia (now southeastern Poland). The region received a stream of political refugees after the German-Polish border was redrawn in 1921. May's job was to establish farming

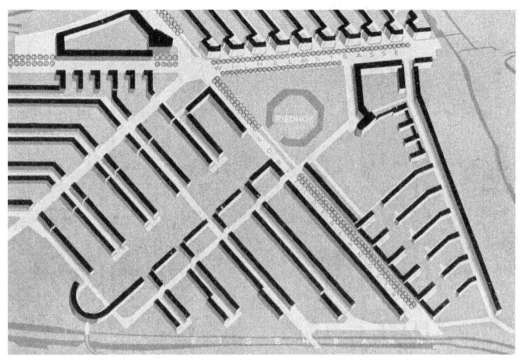

Figure 5.2: May's Riedhof-West plan, detail, 1927. This proposed design featured rows of cul-de-sacs terminating at greenery corridors. Courtesy of Blue Mountain Project at Princeton University.

communities, and by 1925 he had 40 employees and managed three branch offices in addition to the main Breslau office. The 3,000 dwellings that May built in Silesia were generally planned according to garden-city principles.[13]

In September 1925 May was appointed as director of Frankfurt's Municipal Building Department. His mission was to solve the city's housing shortage, and after a few months he issued a ten-year plan. The city would build 10,000 dwellings in self-contained settlements on the urban periphery. His department launched an accelerated construction program of 2,000 units per year, which rose to more than 3,000 by 1928. The department worked in the modernist style; the early projects had decorative features and usually used superblock layouts. The Siedlung Riedhof-West plan (1927) had a superblock with cul-de-sacs pointing inward to a green-space corridor.[14]

People's need for low-cost housing continued to outstrip the supply. The international economy crashed after 1929 and May's funding dwindled. He responded with emergency ultra-cheap settlement schemes that eliminated streets, expanded superblocks, and sited housing in more extensive barracks-like rows.[15]

May's overall achievement during the 1926–1930 period was substantial. He planned some 16 settlement projects, administered at least 3 more, and built 14,000 dwellings. Some of his success can be attributed to marketing skill. May and his staff published the avant-garde magazine *Das neue Frankfurt*; organized lectures, exhibitions, and tours; and hosted the second CIAM congress in 1929. Frankfurt's planning was internationally renowned.[16]

In mid-1930, May traveled with Martin Wagner to the Soviet Union. They both had received invitations to discuss a planning job. The USSR was in the midst of Stalin's first Five-Year Plan, and the *de novo* creation of many mining and industrial

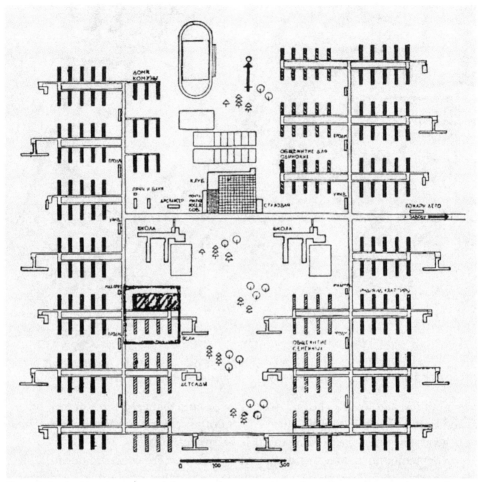

Figure 5.3: The May Group's model quarter for new cities in the USSR, 1931. A settlement for ten thousand people. Courtesy of Heidelberg University Library.

towns was going to require an vast program of city planning and housing construction. Wagner declined the job offer; May accepted.[17]

May and his staff, known as the "May Group" or "May's Brigade," arrived in Moscow in October 1930. May's position was chief engineer of city and new-town planning for the nation's state bank. At the peak of his institutional power from 1931 to 1932, he was in charge of 800 employees, 150 of whom were foreign experts. The demands placed on the May Group were orders of magnitude greater than those in Frankfurt. The solution was the rapid assembly-line production of new towns across the country.[18]

May used a modular, nested planning scheme. The basic unit was the home commune of 400–1,200 people. It was configured as apartment rows perpendicular to a cul-de-sac, and had a communal bath house, dining hall, nursery, and kindergarten. A number of communes combined to form quarters of 8,000–10,000 that had neighborhood buildings and amenities. A number of quarters combined to form a standardized city of 120,000 that had city-level civic buildings and institutions. The superblocks of the standardized scheme were 40 hectares (100 acres) or larger. Street density could be minimized because the need to accommodate motor vehicles was tiny. The minor-street layouts were dendritic; they branched into the superblocks and

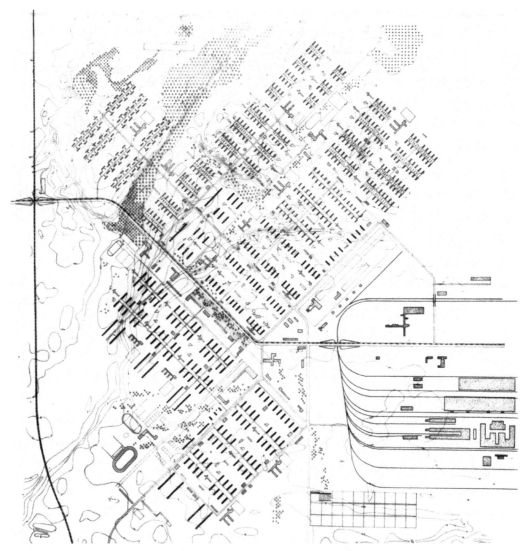

Figure 5.4: Plan of Socialist City Avtostroy, USSR, detail, 1931. A typical new-city plan by the May Group. Quarters are assembled to form a city with superblocks and, at the edges, dendritic extensions. Courtesy of Deutsches Kunstarchiv, Germanisches Nationalmuseum.

urban-fringe areas like ice crystals on a pond surface.[19]

In June 1931, May visited Berlin as a triumphant planning hero. He delivered a lecture on Soviet town planning and highlighted the organizing of residential areas as quarters. He said the socialist town was structured to put all communal facilities and amenities "at a comfortable and functionally optimal distance" from apartment dwellings. Martin Wagner applauded his colleague, writing: "Anticipation of the future, the feeling of liberation after long, frustrating stagnation, the letting in of sun and fresh air into a dark musty workroom—these explain why May's lecture became such an extraordinary event for the people of Berlin."[20]

The triumph was short-lived. In January 1932, May was abruptly fired as a result of a Soviet political power struggle. He continued on in a token position, but the firing marked his permanent break with the Soviet system. To his friends, he complained that the regime was brutal and reactionary, its Five-Year Plans failures, its policies illogical and chaotic. He decided to leave the USSR, and also avoid Germany, where the Nazis had marked him as a political enemy. He purchased a coffee plantation in Tanganyika in East Africa and moved there at the end of 1933. The move was opportune, for all of May's political patrons and allies in the USSR were liquidated by the late 1930s—executed or otherwise vanished.[21]

In the span of 15 months, the May Group had initiated more than 20 projects. They included nine new towns of populations between 50,000 and 250,000, which would have housed 1.4 million in total. The entirety of the May Group's production effect is unknown, but certainly many thousands of dwelling units were built according to its plans. Some were still standing in the 2010s. May's planning effort was the first implementation of strongly dendritic street layouts on a such a huge scale. Its scope was not surpassed until a generation later, when American suburbs adopted dendritic street layouts *en masse* in the 1960s and 1970s.[22]

May lived and practiced in East Africa for twenty years. He returned to Germany in 1954 and worked on more than fifty large-scale development plans until his death in 1970. They usually were in the mold of his earlier Frankfurt projects, but often included high-rise towers and residential slabs. His street layouts generally were configured as superblocks that sometimes contained dendritic access roads. Only a fraction of his postwar plans were realized, yet even so, tens of thousands of dwellings were built according to plans he made or contributed to.[23]

Ludwig Hilberseimer

Ludwig Hilberseimer (1885–1967) was born in Karlsruhe and studied at the technical institute there. He moved to Berlin in 1911, started his own architectural firm in 1914, and began drafting manuscripts about city-planning history and theory. After World War I he wrote for utopian and socialist magazines, covering architecture and planning as well as avant-garde art in Europe and Russia.[24]

Hilberseimer had a very reserved and intellectual personality. He liked to develop abstract architectural and planning models and explore their permutations. As a result, his planning models were at times divergent and contradictory. During the 1920s especially, theoretical exploration was more important to him than consistency.

In a 1923 article, Hilberseimer called for urban decentralization in the form of satellite developments, citing the work of Raymond Unwin, Ernst May, and others. He said the growth of megacities would "produce an entirely new type of city that dispenses with spatial cohesion," and that "the traffic question will become the Alpha and Omega of the entire urban organism." From 1924 to 1930 he also advocated centralized high-rise cities in which transit, autos, and pedestrians circulated on separate levels. Hilberseimer simultaneously argued that both models produced unworkable commuter traffic patterns and that both models were the best possible solution.[25]

Hilberseimer joined the faculty of the Bauhaus in Dessau, Germany, in 1928 and taught modernist architecture and city planning. Over the next several years, he abandoned his high-rise-city vision and returned to a stance in favor of decentralization. He put more emphasis on garden-city principles such as detached houses, green space,

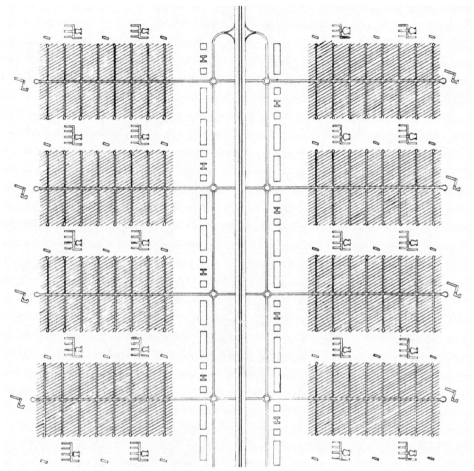

Figure 5.5: Hilberseimer's generic plan for a ribbon of settlement units, 1944. The main highway is paralleled by access highways and commercial and industrial uses. A number of Hilberseimer's plans, like this one, had graphics that were markedly similar to Ernst May's USSR plans. Courtesy of Ryerson and Burnham Archives, The Art Institute of Chicago.

and neighborhood self-sufficiency. Starting in 1931, Hilberseimer began to formulate the ingredients of a development model that he called the settlement unit.[26]

The settlement unit's street layout was purely and absolutely dendritic. A limited-access highway branched into a single central street, which in turn branched into rows of cul-de-sacs. Configuring all local streets as cul-de-sacs would eliminate any possibility of through traffic in the residential area. The green spaces between the settlement units accommodated schools and community buildings, and usually produced enough food to feed the nearby population. Commercial and administrative buildings were placed along the highway, while smokestack industries could be located on the opposite side of the highway, downwind of residences. The settlement unit was sized so that everything was within a 15-to-20-minute walk. Provisions for roadways and parking were minimal; settlement units were generally self-sufficient, so residents had little need to drive.[27]

Hilberseimer's 1932 Dessau plan was his first to feature settlement units. The city had a population of 70,000 at the time, and was home to the Bauhaus school where Hilberseimer taught. He proposed to demolish the city and rebuild it as a ribbon of

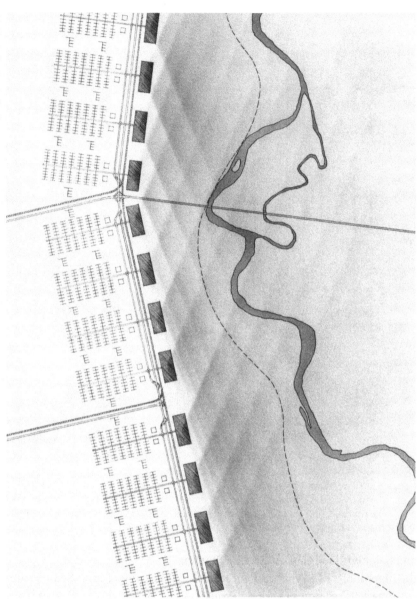

Figure 5.6: Hilberseimer's Dessau plan, 1932. Courtesy of Ryerson and Burnham Archives, The Art Institute of Chicago.

dendritic settlement units. Smokestack industries would be located downwind of the residential clusters. The next year, he made a plan to demonstrate how a big city like Berlin could be decentralized. It consisted of a gigantic grid; the thoroughfares were lined by ribbons of settlement units, each of which could house up to 250,000 people. The grid's megablocks averaged 17 square miles (45 sq km) in area.[28]

The Nazis took power in March 1933, and in April they raided the Bauhaus school and closed its doors. Later that summer, they demanded that Hilberseimer, a dedicated socialist, and Wassily Kandinsky, a "degenerate" painter and suspected Communist, be fired and replaced by sworn supporters of the Fascist ideology. But the faculty had already voted to dissolve the school. Over the next several years, Hilberseimer worked on a book manuscript about urban planning history and the settlement unit.[29]

In 1938, Hilberseimer's longtime friend and colleague Ludwig Mies van der Rohe

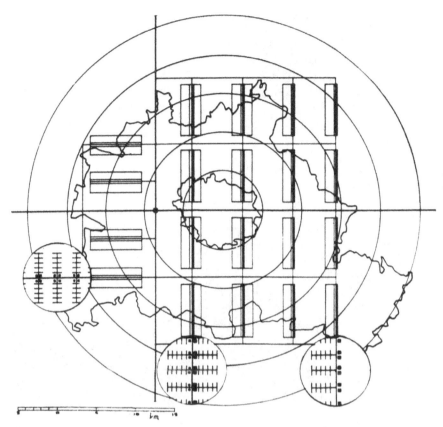

Figure 5.7: Hilberseimer's plan for a decentralized big city superimposed over outline of Berlin, 1933. Courtesy of Ryerson and Burnham Archives, The Art Institute of Chicago.

was asked to become director of the architecture department at the Armour Institute of Technology in Chicago (the school was renamed the Illinois Institute of Technology in 1940). Mies van der Rohe stipulated that Hilberseimer and two other Bauhaus associates would join him as faculty members. Despite his initial inability to speak English, Hilberseimer soon began publicizing the settlement unit through articles, books, and exhibitions.[30]

Through the 1940s and 1950s, Hilberseimer explored various permutations of his theoretical construct. The settlement unit's streets could be wiggly to adapt to hilly conditions, or angled to improve solar orientation. The existing streets in a city gridiron could be selectively removed (a method used by Henry Wright's 1934 plan for Queens, New York) to produce settlement-unit layouts. Centripetal dendritic layouts, like those of Martin Wagner and Walter Gropius at Harvard, could form a small town. A group of settlement units could be located inside variously shaped megablocks that ranged from 2 to 50 square miles (5–130 sq km) in area. Working in the American context, his plans sometimes detailed freeways and cloverleaf intersections. But Hilberseimer himself hated to drive, and he planned for relatively low levels of auto use.[31]

His most sweeping vision was to rebuild existing cities as endless belts of replicated settlement units. He drew plans to decentralize Chicago, Manhattan, Washington, DC, London, and other cities in a gradual stepwise manner over a period of one or two generations. Settlement units would be arrayed along a main highway to form a linear city. As the population grew, the linear city would simply extend across the

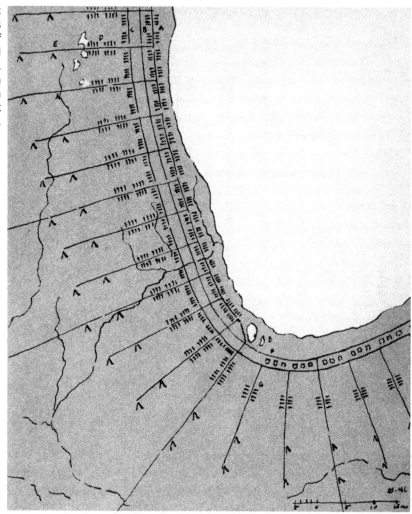

Figure 5.8:
Hilberseimer's
sketch plan of
a decentralized
Chicago, ca. 1939.
Courtesy of Ryerson
and Burnham
Archives, The Art
Institute of Chicago.

countryside, and dendritic settlement units would branch out perpendicularly. In his vision for North America, the linear cities of different regions grew together to span the entire eastern half of the continent.[32]

Hilberseimer said the settlement unit was like a brick: it was modular, yet could be made in a variety of forms, and could be assembled in countless configurations. It could serve every requirement that might arise in any city and "would make a complete traffic solution truly possible." But certain functions were not provided. The settlement unit represented the total elimination of urban streets, urban blocks, and urban fabric. The age-old function of the street as social space—a space for meetings, markets, ceremonies, free speech, entertainment, leisure, and so on—was abolished. And unlike some of his modernist colleagues, Hilberseimer saw no need to provide a substitute.[33]

He offered several reasons why urban populations should be dispersed into settlement units. The concept's greatest advantage was its ability to solve traffic congestion. Traffic safety was crucial too. The traditional street-and-block system was antiquated and its intersections were death traps; in contrast, the settlement unit eliminated as many intersections and pedestrian crossings as possible. The modern city was a locus of crime, pollution, and ill health, all of which the settlement unit would ameliorate.

Military defense was another justification. The lethal potential of air strikes (and later, the hydrogen bomb) made decentralization a matter of survival.[34]

Hilberseimer explained the sources of the settlement-unit idea in his publications. He cited Raymond Unwin and Henry Wright as originators of the cul-de-sac layout, which he called "an old solution." His linear-city vision was similar to that of the Spanish administrator Arturo Soria Y Mata, who proposed continent-spanning linear cities in a 1882–1883 newspaper series; and of the Russian planner Nikolai Miliutin, who diagrammed a plan for unbounded growth in his 1930 book *Sotsgorod* (Socialist City). Hilberseimer never cited Ernst May's USSR plans as an influence, although he certainly must have been familiar with them, and the graphic conventions of his plans were obviously similar to the graphics of May's plans.[35]

Hilberseimer was a private man without intimate friends, yet he was devoted to teaching and beloved by his students. He had little direct impact on the national planning field. (Only one of his neighborhood-scale plans was built: Lafayette Homes, a residential superblock near Detroit's historic core, planned in 1956.) Rather, his ideas were transmitted through his students. As part of the IIT architecture curriculum, all students were trained in the settlement-unit model and used it to re-plan an existing city. Many of Hilberseimer's students attained academic and planning positions at the local and national levels.[36]

During and after Hilberseimer's lifetime, his settlement-unit idea was criticized as being sterile and formulaic. But during the same period, suburban street layouts everywhere grew closer to his ideal of a completely dendritic pattern. Hilberseimer himself may have been relatively unknown, but his ideal pattern filtered into the planning discourse and may have influenced the development field as well. The planning historians Michael Southworth and Peter Owens dubbed the completely dendritic pattern "lollipops on a stick"; it emerged in the 1970s and became dominant in American suburbs in the 1980s.[37]

Wagner in America

Martin Wagner began developing a model for regional development after 1931. Much like Ernst May, he envisioned modular, nested settlement patterns; and like Ludwig Hilberseimer, he envisioned them in linear-city form, strung along transportation corridors. The basic unit was the self-sufficient, mixed-use "township" of 5,000 people and its surrounding agricultural area. Townships could be combined to form larger schemes of 25,000 people.[38]

Political conditions prevented Wagner from developing his model for several years. He was attacked and marginalized as the Nazis took power in Germany. He was forced out of his directorship in 1933, and in 1935 he emigrated to Turkey to work as a city planner. In 1938 Walter Gropius invited him to join the faculty of the Harvard Graduate School of Design.

He soon found his bearings and transplanted his township model to the American setting. In a 1940 article he announced that America's urban and rural communities were obsolete, and that existing big cities were "unfit for the up-growing new life of the twentieth century." All of them had to be replaced by the linear cities of the future. New residential areas would be configured as continuous bands of townships

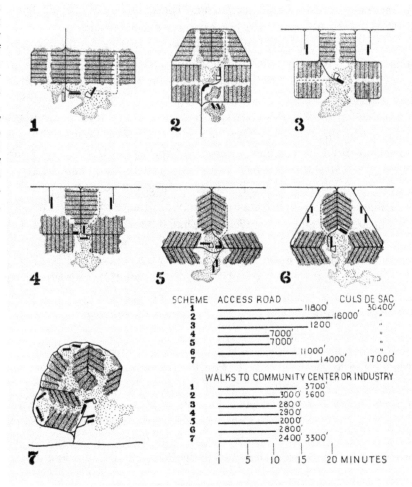

Figure 5.9: Analysis of seven dendritic schemes by Frederic Shurtleff Coolidge, a student in Wagner and Gropius's Harvard studio, 1942. Courtesy of Frances Loeb Library, Harvard University Graduate School of Design.

along combined superhighways and high-speed railways. Residential street layouts generally would be dendritic, and all housing would be sited on cul-de-sacs. Wagner announced that his Harvard classes would be making models of the idea.[39]

But as the academic studio sessions explored the township idea, a different regional pattern emerged. Wagner and Gropius proposed to rebuild existing metropolises as townships "loosely scattered over the whole region" and sited near freeways. One goal, among several, was to increase traffic speed. It seemed preposterous to them that the automobile "must be bridled and policed on an obsolete net of streets by stop lights and speed regulations which contradict the very purpose of its invention."

In an early-1942 studio, the student Frederic Shurtleff Coolidge analyzed a variety of dendritic layouts. The centripetal layout, which had a ring road and cul-de-sacs pointing inward to the center, was said to be the most convenient and economical. The township's area was no more than 500 acres (200 ha), so everything was within walking distance. All local streets were cul-de-sacs, and pedestrians traveled between them on a separate footpath network. Wagner's studios used centripetal layouts through the rest of the 1940s.[40]

These street layouts, like Hilberseimer's, were more completely and systematically dendritic than typical plans of the time—more so even than Radburn. The dendritic

Figure 5.10: Model of proposed development in Weston-Wayland, Massachusetts, by Wagner and Gropius's Harvard students, 1942. Courtesy of Frances Loeb Library, Harvard University Graduate School of Design.

concept started to spread into the design professions. In March 1942, Gropius co-organized the Harvard Conference on Urbanism, which was attended by many reform-minded architects and planners. From mid-1942 through late 1943, the concept reached a tipping point. A flurry of dendritic layouts appeared in proposed projects, architectural journals, popular magazines, and advertising pamphlets. The architecture and planning fields were struggling with a dire shortage of work during this wartime period, and reformist architects and planners, along with Keynesian economists, called for super-enlarged governmental powers to re-plan cities. Strongly dendritic street layouts were a common feature of the postwar settlements they envisioned.[41]

A few years later, in a 1946 studio, Wagner's students proposed street layouts that were looser and more curviform, yet still strongly dendritic. A group of six townships

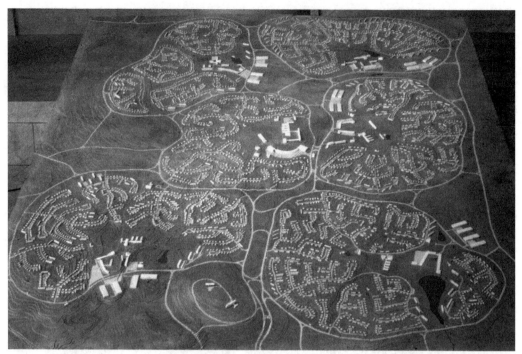

Figure 5.11: Model of township group by Wagner's Harvard students, 1946. This agglomeration would house up to 30,000 people in the Boston suburbs. Courtesy of Frances Loeb Library, Harvard University Graduate School of Design.

could be loosely clustered to form a larger settlement. Parkways could encircle each township, similar to the model that Eliel Saarinen was proposing around the same time. These sprawling layouts presaged the layouts of thousands of American suburbs built after the 1960s.[42]

Wagner was not solely preoccupied with insular suburban townships. His ideal metropolis also needed a major employment center, so in 1942 he and his students devised a wheel-shaped megastructure 1.2 miles (1.9 km) in diameter. Its roadway system comprised sunken and surface expressways that ran both circumferentially and between the spokes of the wheel. Almost no one would live in this "Buck-Rogers-like" complex; it was a district of white-collar business, shopping, hospitals, education, and entertainment. Wagner promoted the scheme for a decade and proposed it as a replacement for Boston's historic core.[43]

During his years in America, Wagner accomplished no built work and made few graphic representations of his ideas. But he continued to publish in professional journals and was exceptionally committed to his students and teaching. He called himself the "most radical and most subversive Harvard professor" and relished his status as an iconoclast. His uncompromising, antagonistic positions repelled his colleagues, including Gropius, who broke with Wagner in the late 1940s. Wagner retired from Harvard in 1950.[44]

Wagner's legacy was realized mainly through the achievements of his students. Many of them became deans of leading architecture schools and founded urban-studies programs. A number of projects spearheaded by Wagner's former students were prominent and influential examples of horizontal and vertical traffic separation, including Reston, Virginia; Don Mills, Toronto; the Underground City of Montreal; and Charles Center in Baltimore.[45]

Clarence Perry and the Neighborhood Unit

Clarence Arthur Perry (1872–1944) was an educator and social activist. He worked as a teacher and high-school principal, and ran school systems in the Philippines and Puerto Rico. He was an investigator for the US Congress's Dillingham Commission on immigration, a job that gave him firsthand knowledge of immigrants' working and living conditions.[46]

In 1909 Perry joined the Russell Sage Foundation's Recreation Division, where he worked until his retirement nearly thirty years later. The foundation had hired him to investigate the use of school buildings for community recreational, social, and civic purposes. Little had been written about the topic, and Perry's book titled *Wider Use of the School Plant* (1910) was a success in its field. He became widely associated with the movement to use school buildings as community centers. He wrote, taught, helped establish advocacy groups, and traveled the United States giving organizing advice.[47]

During the same period, the national community-center movement was gaining energy. It grew from settlement houses, such as Hull House in Chicago, and other community-lecture and community-recreation initiatives. Perry and his fellow reformers were starry-eyed zealots who believed that the community center was a panacea for the toughest social ills:

> ... we fondly dreamed of a time when every neighborhood in the land would possess a copy of this brand new institution. As we envisaged it then, it would be a place where people would meet regularly to discuss their common affairs, sing together, dance and play, study the arts; where the jobless would find employment, where the wealthy would occasionally put their art treasures on exhibition for the benefit of all—an institution which would make one big family out of the whole neighborhood. A heightened social solidarity, the dissolution of class and racial antagonisms, the rise of a civic intelligence that would see through the smoke screens behind which political bosses did their dirty work—these are only a few of the benefits we saw readily following the realization of our dream.[48]

Perry was no bigot, and he appreciated a moderate degree of cultural diversity. But he did exploit contemporary concerns about immigrants to advance his cause. He wrote that mechanized industry and immigrants' "strange manner of living and foreign tongue" created social fissures: they "chopped us up into isolated chunks." Community centers were a means for "breaking down the prejudices which bar the foreigner from native circles and make him a menace in our politics." One of the lecture topics Perry recommended for community centers was "The Neighborhood: The Beginning of Patriotism."[49]

Also, Perry was unusually concerned with the maintenance of proper behavior and cultural norms. He served for many years on the National Board of Review of

Motion Pictures, which was an unofficial arbiter of taste for the US movie industry. He developed a rating system for immigrants' assimilation potential based on their household furnishings. A program he organized for a National Education Association conference had as its motto, "A Community Center is an Americanization Center."[50]

During World War I, Perry developed the Army's system of post exchanges, which he thought of as social centers. He volunteered to serve as a post-exchange officer and, by the end of his tour in France, had achieved the rank of division quartermaster. Perry returned to his community-center work after the war, but when he saw the opportunity to expand in a new direction, he pursued it energetically.[51]

That opportunity was the Regional Plan of New York and Its Environs (RPNY). In 1922 Perry got involved as a contributor to the play and leisure report. His study of recreation planning soon became a more ambitious work about neighborhood planning. He formulated his neighborhood-unit concept in 1923 and drafted a monograph by 1926, which was published by RPNY in 1929.[52]

Perry's neighborhood unit was essentially the concept outlined by the Quarter Section Competition, particularly William Drummond's entry. The differences were a matter of emphasis. For Perry, the school was most important neighborhood institution. The population of a neighborhood unit was the number that could support an elementary school. A neighborhood unit's density and dwelling types could vary considerably, but it was always intended to serve families with housewives and young

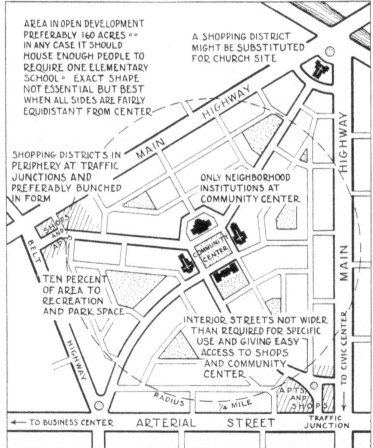

Figure 5.12: Perry's model neighborhood-unit layout, 1929. The diagram, originally published by RPNY, became the most famous visual representation of the neighborhood-unit idea. It appeared to emulate Unwin's model roadway-layout diagram (figure 4.14).

AREA IN OPEN DEVELOPMENT PREFERABLY 160 ACRES °° IN ANY CASE IT SHOULD HOUSE ENOUGH PEOPLE TO REQUIRE ONE ELEMENTARY SCHOOL ° EXACT SHAPE NOT ESSENTIAL BUT BEST WHEN ALL SIDES ARE FAIRLY EQUIDISTANT FROM CENTER

A SHOPPING DISTRICT MIGHT BE SUBSTITUTED FOR CHURCH SITE

SHOPPING DISTRICTS IN PERIPHERY AT TRAFFIC JUNCTIONS AND PREFERABLY BUNCHED IN FORM

ONLY NEIGHBORHOOD INSTITUTIONS AT COMMUNITY CENTER

TEN PERCENT OF AREA TO RECREATION AND PARK SPACE

INTERIOR STREETS NOT WIDER THAN REQUIRED FOR SPECIFIC USE AND GIVING EASY ACCESS TO SHOPS AND COMMUNITY CENTER

HIGHWAY
MAIN
SHOPS AND APTS
BELT
COMMUNITY CENTER
RADIUS — ¼ MILE
APTS AND SHOPS
TO CIVIC CENTER
TO BUSINESS CENTER
ARTERIAL STREET
TRAFFIC JUNCTION
MAIN

children. For a neighborhood of suburban single-family houses, Perry recommended an area of 160 acres (65 ha) bounded by thoroughfares half a mile (0.8 km) apart—identical to the Quarter Section Competition.[53]

Perry was adamant that through traffic must be eliminated. Following the trends of the late 1920s, he discarded immigration as a justification for planned neighborhoods, and instead highlighted automobile danger. The neighborhood unit's interior was a labyrinth made to discourage through traffic and ensure cautious driving. "No motorist can get under very much headway in a maze," Perry noted. Methods for creating the internal labyrinth included civic-space interruptions, landscaped circles, staggered cross streets, and cul-de-sacs. For the sake of safety, all children had to be able to walk to the school and playgrounds without crossing major thoroughfares.[54]

For dense urban areas, Perry envisioned a neighborhood unit on an 18-acre (7 ha) superblock. It had apartment towers 10–33 stories tall, a population of 1,000 families, and its own school, theater, parks, and shops. In the late 1920s, Perry was concerned that such projects might block the "general circulation" of traffic. He suggested that some streets could traverse the site underground. But in the early 1930s, he discarded that concern and proposed a 41-acre (17 ha) superblock with no underground streets.[55]

Perry believed that the automobile was bringing into existence a new type of city, and that the neighborhood unit was the logical completion of that process. He said wide streets, boulevards, parkways, and highways were "cutting up residential areas into small islands separated from each other by raging streams of traffic." Perry called the resulting pattern the *cellular city*:

> It is plain that arterial highways must necessarily run in every direction and turn the street system into a network, and that residential life must occupy the interstitial spaces. We are going to live in cells. The cellular city is the inevitable byproduct of an automobile age. Very well—but what is to be the nature of those cells? . . . the automobile menace has set up an imperative demand for a definition and standardization of the neighborhood district.[56]

He said the design of arterial frontages was a "special problem in planning, and one which will be solved differently for every set of conditions." Residential life must retreat from the bordering arterials. Commercial uses could occupy only a small portion of the arterial frontages because the demand was insufficient to support any more than that. He suggested that arterial frontages might be lined with garages, warehouses, and light industry. Apartment buildings and houses on arterials could be set far back from the roadway and turned to face the interior. Yet he noted that such solutions were not always economical, and he presented several plans that showed apartment buildings fronting directly on the bordering arterials. The treatment of residential frontages on high-speed arterials was never fully solved, and has been a problem in cellular street layouts ever since.[57]

Perry assembled his neighborhood-unit concept from a variety of sources in addition to the Quarter Section Competition. He cited garden-suburb developments, including Hampstead Garden Suburb, Forest Hills Gardens, and Radburn. Raymond Unwin was a major influence, and Perry's important neighborhood-unit schematic diagram was likely adapted from Unwin's 1914 study (figure 4.14). Perry's years of community work and his study of sociological theory informed his discussion of the neighborhood unit's social benefits. The most formative influence, according to Perry himself, was his experience of living in Forest Hills Gardens. He was one of the first occupants; he and his family moved there in 1912, one year after the development opened.[58]

Perry analyzed Forest Hills Gardens in detail in his 1929 monograph. He found much to admire and emulate, but said its planners did not foresee the social revolution caused by the automobile. As a result, the most serious shortcoming was "traffic intrusions" and "evil" speeding on streets that traversed the development.[59]

When Perry moved to Forest Hills Gardens, the surrounding area was mostly farms and vacant lots. During the 1920s, when he was refining his neighborhood-unit concept, the area began to change. Streets and blocks were laid out, houses were built, and traffic began to increase. Yet even then, the area surrounding Forest Hills Gardens was mostly undeveloped and the total number of dwellings was small (see figure 4.15). Perry was sensitive to virtually any amount of through traffic in his neighborhood.

With remarkable rapidity after its 1929 publication, the neighborhood-unit concept gained widespread approval and was adopted internationally. It dominated the planning profession for more than forty years and shaped large portions of the world's metropolitan areas. As the planning professor Jason Brody observed, the concept had a strong identity yet was highly malleable. It was therefore able to serve the needs of many disparate interests, such as planners, real-estate developers, public health experts, policymakers, and traffic engineers. Also, the association with Perry, the Sage Foundation, and RPNY gave the concept an imprimatur of social progressivism. An aura of good civic citizenship was conferred on the interest groups that adopted the concept.[60]

Traffic engineers wholeheartedly absorbed the cellular model of roadway layout and granted it near-universal endorsement. It seemed to address several pressing demands. It promised the tantalizing combination of safe residential environments and high-speed vehicular movement. It offered a model for the automobile age that could structure suburbs and restructure cities. It encapsulated a complex of ideas in a form that was readily understood and propagated through the engineering, development, administrative, and legislative spheres. By the late 1930s to early 1940s, prominent engineers and officials such as H. Alker Tripp and Thomas H. MacDonald were forecasting the cellular model as the future of all cities. The cellular model was embedded in the US Interstate Freeway System and most planning standards of state highway departments. Through the 2010s, it dominated traffic planning and shaped development patterns in the United States and many other nations.

Radburn

When the United States entered World War I in 1917, numerous architects went to work for the federal government, designing new communities to house war-production workers and their families. Many of the architects were "imbued with Garden City ideas," including street layouts that discouraged through traffic on residential streets. The architect Henry Wright was unquestionably one of that group. He worked for the Emergency Fleet Corporation, which designed communities for shipbuilders and erected thousands of dwellings for them.[61]

Wright had been involved with national planning organizations since the mid-1910s and had worked with Frederick Law Olmsted Jr., Thomas Adams, Charles Mulford Robinson, and other advocates of deconcentration, garden cities, and horizontal traffic separation. Wright also was powerfully influenced at that time by Raymond Unwin and his book *Town Planning in Practice* (1909).[62]

Wright's supervisor at the Emergency Fleet Corporation was the New York architect Robert D. Kohn. After the war, Kohn introduced Wright to another architect, his longtime friend and protégé Clarence Stein (1882–1975). Stein and Wright were like-minded. They were passionate about similar issues, particularly the planning of sites, neighborhoods, and regions to improve living conditions and aid social reform.[63]

In 1921 Wright wrote an article for an architectural journal edited by Stein. He described his ideal community plan, which resembled contemporary British and German garden-suburb plans. "My conception of the ideal development of residential areas would take the general form of a broad toothed comb," he explained. Main avenues with commercial uses would form the spines of the combs. Residential areas of attached houses would lie perpendicular to the main avenues, forming the teeth of the combs. Running through the blocks' interiors, parallel to the main avenues, would be corridors of green space; they would contain playgrounds, golf courses, schools, and community buildings. Wright's idea prefigured Radburn's pattern of cul-de-sac rows leading inward to block interiors where parks and schools were sited.[64]

Regional Planning Association of America

In 1923 Stein organized a group of architects, planners, administrators, and advocates into a small but powerful organization called the Regional Planning Association of America. RPAA had no more than sixteen members at any given time, but among them were some of the most visionary planning thinkers of the era, including Benton MacKaye, creator of the Appalachian Trail, and Lewis Mumford, author and critic. The group functioned as a small intellectual salon that was as much a social group as an advocacy organization.[65]

RPAA members were unified philosophically by the goal of decentralizing US cities and moving the population into garden cities. Like the wartime housing programs, their ideal would require an unprecedented degree of government power. One member later described the group's politics: "We were mildly socialist though not at all communist; liberal but willing to abandon large areas of the free market in favor of a planned economy."[66]

Stein was anxious to start building. He encouraged Alexander Bing, a retired developer of Manhattan luxury apartment buildings, to work on low-cost housing. Bing had worked for the Emergency Fleet Corporation and already had an interest in the topic. Wright was called from his practice in St. Louis to join the initiative in 1923. After a year of exploratory research with Stein and Wright, Bing formed the City Housing Corporation (CHC). It was a philanthropic company whose mission was to build low-cost housing and garden cities. The company attracted the participation of prominent New Yorkers, including Eleanor Roosevelt, who served on CHC's board until 1928. CHC and RPAA were separate but closely linked: Bing was RPAA's first president; Stein and Wright were Bing's designers.[67]

Bing sent Stein and Wright on a tour of British garden cities in 1924. Ebenezer Howard showed them around Welwyn, the second garden city, and they met Raymond Unwin at his home in Hampstead Garden Suburb. About Hampstead, Stein commented that "I know nothing finer of that romantic age before life and cities were molded to serve the requirements of speeding automobiles rather than humans." When Howard and Unwin traveled to New York the next year to lecture at a garden-cities conference, Stein hosted both. He called himself a disciple of the two movement founders.[68]

Development of Radburn

In 1927 CHC decided the time was right to build a garden city. It had successfully built Sunnyside Gardens, an affordable-housing development in Queens, New York. Also, the George Washington Bridge was scheduled to begin construction. CHC probably anticipated that the auto commute to Manhattan would become much quicker and more convenient. The company eventually acquired over 1,200 acres (485 ha) of farmland in Fair Lawn, New Jersey, about 11 miles (18 km) west of the bridge site.[69]

Clarence Perry had participated in some RPAA meetings, and in October 1927 the group discussed his neighborhood-unit idea in detail. Herbert Emmerich, who was CHC's vice president and Radburn's project manager, seems to have been inspired by Perry's idea. In December Emmerich sketched a theoretical neighborhood unit that was contained in a single superblock. The modular superblock and its uniform cul-de-sac rows were eminently suitable for mass production.[70]

Stein and Wright's drawing of the concept showed a superblock approximately 54 acres (22 ha) in size, with about 500 houses on 18 cul-de-sacs. It had parks and a school in the interior, and retail stores and garages at the ends. Wright himself had

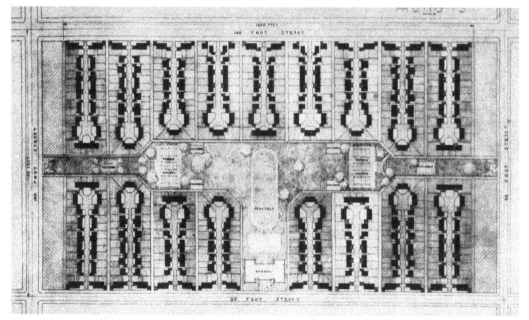

Figure 5.13: Stein and Wright's preliminary study of a superblock neighborhood unit, ca. 1928.

developed a similar idea during the planning of Sunnyside Gardens. His 1924 sketch showed a street segment converted to a grassy "street park" to form a superblock with loop roads, dead-end alleys, and internal park and school spaces.[71]

Stein and Wright invited Raymond Unwin to consult on Radburn's site planning after they had completed a preliminary plan. Unwin worked with the design team for several months during 1928, walking the land and identifying the best locations for important buildings such as the high school. In September he wrote, "I am deep in planning their new Garden Suburb." Radburn was planned to house 25,000–30,000 people and have commercial and industrial districts—essentially like Letchworth.[72]

Radburn's street layout was modeled on Unwin's previous work and other British garden suburbs, but scaled up and standardized to suit American market preferences and driving habits. Residential superblocks were up to 70 acres (28 ha) in size. Most of the houses were located on cul-de-sacs, which minimized the number of driveways on streets that bounded superblocks. Radburn's major streets were designed with medians and traffic circles to eliminate intersecting traffic paths; that was intended to reduce crash danger and ensure brisk flow. The major streets would connect to a nearby partially limited-access parkway. Thus the plan established a range of roadway types specialized for either dwelling access or traffic flow. A separate footpath system ran past every house, traversed the superblocks' internal parks, and crossed major roadways via one underpass and one footbridge.[73]

Henry Wright was largely responsible for melding Radburn's influences and goals into a unified plan. Radburn had a coordinated set of elements that included single-use zoning, neighborhood units, superblocks, and roadways specialized for traffic type. Stein called this complete set "the Radburn Idea"—the garden city adapted for the motor age. The intent of the street and footpath networks was to ensure children's safety, minimize traffic impacts in residential areas, and reduce paving costs, while allowing easy, fast auto travel.[74]

House sales began in May 1929, five months before the stock market crashed. Sales remained strong through 1930. But as the Great Depression spread, homeowners defaulted and the stream of new residents slowed to a trickle. CHC donated land for a new highway to the George Washington Bridge (Route S-4B) in the hope that it would re-ignite sales. That did not happen. The developer's situation grew precarious; Radburn had been financed by a mortgage-bond scheme that depended on uninterrupted growth to maintain profitability. The scheme collapsed, construction stopped in 1933, and CHC went bankrupt in 1934. In total, CHC had built one 40-acre superblock, two half-superblocks, two apartment buildings, and a commercial center. About 500 dwellings housed 1,500 residents.[75]

Influence of RPAA and the Radburn Idea

Although only a small portion of Radburn was built, it had a large influence on American suburbs. That was due in part to RPAA's relationships with policy makers, in part to promotion and favorable press, and in part to the planners, designers, and developers who acclaimed Radburn and adopted some of its elements.

Radburn received positive attention from the Hoover administration. New York governor Franklin D. Roosevelt was familiar with RPAA's ideas and spoke at a

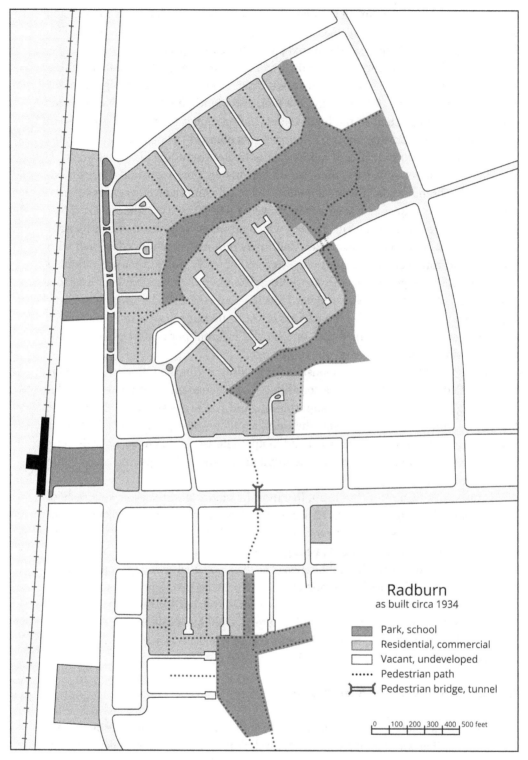

Figure 5.14: Radburn as built, ca. 1934. The CHC developed 150 of its 1,250 acres before going bankrupt. The pedestrian bridge was later demolished.

conference that RPAA co-organized. Several RPAA members later took positions of authority in Roosevelt's presidential administration. Through the 1930s, the Radburn model was prominent in US land planning and development policy.[76]

The federal government's greenbelt-town program was an immediate outcome of those relationships. Three projects were built using the Radburn Idea: Greenbelt, Maryland; Greenhills, Ohio; and Greendale, Wisconsin. The RPAA members Stein, Wright, Kohn, Frederick Bigger, and Catherine Bauer were directly involved in the program.

Radburn was extensively covered in architectural magazines, academic journals, national newspapers, and professional manuals. The Radburn Idea influenced numerous plans and planning policies in the United States, Great Britain, Australia, and throughout Europe. The period from the mid-1950s to mid-1960s was the peak of Radburn's influence in Great Britain, as a number of British New Towns were modeled on it. In turn, the British New Towns were models for the American New Towns of the late 1950s to 1970s.[77]

After Wright's death in 1936, Stein continued to be a leading promoter and practitioner of the Radburn Idea. He maintained a professional stance in opposition to big cities for the rest of his career. He was unwavering in his call to deconcentrate urban populations and move them to Radburn-type garden cities. Contrary to his professional stance, however, Stein loved the cultural life of Manhattan and his high-rise apartment overlooking Central Park, where he lived for most of his life.[78]

The Federal Government Steps In

Radburn's construction start and the publication of Perry's neighborhood unit coincided with the advent of the Great Depression. The US real-estate market collapsed amid the global economy's greater wreckage. Two of the federal government's early responses were to organize housing and planning research, and to sponsor public housing projects. Those initiatives amplified and spurred the evolution of the new residential-planning ideas. Planners and designers explored a multitude of street-layout concepts that aimed to insulate streets and communities from through traffic.

President Hoover's Commission

As the Great Depression deepened, leaders of the real-estate industry decided that government action was needed to stimulate business. They wanted single-use zoning, subdivision regulations based on approved models, and local and regional planning. Those policies, the major builders believed, would encourage large, standardized subdivisions, enhance the market appeal of their products, and protect long-term property values. Not coincidentally, those policies also would give the major builders a competitive advantage. They would help eliminate smaller, less-professionalized builders who developed single lots and small areas.[79]

The Hoover administration, as always, was eager to foster a voluntary model of regulation in which private businesses governed themselves. In September 1930 the president convened the President's Conference on Home Building and Home Ownership. It was a gigantic, privately-funded research and publicity initiative—larger than any before on the topic of housing—that involved 540 volunteers working on 31 committees. It brought together leaders from real estate, construction, planning, government, the press, and related fields. The findings and recommendations were presented in December 1931 and published in eleven volumes during 1932.[80]

Among the participants were many advocates of superblocks, cul-de-sacs, and neighborhood units. Frederic A. Delano, former chairman of the RPNY initiative, chaired the City Planning And Zoning Committee. Alexander Bing, developer of Radburn, was a conference organizer. Henry Wright, Robert Whitten, and Thomas Adams served on the Subdivision Layout committee and worked on research. (Whitten was president of the American City Planning Institute and a leading neighborhood-unit advocate.) The Subdivision Layout committee was dominated by the real-estate perspective because most of the participants were affiliated with the nation's primary real-estate-industry association.[81]

Wright, Whitten, and Adams had been focusing on the economics of superblocks and cul-de-sacs before the President's Conference. One planning journal described Wright's presentation on the topic at a 1929 real-estate convention. He demonstrated "with what seemed almost the art of a magician" that developers could provide parks and wide arterial streets while also reducing development costs. "Large blocks constitute one of the magic keys," enthused the journal.[82]

In 1930 Wright published his version of an ideal city. Multiway expressways were spaced 3,000 feet (914 m) apart in a citywide grid, and had grade-separated intersections. The expressways bounded neighborhood-unit cells that contained various land uses and housing types. The lower-density residential cells would be laid out like Radburn, with superblocks up to 64 acres (26 ha) in size. Pedestrians moved from cell to cell via pedestrian bridges.[83]

Whitten and Adams published their book *Neighborhoods of Small Homes* in 1931.

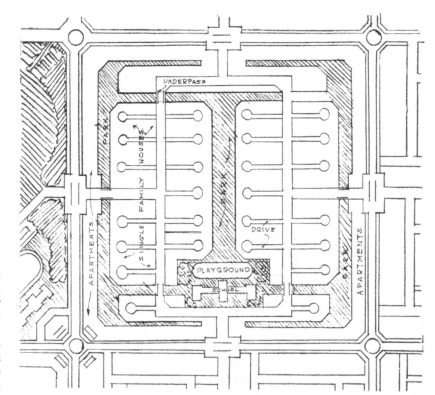

Figure 5.15: Wright's model neighborhood unit, 1930. Radburn-style superblocks had single-family dwellings on cul-de-sacs and low- or medium-rise apartments along the arterials.

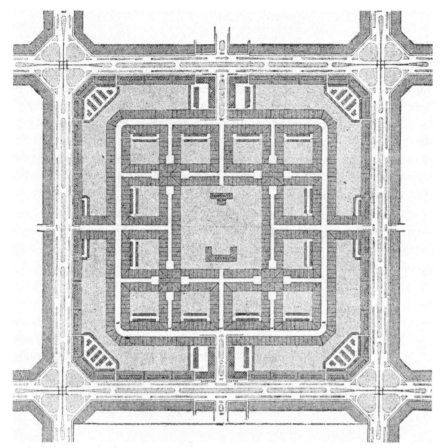

Figure 5.16: Whitten's neighborhood unit plan, 1931. The bordering multiway arterials have cloverleaf intersections.

In it, Whitten performed a cost analysis of different street layouts such as gridiron, hexagonal, and superblock with cul-de-sacs. Following Wright's lead, Whitten found that larger blocks were less costly to develop, and he modeled a 180-acre (73-ha) neighborhood unit that had an 80-acre (32-ha) central superblock. His neighborhood units were bounded by major arterials that intersected at cloverleaf interchanges.[84]

As the President's Conference got underway, Adams was working on a follow-up book that expanded Whitten's analysis. Adams inserted his analysis into the President's Conference report. Like the 1913 Quarter Section Competition, he compared identically sized neighborhood units that had different street layouts, such as gridiron, curvilinear, hexagonal, and cul-de-sac loop. Most of his neighborhood units were composed of superblocks, which ranged from 20 to 40 acres (8 to 16 ha) in size. Like Wright and Whitten, Adams found that development costs were closely linked to the amount of street area, and therefore superblock layouts were the least expensive to develop.[85]

In the President's Conference report, the Subdivision Layout committee asserted that larger subdivisions were better. The ideal was a developer in control of a 160–640 acre (65–260 ha) parcel. Large subdivisions simplified procedures and assured "greater protection" for the developer. Large cellular developments also improved traffic flow on the bounding arterials. Long blocks on major arterials could reduce intersection frequency, said the committee, and it noted that blocks 1,000 feet (305 m) or more in length were becoming more common.[86]

The President's Conference report delivered a wholehearted, even gushing, endorsement of the Radburn and neighborhood-unit development models. A photo of Radburn appeared on the frontispiece of the first volume, and the text cited Radburn more than any other project. The neighborhood unit was important for investment and permanence; for safeguarding the health, safety, and morals of residents; and for fostering community pride, happier home life, and better government. It would provide "peace from the noise and dust of heavy through traffic arteries," and, unlike the gridiron, it would check the "endless spread of urban expansion" into residential districts.[87]

The President's Conference formally recommended large blocks, cellular street layouts, and city planning that enforced the neighborhood-unit model. Many cities and government agencies followed those recommendations with confidence. The Conference also recommended that only houses of sound design should receive mortgage financing, and stated that one aspect of sound design was a neighborhood plan. Those recommendations were later adapted by the Roosevelt administration and became an important part of federal housing policy.[88]

Federal Public Housing and Related Proposals

Franklin D. Roosevelt was elected president in 1932. In contrast to Hoover, he had a strong belief in central planning and large public-works programs. One of the administration's first initiatives was the Housing Division of the Public Works Administration (PWA), established in summer 1933. The Division announced funding for low-cost housing, and specified that projects should be "a unit in a neighborhood community" and isolated from through traffic. More than 600 projects were submitted for financial and design review, but only seven were deemed acceptable for funding. The Division favored slum-clearance projects in the form of row housing and garden apartments arranged on superblocks.[89]

The Division's design standards were formulated during its first year when Robert D. Kohn was the director and Henry Wright was an architectural consultant. Kohn was an RPAA member and had helped design Radburn. Wright had worked for Kohn during World War I, designing housing for shipyard workers. Also, Wright had recently made a four-month study tour of European housing projects and returned with a deep admiration for European modernist settlements. Projects by Wright, Stein, and their colleagues were among the Housing Division's design models.[90]

Some of the submitted proposals introduced novel variations on the Radburn and neighborhood-unit ideas. One example was Pennypack Creek Homes by the architect Edmund B. Gilchrist. Proposed for a 120-acre (49-ha) site in the Philadelphia suburbs, it had five curvilinear superblocks that were filled with cul-de-sac bulbs. The plan was dominated by private yards; only two pedestrian paths cut through the blocks. This "definitely modernistic" plan was said to provide "privacy without isolation." The site was later developed as a federal war-housing project named Pennypack Woods (1941–1943). The roadway layout, designed by the modernist architecture firm Howe, Stonorov & Kahn, was very similar to Gilchrist's.[91]

One proposal that gave extra attention to major roadways was located near the historic center of Detroit, Michigan. It was a 150-acre (61-ha) neighborhood unit composed of four superblocks between 21 and 45 acres (8 and 18 ha) in size. The project's

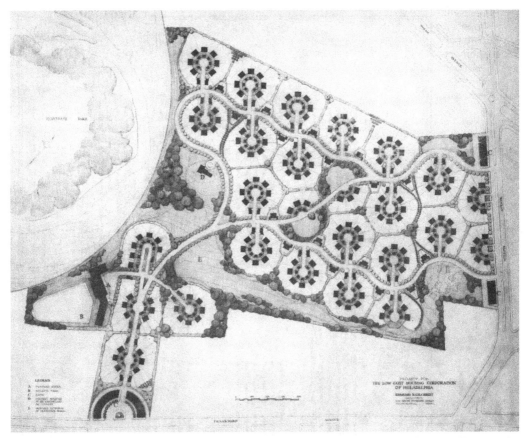

Figure 5.17: Pennypack Creek Homes plan by Gilchrist, 1933. Edmund Beaman Gilchrist Collection, The Architectural Archives, University of Pennsylvania.

stated goals were slum-housing clearance and transformation of the city's gridiron. As an unstated consequence, the project would eradicate a vital center of Black culture and entertainment along Hastings Street, which ran through the center of the site. A depressed limited-access highway was envisioned along the northern border, and Hastings Street would become a partial-access arterial with grade-separated intersections. Three pedestrian underpasses would connect the superblocks.[92]

In 1934 PWA switched to a fast-production strategy, and over the next three years completed 51 affordable-housing projects. The program's impact was large: a total of 2,200 designers worked in 35 cities while another 100,000 people were employed in fabrication, transportation, and construction. Some neighborhoods were altered beyond recognition. For example, a 28-acre (11-ha) portion of the earlier Detroit proposal, now named the Brewster development, was built from 1935 to 1938. Its layout of oversize blocks was formed by closing alternating streets of the existing gridiron. Eleanor Roosevelt broke ground for the development; it was one of the first public housing projects for Black Americans. And with crushing inevitability, Hastings Street was demolished to make way for the Chrysler Freeway (Interstate 75) in the late 1950s and early 1960s.[93]

From early 1933 through spring 1934, Henry Wright and four colleagues worked on a planning study named Queensbridge Dwellings. The study may have reflected the

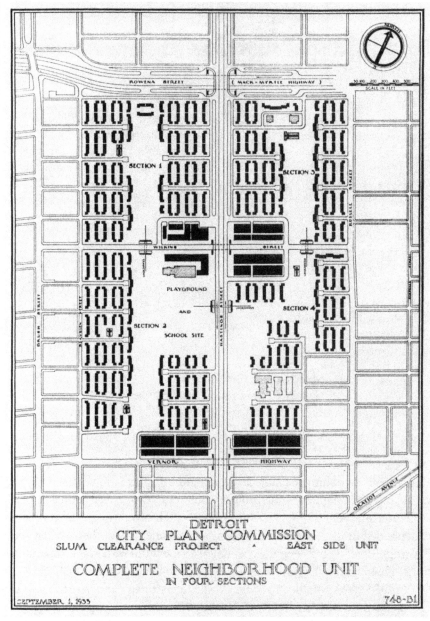

Figure 5.18: Proposed superblock redevelopment of the Hastings Street neighborhood in Detroit, 1933.

authors' frustration with PWA's overall strategy. "Isolated attempts at model housing are powerless to change their surrounding slums which sooner or later engulf them," they argued; therefore, "slum clearance is ineffective socially on the small scale." To demonstrate larger-scale replanning, they proposed to demolish a "slum" in Queens, New York, and rebuild it as a 528-acre (214-ha) neighborhood unit. Streets in the existing gridiron would be selectively removed and rerouted to create a layout of cul-de-sacs and superblocks. The arrangement of low- and mid-rise apartment rows would be a hybrid of Radburn and modernist German *Seidlungen* plans. The designers imagined that similar projects in every large US city would be the seeds of a long-term national housing program, which they labeled "Garden Cities within the City."[94]

One motive of the Queensbridge plan was to reconfigure the area's street layout

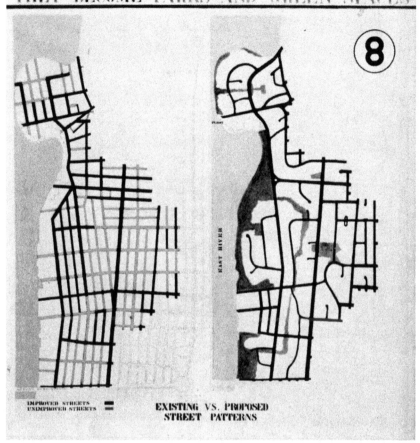

MORE STREETS THAN TRAFFIC REQUIRES THEY BECOME PARKS AND GREEN SPACES

EXISTING VS. PROPOSED
STREET PATTERNS

IMPROVED STREETS
UNIMPROVED STREETS

Figure 5.19:
Existing street
grid and proposed
layout for
Queensbridge
Dwellings in
Astoria, Queens,
New York City.
Henry Wright and
colleagues, 1934.

before it was inundated by traffic from Robert Moses's Triborough Bridge (the bridge opened in 1936). In 1937 Moses said he was "impressed by the possibilities" of the plan, and said it was "too good not to push through." Although the plan was not built, it became a reference for the city's public housing program over the following years. It directly influenced the Queensbridge Houses project (1939), which was built on a portion of the same site. The 47-acre (19-ha) development was the largest public housing project in America, having more than 3,100 apartments. By removing alternating streets, the project's designers converted 12 gridiron blocks to 6 oversize blocks, each about 6 acres (2.4 ha) in size.[95]

President Roosevelt's FHA

The real-estate industry eagerly supported the creation of the Federal Housing Administration (FHA) in 1934. Normally the industry would have opposed such government activism because of its antipathy to what it viewed as federal meddling in local affairs. But FHA was largely staffed by the real-estate and banking industries, so real-estate executives could be assured that any actions would benefit the biggest and most standardized operators. Moreover, as an official FHA history later noted,

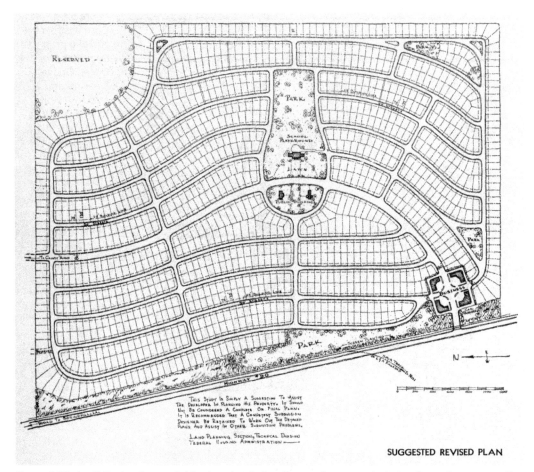

SUGGESTED REVISED PLAN

Figure 5.20: An FHA plan for a neighborhood unit that featured extreme isolation from the surrounding street network. It had an area of about 460 acres (186 ha) and a perimeter of 3.4 miles (5.4 km). It had two external connections, and so averaged one external connection per 1.7 miles (2.8 km) of perimeter length.

"It was the last hope of private enterprise. The alternative was socialization of the housing industry."[96]

The motor industry too had a significant presence in FHA. James A. Moffett, a Standard Oil executive and personal friend of President Roosevelt, was appointed to lead the agency. Stewart McDonald, former president of Moon Motor Car in St. Louis, succeeded Moffett and served from 1935 to 1940. Ward M. Canaday, an advertising man long associated with the Willys-Overland motor company in Toledo, Ohio, was named director of pubic relations. The 1934 promotional campaign for FHA-backed loans was "comparable to a government war bond drive" and turned FHA into a household name.[97]

America's home-mortgage system had collapsed, and FHA's purpose was to revive and reform it. FHA did not issue mortgages itself; instead, it guaranteed mortgages, which meant that it would repay a loan if a homeowner defaulted. FHA-backed loans were virtually risk-free for developers. Few wished to refuse such a bonanza.

Developers had to submit detailed project plans to qualify their dwellings for FHA mortgage guarantees. FHA staffers worked with developers to conform the project plans to FHA standards, which were mainly derived from the 1931 President's Conference on Home Building and Home Ownership. Beginning in 1935, FHA issued a series of booklets to explain its design principles. The agency recommended neighborhood-unit planning, cellular street layouts, and large blocks (600–1,300 feet or 180–400 meters long). It said cul-de-sacs offered distinct advantages: protection from traffic noise and hazard, cheaper development costs, and the ability to exploit oddly shaped remnant areas. A "Radburn-type plan" was featured as a desirable development pattern.

FHA said existing highways and main thoroughfares should always be extended—preferably around developments, but through them if necessary—"so that circulation will not be restricted and whole areas cut off from ready access to the main body of the city." Minor streets should be indirect in order to make fast through traffic impossible. The agency affirmed its support for insular street layouts by stating that the number of external connections to bordering roadways should be limited. That would protect a neighborhood from objectionable or inharmonious uses on adjacent land parcels. In general, said the agency, plans should made with the assumption that all households would own at least one car. Meanwhile, a federal survey found that 60 percent of US households did not own a car in the mid-1930s.[98]

Impacts of the FHA Standards

FHA often pointed out that its design standards were implemented by voluntary incentives rather than prescriptive rules—carrots rather than sticks. But comparable financing was unavailable on the open market, which meant that the voluntary nature of the FHA standards was basically a politically convenient fiction. In practice, the standards were backed by an unprecedented degree of power. Administrator Moffett acknowledged confidentially that the agency could use presidential authority to control the amount and location of development, the neighborhood standards, and "everything else."[99]

FHA's effect on the pattern of American suburbs was colossal. By the late 1930s it was guaranteeing loans for one-third of dwellings built annually; that figure spiked to 50–80 percent during World War II. The agency's influence pervaded the development, banking, and planning fields. Its design standards were considered the exemplar of sound and profitable development practice. Some developers found it worthwhile to obtain FHA approval even when they used other financing sources. Many local planning commissions adopted some form of FHA's design standards, making them the basis of legally required growth patterns in a multitude of American suburbs.[100]

By 1967 FHA had guaranteed more than ten million home loans, which represented about 30 percent of private dwellings built since 1935. That year, the agency began to dismantle its location-based loan restrictions and its design requirements. The new political attitude was that FHA standards discriminated against Black Americans and did little to support central-city economic development. In addition, a revived private mortgage insurance industry was gaining market share from FHA. In 1968 the majority of FHA's loan activity was spun off to a newly privatized Fannie Mae. FHA continued to promote cellular street layouts, superblocks, and cul-de-sacs through the 1970s—for instance, in its recommendations for planned unit developments. But as the agency's budget and market participation shrank, so did its influence on the national financial establishment. Its street-layout biases were carried forward by developers, bankers, appraisers, and other private-sector operators, as well as the many official state and local practices that had solidified into conventional wisdom over the decades.[101]

Chapter 5 Summary

In late-1920s Germany and early-1930s Russia, modernist architects developed repetitive superblocks and standardized dendritic layouts under emergency conditions. Their street layouts were designed for contexts where few private cars were used, and were intended to maximize uniformity and construction speed, minimize costs, and provide green space. Several of the modernists emigrated to America and adapted the patterns to the American market. Their ideas had notable impacts on the American design professions.

Clarence Perry published his neighborhood-unit monograph in 1929 with the aim of promoting neighborhood social cohesion and schools, ensuring safety, and directing fast traffic onto arterials. Radburn, New Jersey, was the preeminent built example, and its lead planner, Henry Wright, emerged as an influential advocate of cellular roadway planning. US state and federal agencies actively promoted cellular roadway networks; of all of them, the Federal Housing Administration had the most powerful effect on suburban residential development. For traffic engineers, the cellular model promised a tantalizing combination of safe residential environments and high-speed vehicular movement. It rapidly became the dominant, widely accepted model for structuring suburbs and restructuring cities.

The most commonly stated objectives of insular roadways in the twentieth century were to reduce traffic noise, pollution, and crash danger; reduce development costs; deconcentrate cities; increase open space and greenery; and support residents' health. Advocates said cellular planning would ensure neighborhood stability, give protection from "inharmonious" land uses, and keep traffic speeding on the bordering arterials.

A less commonly stated objective was classism. The physical separation of social classes was an early reason for insular layouts and, judging from developers' techniques and real-estate marketing methods, it continued to be important throughout the twentieth century. Some suburbanites believed that insular, semi-impermeable neighborhoods helped exclude lower classes, and thus maintained standards of behavior and house prices.

Racism was probably a major motive for insular neighborhoods in the United States, especially from the 1890s to the 1970s. Racial and ethnic exclusion was an important selling point of many suburban developments of that period. Chinese, Greek, Italian, Japanese, Jewish, Mexican, and Native American people were excluded over varying periods, and to different degrees in different regions. But it was Black Americans above all who were excluded most frequently, most extensively, and most completely. The large majority of unplanned suburbs created between 1890 and 1960 were White-only. During that period Blacks were less than 5 percent of the suburban population, even though Blacks were 10 percent of the national population.[102]

The record for planned suburban communities was even worse. That describes the developments named in this chapter, no matter how progressive they claimed to be. For instance, in 1912 the Black sociology professor and civil-rights intellectual W. E. B. Du Bois tried to buy a house in Forest Hills Gardens. The Sage Foundation's president refused him because of his skin color. In 1929 Du Bois told Alexander Bing that an all-White Radburn would aggravate race relations everywhere. Bing replied, "I realize the seriousness of the problem . . . I do not see any other way of handling the matter."[103]

FHA infamously exerted the full weight of its authority in order to support and enforce racial segregation from 1934 to 1948. Furthermore, the agency ignored many types of racial discrimination in private housing until 1968. More than 98 percent of FHA- and VA-guaranteed loans issued after World War II were available to Whites only. Insular and mazelike roadway layouts were possibly a part of the racial-exclusion mindset. Clarence Perry intimated as much when he said that "a certain degree of racial and social homogeneity must be assured among playground patrons or a healthy play-life will not occur," and that the neighborhood unit, "walled in with highways and provided with its own special street system," would best promote such "normal neighborhood life." But historical evidence on this point is scanty, because most exclusionary policies were unwritten and enforced by oral agreement, and many written records were lost or purposely destroyed.[104]

CHAPTER 6
Horizontal Traffic Separation:
Fast Roadways

Fast roadways are those designated to carry traffic that is faster than usual city traffic. Fast speed on city streets was, through most of history, the speed of a trotting horse. Toward the end of the nineteenth century, bicycles, cable cars, and electric streetcars raised the threshold of maximum operating speed for city vehicles. In response, cities instituted speed limits for each vehicle type. Speed limits were set at the speed of a trotting horse until the early 1900s; then the automobile broke the city speed barrier. As auto engine power increased from the 1910s to the 1930s, city speed limits increased to 20–30 mph (32–48 kmh), and on some urban parkways and expressways reached 35–45 mph (56–72 kmh).[1]

Speed driving was often associated with feelings of personal excitement and dominance. The first expression of that urge in cities was road racing for recreation and status.

Speed Driving and Speedways

One of the most popular sports in America in the nineteenth century was trotting, or harness racing. Trotting developed from everyday-vehicle use: the horses pulled a lightweight carriage and used a trotting gait when they raced. Trotting had a long history as a popular pastime in European countries such as the Netherlands and England. In America it became a national craze and an organized sport. It was considered more democratic than thoroughbred racing because middle-class hobbyists could afford to participate and common breeds of horses could win. After the 1870s, wealthy owners took control of the best breeding stock, and the sport turned into a big business that depended on large audiences for its profits. Although most high-profile races were held on race tracks, informal speeding and racing took place on suburban roadways.

New York City was the epicenter of the trotting sport. Organized and impromptu races, as well as solo speeding, occurred on the developing outskirts of the city. The popular locations shifted outward as the city grew. Third Avenue was the city's most popular speed road until the 1850s; from the 1860s through the 1880s Harlem Lane

Figure 6.1: Trotting drivers are posed before a racing club, Harlem Lane, New York City, ca. 1870. Separate entrances are marked for men and women.

(now St. Nicholas Avenue) and Seventh Avenue north of Central Park served similar roles. The speed roads attracted hard-charging racers, sedate promenading drivers, and spectators of all classes. Racing taverns and clubs opened along the routes.[2]

Many of the parkways designed or inspired by Olmsted and Vaux served as speed-driving facilities. Many were conceived from the outset to serve swift yet genteel driving. In some cases, the speed-facility role was formalized by rules issued years after construction. The parkways were unusually wide, well surfaced and drained, and ran through low-density areas, creating ideal conditions for fast driving. Sleigh racing was popular when snow blanketed the ground.

Olmsted and Vaux, in their initial proposal for Brooklyn parkways, suggested the carriage lanes could be used for fast trotting. But they likely felt that organized racing was too rambunctious—one of the many stressful "embarrassments" that should be banned to maintain an elegant neighborhood character. After Ocean Parkway opened in 1876, it carried the fastest traffic in Brooklyn and, regardless of the designers' feelings on the matter, hosted many races both formal and informal.[3]

James Stranahan, president of the Brooklyn park commission and himself a driving enthusiast, wrote that one purpose of Ocean Parkway was to inculcate a "taste for driving" and a "desire to move along at a higher rate of speed." Later commissioners minimized cross traffic that might interfere with the parkway. Only one trolley route was allowed to cross Ocean Parkway, in a tunnel under the roadway.[4]

Grand Boulevard in Chicago was one of the parkways suggested by Olmsted and Vaux in their South Parks plan. Shortly after it opened in 1873, speed limits were suspended at specific times to allow racing and fast driving, and in 1882, a half-mile (0.8 km) of the boulevard was designated as a speeding track. Racing was also allowed on

Drexel Boulevard, another Olmsted-inspired parkway in Chicago. Delaware Avenue, an Olmsted parkway in Buffalo, New York, was designated for fast driving and informal races during the 1880s. Commonwealth Avenue, a Olmsted-designed boulevard in Boston, hosted races until the 1890s, when residents along the avenue began to agitate for speed limits. Another Olmsted boulevard in Boston, Beacon Street, was for years the center of the city's sleigh-racing scene.[5]

Other urban thoroughfares were used as speed drives as well. For example, Boston's Blue Hill Avenue was used as a speedway until a dedicated racetrack was built in 1909. In Cleveland, Ohio, speed limits were removed to allow racing on Euclid Avenue. But the streets in most cities could not accommodate seven distinct traffic streams as Ocean Parkway did. Conflicts became untenable as urban neighborhoods grew along the speed-driving routes and the swelling flows of everyday traffic interfered with racing and speeding. Bicycles were felt to be especially annoying; in Manhattan the "clanging scorcher" was a "constant nightmare" that drove away trotting racers and fans. Manhattan's cyclists also campaigned successfully to pave the streets with hard asphalt, which was unsuitable for horse-powered speed driving.[6]

The wealthy of Manhattan clamored for dedicated thoroughfares to speed on. Peter B. Sweeny, a former commissioner of parks and inside member of the corrupt Tweed ring, complained that there was no place left "where a man can speed his horse and get the enjoyment he is entitled to without being chased by a policeman and hunted as if he had committed a crime of the blackest magnitude against the law." Sweeny peddled unvarnished Gilded Age paternalism as he promoted a speed-drive viaduct for Riverside Park. He called for a thoroughfare "where fashion can reign supreme and where wealth can be displayed as an educator."[7]

A more common view advanced by wealthy speed-driving enthusiasts was that their recreation was entertainment for lower-class spectators. Speed drives should be built on public land because they benefited all classes. The industrialist Russell Sage propounded that view:

> Well, then, if we like to speed our animals now and then, and in such a splendid place as that drive up Riverside way can be made, wouldn't thousands of people like to see the sport? I tell you there are some horses that would be seen on that drive that people would go a long way to see. So the driveway would be a public benefit for that reason alone, if for no other.[8]

Judging by the lack of widespread protest or dissent, the public may have agreed with that position, or at least was indifferent. The specific efforts to install speedways in Central Park and Riverside Park failed because working-class groups opposed the use of scarce parkland for wealthy people's recreation, and because abutting residents opposed the noise and raucous crowds. But trotting and promenading remained very popular and continued to draw large crowds of spectators through the first decade of the twentieth century.[9]

The trend of ever-faster carriage drives reached a climax after the mid-1890s with the appearance of speedways. Speedways were roadways specialized for high-speed traffic. Only fast horse-travel modes were allowed, such as equestrians, sulkies

Figure 6.2: Harlem Speedway, 1900. Well-to-do spectators watch speedway races from the heights.

(two-wheeled trotting carts), and other lightweight speed carriages. Slower traffic, including everyday heavy carriages, freight wagons, and pedestrians, was prohibited. Speedways were usually built in the low-density fringes of cities or in park settings. Where speedways ran through inhabited areas, intersections were sometimes grade separated and access to abutting properties was sometimes barred.

The most famous was the Harlem River Speedway in northern Manhattan, which was built from 1894 to 1898 at a cost of $4 million. It ran 2.5 miles (4 km) along the Harlem River from 155th Street to Dyckman Street. The site was a steep, rocky river frontage that required complicated engineering. The construction process was fraught with internecine power struggles. Calvert Vaux was appointed landscape designer after several years of disputes, but even Vaux could not disguise the relatively raw character of the site.

Well-to-do spectators flocked to the speedway in the years after its 1898 opening. Its traffic-separation regulations were strict. State law prohibited pedestrians, bicycles, streetcars, and commercial traffic. Both fast carriages and equestrians were permitted

Figure 6.3: Harlem Speedway pedestrian underpass, 1898.

initially; equestrians were banned two years later. Automobilists clamored to gain access but were denied. The law required all crossings to be grade-separated, so three pedestrian tunnels were built beneath the speedway. *Scientific American* described the pedestrian tunnels as "a necessary provision where the roadway is devoted to fast driving."[10]

The Grand Boulevard and Concourse in the Bronx, New York, was conceived in 1891 by Louis A. Risse, chief engineer of the streets department. It was a curious and unique amalgam of roadway concepts. It was a grand multiway boulevard that ran 4.3 miles (6.9 km) along the crest of a north-south ridgeline. It was a speedway that served the region's growing ranks of recreational speed drivers. It was a quasi-parkway that linked Manhattan to the Mosholu Parkway (1888) and the rest of the Bronx's park and parkway system. And it featured perhaps the most extensive program of grade-separated intersections yet proposed for a major thoroughfare: nine underpasses carried cross streets under the Grand Concourse. Development of the corridor would be "a magnificent real estate speculation," but Risse was positive that the Grand Concourse would not become a commercial thoroughfare. The underpasses would draw away cross-Bronx commercial traffic, keeping the thoroughfare "secure forever against the intrusion of trade."[11]

The Grand Concourse was authorized in 1895, began construction in 1902, and opened in 1909. It developed much differently than Risse had envisioned. The horse-carriage speedway was replaced by motor-vehicle lanes, which carried heavy trucks

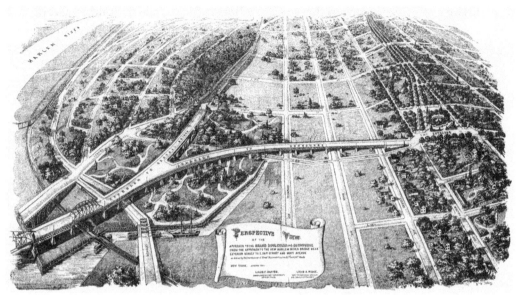

Figure 6.4: Grand Concourse proposal, 1895. The design of the stream-form flyover ramps anticipated the design of twentieth-century urban freeways.

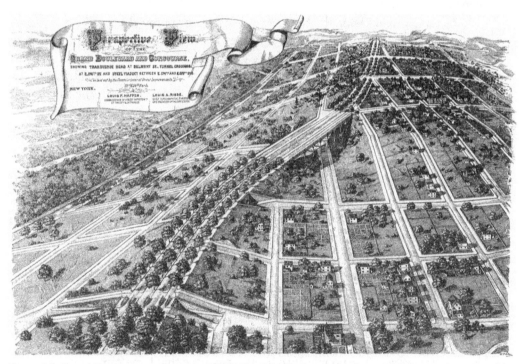

Figure 6.5: Grand Concourse proposal, ca. 1895. The ridgeline's topography provided natural opportunities for grade separation.

and heavy streams of commuter traffic. Risse's vision was more prophetic in terms of large-scale landscape design. The 1895 aerial renderings featured entry ramps and viaducts on elevated sweeping curves. The broad thoroughfare cut through the surrounding grid on a winding, sinuous route, following its own functional and topographical dictates. Thus in certain respects the Grand Concourse anticipated the layouts of urban expressways, such as those built by Robert Moses, and later urban freeways.[12]

In Brooklyn, speed enthusiasts envied Manhattan's Harlem River Speedway. Brooklyn had banned street racing in the early 1890s, yet the appetite for the sport remained high. Racers and speed drivers agitated for a speedway in early 1900. That summer, the park commission formally designated a 1.25-mile (2-km) stretch of Ocean Parkway's center lane as the Ocean Parkway Speedway. The speedway was bordered by a cemetery along half its length, so few cross streets could interfere with the racing vehicles. Signs posted at each end reminded everyone that autos were banned and had to use a side lane. After 1910 the growing volume of motor traffic caused continual friction and disputes; the speedway was discontinued in 1921.[13]

The conflicts on Ocean Parkway's speedway were not unique. The Bayonne, New Jersey, speedway opened in 1900 as a wide macadam road that ran nearly 3 miles (4.8 km) from the Arlington Casino in Bayonne to Bergen Point. It had been "secured for speeding purposes" by a local association of enthusiasts. Soon thereafter, the Pennsylvania Railroad Company attempted to build a low bridge across the speedway and depress the speedway's surface to create height clearance. The city fought that plan. Matters came to a head on 28 February 1902, when the city arrested two railroad engineers at the bridge site and posted a police guard "to prevent any surprise or construction work."[14]

Just a few weeks later, the New Jersey legislature approved a speedway law, possibly spurred by the conflict in Bayonne. New Jersey's counties were authorized to build and maintain speedways that were guaranteed limited-access status. The law stipulated that "no public streets or highways shall be laid across or intersect" any speedway without the consent of county legislators. It was perhaps the first law to authorize limited-access thoroughfares in the United States.[15]

In Washington, DC, a pleasure drive described as "one of the finest roadways in the South" opened in October 1903. It ran one mile (1.6 km) from the Tidal Basin, across the Mall, to the Ellipse at the White House. On two days each week, and when snow permitted sleigh riding, the speed limit was lifted and the drive was used as a speedway. These events were so popular that a local drivers' association sought to build a dedicated speedway nearby. Enthusiastic federal officials granted permission, and the Century Speedway was built on reclaimed land that extended from the Washington Monument to the Potomac River (now the National Mall and Constitution Avenue). It opened in May 1904 with the understanding that it would operate until the area was re-landscaped according to the McMillan plan. The presence of these facilities in the District's monumental core symbolized the fact that speedways had become ubiquitous in urban America.[16]

By 1905 every major city in the United States, and many smaller ones, had at least one speedway. The popularity of trotting assured that large sums of money were spent to build these special roads dedicated full-time or part-time to speed driving. They shared similar governing rules; for example, only open-top four-wheel horse-drawn vehicles were allowed. Local driving clubs provided the social glue and political organization that enabled speed drivers to claim exclusive use of the roadways.[17]

But the appropriation of public thoroughfares and establishment of exclusive rules was the last gasp of political power for the carriage-racing old guard. Speedways declined after 1910, victims of the explosive growth of motor vehicles and resulting increase of traffic conflicts. In addition, limited access caused problems in developing areas. Abutting landowners believed that direct access was very important to land value and essential for the success of businesses that fronted on thoroughfares.

As speedways lost popularity, most were converted to open-access thoroughfares. Sometimes the conversions resulted from citizen pressure. A speedway in Essex County, New Jersey, was built in 1904, but within a few years the abutting landowners had become deeply disgruntled. Like the Harlem River Speedway, it was reserved for fast horse-drawn vehicles and prohibited ordinary carriages and business wagons. In addition, it was lined by a high iron picket fence that blocked abutters' access. By autumn 1909 the abutting landowners had organized a movement to abolish the speedway. One complained, "It might just as well be a wall fifty feet high so far as we are concerned. We cannot get by it and our land is isolated."[18]

Other speedways simply lost patronage and faded from memory as auto ownership came within reach of the middle class, and as auto racing on oval tracks drew the speed enthusiasts. Speedways were often subsumed into the larger national movement to pave and widen all streets for use by motor vehicles and bicycles. Sometimes the thoroughfares retained *speedway* in their names. The general meaning of *speedway* changed to refer to a fast motor-vehicle arterial or a professional motor-racing track. The word's origin in carriage racing was forgotten.

Horse-carriage speedways established the legal and cultural precedents for high-speed motor traffic in urban settings nationwide. The most advanced speedways barred all but a select class of vehicles, eliminated access to abutting properties, banned at-grade street intersections, and required other travel modes to cross above or underneath the roadway. Motor-vehicle drivers took note and began campaigning for similar treatment.

Introduction of the Motorcar

In the 1890s the automobile was an upstart invention whose role in society had yet to be determined. It was alternately a hobbyists' curiosity, an amusement for thrillseekers, or an expensive status symbol for technology-minded elites. Attitudes toward the new invention spanned a wide range. At one extreme was the boundless optimism of automobile boosters; at the other was the outrage of automobile critics.

The automobile press trumpeted an epochal future for the industry. "Again, but with greater emphasis, will the history of the bicycle repeat itself," wrote *Horseless Age* in 1896. "Fortunes will be made. A giant industry will be the outcome, and those who wisely venture first will mold its destinies." Some anticipated the environmental benefits cities would enjoy after horses were replaced. "The deafening rattle of hard tires over Belgian blocks would give place to the silence of the pneumatic or cushion tired wheel; and its streets would be largely rid of the ever present filth," wrote *Scientific American*. Autos would reduce traffic blockages because they were more manageable than horses and more maneuverable than carriages. Autos, like streetcars and bicycles before them, would promote suburbanization, transporting the working class to "the meadows and flowers of the country." In short, the boosters, manufacturers, and other visionaries believed the automobile was a chief agent of cultural progress and a panacea for the traffic and environmental problems of cities.[19]

But the many drawbacks of early automobiles were all too apparent. Nineteenth-century autos were noisy, polluting, and subject to frequent breakdowns. They were perceived by the general population as strange or frightening. Apart from perception, they were objectively dangerous: liable to catch fire, spill acid, or careen out of control. Their high cost put them out of reach to all but the wealthiest of buyers, so they were ripe for pillory as symbols of class injustice.

The most grievous troubles were reckless driving and speeding. Motorists were often viewed as thrill-seeking speeders who exulted in the power of their vehicles and bullied horse-drawn vehicles, cyclists, and people on foot. As a result, anti-automobile feelings were common throughout Europe, the United Kingdom, and the United States

Figure 6.6: *Life* magazine, "Our Leisure Class Must Be Amused," detail, 1902. Invading hordes of motorists arrayed against all other street users.

(although not as common as pro-automobile fascination and devotion).[20]

Editorials and cartoons portrayed motorists as callous, irresponsible daredevils and prodigals. *Life* magazine, which was a humor magazine in the early 1900s, took the most zealous anti-car stance. Its cartoons depicted auto drivers as decadent avatars of mayhem, their shadowy goggled faces grim as they brutally attacked nondrivers and left broken bodies strewn in their wake. Speed contests were likened to pagan ceremonies of human sacrifice. Automobiles were noxious, invasive pests that soon would envelop the whole planet.

Of all of the automobile's negative impacts, road racing and racing crashes were the most visible. Road-race crashes caused the most damage, grabbed the biggest headlines, and stirred up the angriest public responses. In the 1890s France was the leading region for road racing because of the excellent quality of its cross-county roads. French races drew top international competitors, large crowds of spectators, and eager press coverage. But the country experienced many deaths and injuries from road races, and by 1900 authorities began to issue prohibitions. That marked the start of a cycle that was repeated in Europe, the United Kingdom, and the United States: road races were held, deaths and injuries were suffered, public outrage was expressed, and governmental restrictions were imposed. The racing community, which included many wealthy and politically connected elites, would then negotiate exceptions and the cycle began anew.

Automobile technology was progressing incredibly swiftly. In the earliest races of the 1890s, any car that could reach the finish line was a winner. The Paris–Marseille–Paris race of 1896 was the first competitive long-distance road race, and was won at an average speed of 24 kmh (15 mph). The average winning speed increased steadily through 1900, and then leaped upward. By 1903 road races were won at 106 kmh (66 mph). The legal systems of host countries struggled to keep pace.

Vanderbilt and the Long Island Motor Parkway

William K. Vanderbilt Jr. (1878–1944) was a leading promoter of road racing in the United States. He was athletic and dashing, a fearless daredevil, fascinated with motor vehicles, and wealthy enough to indulge his every whim. "To William K. Vanderbilt Jr., nothing seems worth while but automobiles," wrote *Cosmopolitan*. "It is a matter of wonder that he has not been killed, for a more reckless driver and a more daring, speed-mad rider has never been known."[21]

Vanderbilt traveled frequently to Europe to compete in road races and won respect as a serious competitor who often placed second or third. As racing opportunities dwindled abroad, Vanderbilt sought to develop road racing in America. In May 1902 Vanderbilt and a group of auto enthusiasts proposed a automobile speedway extending from New York City along the length of Long Island. It was an ideal location; it had flat topography, well-maintained roads, and a supportive political establishment. Over the following year, the group proposed a variety of routes that ranged from 20 to 112 miles (32 to 180 km) in length. The routes generally served areas where auto enthusiasts owned grand country estates, and the speedway was envisioned as a private facility, perhaps for the exclusive use of Automobile Club of America members. County political leaders endorsed the concept and pledged permitting assistance.

Media reports highlighted the potential for long-distance high-speed auto commuting to New York City. *Motor World* said the speedway would gratify the millionaires' desire for speed and "permit them to travel between their homes and offices at a pace in excess of that made by even the fastest express trains." *Brooklyn Life* commented that "the run to and from town will be mere child's play."[22]

But all was not smooth sailing for the speedway effort. Vanderbilt and his colleagues encountered angry resistance from certain quarters. A scathing editorial in the *New York Times* roasted Vanderbilt's idea and automobiles in general. A motor speedway would rob drivers of "the pleasures of the chase" because "close misses are the sweetener of the automobilist's existence." The editorial continued, "With no chance of beating another machine, and no chance of killing an old lady, the sport will become weary, stale, flat, and unprofitable."[23]

Figure 6.7: *Life* magazine, "Where They Belong," 1903. Millionaire motorists are relegated to a depressed limited-access speedway where they can smash at will.

An anti-speeding group was organized in Nassau County, where Vanderbilt and other motorcar enthusiasts had purchased estates. The Long Island Highway Protective Association noted that Long Island had become "the Mecca of the scorchers" and declared that reckless speeders "who drive madly through village streets and around corners, who respect none of the rights of pedestrians or horsemen, will no longer be tolerated. War is to be waged against all such offenders."[24]

The Protective Association drafted a bill to control reckless automobiles. The Automobile Club of America, fearing the bill might pass in the state legislature, negotiated to remove its most drastic provisions and in exchange gave its endorsement. The "Bailey Bill" became law in 1903. It required that autos pass pedestrians and horse-drawn vehicles slowly (no more than 8 mph, or 13 kmh) and come to a full stop if the driver of a horse-drawn vehicle requested it. The bill declared that speedways were exclusively for horse-drawn vehicles. However, it gave autos the right to travel on all other roads, and gave localities the right to organize road races.[25]

Road racing received a shock when the horrific Paris-Madrid race of 1903 left at least eight dead and ten seriously injured, including several spectators. France banned road racing nationwide. American auto manufacturers condemned road racing with near unanimity. One large automaker called it "an outrage and an infringement upon the rights of users of other vehicles" and rejected the claim that racing helped develop vehicles for practical everyday work. US automobile clubs found themselves in a difficult position. Not wanting to inflame public opinion, they gave lip service in opposition to road racing even as they continued to organize races in the United States to serve their members' desires.[26]

Vanderbilt's speedway effort faded, probably because of the difficulty of acquiring right of way, as well as the newly enshrined status of racing on public roads. With the backing of the American Automobile Association (AAA), Vanderbilt organized the Vanderbilt Cup road race in 1904. It was to be run on public roads on Long Island and was meant to be the most prestigious auto road race in the country. The races were an enormous popular success. They drew at first tens and then hundreds of thousands of spectators. The excitement spilled over to popular culture; a musical titled "The Vanderbilt Cup" played on Broadway in 1906 and 1907 and toured to other cities.[27]

During this period anti-auto sentiment rose in the United States and violence reached a crescendo. New York City recorded thirteen incidents of anti-auto violence in 1904. On the Lower East Side of Manhattan, groups of boys pelted motorists with sticks and rocks. The Vanderbilt Cup continued with great public popularity, but given the dismal safety record of other road races, it was only a matter of time until a crash occurred. In the 1906 race a spectator was hit by a race car and died instantly.[28]

Vanderbilt conferred with AAA. Twelve days after the crash, he announced the resurrection of his speedway idea. Many automakers expressed support and promised funding. The head of Thomas Motor said a private speedway was "an absolute necessity for the development and perfection of automobiles." The head of Locomobile Company said, "The proposed automobile speedway is what the automobile manufacturers have been waiting for for years." The nomenclature of this new type of facility was a challenge. At first the press called it a speedway because that was the most apropos term. But Vanderbilt and his associates wished to avoid labels that were strongly associated with racing. They considered various terms including *automobile highway, automobile toll road*, and *motor roadway*, finally settling on *Long Island Motor Parkway*. That name recalled the exclusivity and ease of the Olmstedian parkway, and reassigned it to high-speed automobile pleasure driving. The altered definition took hold. By the late 1920s the term *parkway* had come to refer mainly to segregated, buffered, and exclusive automobile pleasure roads.[29]

Although the Motor Parkway was designed for racing, for most of the year it would operate as a toll road for touring. In their promotional efforts, Vanderbilt and his associates emphasized economic development and quick access to the pleasures of country life. The manager of the Motor Parkway predicted that within two years it would be bordered by many high-class inns and cafes catering to the "outdoor, sport-loving class" of recreational auto drivers. Vanderbilt saw the Motor Parkway as a model and envisioned similar roadways extending from New York to cities and towns up and down the eastern seaboard.[30]

At the June 1908 groundbreaking ceremony, the president of AAA congratulated Vanderbilt on behalf of the thousands of motorists "to whom a road restricted to automobiles is like a glimpse of paradise." Other attendees vaunted that the event was the start of a new epoch and predicted that exclusive motor thoroughfares would soon be common in all great cities of the United States.[31]

The route traveled approximately 43 miles (69 km) from the outskirts of Queens, New York City, to Lake Ronkonkoma in central Long Island. The Motor Parkway had features similar to trotting speedways, such as limited access, grade-separated road crossings, and exclusive use by certain vehicle types, as well as auto-racing features such as concrete pavement and banked curves. The roadway was initially 16 feet (4.9 m) wide, and was later widened to 22 feet (6.7 m). The right-of-way, being 50–100 feet (15–30 m) wide, formed a green buffer along most of its length. The right-of-way also was lined along most of its length by fencing made of durable concrete posts and steel-wire mesh. A road reserved exclusively for pleasure automobiles was new and unfamiliar to everyone, so no-trespassing signs were posted that prohibited all other vehicles, bicycles, equestrians, and pedestrians—under threat of prosecution.[32]

Vanderbilt's team believed those measures would ensure safety, but both race cars and spectators managed to break through the barriers. And the 1908–1910 Vanderbilt Cup races ran on ordinary public roads in addition to Motor Parkway segments. Meanwhile, automobile critics called for stricter speed controls on vehicles. A New York state legislator introduced a bill to mechanically limit all cars manufactured in the state to 20 mph (32 kmh). *Atlantic Monthly* wrote in favor of mandatory speed governors. When several crashes during the 1910 Vanderbilt Cup race caused two deaths and at least sixteen serious injuries, the press was apoplectic. The normally staid *Scientific American* called the race a "slaughter" and likened it to the "unspeakable cruelties" of the Roman Coliseum. The crashes spelled the end of road racing on Long Island.[33]

The major portion of the Motor Parkway's construction was completed in June 1912 and its traffic increased steadily over the following years. It was a highway for the wealthy: the one-way toll was $1.50, equal to four hours of unskilled labor. Other Long Island highways were improved during the same period as suburban areas sought to make commuting trips "as pleasant and attractive as possible." Land 50 miles (80 km) from New York City became accessible for commuting. One real-estate operator estimated that 20,000 acres (8,100 ha) of farmland were developed from 1912 to

1913, mostly as large estates of 100 acres (40 ha) or more. A constant stream of auto commuters arriving in Manhattan from distant points was a daily morning sight. As the fastest and most exclusive highway on Long Island, the Motor Parkway had a large effect on the population growth and development of the areas it ran through. It was part of the new phenomenon of extensive automobile-based suburbanization.[34]

The Motor Parkway's business peaked in the 1924–1930 period with about 410 trips logged daily. Although it charged high tolls, it was not a profitable investment. New Yorkers instead crowded onto ordinary roads as they sought weekend escapes of outdoor recreation. An ambitious park administrator named Robert Moses was quite willing to serve the public's desire for free competing parkways—and in the process drive Vanderbilt's parkway out of business. The Motor Parkway officially closed in 1938 and Moses's Department of Parks promptly converted the westernmost segment to a 2.5-mile (4-km) bicycle path. A few other segments were used as public roads or electricity transmission corridors, but most of the Motor Parkway was abandoned to decay.[35]

The Motor Parkway was a pioneering facility that taught many lessons, even as its specific dimensions and configurations became obsolete. Generally, it was not cited as an influence on later designers, planners, or highway engineers. That was most probably because of its record of racing fatalities and its association with gilded aristocracy. But it was internationally famous. To the real-estate industry, it demonstrated that a high-speed limited-access auto highway could boost property values and accelerate suburbanization. It helped awaken an appetite for long-distance auto commuting, and that had powerful implications for the future form of cities.

Bronx River Parkway

The Bronx Zoo was founded and developed by Madison Grant (1865–1937), a New York lawyer, big-game hunter, and conservationist. The zoo was established in 1895, opened in 1899, and continued to develop under Grant's leadership of the New York Zoological Society. Within ten years it was widely considered the largest and most beautiful city zoo in the world. It was one of the most popular attractions in New York City, drawing one million visitors per year in 1903 and two million by 1914.

Grant and his fellow directors felt very possessive about the zoo. Any threats to its character were almost a personal affront. The Bronx River, which flowed through the zoo and fed its ponds, was one such threat. It was badly polluted by sewage and industrial waste from many sources located along miles of river valley upstream. The zoo's 1903 annual report called it "a menace to public health" that required radical measures to prevent further degradation. The idea of a sewer and highway project to protect the river valley had been discussed by state and local leaders since 1895. One of the zoo's directors, William White Niles, wanted to take the initiative on cleaning the river and restoring the land along its banks.[36]

In the summer of 1904, the river's pollution was so bad that waterfowl using the zoo's ponds became sick. Grant decided to pursue Niles's idea. He and his colleagues determined to create a parkway 15 miles (24 km) long, extending from the zoo north to the Kensico Reservoir. Niles, who was a lawyer and state legislator, drafted a bill to create a commission of inquiry. Grant reviewed and approved the bill.

The bill passed the state legislature in 1906 and the governor appointed three

Figure 6.8: Race car in Fairmount Park, Philadelphia, 1909.

men to run the Bronx Parkway Commission, their names having been suggested by Niles. Grant took the position of chairman and served in that role for nineteen years. The treasurer was James G. Cannon, a prominent bank executive who dabbled in not-for-profit land development in Scarsdale, New York. Dave H. Morris served during the commission's first year of inquiry and report writing. He was the president of the Automobile Club of America, an auto-racing enthusiast, cousin-in-law of William K. Vanderbilt Jr., and a member of the Long Island Motor Parkway planning committee. Niles served as secretary and took Morris's place when the parkway was authorized in 1907. All four men were officers or members of the Zoological Society.[37]

The commission identified two models for its parkway. For grade separation and access control, the model was the system of East and West River Drives along the Schuylkill River in Fairmount Park, Philadelphia. There, a complicated mix of roads, walking paths, trolley lines, and railways were sandwiched between the riverbanks and steep bluffs. Limited access was ensured by two conditions: through road and rail traffic was carried on several bridges that spanned the river and crossed over the drives; and the drives were bordered by parkland that prevented most city streets from connecting. The drives were generally 100 feet (30 m) wide and were easily adapted to auto traffic. When auto races were held in Fairmount Park from 1908 to 1911, West River Drive was a major part of the course. During the 1909 race, the fastest laps were driven at an average speed of 63 mph (101 kmh), and higher speeds were reached on West River Drive, which *Motor Age* described as "a 3-mile opportunity to beat it."[38]

The commission's other model was the Boston park and parkway system (1878–1895), designed by Frederick Law Olmsted. It was a chain of public parks and linking parkways that spiraled from the city's heart to its outer suburban districts. One of the parks, the Back Bay Fens, was created to improve the mouth of the Muddy River. The area was an ecological disaster zone—a fetid sewage basin that repelled all human life within a half mile. Extensive dredging, land shaping, and planting was required to transform the river course into an amenity. The Fens and associated sewer improvements rehabilitated the adjacent neighborhoods; by the 1890s grand houses were being built and prestigious institutions were locating nearby. To the Bronx parkway commissioners, the Boston system was an exemplar of pollution cleanup, property-value increase, and a rustic, naturalistic aesthetic.[39]

The commission's first report endorsed the original concept. It would be a linear reservation of reclaimed land with an attractive, scenic roadway restricted to noncommercial vehicles. All minor streets in the reservation would be acquired and extinguished. Only important, busy streets would be retained. The commission hailed the parkway as a "transformed life artery" running through local communities, and said the progress it impelled would be of inestimable value. The commission anticipated that the parkway would become part of a future network of parkways in and near Westchester County.[40]

The commission noted many complicating conditions. Railways and a water pipeline occupied the proposed reservation, and preliminary work on a trunk-sewer line was underway. The report also warned of "a low class of development and increasingly unsanitary conditions" within the reservation that threatened to cause a disastrous epidemic. That began the commission's years-long campaign of denigrating working-class immigrants' housing in order to justify, and even celebrate, its removal.[41]

Environmental improvement was the primary reason used to justify the parkway. Another reason, stated less explicitly, was bigotry. Madison Grant was a white supremacist, eugenicist, and defender of slavery. He abhorred the swarming, racially diverse contemporary city, especially New York, which was producing "ethnic horrors that will be beyond the powers of future anthropologists to unravel." Aryans could not thrive in cities, said Grant; they needed country villages and farms. With the publication of his book *The Passing of the Great Race* (1916), Grant became an internationally known leader of the white-supremacist and anti-immigration movements, and one of the most prominent racists in America. Grant's fellow parkway commissioners echoed his bigoted sentiments. Several times, the commission identified working-class Italian neighborhoods as the type of the dirty, ramshackle development it took pride in demolishing.[42]

Grant's bigotry was but an extreme expression of sentiments that were widely prevalent in the United States at the time. The *Scarsdale Inquirer* was particularly concerned about nearby Bronx, "a hodge-podge of farm lands, shanties and tumble-down buildings, which inevitably give way to the cheapest sort of city development." It warned that Scarsdale might someday become like Harlem and Yorkville (Manhattan tenement neighborhoods inhabited by Blacks, Jews, and immigrants). The Bronx Parkway and other suburban-style developments served as a bulwark against "the menace of city growth." They guaranteed that Scarsdale would become a "permanent suburb" where single-family houses, lawns, and trees would predominate for the foreseeable future.[43]

In 1911 the engineer Jay Downer (1877–1949) was hired by the commission to direct the mapping and acquisition of parkway land. Downer previously had worked on railways, industrial facilities, and residential land developments. He likely was familiar with the Long Island Motor Parkway because he had worked for the Island Cities Real Estate Company while it developed Hollis Hills Gardens near the Motor Parkway's terminus in Queens.[44]

By 1914 Downer had taken the position of chief engineer. He made a preliminary plan of the parkway's motor drive that year, but much of the design work was yet to be done. In 1915 Downer and the commissioners visited and took measurements of the drives in Central Park, other thoroughfares in the New York City region, and parkways in other eastern states. Hermann Merkel began to refine the plan in 1915, working in constant consultation with Downer and the commissioners. Merkel was in charge of the Bronx Zoo's landscaping and was the commission's chief forester and landscape architect. Gilmore D. Clarke, a recent Cornell graduate, was appointed superintendent of construction. Downer and Clarke formed a close working relationship that would be significant for parkway planning in the years to come.[45]

Construction of the parkway drive began in 1917. After various delays, including World War I and a lawsuit forcing New York City to pay obligated funds, the first segments opened in summer 1921. By 1923 large sections were open and the parkway was regularly experiencing a crush of traffic on weekends and holidays. The formal opening was held in November 1925.[46]

The parkway reservation was 15.5 miles (25 km) long and ranged from 200 to 1,200 feet (61 to 366 m) wide. The drive generally hewed to the valley bottom and was separated from local streets by landscaped strips, walls, or rail tracks. From the start of design work, Downer and the commissioners had recognized the importance of grade-separated intersections. Nine of the busiest cross streets were routed to bridges that spanned the valley and crossed over the parkway. The commission believed the bridges were needed to avoid crash danger and expensive traffic-control measures. Several bridges were requested and paid for by adjacent communities, which had similar safety concerns and wanted to avoid traffic jams.[47]

Access control was also implemented by additional means. Bicycles and pedestrians were prohibited from the parkway drive, and instead used the parkway reservation's 20 miles (32 km) of pedestrian paths. Access control was reinforced when the commission installed guard rails along the motor drive in the early 1920s. The rails were supposed to prevent bad behaviors such as driving and parking on the roadside lawns, peddling wares, littering, and stealing shrubbery.[48]

But while often cited as a pioneering example of limited access, the parkway in actuality was a hybrid. It had at least six at-grade intersections with cross streets. Also, private driveways were connected directly to the parkway along a segment in White Plains. Pedestrian paths crossed the parkway at grade at several points.[49]

The parkway was lauded as a terrific success. The idea of motor parkways leading to parks enjoyed boundless public approval, to which politicians paid keen attention. Real-estate interests viewed the parkway as a regional amenity that would attract homebuyers and help make Westchester County the richest county in the state. As the county's suburban communities boomed in population, Downer and other advocates harped on the property-value impacts. Between 1918 and 1932 the assessed value of lots along the parkway increased 500 percent. By the late 1920s the parkway was a busy commuter thoroughfare and, according to National Park Service historians, was one of the most heavily traveled roads in the eastern United States.[50]

Figure 6.9: Bronx River Parkway traffic congestion, 1926. Courtesy of Westchester County Archives.

The parkway also had a number of drawbacks. When it opened, the parkway received universal praise for its environmental improvements, but later reports were less glowing. It suffered from periodic floods that created traffic jams. The flooding was exacerbated by the suburban development that the parkway had encouraged. The sewer line continued to overflow into the river during the biggest storms. Stormwater runoff from adjacent suburbs polluted the river, as did runoff from the parkway itself, which carried oil, rubber, road salt, lead, and other toxins.[51]

The parkway increased separation between neighborhoods and land uses by rein-forcing the divisive effect of the Bronx River and the parallel railway. The impact was pronounced for people on foot. The southernmost segment of the parkway, which ran through working-class communities, was difficult to access on foot, entailing hazard-ous road crossings at some points. The parkway's path system had gaps and dead ends that hampered longer-distance walking and bicycling trips.[52]

Fast drivers delighted in the high speeds enabled by limited access. Speeding was a continual problem. The parkway's speed limit in Westchester County was set at 30 mph (48 kmh) initially, and was raised to 35 mph (56 kmh) by 1929. Speeders were regularly ticketed for going above 50 mph (80 kmh). The parkway had a high crash rate relative to later parkways, most likely the result of inexperienced drivers and heavy traffic volumes, and possibly also because of sharp bends, lack of lane striping, and other design features. In 1932 Downer defended the parkway's design, saying it was "a fine, safe driveway for any sane driver at speeds up to 45 miles per hour, depending on the amount of traffic." Furthermore, he argued, parkways designed for midrange speeds were safer than higher-speed facilities: "We could spend a couple million dol-lars in changing the driveway to a modern speedway, upon which experience indicates there might occur more accidents than on the present parkway." Nevertheless, during the 1950s and 1960s, much of the parkway was rebuilt to a near-freeway standard to reduce crashes and allow higher speeds.[53]

Westchester County Parkways

In the years immediately after World War I, leading citizens and politicians of Westchester County began to think seriously about a countywide parkway system, which had first been suggested by the Bronx Parkway Commission in 1907. According to Jay Downer, the parkway system was motivated by trends that were definite and growing. He pointed to the automobile, demand for more roads, booming suburbs, budding popularity of outdoor recreation, and increased interest in regional planning. The Bronx River Parkway itself was a major motivator because it "strongly influenced sentiment in favor of additional parkways." County leaders could not help but notice the traffic and the international praise it drew. By the end of 1921, public support for a comprehensive parkway system was assured.[54]

In February 1922 a state bill was introduced to authorize a comprehensive park and parkway system in Westchester County. It was widely endorsed and hyped in the media. "A chain of parks, connected by parkways . . . would form, as planned, one of the most extensive and elaborate pleasure grounds in the world," effused the *New York Times*. "The bill has the backing of . . . a great many of the wealthy and prominent persons who maintain residences in what has come to be regarded as the richest suburban colony in the United States and probably the world." The bill passed quickly and the Westchester County Park Commission was formed in April.[55]

The commission publicized its general parkway concept in January 1923. Population movement into Westchester County "is now unprecedented," noted the commission's president. It was "a surge actuated by the pressure of the millions confined within city limits. People are coming to Westchester just as fast as the builders can provide homes for them." Fortuitously, the county's topography was aligned with its commuting patterns. "The three Westchester County river valleys parallel to its north and south axis and the direction of greatest traffic, are natural parkways," the president contended.[56]

Starting in 1923, several of the Bronx River Parkway's staffers moved to the Westchester County Park Commission. Jay Downer, as chief engineer, had executive control. Gilmore D. Clarke, as landscape architect, was responsible for planning and landscape design. System planning and land acquisition began immediately.[57]

Downer understood that his parkway network would set the pattern of suburbanization for years to come. He called it "a great skeleton plan for the county's future growth," and explained how it would open vast areas to upper-income, auto-dependent development:

> The spreading growth of cities and widening circles of intensive suburban development is largely shaped by transportation facilities, and motorized transport has brought about an entirely new phase of suburban development which will be largely influenced by the parkways. . . . Some of the new parkways traversing large open areas away from the railroads will start entirely new trends of subsidiary growth of the substantial quality usually attracted to park frontages and adjoining areas.[58]

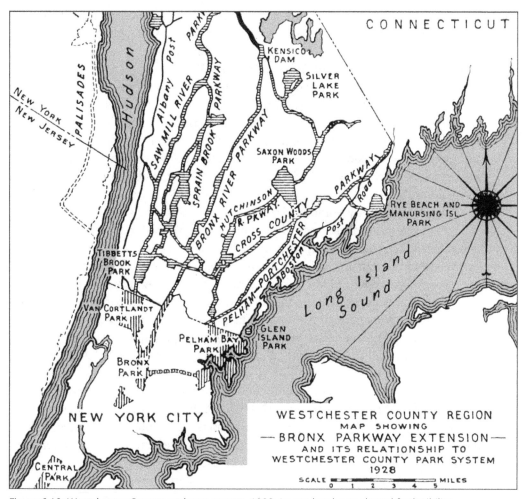

Figure 6.10: Westchester County parkway system, 1928. Image has been altered for legibility.

By 1925 the county had authorized a tangled network that comprised 122 miles (196 km) of parkways in addition to the 15.5-mile (25-km) Bronx River Parkway. Not all were realized. Three parkways were cancelled, while others were built by Robert Moses after World War II as mixed-traffic expressways and freeways. The parkways nearest to New York City were the most influential in terms of furthering the metropolitan parkway concept. They were the Bronx River Parkway, Saw Mill River Parkway (planned 1923, began construction 1925, first section opened 1926), Hutchinson River Parkway (planned 1923, began construction 1927, opened 1928), and Cross-County Parkway (planned 1925, began construction 1927, first section opened 1928).[59]

Those parkways bolstered the idea that responsible highway planning put major vehicular routes in small stream valleys. Downer argued that parkways turned stream valleys into assets, while unprotected stream valleys became nuisance zones that depressed property values.[60]

A separate but linked parkway was launched in 1925. It continued the Bronx River Parkway extension from the Westchester County border to an area 75 miles (120 km) to the north. Eventually named the Taconic State Parkway, it was funded by the state and was directed by its own commission. The commission included Franklin D. Roosevelt as chairman, William Niles, and Madison Grant. Although it was a separate state project, it used the Westchester parkways as models and drew on the assistance and advice of Jay Downer and Gilmore D. Clarke.[61]

Limited access was an ongoing concern of the parkway builders, and the topic occasionally flared into political disputes and court battles. According to Joseph Barnett, an engineer who worked on Westchester's parkway bridges, the park commission had "considerable doubt" that mere ownership of a property established the legal authority to prohibit abutter access on it. Therefore, whenever the park commission acquired a property for right of way, it was careful to state in the deed that it had control of access.[62]

Westchester County residents, for the most part, were pleased with the parkways and accepted any inconveniences without protest. In contrast, the Taconic State Park Commission faced indignant opposition to its limited-access plans. The Westchester parkways ran through areas of speculative residential development, but the Taconic ran through farms operated by working-class residents. Many farmers owned just one vehicle, a pickup truck, which was barred from the parkway. The parkway interrupted the existing network of farm roads, creating permanent detours and increasing the residents' inconvenience. Also, the parkway cut through a number of farm properties, and farmers felt they were not being fairly compensated for the loss of land and livelihood.[63]

Both the Westchester and Taconic commissions were forced by circumstances to build hybrid road segments. The Saw Mill River Parkway, for example, had more than a dozen at-grade intersections. The Taconic commission granted abutter access where the parkway severed a farm and isolated the land on one side. The Taconic commission's willingness to compromise showed that it too harbored doubts about its authority. It was challenging longstanding common law that gave property owners access to all adjoining public roads, and the widespread cultural view that abutter access was necessary to conduct business and retain property value.

In an effort to clarify its legal standing, the Taconic commission took a case to court about one of the farms that was split by the parkway. The jury sided with the commission. It confirmed that abutting farmers had no right to drive a tractor on the parkway. Tractors had to be driven to the nearest overpass in order to reach the other side of the parkway. But that was infeasible for cattle, so the jury ruled that the farmer's cattle were allowed to cross the parkway at grade—and motorists had to yield the right of way. The uncertain legal status of limited-access roadways would not begin to be resolved until 1937.[64]

Between 1922 and 1932 a total of $37 million was spent by the county, the state, and New York City to build Westchester's parkway system. In 1932 about half of the planned 160 miles (257 km) of parkways was completed or under construction, and the parks and parkways together occupied 27 square miles (70 sq km). The park commission proudly called it "a park system thus far unequalled." Downer, rather uncharacteristically, boasted that "the fame of Westchester has been carried literally to the four corners of the Earth." Westchester's parkways were acclaimed by a wide variety of commentators, from hard-headed engineers to visionary designers, from corporatists to socialists, from village mayors to top federal officials.[65]

Jay Downer and Gilmore D. Clarke worked on many of the renowned parkways of the 1920s and 1930s, including parkways built or administered by Robert Moses, the federal Mount Vernon Memorial Highway in Alexandria, Virginia, and other federal parkways. The two had complementary personalities. Downer was a discreet and quiet man interested in engineering practicalities and financial matters. Clarke was a forceful and commanding type (having the initials G. D., he was known as Major God Damn Clarke during World War I) who was passionate about landscape beauty. Downer capped his career by engineering Idlewild Airport (now John F. Kennedy Airport) in the 1940s. Clarke began teaching in the 1930s at Cornell, his alma mater, and later became the school's dean of architecture. Both men wrote and lectured as parkway advocates, and both were internationally respected in their fields. Their work greatly influenced thinking about limited-access roadways and the role of parkways in structuring urban regions.[66]

Robert Moses

As a young child, Robert Moses (1888–1981) aspired to be the governor of Connecticut. Although he never won elected office, he held many positions of authority throughout his long career as a public administrator. In his chosen sphere of action—building parks, parkways, freeways, bridges, public housing, and other infrastructure—he exercised a degree of power that rivaled, even exceeded, that of governors. The urge to wield great government power was the defining attribute of his career.

He was born to a wealthy family that lived in a leafy traditional neighborhood near Yale University. He felt comfortable in New Haven, and when his family moved to Manhattan in 1897, he disliked the crowds, noise, and confusion of the big city. After studying at Yale and Oxford, and writing a PhD thesis on government administration, Moses joined the Bureau of Municipal Research, a government-reform think tank in Manhattan. In his free time, he enjoyed outdoor recreations like hiking, boating, and picnics in the country. He also trekked about the city, examining places such as the Hudson River waterfront and dreaming of the physical improvements that ought to be made.[67]

Moses was familiar with the Bronx River Parkway during its construction and occasionally mentioned it in policy recommendations. But he had no special concern for parkways; his aims were bigger. By the late 1910s, he was a recognized expert in the public-administration field and was assisting the reform of the US federal civil service.[68]

Moses began working for Governor Al Smith's administration in 1918. When Smith lost the election two years later, Moses was hired to lead the New York State Association, which was a nongovernmental group organized to carry Smith's reform agenda forward. One of its goals was to create a state park plan. In January 1921 Moses reconvened the Committee on the State Park Plan, which previously had been a part of Smith's administration. Madison Grant was the chairman and Jay Downer was a member.[69]

Moses and Grant served together for three years, until the committee issued its final plan in 1924. Grant had the potential to be a role model in many ways. He was adept at drafting legislation at the city, state, and federal levels. He built parks and parkways that were prized by reformers, business interests, and the public. He gained

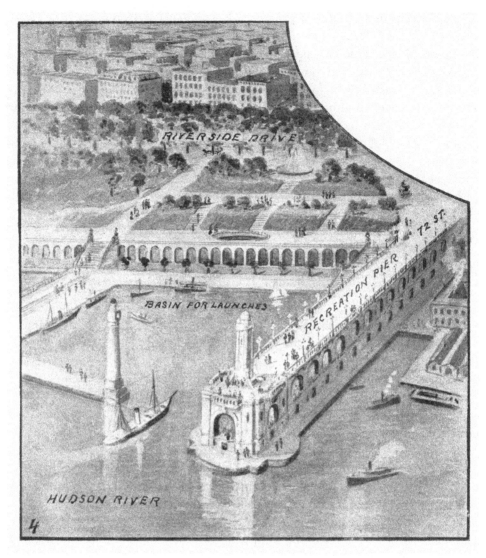

Figure 6.11: Hudson riverfront vision by Harry M. Pettit, 1905. Robert Moses's dreams resembled plans that were publicized when he was a high-school student.

the support of key politicians and outlasted most of them. He influenced state and national policy for both better and worse, in ways that altered American culture over many decades. To a man like Moses, who reserved his ultimate admiration for those who achieved big, tangible results, Grant's career may have offered a number of lessons in the exercise of bureaucratic power.

Moses was not known for crediting the influences of others upon his work, but he freely credited the Bronx River Parkway. In the 1950s, at the apex of his career, he said it was "the pioneer and father of all genuine parkways." One lesson Moses may have learned from Grant and Downer was that parks were sacred in political terms, and parkways were almost as popular. He liked to tell his colleagues: "As long as you're on the side of parks, you're on the side of angels. You can't lose." Political sanctity was important when one had an abrasive, aggressive personality, as Moses did. In the months before the 1922 election, for example, he was chastised by the *New York Times* for his megalomanic propaganda against the sitting governor.[70]

By the time Al Smith regained the governorship in 1922, Moses had become a trusted advisor on all facets of state government. He could have chosen any number of paths to get the power and fame that he craved. The topic that increasingly absorbed his attention was park and parkway planning. He trekked all over Nassau County, Long Island, to discover potential building sites, and he constantly described his ideas to Governor Smith. When Smith suggested in the summer of 1923 that Moses direct the Long Island Park Commission, Moses readily accepted.[71]

His Long Island parkway efforts closely followed the activities of Westchester County. Moses copied each of Westchester's steps with a lag of 1–2 years. His comprehensive network plan was released in 1924; the first parkway began construction in 1926; and the first parkway segments opened in 1927. He hired Gilmore D. Clarke to work on the designs.[72]

Moses's vision for Long Island emulated Westchester County: it would be primarily residential and recreational. Commercial traffic was banned on its parkways, and the land bordering the parkways was zoned residential by localities, as Moses had urged. The parkways were intended to promote diffuse residential development rather than compact mixed-use settlements. Advocates presented that as a beneficial effect. "Access to the [Southern State] Parkway will be only at fixed places, so it will never become a main street of new villages," argued a supporter of Moses's parkway plan. In that goal, the parkways were successful. They stimulated extensive low-density development that mostly took the form of auto-dependent bedroom suburbs.[73]

Long Island's parkway system also had notable differences from Westchester's. One, the parkways were not routed along stream valleys. Instead, they traversed a variety of terrains. Their routes were determined by park locations, politics, and expected demand. Two, Moses ensured that his parkways were entirely limited-access. His ability to achieve that might be ascribed partly to his hyperaggressive land acquisition methods, which at times verged on extralegal abuse and vindictive bullying.[74]

Before Moses started his construction program, Long Island had virtually no parks, and few ways to reach them even if they had existed. Public roads were in poor repair and jammed on weekends. The Long Island Motor Parkway was too expensive for the working class. By 1929, Moses had created 14 parks totaling 8,200 acres (3,300 ha), and had completed portions of the Southern State and Wantagh parkways. Park attendance zoomed from near zero in 1926 to three million in 1930. New Yorkers felt that Moses had given them a gift. He became a popular hero and amassed considerable political capital, which carried him past many enemies and through many administrative conflicts over the following decades.[75]

Moses's 1920s parkways were built mostly on farms, rural estates, landfill, and other undeveloped land. As he later explained, he started building parkways outside the city "and worked in, because that was the easiest way to make progress." He had been urging more major roads and bridges in New York City since 1926, but was unable to hire long-range planners because of legal restrictions. So he adapted the highway plan developed by the Regional Plan of New York and Its Environs committee and, in February 1930, presented it as his own. The proposed system would pervade and traverse New York City, and link the Long Island and Westchester County parkway systems.[76]

Moses's plan began to grind forward with consistent support from Governor

Franklin D. Roosevelt. Most histories portray Moses and Roosevelt as enemies, but on the issue of parkways running through cities, they were simpatico. In October 1930, Roosevelt endorsed Moses's five-year program of parkway construction. In July 1931, Roosevelt launched construction of the Grand Central Parkway in Queens. The governor said he wanted the Long Island parkways to continue into the city and connect to Westchester County via the Triborough Bridge.[77]

In 1932, responding to the economic collapse of the Depression, the state legislature cut parkway funding. Roosevelt was adamantly opposed to the cuts. "These express arteries are not merely a luxury; they are a commercial and economic necessity," he told the legislators. According to the *New York Times*, Moses "apparently was well-pleased" with Roosevelt's support.[78]

After Roosevelt won the presidency, he was able to allocate large amounts of federal funding to the city's parkway construction program. Thus reassured, in May 1933 the city approved a 30-mile (48-km) parkway network for Queens along the lines that Moses had proposed. In July 1933, the Grand Central Parkway opened to Kew Gardens, Queens. The 8-mile (13-km) segment was the city's first limited-access parkway.[79]

Moses's power to build in New York City took a quantum jump when he joined Mayor LaGuardia's administration in 1934. He took control of the parks department and Triborough Bridge Authority, and waged a blitz of parkway construction. He favored routes on low-value land: vacant properties, undeveloped parklands, industrial waterfronts, and new water frontages that he created with landfill. The parkways barred walking and other recreational uses from miles of waterfront, a legacy the city has struggled to overcome through the present day.[80]

In 1937 the state enacted a law that allowed any road to be built or reconstructed as a limited-access freeway. Abutting property owners had no right of access and administrators could fence the right-of-way at their discretion. That gave Moses more power to ram parkways and expressways through built-up areas, particularly poor and minority communities where residents were unable to muster strong opposition. His projects became more invasive and destructive to neighborhoods, involving condemnation, displacement, and relocation of residents and businesses on large scales.[81]

By 1943 Moses had completed 87 miles (140 km) of parkways and limited-access drives inside the city's boundaries. New York City had more miles of limited-access highways than any other city in the world, by a wide margin. Local and national media lionized Moses as "the master builder" for his accomplishments. His status ascended from local hero to national legend; he stood as a singular figure in the transportation world. Teams of engineers from across the nation toured Moses's works and, in their home cities, applied the lessons and methods they had learned. Officials and public-works experts visited from Britain, Europe, Scandinavia, and Latin America. Moses was in high demand as a consultant and contributed to planning studies in more than a dozen cities and regions in the United States and abroad.[82]

That period of great acclaim coincided with the end of the urban-parkway era in America. Construction experience had brought a better understanding of the drawbacks. Parkways were expensive, land acquisition was time consuming, and the wider right-of ways were more difficult to fit into constrained urban sites. Leading planners, such as John Nolen and Harland Bartholomew, declared that only the wealthiest jurisdictions could afford such extravagances. Burdened by the Depression and World

War II, highway administrators and engineers gave priority to hardheaded efficiency over scenic and recreational values. The practice of banning commercial traffic from urban highways was viewed as wasteful and impractical.[83]

Conservationists were disillusioned about the environmental impacts. Where parkways ran through natural land, they destroyed local ecologies and the quality of quiet, restorative refuge. In 1942, Harland Bartholomew stated the current progressive opinion of stream-valley parkways. He noted that they had once seemed an ideal solution to congestion, but in reality they only accelerated the automobile-commuting trend, which led to an unending cycle of road expansion and park destruction.[84]

In addition, the legal need for parkways was fading. By 1943, seventeen states had adopted laws enabling limited-access highways. Highway administrators had less and less need to acquire strips of roadside property in order to prohibit abutter access. Backed by the new laws, they had more power to insert unbuffered facilities directly into the urban fabric of streets and blocks.[85]

After World War II, Moses maintained a rapid pace of construction as he added some 85 miles (137 km) of limited-access roads in New York City. Most were utilitarian, mixed-traffic freeways that de-emphasized or omitted scenic landscaping and space for recreation. During the 1960s, Moses lost his positions of authority. Public attitudes toward urban freeways underwent a stunning reversal, and the launching of new freeways in the city ceased. Even so, the New York urban area today has more limited-access roadways than any other in America. They are the primary legacy of Moses's 44-year career as a highway administrator.[86]

Moses's legacy also extended nationally. He advised the planners of the US Freeway System, helped promote it, and was a major influence on its administration. Bertram D. Tallamy, the federal official who directed the initial construction of the Freeway System, said it was built according to Moses's principles.[87]

Edward Bassett and Freeways

Edward M. Bassett (1863–1948) was a lawyer and planner who led the creation of New York City's 1916 zoning code. It was the nation's first comprehensive zoning code—the famous law that prescribed wedding-cake setbacks for the city's skyscrapers and prompted hundreds of American towns and cities to adopt zoning. For that achievement, Bassett was honored by design professionals and named "the father of American zoning."[88]

In 1921 Bassett joined the Regional Plan of New York and Its Environs initiative (RPNY) as head of the legal team. His assignment was to investigate legal issues that might arise when implementing a comprehensive regional plan. One question identified early in the process was how to create and stabilize official highway layouts. Jay Downer may have helped answer that particular question, because he served as an RPNY engineering advisor from 1921 until the final report was issued in 1929.[89]

RPNY said that existing traffic congestion in New York "places intolerable burdens upon commerce and endangers human life." Therefore, one of RPNY's primary tasks was to plan a regional network of expressways, which were highways designed for high-speed through traffic. It issued its plans in 1929. RPNY said that express travel through intensive urban areas required roads that were fully grade separated. They should be either elevated above existing streets, or tunneled below them, or placed in a depressed trench with parallel access roads at grade. Those options gave property owners access to abutting streets and avoided legal disputes over access rights.[90]

As RPNY's engineers were developing regional highway plans, Bassett worked as an attorney on several cases involving the Long Island parkways built by Robert Moses. He began thinking about land planning in terms of abutter access. He was concerned that weak legal frameworks allowed buildings to be built in the path of planned arterial routes, which caused arterial plans to fail. For a 1929 RPNY survey report, he created access-based definitions of streets and parkland. Similar access-based definitions of boulevards and parkways were presented in RPNY's 1929 final plan, highlighting the ability of parkways to speed traffic.[91]

The following year, Bassett wrote a brief yet remarkably influential article. He envisioned a "new kind of thoroughfare" that limited access like a parkway, but carried all auto and commercial traffic like a highway. "We have no name for such a thoroughfare," Bassett wrote. "I suggest the name of *freeway*. This word is short and good Anglo-Saxon."

The *free* in *freeway* was not a reference to tolls or any other financial arrangement. It referred to freedom from at-grade intersections, abutter access, roadside businesses, parked cars, and pedestrians. It referred to the free flow of traffic. On a freeway, all activities not related to fast vehicular movement would be stripped away. Bassett devised the term *freeway* with a particular concern for facilitating traffic through urban areas. He pointed out that freeways could be adapted to the most congested districts of the largest cities. In addition, Bassett noted that no laws in the United States permitted the total denial of abutter access from roads that carried commercial traffic. Implicit in his definition was a call to create such laws.[92]

The freeway concept was rapidly accepted in the planning and engineering fields. It was strongly endorsed by the Regional Plan Association (the new name of RPNY) in 1933, when Bassett was still a consultant to the organization. Bassett apparently envisioned freeways as having generous landscaped borders like parkways. He expected that housing built along freeways would be extremely desirable and valuable. That was not a bizarre expectation at the time, because parkways were only four to six lanes wide and set in lush, generously sized reservations. And the dominant organization of highway engineers, the American Association of State Highway Officials, was on record supporting highway beautification and the conservation of roadside greenery.

In practice, however, urban freeways were squeezed by financial and political demands. Engineers gave priority to traffic capacity and low cost above other values, and designed urban freeways with minimal landscaping and aesthetic quality. Bassett's expectation proved wrong. Urban freeways lowered residential property values; at worst, they blighted entire communities.[93]

Thomas MacDonald and Roosevelt's Interstates

No individual had a greater influence on American highways than the civil engineer and career administrator Thomas H. MacDonald (1881–1957). He was chief of the US Bureau of Public Roads (and its alternately named iterations) for 34 years, from 1919 to 1953, serving seven presidential administrations. He oversaw the construction of the National Highway System in the 1920s and established the guiding vision for the Interstate Freeway System in the 1930s and 1940s. During his tenure, the car-based society evolved from a exploding phenomenon to a firmly entrenched regime. The US highway system today is a reflection of MacDonald's priorities, perspectives, and preferences.

MacDonald grew up in the small town of Montezuma, Iowa, and as a teen worked in his father's lumber and grain store. He studied civil engineering at Iowa State College and wrote his thesis on highway construction methods specific to the state. In 1904 the Iowa legislature created the State Highway Commission as a research unit within the college. The dean chose MacDonald to handle day-to-day operations.

The commission was essentially a college extension service and MacDonald was its only employee for the first seven years. He traveled the state and consulted on projects when asked, ran research and educational programs, and issued pamphlets on construction methods and good roads. He developed a reputation for sound engineering advice and high integrity. On occasion, he uncovered corruption in road projects, and his findings sent local politicians to jail.[94]

Relative to other state highway departments, Iowa's commission was small and weak. Through most of the 1910s, it did not control road-building funds and its only power was the authority to approve plans and enforce uniform standards. Road-building power in Iowa was decentralized among the county engineers. Perhaps as a result, MacDonald developed a collaborative leadership style based on professional partnerships and consultation. That style, combined with the commission's strict quality-control work, was very successful. The commission boasted that it maintained road standards that were more uniform than those of any other state. And the people of Iowa responded by purchasing cars at an unprecedented rate: from 1915 to 1918, Iowa ranked first among US states in motor vehicles per capita.[95]

Although Iowa was a predominantly rural state, MacDonald's commission did make recommendations for urban policy and legislation. The commission called for county roads to extend into and through small towns. It said the construction of main routes leading into city business districts was one of the most serious street problems of larger towns and cities. The problem of deficient roads was also acute in suburban areas, and the commission said the highways leading into every large city must be permanently improved.[96]

The American Association of State Highway Officials (AASHO) was formed in 1914 and MacDonald, as a member of its executive committee, became involved in federal policy. He led the AASHO group that drafted federal road legislation based on the ideas of his friend Logan Page, head of the federal Office of Public Roads. That draft became the 1916 Federal-Aid Highway Act, and AASHO and its ally the American Automobile Association dominated the successful effort to pass it. The Act gave the federal government a lead role in funding and oversight of the nation's highways, and enshrined the state highway departments' authority over planning and construction.[97]

When the position of director of the federal Bureau of Public Roads (BPR) became available in 1919, AASHO recommended MacDonald for the job. One of his first actions was to change his title to "Chief," and for the rest of his career, he was called "Chief" by his colleagues as well as presidents, senators, and other luminaries. MacDonald was a reserved, formal man who quietly prized status and authority. At home, his family called him "Sir" or "Mr. MacDonald." As BPR's chief, he built a substantial power base outside of government. His network of allied interests included automakers, road builders, highway officials, auto clubs, and chambers of commerce. It provided a potent combination of money, political sway, and technical expertise.[98]

MacDonald, in close partnership with state highway departments, embarked on the vast multi-decade task of planning and building a national highway system. The government could fund only a fraction of all road-building requests, so he tightened the standards that determined which roads were eligible for funding. At the same time, he shoveled money to the states as fast as they could spend it. The results were stupendous. By 1931, BPR had distributed over $1 billion to the states and had built or improved 89,000 miles (143,000 km) of highways. Of the total, some 37,000 miles (60,000 km), or 42 percent, were paved.[99]

The early federal-aid highway system was wholly rural because BPR was prohibited from spending money on urban highways. But BPR was quite interested in studying urban traffic, and its findings suggested that federal funds ought to be distributed very differently. MacDonald reported the studies' general conclusions in 1925. The traffic importance of highways provided "the only proper index for the distribution of highway funds"—and the most important traffic routes were those in densely populated areas and intensive industrial areas. Major highways entering large cities were necessary, as were belt (circumferential) highways encircling them. The long-distance portion of highway traffic was relatively minor: "Highway traffic, both of passenger cars and motor trucks, is predominantly local in nature," MacDonald wrote. MacDonald would continue to argue these points throughout the 1930s and 1940s. They would become the basic principles of nation's urban freeway system.[100]

BPR and Limited Access

MacDonald was also an enthusiast of limited-access motor parkways. In 1924 he observed that the public was using parkways for the utilitarian purpose of avoiding congested city streets. That might "invade violently" the original intent of the parkways, but MacDonald found it "very much more encouraging" that the "big visioned" parkways were operating as fast traffic conduits. He recommended a regional spider-web (radial-circumferential) pattern of high-speed parkways, saying it was "the only way traffic congestion will ever be solved." MacDonald admitted that his vision would be expensive but felt the expenditures would prove "sane and worthwhile" because of the parkways' many benefits, which included congestion relief, traffic safety, increased property values, beautification of cities and towns, and better living conditions in suburbs.[101]

BPR got its opportunity to build a parkway when the US Congress decided to commemorate George Washington's birthday bicentennial with a new road. The Mount Vernon Memorial Highway, covering 15 miles (24 km) from the District of Columbia to Washington's historic estate, was authorized in May 1928. That summer, BPR designers toured various East Coast parkways and chose the Westchester County parkways as the best model. In May 1929 MacDonald hired Jay Downer, Gilmore D. Clarke, and two other Westchester personnel as consultants. Construction began in October 1929 and the parkway opened in January 1932. Access was limited along much of the route, while a few minor road crossings were at-grade. Commercial traffic was banned, but the parkway did have public bus stops.

BPR rigorously documented every stage of development and disseminated the information in a flood of articles, exhibits, agency publications, and tours. The Memorial Highway became better known than the Westchester parkways. Its influence persisted for years, owing to BPR's promotion, and one of its main impacts was to institutionalize the limited-access highway concept within BPR.[102]

When Edward M. Bassett invented the term *freeway* in 1930, he noted the lack of enabling legislation. Various initiatives soon began trying to rectify that lack. In January 1933, a bill was introduced in the California legislature to enable freeways. It used Bassett's definition, allowed any roadway to become a freeway, and permitted any crossing road to be closed off. The bill was blocked by rural legislators.[103]

BPR was an early proponent of the freeway concept, and in 1934 it wrote a summary of freeway principles to serve as a basis for legislation. It too used Bassett's definition, and said the New York law that enabled parkways in Westchester County provided the most helpful model. Also in 1934, a freeway bill was introduced in the Connecticut legislature.[104]

The Restriction of Ribbon Development Act, adopted in the United Kingdom in 1935, established another legal model. Professionals, reformers, and members of Parliament agreed that ribbon (strip) development along suburban highways had to be regulated. They argued that it caused congestion, crashes, and social and community fragmentation. The Act gave highway authorities the power to prohibit new means of access on 33,000 miles (53,000 km) of major highways, although it did not allow them to close off existing means of access. Application of the Act was slow and piecemeal, and some highway authorities granted access requests quite freely. Critics said ribbon development paid for the roads it lined, which created an incentive to perpetuate it.[105]

In America by 1936, six states were considering legislation. On 19 April 1937, New York became the first state to pass a law enabling freeways. Rhode Island followed a week later. Rhode Island's law was more broadly and clearly phrased; it specified that both new and existing roads could be designated as limited access, and that existing access rights could be extinguished by the government.[106]

By 1943, seventeen states had passed freeway-enabling laws and six were considering legislation. But despite the improving legal context, the total mileage of limited-access facilities was relatively tiny. About 315 miles (507 km) of parkways and freeways had been completed in US metropolitan areas by 1943. A remarkable two-thirds of that mileage was located in the New York metropolitan area. In comparison, the nation had 32,100 miles (51,660 km) of state highways running through municipalities, 12,500 (20,120 km) of which were three or more lanes wide.[107]

In early 1943, MacDonald's agency issued a model law that was a composite of existing state laws. It had a strong influence on subsequent state laws, which were more comprehensive and gave more jurisdictions more power to limit access on more types of roadways.[108]

BPR and Urban Freeways

Automobile use reached record highs in the mid-1930s, yet the national economy was mired in the doldrums. The demand for federal highway spending outstripped BPR's foreseeable budget. Choices had to be made, and interest groups pushed differing ideas about the top spending priorities. Rural officials wanted more spending on rural roads. Many US officials and highway boosters wanted a transcontinental system similar to Hitler's autobahns, and President Roosevelt supported that idea with enthusiasm. MacDonald and his allies in the motor industries believed the top funding priorities were the same as those identified a decade earlier: major highways through and around cities.[109]

MacDonald had long felt that research data and expert planning were the best means to resolve contentious policy issues. So in 1936, BPR launched a program of state traffic surveys to set funding priorities and forecast future needs. Forty states performed surveys according to BPR's uniform guidelines (and after 1938 Congress required the remaining eight states to participate). The nation was able to make a portrait, for the first time, of the origins, destinations, and volumes of traffic on its major highways.[110]

In 1937 President Roosevelt asked MacDonald for a study of a transcontinental toll-highway system, and Congress made a similar request the following year. BPR completed the report titled *Toll Roads and Free Roads* in 1939. Half of it explained why a system of toll highways would not serve the nation's needs. The other half laid out a vision of an extensive system of free highways, based on the state traffic surveys. The surveys indicated that the great majority of highway traffic in and near cities was local. For example, in Baltimore 86 percent of highway traffic entering the city was daily local trips; in Washington, DC, the figure was 89 percent.[111]

Therefore, *Toll Roads and Free Roads* proposed a fundamental shift in the nation's highway policy. Previously, rural service had been the foremost concern. Now the first priority was limited-access express highways leading into city centers in a radial pattern. The second priority was belt (circumferential) express highways for all large cities and many small cities. Like the radial highways, their main purpose was to serve local trips within metropolitan areas. MacDonald appeased other interest groups by making intercity highways the third priority and reconstruction of rural highways the fourth priority. Limited access on rural routes was needed to prevent ribbon development, BPR argued.[112]

Toll Roads and Free Roads took an extremely aggressive approach to urban reconstruction. The automobile had encouraged the middle class to decamp for the suburbs, leaving central-city areas to the lower classes. Those so-called blighted areas were deemed suitable for express-highway routes. Using Baltimore as an example, BPR stated that "the whole interior of the city is ripe for the major change that it must undergo" to adapt to twentieth-century traffic. Only the unfettered circulation of traffic on express highways would stop the decay of city business districts. Traditional street grids were described as archaic.[113]

But BPR's position on urban regeneration was opportunistic and contradictory. In some blighted areas, it noted, "substantial new properties of various sorts are beginning to rise." There was a "growing danger" that these buildings would block future express highway routes. Therefore, new routes had to be planned quickly, before further regeneration took place. Inner-belt expressways could be built in the "ring of decadent property surrounding the central business area."[114]

Figure 6.12: According to BPR, this was a "decadent area" that needed to be replaced by a freeway. Note the curtained windows, active retail, and several pedestrians, all Black.

In large cities, nothing less than fully grade-separated highways would suffice to carry masses of daily local traffic throughout the city and into its heart. BPR was writing at a time when only a handful of states had passed freeway enabling laws, so it made recommendations similar to those of the Regional Plan of New York. Limited-access highways in large cities should be elevated or depressed; the latter was preferred. Outstanding examples of the needed city improvements, in terms of both design and execution, included Manhattan's West Side Elevated Highway, Robert Moses's Henry Hudson Parkway, and the Westchester County parkways.[115]

Paul G. Hoffman, president of the Studebaker auto company and head of the Automotive Safety Foundation, said the significance of BPR's report could not be overemphasized. He covered it in the *Saturday Evening Post*, a popular national magazine, using language that was blunt and aggressive. "Chief MacDonald insists that we must dream of gashing our way rather ruthlessly through built-up sections of overcrowded cities, in order to create traffic ways capable of carrying the traffic with safety, facility, reasonable speed," Hoffman reported. MacDonald's statements were equally blunt. "We are trampling on tradition," he said proudly. Continuing to use "streets that grew up from cowpaths," said MacDonald, "would only prolong the agony. No city can be said to be equipped for the motor age unless all of its express highways are some type of limited-way facility."[116]

Toll Roads and Free Roads did not quell dissent among highway advocates as MacDonald hoped. Strenuous debate continued for another seventeen years about the priorities and funding of the national system. "Yet even though no one realized it," observed the historian Bruce Seely, "BPR's 1939 report had laid the groundwork for a future consensus on American highway policy." With the help of his allies, MacDonald advanced BPR's positions until they became mainstream and broadly accepted.

President Roosevelt created the National Interregional Highway Committee in April 1941 to flesh out the details of a national freeway system. MacDonald was the chair and G. Donald Kennedy was the vice-chair. Kennedy was a highway engineer, the head of the Michigan State Highway Department, and the president of AASHO. To represent the urban planning perspective, Roosevelt appointed Harland Bartholomew, Rexford Tugwell, and his uncle Frederic Delano. But BPR determined the final outcome in all important respects.[117]

The *Interregional Highways* report was mostly finished by November 1941 and was submitted to Congress in 1944. It recommended a total system length of 39,000 miles (62,800 km). About 7,300 miles (11,700 km), or 19 percent, were routes in cities and large towns (those with population over 10,000). The urban mileage was a small portion of the total, but urban expressways were the most elaborate and expensive. The report recommended spending $750 million annually to build the interregional system: one-third for the rural sections; two-thirds for the urban sections.[118]

The report elaborated the guidelines for routing expressways through cities. Most cities had "fingers" of development along older highways and "wedges" of undeveloped land between them, which extended from central areas to suburban fringes. The wedges could be the best locations for expressways to enter the city because the land was cheap and easy to acquire. Other routes along riverbanks and railways offered the advantage of near-total access control on one side. The report also repeated the reasoning made by the Bronx Parkway Commission thirty years earlier. Small stream valleys offered excellent opportunities for expressways to penetrate the city. In some cases, they were "neighborhoods of cheap, run-down houses and shacks, abject poverty, squalor, and filth" whose eradication would only benefit the community.[119]

Although the report recommended both depressed and elevated expressways in large cities, it accentuated the drawbacks of elevated expressways. They created divisions between communities and acted as psychological barriers. Cramped conditions underneath their decks tended to impair local traffic. They were acceptable only in commercial districts and were aesthetically undesirable other parts of the city, such as residential areas.[120]

The report acknowledged that urban expressways generally had negative impacts, but asserted that proper design could fix those problems. Adequately landscaped borders would "insulate adjacent residential and business properties, churches, and schools from the noise, dust, and fumes of traffic." When urban expressways were well designed and landscaped, they would become "not the unsightly and obstructive gashes feared by some—but rather elongated parks bringing to the inner city a welcome addition of beauty, grace, and open green space." A reader could conclude that a happier urban destiny would thus triumph.[121]

The recommendations of *Interregional Highways* were widely supported by state highway engineers and city officials. In 1944, Congress put many of the recommendations into law and established the 40,000-mile (64,400-km) Interstate Highway System. BPR and AASHO worked together to create the system's design standards, which were adopted in 1945. The standards recommended limited access everywhere that it was legally and economically possible. In the years after the war, when car sales and car-oriented suburbs were booming, Congress authorized hundreds of millions of dollars for urban highways. From 1943 to 1954 the mileage of limited-access highways (both urban and rural) increased more than fivefold. During the same period, an additional 22 states adopted limited-access laws to enable that increase.[122]

Opposition to urban freeways during those years was minor but vocal. Opponents complained that freeway construction razed large numbers of dwellings, eliminating stocks of much-needed housing. They said depressed freeways disrupted communities and created barriers between neighborhoods. Above all, urban freeways cost too much.

MacDonald refuted the objections. He said that expressways usually passed through blighted areas where "most of the buildings are of the type that should be torn down in any case, to rid the city of its slums." MacDonald rejected the notion that depressed freeways created barriers. Overpasses that bridged the freeways provided fast links and increased "the ease of communication and business interchange between adjacent neighborhoods." He said the cost of urban freeways was outweighed by the benefits they provided. They would speed traffic, reduce congestion, and improve safety. They would help stop the decay of city centers and the spread of blighted areas.[123]

Speaking to the American Society of Civil Engineers, MacDonald explained how freeways would alter urban form. Interstate freeways, in combination with similar expressways, would restructure cities according to the cellular principle. They would "provide the occasion for the remodeling of the city—now more or less an amorphous mass—and for converting it into an orderly arrangement of neighborhood cells." Furthermore, MacDonald believed that the conversion into cellular layouts was a matter of life and death for cities. The Interstate System, he said, "may well constitute the key to the functional rebuilding of our cities. But the cities themselves must recognize that while that opportunity is at hand, they must exploit it to the fullest if they are to survive." Over the following years, engineers, interest groups, and state and federal officials instituted the rules and standards necessary to realize MacDonald's forecast.[124]

MacDonald devoted more than a decade to formulating and promoting BPR's Interstate System vision. (He retired in 1953 to College Station, Texas, and joined the Texas Transportation Institute.) When the pressure to accelerate and fund the national system reached a critical level of urgency in 1956, there was no other plan available with as much political support, industry consensus, research, and promotional effort behind it. MacDonald had made his plan the default, and it significantly shaped the Federal-Aid Highway Act of 1956 in terms of funding priorities and planning principles.

The 1956 Act required uniform design standards for the entire Interstate System. Once again, BPR and AASHO collaborated to write the standards. One major standard was the requirement that all interstate freeways be limited access. A few states still had not passed freeway enabling laws, while others had passed laws that were too weak and slow for the Interstate System's construction schedule. So the 1956 Act allowed the federal government to take property and access rights from landowners and convey them to the states. A few of the lagging states used that mechanism, but most passed access-control legislation that allowed the interstate freeway construction to proceed apace.[125]

The mileage of federally funded freeways increased from 4,000 (6,400 km) in 1956 to 41,000 (66,000 km) in 1970. About 7,400 miles (11,900 km), or 20 percent, were located in urban areas. The 1970 statistics were remarkably close to the numbers that MacDonald and the Interregional Highway Committee had proposed in 1944.[126]

Urban freeways rumbled through the nation's cities like an avalanche, causing much destruction and leaving long-lasting scars. They eradicated many viable urban neighborhoods, usually communities of racial and ethnic minorities. They devastated large tracts of parkland and other natural environments. They often formed permanent divisions and barriers, and tended to degrade the adjacent pre-existing neighborhoods. Rather than save central cities, the freeways accelerated middle-class flight and sub-urbanization. In suburbs, sprawling tangles of freeway infrastructure scattered and divided nearby new development. Today, Americans are not necessarily pleased with the quality of urban environments near freeways, but the system is in place, heavily used, and difficult to reform.[127]

Chapter 6 Summary

A segment of human society, especially teenage to middle-age males, has always been entranced with speed and its overtones of aggression and conquest. Road racing was one way to satisfy those desires, particularly in America where trotting was the most popular sport during much of the nineteenth century. The functions of fast roadways and divided roadways sometimes overlapped in service to road racing. For instance, many of the parkways designed or inspired by Olmsted and Vaux served as speed-driving facilities.

Speedways arose in the United States in the 1890s and were ubiquitous in large US cities by first decade of twentieth century. They generally banned slow traffic and pedestrians, and some featured both grade-separated intersections and limited access. The 1895 design of the Bronx's Grand Concourse prefigured freeway geometry. It had entry ramps and viaducts on elevated sweeping curves, and cut a sinuous route through the surrounding street grid. In 1902 the New Jersey legislature authorized speedways throughout the state. It was perhaps the first law anywhere to authorize limited-access public thoroughfares.

The Long Island Motor Parkway grew from road racing, and was designed for racing and touring. It was a toll road with features such as limited access, vehicular exclusions, high-speed geometry, and fenced right-of-ways. A short distance to the northwest, in Westchester County, a system of parkways opened to traffic beginning in 1921. Its designers said the system would shape future growth and open vast areas to upper-income, auto-dependent development. The parkways were admired by engineers and officials around the world, and notably were copied by the US federal government.

Robert Moses, with the full support of Governor (and later President) Franklin Roosevelt, launched a parkway-system construction blitz in New York City in 1931. By the early 1940s, he had installed more miles of limited-access highways than existed in any other city in the world, by far. And in 1930, Edward Bassett invented the legal concept of the freeway and called for its authorization nationwide. By 1943 seventeen states had legalized freeways. The laws affected the type and design of urban express-ways that were built in the United States, and helped end the urban parkway era.

Thomas H. MacDonald, chief of the US Bureau of Public Roads for 34 years, established the guiding vision for the US Interstate Freeway System. By 1925, if not earlier, he believed that highways penetrating city centers were the most important traffic priority. He believed that freeways and expressways would restructure cities according to the cellular principle, and felt that such restructuring was a matter of life and death for cities.

Engineers, officials, automakers, and allied business interests couched their advocacy for high-speed expressways in terms of efficiency, economy, convenience, safety, congestion reduction, and prosperity. But next to that realm of rationality and dispassion was an entirely dissimilar realm of turbulent, sublime emotions. Salespeople, advertisers, literary writers, filmmakers, and other cultural observers explored and exploited the psychological and sensual appeals of fast driving.

From the 1890s to World War I, the speeding car became an object of fantasy. It offered sensations of adventure and flying, and associations with lust, eroticism, aggression, and conquest. It aroused the macho celebration of danger and near-death, and a fascination with cruel violence. As the historian Gijs Mom described, it provided a "mixture of fear and rush that led to a multisensorial transcendent experience." After World War I, car culture was domesticated and its blatantly violent aspects were tamed or hidden. Highway cruising was described as dreamlike or similar to flying; the nearby objects that ordinarily provided visual speed cues were removed, creating a sensation of hypnotic slowness at high speed. Automobile speed was advertised as a hedonistic indulgence in sensations of fun and power.[128]

During the 1930s, support for urban freeways burgeoned among state and federal officials. Downtown business interests, automakers, road builders, and driving enthusiasts led calls for an ambitious government construction program. A small minority of planners, engineers, and transit spokesmen expressed doubts. They argued that urban freeways were prohibitively expensive, would displace thousands of residents, and would degrade the quality and character of urban environments. They said freeways would neither solve congestion nor halt the emptying of city centers.

The objecting voices were overpowered by widespread support from government, professional organizations, automakers, the highway lobby, downtown business interests, and many motorists. America decided that uninterrupted high speed should be the top priority in urban roadway planning. Cities were retrofitted to accommodate fast traffic, and new suburban roadway networks were designed for fast traffic first and foremost. The American obsession with fast urban auto traffic was also exported worldwide. It had the greatest direct influence in Latin American cities and various European suburbs. Since the 1990s, China has undertaken huge programs of urban arterial and expressway construction, and the size of those systems may eventually surpass the size of US systems.[129]

CHAPTER 7
Blending and Winnowing

The first six chapters of this book cover different types of functional traffic separation: vertical separation, divided roadways, insular roadways, and fast roadways. Until the early twentieth century, the advocacy for those different types tended to be distinct. For example, those who advocated vertical separation tended to favor urban centralization and greater building density, while those who advocated horizontal separation tended to favor decentralization and reduced density. Another example can be found in the advocacy for insular and fast roadways. The designers who advocated insular residential roadways tended to have different sensibilities and goals than the racers who pushed for urban speedways.

In the early and mid-twentieth century, those various strands became more blended. Planners, designers, and engineers drew from the established body of traffic-separation ideas to assemble new combinations. They borrowed and mixed freely to create new traffic-planning practices that would respond to mass auto ownership and stimulate ever more auto use.

Regional Plan of New York

Charles Norton, the civic-minded businessman who had initiated the Chicago Plan, moved to New York in 1911 to work as a bank executive. He volunteered for many civic groups and causes, one of which was a city advisory committee concerned with land planning. Norton believed that planning should encompass the entire region. "Let some Daniel H. Burnham do for this immense community what Burnham did for Chicago and its environs," he urged in 1915. He wanted the committee to lead a large public-private planning initiative that would study the region for at least five years. But Norton's ambitions were blocked by political opposition, and the committee was disbanded in 1917.[1]

Norton got another chance the following year when he joined the Russell Sage Foundation's board. The foundation was a philanthropic organization charged with a mission of social reform; it generally operated in the fields of housing, social work, and public health. It had first gotten involved in land planning when it developed Forest Hills Gardens in the Brooklyn suburbs.

The foundation's president asked Norton to suggest new projects. Norton gave the board his regional-plan proposal. The board was chary of the scale and cost of the initiative, so in 1920 it approved a small sum for preliminary study. Frederic A. Delano, who had worked with Norton in Chicago, joined the foundation's board at the same time. Finally, in May 1921, the board granted full funding to the Regional Plan of New York and Its Environs (RPNY) initiative. Norton and Delano were once again paired on a major multiyear city-planning effort.[2]

Early news articles reported that RPNY's goal was to deconcentrate and decongest the city. It wanted to encourage a constellation of self-contained yet economically linked community units in the wide-open suburbs. RPNY invited Raymond Unwin to give a consultation, so Unwin traveled to New York in September 1922 for a ten-day work session. Unwin said that deconcentration of population and jobs was "the main hope of relief" for traffic congestion, and that without deconcentration, "the evil may well reach quite unmanageable proportions." His vision called for new "suburbs, satellite towns, or garden cities, which should be as self-contained as possible." In regard to roadway design, he advised minimizing the number of at-grade intersections on main routes. He said RPNY itself should build a garden suburb that would "enormously stimulate public opinion" by demonstrating town amenities and satisfactory workers' housing.[3]

But RPNY was too big and diverse to follow the garden-city program exclusively. It gathered many leading figures from the fields of planning, engineering, architecture, transportation, housing, and economics to contribute to the effort. The advisors and staff had a wide range of opinions about regional planning. Some favored deconcentration into new, relatively self-sufficient garden cities. Others favored continued growth in high-density areas, new skyscrapers, and vertical traffic-separation schemes. The final plan reflected this variety of uncoordinated and sometimes-conflicting propositions.

Charles Norton died of influenza in 1923. Delano took over as chairman, but because he was unable to work full-time on RPNY, he named Thomas Adams as director. Adams was an accomplished planner and manager who had served as secretary of the British Garden Cities Association, co-founded the British Town Planning Institute, and founded the Town Planning Institute of Canada. Adams served as RPNY's director until 1931, which was long enough to shepherd the plan to completion.

Adams ran RPNY as a conciliatory mediator, always striving for an inclusive middle ground among the plan's many skilled and powerful contributors. Unlike a standard city plan, RPNY's plan was indefinite; Adams said that was good, because indefiniteness allowed flexibility. The plan was reactive rather than proactive. It followed existing trends rather than blazing new ones.[4]

RPNY's copiously detailed background studies were released in eight "Regional Survey" volumes from 1927 to 1929. The final plan was released as two volumes in 1929 and 1931. It was a large, wide-ranging compendium of ideas that addressed the region's needs through the year 1965. In regard to roadways, it recommended vertical traffic separation for Manhattan locations, and horizontal traffic separation for newly developing suburbs. It was the first time that hyperurban and deconcentration proposals were brought together in a comprehensive regional plan.

In its discussion of Manhattan, the final plan reviewed multilevel proposals from the past sixty years. It showed numerous schemes that were similar to C. McKnight Smith's street sections, and even reprinted the Broadway Arcade Railway illustration of 1868. Based on its review, the plan recommended a collection of networks to relieve congestion. It recommended elevated highways along the riverfronts; underground, depressed, and elevated expressways inland; and a system of elevated pedestrian arcades in Midtown (using the 1923 template and illustrations created by Corbett and Ferriss). It stated that multilevel solutions should be used only in existing high-intensity areas. The plan argued that multilevel highways were unjustified in redeveloping areas and suburbs; it noted that the West Side Elevated Highway cost eleven times more per mile than a surface parkway in Westchester County.[5]

At the regional scale, the plan recommended a network of limited-access expressways that would criss-cross the region in a large grid, and also traverse Manhattan. Some existing neighborhoods would be demolished to make way for the new expressways. The expressways would run on the surface, buffered by access lanes; or would be elevated or depressed below grade. The Route 1 Extension was an "excellent example." The plan also recommended an extensive regional parkway network that was modeled on Westchester County's parkways.[6]

If the plan's catholic, pragmatic approach to traffic planning resembled the perspective of any one contributor, it was that of the civil engineer and city planner Ernest P. Goodrich. During the 1910s, Goodrich had advocated both vertical and horizontal traffic separation. He had called for skywalks and tunnelwalks in Manhattan, and supported elevated roadways in dense districts. For lower-density districts, he had advocated the horizontal segregation of autos, trucks, and rapid transit on dedicated lanes or dedicated thoroughfares. Goodrich co-wrote RPNY's Regional Survey volume on highway traffic and was RPNY's consultant on traffic studies; his perspective informed the final recommendations.[7]

For new construction in outlying areas, RPNY's final plan recommended Radburn-type residential areas in garden cities and suburbs. The plan described Radburn with approval, especially its traffic-separation scheme. Indeed, Alexander Bing had invited Thomas Adams to consult on Radburn in early 1928, and Adams had taken an active role during the planning phase.[8]

As lead author of RPNY's final plan, Adams commented on the "impossible utopias" envisioned by grandiose planners and criticized the political arrangements they would require. That seemed to refer especially to Le Corbusier and his perfectly immutable schemes of large-scale city replacement. "The world would be poorer without these pictures of utopias, but every one has to be examined in the light of reality," Adams warned. "A utopia can be achieved only on a basis of despotism." But Adams also expected that utopian visions would continue to influence development patterns, resulting in both deconcentration and hyperurbanization:

> It is probable, therefore, that the utopia of the perfect "garden city" will influence future urban growth in the New York region at least as much as the utopia of the perfect "skyscraper city" and that the expansion of the city-region will evolve along lines that will show an attempt, at least, to embrace the best features of both.[9]

Influence of the Plan

Although the RPNY committee was a nongovernmental organization, it hoped the breadth and detail of its plan, the aptness of its ideas, and the expertise of its members would persuade officials and the public to follow its recommendations. RPNY was widely hailed as the largest and most thoroughly researched regional plan yet made, and it exerted a powerful influence on American urban planning and theory. The historian David Johnson wrote that the plan's ideas "altered the way American urbanists looked at their large cities and imagined their futures."[10]

Governor and soon-to-be-president Franklin D. Roosevelt attended the celebration dinner for the plan's completion in December 1931. Roosevelt spoke fondly of "the days nearly twenty years ago when Mr. Norton and my uncle, Mr. Delano, first talked to me about regional planning for the city of Chicago. I think from that very moment I have been interested not in the planning of any one mere city but in planning in its larger aspects." Roosevelt concluded by saying that "this regional plan will mark, I have no doubt, the foundation on which all building in the future will be based."[11]

The ideas and techniques introduced by RPNY spread rapidly to planning efforts in other cities as well as academic realms. Traffic engineers noticed too. Over the following decades, elements of RPNY's highway-planning process were refined and used in state and federal highway planning.[12]

Many cities looked to New York and the Regional Plan as guides for their own futures. In the dense, compact downtown they would build towers, streets dedicated to fast traffic, and grade-separated pedestrian facilities. Outside of downtown, they would create low-density development that hewed to the cellular neighborhood-unit model. A network of limited-access expressways would tie the region together. In suburbs, the expressways would run on the surface, creating barriers between communities and different land uses. In central districts, the expressways would be lifted on viaducts or dropped below grade to slash through industrial areas and wipe out "blighted" neighborhoods. That bifurcated regional pattern became the standard prescription for urban prosperity and improved quality of life, and was vigorously promoted by various US federal government agencies.

Paul Hoffman and Miller McClintock

Paul Gray Hoffman (1891–1974) was an auto industry executive and a leader in the traffic-safety field during the 1930s and 1940s. He established several organizations that helped determine the principles and practices of US traffic planning well into the 1960s and beyond.

Hoffman grew up in Western Springs, Illinois, which was an upper-middle-class railroad suburb of Chicago. He was a sociable and self-confident man, cheerful and optimistic in nature. He attended the University of Chicago in 1908 and enjoyed his fraternity and social life, but the classwork bored him and his professors did not encourage him to continue. Despite that experience, he always respected scholarly research. Later in his life, when he was developing plans and policies, he typically began by commissioning a study to understand the facts of the situation.[13]

Hoffman left college at age eighteen and within two years was earning a comfortable salary as a Studebaker car salesman. He followed his family to Southern California in 1911, where he continued to work for Studebaker and rose swiftly to the position of sales manager for Los Angeles and Orange counties. During World War I, he joined the Army as a private and completed his service as a first lieutenant. He returned to Los Angeles and in 1919 decided to go into business for himself. The Studebaker Corporation tried to keep him on the company payroll, offering to put him on the board of directors and make him manager of the New York City distributorship (the company's largest). But Hoffman told company president Albert Erskine that he wanted to purchase the Los Angeles distributorship. Erskine agreed.

His advance was meteoric. He opened six dealerships in the first few years and by 1925 was a millionaire. His operation was Studebaker's second largest, selling four thousand vehicles annually. His success was partly a result of his outstanding personal skills in sales and management. Hoffman had a quality of decency and sincerity about him. He held a lifelong belief that corporate profits and the public welfare were compatible, and that automobility was not only beneficial to the greater good of society, but necessary to the American way of life.[14]

He was a great believer in advertising and was quick to try innovative methods. With a $35,000 investment, he helped launch one of the first radio stations in the city. KNX radio, "the voice of Hollywood," was broadcast from Hoffman's showroom on Hollywood Boulevard. Hoffman's success was also a matter of being in the right place at the right time. Automobile sales were surging nationwide and Los Angeles was a leader. From 1920 to 1930 the number of registered cars in Los Angeles County multiplied more than fivefold, and during most of that decade the city had the highest rate of car ownership in the United States. But while Hoffman was busy amassing a personal fortune, serious problems for the auto industry threatened to disrupt the boom.[15]

Efficiency vs. Expansion

Until the 1910s in America, city dwellers shared an understanding about the use of roadway space. Roadway space was available to all on equal terms, with the exception of certain boulevards and speedways. Pedestrians, animal-drawn carriages and carts, cycles, streetcars, and motor vehicles possessed equal rights to use the entire right-of-way. Delivery wagons parked in front of any business. Peddlers set up shop by the side of the street. Pedestrians tended to keep to the sidewalk, but were free to walk in the street, or simply stand and talk in the street. "Under this construction of the city street," wrote the historian Peter Norton, "even children at play could be legitimate street users, and even careful motorists were under suspicion."[16]

That historical regime came into direct conflict with mass motorization. Officials and engineers noticed a quantum change in traffic conditions in the mid-1910s. Twice-daily traffic jams appeared in every large American city during the summers of 1914 and 1915. Traffic was moving faster, but at certain times and locations it was more liable to congeal. The term *traffic jam* originated during this period.[17]

City engineers of the period believed that roadways should be managed to maximize the public good for the greatest number of people. Roadway space was necessarily limited, so traffic should be regulated to use every square foot as efficiently as possible.

TRAFFIC CONGESTION IS YOUR PROBLEM

STREET cars, motor cars, busses, trucks, taxis, pedestrians — all struggling through the same narrow street. Subways years distant. Street widening impractical. Immediate relief demanded. What is the answer?

First, *get the right point of view*. Traffic congestion is a public problem. It will be solved, not by favoring one type of vehicle at the expense of another, but by utilizing all types — street cars, motor cars, busses, taxis, trucks — each where most useful to the public.

Take street cars as one illustration. The more congested the area, the more efficient street cars become — *provided free from interference by other vehicles*.

In the Loop district of Chicago, for example, street cars form 2 per cent of a day's traffic, yet haul 74 per cent of the passengers; in down-town Baltimore they form 14 per cent of rush-hour traffic, yet haul 89 per cent of the passengers; in down-town Los Angeles, they form 4 per cent of rush hour traffic, yet haul 66 per cent of the passengers.

Such being the case, it's an obvious betterment to restrict parking on crowded car lines, and to segregate or reroute vehicles so as to facilitate car movements. Such improvements speed up vehicles. They shorten street car and motor coach schedules, make runs more regular, bring greater comfort, speed, and safety to the public.

Everybody depends on street cars — a large percentage directly, as the above figures show; the balance indirectly. Give the street car and the regular motor coach *room to give you better service.*

WESTINGHOUSE ELECTRIC & MANUFACTURING COMPANY   ·   *Offices in All Principal Cities*   ·   *Representatives Everywhere*
Tune in sometime with KDKA—KYW—WBZ—KFKX

Westinghouse

© 1924, by the Westinghouse Electric & Manufacturing Company

Figure 7.1: Westinghouse Electric Company, editorial ad for dedicated streetcar space, 1924. From the text: "Give the streetcar and the regular motor coach *room* to give you better service."

Engineers, police, and elected officials were often united in support of this approach, which was called *traffic control*. Chambers of commerce viewed it as pro-business.[18]

City engineers responded to rising city congestion with a range of traffic-control measures. They denied walkers their historical right to use the entire roadway, and restricted street crossings to crosswalks only. They restricted or banned on-street parking. Some motor-vehicle restrictions were more obtrusive, such as time-of-day limits on freight trucks, which were common in big-city downtowns. Some engineers and advocates made more radical proposals, urging that freight trucks or passenger autos, or both, should be banned at all times in congested districts. In addition, engineers and streetcar companies spotlighted the fact that autos needed much more space than streetcars to move an equal number of people. They contended that streetcars should have exclusive lanes and right-of-way priority.[19]

As the number of vehicles exploded, traffic fatalities did the same. Between 1914 and 1923, US traffic fatalities quadrupled and the per-capita traffic-fatality rate more than tripled. The shocking headlines about children, women, and seniors killed by cars sparked a nationwide grassroots safety movement in the early 1920s. Citizens protested and gathered in angry mobs. They held large memorial events and raised monuments to the dead. Autos were demonized in the press. Safety clubs demanded strict speed regulations, and police and public officials lent their support.[20]

Public anger about traffic deaths and injuries rose to such extreme levels that the auto industry believed its business was threatened. In 1923, safety activists in Cincinnati, Ohio, gathered 42,000 signatures for a referendum to require 25 mph (40 kmh) mechanical speed governors in all vehicles. A doctoral student named Miller McClintock, who was touring the nation's cities to research traffic-control methods, reported that "there is a widespread feeling that sooner or later the law will require that every vehicle be equipped with an automatic speed governor."[21]

More alarming than the safety battles was the slump in automobile sales from 1923 to 1924. Even though a national recession was affecting all sectors of the economy, the motor industry put the blame on downtown traffic congestion. Crowded city streets simply lacked room for new cars. The automakers believed that the lack of room was choking car sales. They felt that the traffic-control approach had failed to reduce congestion and now imperiled their survival. Downtown business owners, who had begun to lose market share to the suburbs, felt similarly.

The automobile and roadbuilding industries decided that the traffic-control approach was wholly unacceptable. They determined to institute a different philosophy based on the idea of market supply. According to this new model, cities should supply an unlimited amount of street space—whatever was needed to accommodate demand, no matter how inefficient that strategy might be. The industry coalesced into a unified lobbying force and overwhelmed the passionate yet uncoordinated voices calling for motor-vehicle restrictions (which included grassroots safety groups, streetcar companies, police, municipal engineers, and streetcar engineers). Using its superior funding, organization, and political connections, the industry elevated the market-supply philosophy to a cultural axiom.[22]

Charles Clifton, president of the National Automobile Chamber of Commerce, explained the philosophy in the pages of *Collier's* magazine. The traffic-control advocates "have forgotten the laws by which progress operates," he said. "The fact that traffic is congested means, not that traffic will be restricted, but that more facilities will be provided." Clifton thus presented roadway-space expansion as an outcome of natural law rather than a self-determined choice made by a city or community.[23]

Traffic experts completed scores of traffic congestion studies in the 1910s and 1920s, mainly funded by downtown business interests. Those who were oriented to the market-supply philosophy recommended that cities widen existing streets and carve new through streets. Many cities pursued that program with zeal. They condemned and demolished abutting properties to widen streets. They sacrificed landscaping, street trees, benches, and sidewalk space. By spending millions of dollars raised through bonds, special assessments, and vehicle taxes, US cities were able to accommodate many more automobiles by the end of the 1920s.[24]

Hoffman and McClintock in the 1920s

Paul Hoffman contributed to the effort in his home territory. In 1922 he co-founded a private organization of business interests named the Traffic Commission of the City and County of Los Angeles, and took command as its president. The commission hired Frederick Law Olmsted Jr., Harland Bartholomew, and Charles Cheney to formulate a street plan for the city.[25]

The trio of planners issued the *Major Traffic Street Plan* in 1924. It proposed a citywide program of street widening and new thoroughfares. It called for traffic separation to reduce the "promiscuous mixing" of traffic types. It proposed auto-only parkways, wide streets with streetcar lines, and streets designated for heavy-truck traffic. It claimed that concentrating fast through traffic on a few broad, straight thoroughfares would improve safety and reduce maintenance costs.[26]

Hoffman led the energetic and comprehensive campaign to adopt the plan. The Traffic Commission used billboards, theaters, newspapers, handbills, and even educational booklets handed out by Boy Scouts. With the solid support of the city's business establishment and other vested interests, Los Angeles adopted the street plan in 1924.[27]

The plan was more influential as a rhetorical device than as a shaper of the street network. Implementation was underfunded and piecemeal, and some attempts to construct new arterials and highways met with determined protest. But the mythos of Los Angeles as a uniquely car-oriented culture was mightily boosted by the publicity campaign for the *Major Traffic Street Plan*.[28]

In the midst of his Traffic Commission work, Hoffman met Miller McClintock. The Harvard doctoral student was on a research tour during the summer of 1923 and was invited to lecture to the commission. Evidently Hoffman was impressed. The following year, McClintock joined the commission's technical staff and drafted a new traffic code for Los Angeles, which was adopted immediately.[29]

McClintock's doctoral thesis, published as *Street Traffic Control* in 1925, became the leading traffic textbook of the 1920s. It was not an engineering text; rather, McClintock wrote in terms of administration and management. He argued for multilevel travelways as the "ultimate solution" to traffic conflicts. Ideally, motor vehicles, streetcars, and pedestrians each had their own grade-separated, dedicated facilities to achieve "complete segregation of the warring elements." But that was costly and infeasible for most cities. Therefore, McClintock recommended that streetcars should be given "reasonable right-of-way" in conflicting or congested conditions. Automobiles should have second priority. Pedestrians should have right of way only at crosswalks; otherwise they should be kept out of the street—preferably by physical barriers. In a 1924 lecture, McClintock forecast that within ten years, major express streets would be "as well protected against casual pedestrians as are some of our great railways at the present time."[30]

Bureau for Street Traffic Research

Hoffman was so successful in his many endeavors that the president of Studebaker, Albert Russell Erskine, brought him into the company's leadership. Hoffman became a vice president of Studebaker in 1925 and moved to South Bend, Indiana, where the company was headquartered. It was a prestigious assignment. In the early 1920s Studebaker was the nation's number-three automaker in terms of assets, and at its peak it ranked sixth in auto sales.[31]

One of Hoffman's first actions as an executive was to establish a corporate relationship with Miller McClintock. He called McClintock to Studebaker's headquarters and told him that the solution to traffic congestion would determine the ultimate future of the automobile. "Tell me just what I can do to help you," Hoffman said. "Make it possible for me to set up a traffic research bureau to train young men," McClintock answered. Hoffman arranged a $10,000 annual grant to support the Albert Russell Erskine Bureau for Street Traffic Research, which was headed by McClintock. The Bureau was based at UCLA for one year; then in 1926 Hoffman persuaded Harvard to host it. The Bureau systematized McClintock's traffic-planning principles and offered his program to cities nationwide.[32]

McClintock was soon in great demand as a traffic consultant. The Erskine Bureau produced street-traffic reports for large cities such as Chicago, San Francisco, Los Angeles, Boston, New Orleans, and Knoxville. The Bureau also trained several generations of traffic engineers. It was a key supplier of manpower to the profession, training 800 traffic engineers and transportation planners over its 57 years of existence.[33]

Inevitable Expressways

In the early 1920s, rebuilding cities with elaborate grade-separated pedestrian facilities and limited-access expressways was considered excessively difficult and costly. It was a goal for the far future. By the mid-1930s, many believed that urban expressways were not only feasible, they were necessary. It was a major shift in the mainstream vision for city streets, motivated by several factors.

One, the booming 1920s economy established a high level of government road-construction spending, auto sales, and corporate profits, which the motor and road-building industries dearly wanted to preserve. Two, only 11 percent of autos were located in big cities, compared to 17 percent of the population; automakers saw cities as the next great opportunity to expand sales. Three, downtown congestion remained as bad as ever. Four, the opening of limited-access roads in America and Europe was widely reported and excited further action. Five, Americans were enamored with future-city transportation ideas, especially those that had awe-inspiring visuals.[34]

As early as 1928, Miller McClintock was ready to declare that a new day had arrived. Grade separation of all major intersections on urban thoroughfares and highways was "a development that I should have looked upon as extremely visionary six or seven years ago, but which I think so inevitable now that I can speak about it with entire confidence." Urban elevated highways were equally inevitable, and examples like the $50 million Holland Tunnel complex "should give us an inspiration to have rather large visions for our own communities." In 1930 he assured readers that "the second-story sidewalk arcade with bridged intersections might have appeared as a fantastic dream a decade or less ago. Today it appears as a natural and logical development."[35]

McClintock in Chicago

McClintock's work in Chicago illustrated the shift in thinking. In 1925 the Chicago Plan Commission said that selected streets should be designated to form a citywide through-traffic network. Within a year, Chicago had created a network of 48 through-traffic streets. In 1926 McClintock wrote a lengthy report on new traffic regulations for the city. He recommended a "more drastic method of segregation" for the through-traffic streets: they should be reserved exclusively for fast auto traffic, while commercial traffic should be relegated to its own separate network. Meanwhile, the Chicago Plan Commission decided that a network of limited-access superhighways was needed. In 1927 the commission outlined a proposal for three or four superhighways radiating from the downtown Loop, as well as extensions of the two existing at-grade lakeshore parkways. At least one of the radiating superhighways, Avondale Avenue, would be elevated along its entire 10-mile (16-km) length. For nine of those miles, the super-highway would adjoin an elevated rail line and would make identical crossings over surface streets. The superhighway would be 160 feet (49 m) wide and would have center-median bus stops with passenger waiting platforms.[36]

Working as a consultant to the City of Chicago from 1931 to 1933, McClintock transformed the commission's sketch proposal into a complete plan. He recommended 160 miles (260 km) of fully grade-separated "limited ways" (his term for limited-access highways). Eleven elevated highways would crisscross the city or radiate from downtown, and the two existing lakeshore parkways would be extended. The limited

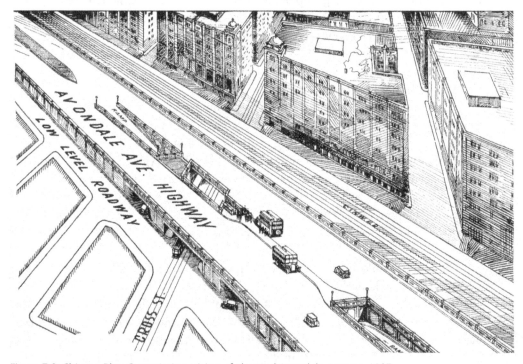

Figure 7.2: Chicago Plan Commission, vision of elevated Avondale Avenue, 1927.

ways would generally be restricted to passenger automobiles. Several elevated railways would be converted to elevated highways, which would produce less noise and no perceptible vibration. The elevated highways would not damage the amenities of any district; in fact, users would be wealthier than average, and therefore the limited ways would spur vigorous business growth. Limited ways would provide such great benefits that "an entirely new automotive era will be introduced."[37]

Hoffman pitched McClintock's limited-way plan in the *New York Times*. He said it was a "permanent solution of traffic congestion and hazards, and its adoption would completely revolutionize the use of motor vehicles in urban areas." Hoffman made no secret of his interest in promoting car sales, and never recognized any conflict between that position and the greater good of society.[38]

Through the 1930s, America's downtowns declined even as the larger economy showed signs of moderate recovery from the Great Depression. McClintock, his traffic-engineering colleagues, the motor industry, and the Bureau of Public Roads issued similar prescriptions for the economic woes of downtowns: limited-access expressways were needed. Downtown business interests came to agree. Limited-access expressways would speed commuters and shoppers from bedroom suburbs directly to downtown. They would clear away gridlock and make downtown businesses competitive again. Critics warned that those hopes were improbable, but the downtown boosters were desperate. "The downtown business interests did not know how much damage the freeways would do," wrote the historian Robert Fogelson, "but had they known, they would have supported them anyway."[39]

Founding of ITE

In the late 1920s, the small group of men who worked in the traffic-engineering field began to discuss the need for a professional organization. In the fall of 1930 they sought an official endorsement from the American Society of Civil Engineers. The ASCE refused, saying the traffic-engineering profession was not advanced enough. So the traffic engineers founded their own organization on the spot, and named it the Institute of Traffic Engineers (ITE).

ITE had an initial membership of thirty. The president was Ernest P. Goodrich, a civil engineer with an extensive background in city planning. He was a strong supporter of both horizontal and vertical traffic-separation techniques and had co-written RPNY's regional highway plan. Miller McClintock was vice-president. Burton W. Marsh, a civil engineer (and the first person ever to work as a full-time traffic engineer), was one of the two board directors. Paul Hoffman was a co-founder and later was named an honorary member. During its early years, ITE was housed in the offices of the National Conservation Bureau, which was a safety organization created by the insurance industry.

ITE had multiple goals. It wanted to encourage professional and social contact. It aimed to research, exchange, and disseminate traffic-engineering ideas and methods. It advocated the establishment of traffic-engineering departments in city and state governments. Not least, ITE wanted to make traffic engineering a recognized discipline so that traffic engineers could be licensed to practice (a goal that remains a challenge in some jurisdictions in the present day). *Fortune* magazine, in a profile of McClintock, described the profession's image during its early years: "The swaddling traffic engineer, with his traffic separations and segregations, was scorned as an intellectual who might have fancy ideas but no practical knowledge of the business of laying out a highway." The description seemed to apply to McClintock specifically.[40]

New traffic-planning concepts and implementation strategies were exchanged between ITE members and disseminated through their offices, clients, and communities. Like the Bureau for Street Traffic Research, ITE was an organizing nexus for the fledgling field of traffic engineering.

McClintock and Bel Geddes

McClintock had multiple careers during the Depression. In addition to his traffic-related work, he was deeply involved in advertising. In 1931 he led a 150-city study of traffic counts for billboard advertisers. As a result, he became the chief of the Traffic Audit Bureau of the Association of National Advertisers, where he performed research for advertisers. Later in the decade he became a director of the Advertising Research Foundation.[41]

Therefore McClintock was superbly qualified when a Shell Oil advertising campaign needed a technical consultant. In 1936 he was hired to advise Norman Bel Geddes (1893–1958), the lead designer of the campaign.

Bel Geddes started his career as an advertising illustrator and theatrical designer, and worked on many Broadway productions. In the late 1920s he turned to industrial design and became renowned for the streamlined style he applied to appliances, buildings, and vehicles. He was a voluble self-promoter with an irrepressibly boyish personality—*Fortune* magazine called him "the P.T. Barnum of industrial design"—and had an endless fascination for large, intricately detailed landscape models. His working models of sports matches, horse races, and military battles were the bases for serious gaming sessions that involved leading society figures, betting, and heavy drinking. Around 1933–1935, he had a hobby of filming small creatures, and amassed a collection of two thousand living reptiles and insects in his Manhattan homes.[42]

Bel Geddes became interested in traffic congestion and safety issues in the early 1930s. His said his thinking about cities was influenced by Le Corbusier, Ernest Flagg, and his friend Harvey Wiley Corbett. Judging by appearances, he was most influenced by Hugh Ferriss's spectacular illustrations. Bel Geddes built a future-city model for the Shell Oil campaign that was 6 feet (1.8 m) long and could be photographed from any angle. It showcased a city rebuilt for fast traffic, and featured towers, a large-scale grid of broad freeways, and a comprehensive elevated pedestrian network.[43]

During the model's design process, Bel Geddes repeatedly suggested that private automobiles be banned from the downtown area. Parking garages would be erected at the urban fringe, and shuttle buses would take commuters downtown. McClintock quashed the idea because he believed the bother of switching transportation modes was too much for motorists to accept.[44]

Shell Oil used the model in ads and films intended to build public support for urban freeways and a national highway system. Miller McClintock was the leading promoter and spokesman for the scheme. He toured the United States throughout 1937, using slides and drawings of Bel Geddes's model to illustrate a desirable urban

Figure 7.3: Bel Geddes's city model made for a Shell Oil ad campaign, 1937. A typical American city street grid retrofitted for hugely increased traffic volume and velocity. Freeways were spaced at ten-block intervals and had about 22 lanes. The elevated pedestrian network apparently did not cross the freeways. Image © The Edith Lutyens and Norman Bel Geddes Foundation, Inc.

future. He lavished praise on Bel Geddes, the "master of functional shape and form," who had glimpsed "the automotive city of tomorrow."[45]

The vision McClintock advocated was colossal. As *Scribner's* magazine described it, America needed to scrap its urban streets and "do the whole thing over again, in the way we have seen depicted on the covers of popular science magazines for the past twenty years." McClintock said that unless America's "useless" street system was replaced, the automobile would become "a malignant growth." He predicted that American cities would be rebuilt over the next 25–50 years at a cost of $57 billion, and said the system would generate sufficient revenue to pay for itself. A *Wall Street Journal* editorial commented that "this huge prospective outlay leaves us aghast," but the newspaper supported the basic vision and noted that it was certain to increase auto sales.[46]

Hoffman and the Automotive Safety Foundation

McClintock and his research bureau were a major force promoting grade-separated facilities and limited-access urban highways. But it was Hoffman's own work in the field of safety advocacy that ultimately would have the greater influence on traffic separation and American land-development patterns.

After the financial crash of 1929, Studebaker struggled to meet its obligations. Albert Esrkine, the corporation's president, overextended Studebaker's debt and within a few years drove the company into bankruptcy. Tragically, he committed suicide by gunshot to obtain life-insurance money for his family. Hoffman took over as Studebaker's president in 1935 and oversaw the company's return to profitability. (Meanwhile, Erskine's name was quietly dropped from the title of the Bureau for Street Traffic Research.) Hoffman's new position gave him greater authority and sway within the auto industry.

Hoffman was convinced that bad publicity about traffic crashes hurt auto sales. In 1932 he had become chair of the Traffic Planning and Safety Committee of the National Automobile Chamber of Commerce, and had been mostly unsuccessful at persuading other automakers to participate. NACC (which was renamed the Automobile Manufacturers' Association in 1934) was more concerned with problems like the threat of labor strikes. But events were once again forcing the automakers' hand. As the number of automobiles resumed its rapid growth, the number of traffic deaths and serious injuries shot up too. The human toll made the American public simmer with grief and anger.

In August 1935, *Readers Digest* published a vivid, gruesome article titled "—And Sudden Death." In the manner of a pulp crime thriller, it described the "savage mutilation" caused by auto crashes, warning that "every time you step on the throttle, death gets in beside you, hopefully waiting for his chance." The article was a cultural sensation and achieved an extraordinary degree of visibility. Its total circulation was estimated at 35 million; it was reprinted in 2,000 newspapers and magazines, and 3.5 million individual reprints were requested. Hoffman called it "the spark that touched off a tremendous explosion of public interest and concern." A 1936 poll found that two out of three Americans were in favor of mandated speed governors on motor vehicles.[47]

It was not the type of publicity that Hoffman wished to see, but it was advantageous for his safety advocacy goals. He convinced the automakers to act. He characteristically started with a study, written by McClintock and a few other safety advocates friendly to the auto industry, that recommended a program of grants to traffic engineering schools, highway safety agencies, and other groups involved with traffic safety. That strategy of direct giving was intended to coordinate the highway safety movement and provide direction to recipients.

At the request of the automakers, Hoffman brought co-funders into the program. They were from industries ancillary to automaking: steel, petroleum, rubber, cement, and insurance. In 1937 the Automobile Manufacturers' Association spun off Hoffman's initiative as a separate organization that would administer the program and disburse the grants. It was named the Automotive Safety Foundation (ASF). Top-level industry executives sat on its board and operating committee. Participating vehicle manufacturers included General Motors, Chrysler, Studebaker, Packard, Hudson, Mack, International Harvester, Nash-Kelvinator, and White Motor. The lengthy roster of trustees included manufacturers of auto parts, accessories, and tires, along with cement, oil, and finance companies.[48]

Hoffman was ASF's leader and most active promoter. During his five years as president, he lectured to business and civic groups, wrote numerous articles, gave interviews in print and on radio, won service awards from business and safety organizations, and published a book, *Seven Roads to Safety* (1939). He became the industry's chief spokesman for auto safety, pitching a comprehensive program that was largely borrowed from McClintock.[49]

ASF under Hoffman supported a variety of pre-existing programs and initiatives. Traffic engineering was a primary focus. ASF supported initiatives to train traffic engineers and staff; place traffic engineers in every state and major city; and study traffic crashes, traffic congestion, and the effectiveness of solutions. Those initiatives were carried out by the Bureau for Street Traffic Research (which moved to Yale in 1938), the American Automobile Association, and other industry-friendly schools and organizations. ASF also supported efforts to standardize traffic laws, traffic signage, and driver licensing; and it supported driver education, safety instruction programs, and increased police traffic patrols. Above all, Hoffman saw ASF as a coordinator of policy, methods, and procedures. Over the next three decades, it operated as a leading agent of consensus within the traffic-safety establishment.[50]

The link between Hoffman and McClintock was underscored in 1938 when the two were featured as a pair in *Life* magazine. They were hailed as the nation's authorities on automobile safety and traffic planning—Hoffman the "civic leader of the safety movement," McClintock the "foremost U.S. traffic engineer."[51]

Hoffman strongly believed in the social benefits of mass suburbanization, which was a position in happy accord with his business interests. The auto industry had long viewed suburbanization as a trend that would multiply its profits. In 1922 the head of National Automobile Chamber of Commerce had stated, "The movement toward the suburbs manifest everywhere during the past 10 years will continue to be augmented through motor travel and in turn will increase the demand for automobiles."[52]

Throughout his time as an auto executive, and most vigorously in the late 1930s, Hoffman advocated limited-access highways that would accelerate suburbanization. He repeated the urban-expressway principles that had been propounded by Thomas H. MacDonald and BPR. America needed to remake its cities to permanently solve the congestion problem, said Hoffman. Expressways had to plow through blighted areas. The urban poor needed to suburbanize—to move to garden cities or rural houses. Americans would be thankful for these great changes in their cities, "just as we're thankful we no longer have to wallow in mud on country roads." The automakers would be thankful too. Reconstructing American cities for the automobile would open enormous new markets. "The greatest automobile market today, the greatest untapped field of potential customers," said Hoffman, "is the large number of city people who refuse to own cars, or use the cars they have very little, because it's such a nuisance to take them out."[53]

Safety Statistics

Given the great amount of money and public-relations effort that they had invested, Hoffman and the auto industry had a definite interest in proving that their traffic-safety ideas were effective. But they had a problem. Different statistical metrics showed drastically different results. By some metrics the traffic fatality rate was increasing—even

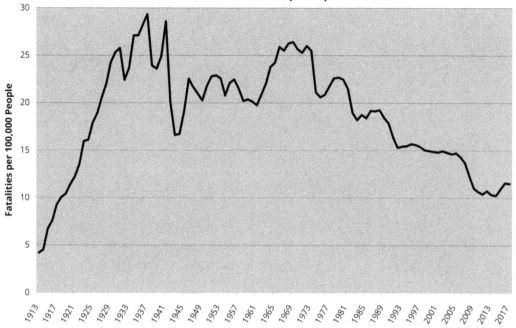

Figure 7.4: US traffic fatalities per capita over a 104-year period. The 2017 death rate was the same as the early 1920s death rate.

reaching record highs. So the auto industry consistently used metrics that interpreted the raw numbers in the best possible light.

The most basic metric, the number of traffic fatalities, reached record high levels in the late 1930s and early 1940s. The number of traffic fatalities per capita also reached record high levels. In the field of public health, fatalities per capita is a standard, widely accepted metric of risk at the scale of an entire society, and is used to calculate annual or lifetime risk. The auto industry never preferred it.

Early in its history, the industry had adopted the metric of fatalities per registered car to prove that safety was improving. A 1921 industry yearbook crowed, "Automobiles Now Twice as Safe: Ratio of Fatalities per Car Halved in Five Years." But that outcome was mainly an artifact of the tremendous growth in car ownership. Conditions were much different during the late 1920s and early 1930s. The car-ownership rate stagnated as the number of fatalities increased, and so the fatalities-per-car statistic rose to a 15-year peak. The rate dropped somewhat over the next few years, but at the end of the decade it still showed that no improvement had been made since the mid-1920s. The metric no longer served the industry's purposes. The industry needed a replacement.[54]

In 1931 the National Safety Council (an organization backed by the industrial and insurance sectors) used for the first time the metric of traffic fatalities per gallons of gasoline consumed. NSC claimed that increased gasoline consumption was the single factor that could explain the recent increase in traffic fatalities. Soon other writers and engineers began to analyze fatalities using NSC's metric.[55]

Hoffman translated NSC's metric into fatalities per miles driven, and then led the auto industry's use of that metric. In 1936, before ASF was formed, he spotlighted the

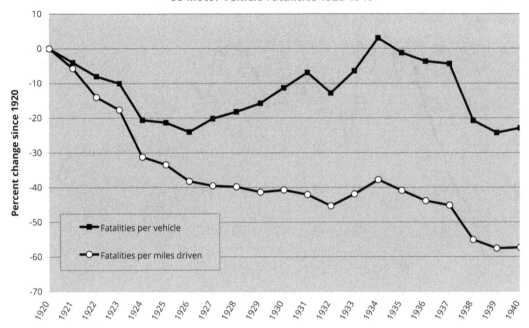

US Motor Vehicle Fatalities 1920-1940

Figure 7.5: US traffic fatalities by two metrics. In the mid-1930s, the fatalities-per-vehicle metric was reporting no improvement since 1920.

great improvement in traffic fatalities when measured in those terms. In 1938 an ASF press release trumpeted that "Traffic Fatality Rate Is Lowest in History." Hoffman said the improvement was the result of education, enforcement, and engineering—"the now famous three E's of safety" that were also ASF's core program. In speeches, articles, and publicity materials, Hoffman claimed that ASF's program was scientifically proven to reduce traffic deaths, and advised that every state should adopt it. Allied organizations, such as the American Automobile Association, lent their voices in support. A number of those organizations received ASF funding, such as NSC itself.[56]

The automotive engineer Arthur W. Stevens criticized Hoffman at length in his 1941 book on auto safety, arguing that the metric of fatalities per miles driven was inaccurate and unreliable. Hoffman acknowledged that the raw number of fatalities was a matter of terrible concern to the general public. However, he said, a knowledgeable field of practice such as highway safety should view statistical comparisons based on raw numbers as "wholly meaningless." Raw numbers had to be adjusted to account for risk exposure, and Hoffman defended the fatalities-per-miles-driven metric as a proper way to accomplish that.[57]

But the metric had more basic flaws than those that Stevens had identified. One, it did not account for the speed of travel. Therefore, for any given amount of travel time, and assuming that all other conditions were the same, it would always find that faster speed was safer. The evidence from actual crashes showed the opposite: faster speed tended to be riskier. Two, driving itself was a risk factor. The more people drove, the more risk they were exposed to. The metric did not represent that essential systemic aspect of the transportation safety problem.[58]

Despite scattered objections, the metric entered into general usage worldwide. When the US Congress established a federal traffic safety agency in 1966, it followed the industry's lead and reported fatalities in terms of miles driven. The practice has continued through the present day. It is frequently used to portray raw fatality figures in a more optimistic light.[59]

During and After World War II

In 1942 Hoffman stepped down as president of ASF to work on war-production planning. He retained his position as chairman of ASF until 1948, when President Truman appointed him to lead the Marshall Plan to help rebuild war-torn Europe. In addition to pursuing trans-European political cooperation and financial stabilization, the Marshall Plan assisted the agriculture, energy, and transport sectors. Hoffman's deputies and nongovernmental allies in Europe promoted auto-oriented traffic planning and encouraged the construction of a transcontinental highway network. In later decades, Hoffman led the United Nations' economic development program for low-income countries.[60]

McClintock left the transportation field in 1942 to head the War Advertising Council, a private organization of advertisers involved in the war effort. The council conveyed war-related information, advertising, and propaganda from the government to domestic audiences. The next year, he became president of the Mutual Broadcasting System, one of the "big four" US radio broadcasting networks and, after that, developed educational television programs.[61]

The position of ASF president was taken over by Pyke Johnson. He had started his career as a reporter for the *Rocky Mountain News*, and after World War I was secretary of the National Automobile Chamber of Commerce (renamed the Automobile Manufacturers' Association in 1934). He served as the Washington representative and lobbyist for that organization, and in 1939 became its executive vice-president. He also collaborated with Hoffman and McClintock on the formation of ASF.[62]

Under Johnson, ASF began a new, professionalized phase of operations. It entered the consulting business, giving direct planning assistance to cities and states. It created numerous major-roadway plans for cities and states, and many of those plans included major-roadway classification schemes. Thanks to Hoffman's groundwork, ASF enjoyed a sterling public reputation. It had the firm support of presidents and— more important for its everyday work—state and federal highway bureaucracies.

Thus, in years after World War II, ASF was centrally positioned as an organizer, mediator, and information clearinghouse. It would play a major role in realizing state and national traffic-planning policies that were aligned with the interests of the auto industry.

1939 World's Fair and Futurama

The 1939 World's Fair in New York City was motivated by goals both stated and unstated. The Fair's planners and sponsors hoped to bring billions of dollars of business and investment to the city. They wanted to promote technological progress and material abundance, restore faith in the nation's economic and political systems, and normalize a future dominated by corporations. A key goal was to mount an event so powerful, of such great import, that it would change American culture. Grover Whelan, president of the Fair, wrote that "the fair of 1939 will predict, may even dictate, the shape of things to come." President Roosevelt wrote that "millions may visualize the national life that is to come" and that the nation hoped the Fair would "profoundly influence our national life for many years."[63]

The Fair brought together many of the individuals, organizations, and firms that had engaged in transportation futurism over the previous twenty years. Jay Downer, Gilmore D. Clarke, Clarence Stein, and Hugh Ferriss were just a few of the local designers involved with the Fair. Philosophical unity was by no means assured; aggressive corporatism and idealized communalism sat uneasily side by side. The Fair combined multifarious visions of hyperurbanism and decentralization in a gleaming, stylized buffet of amusements.

RPA and Robert Moses

The Fair was organized in 1935 by the Regional Plan Association (the new name of the Regional Plan of New York and Its Environs initiative). The site of the Fair was a enormous trash dump on the shore of Flushing Bay, Queens, which RPA had first envisioned as a waterfront park in 1922. Before seeking any sponsors, RPA enlisted the help of Robert Moses. Moses enthusiastically adopted the project as his own. He wanted to reclaim the site and make it the jewel of his regional park system. That is not to say that Moses and RPA were on amicable terms; they squabbled and sniped over who got credit for this and other projects. But they also depended on each other. RPA organized political support, sought private investors, and handled preliminary mapping and rezoning. Moses received $93 million in federal, state, and city funding to acquire the land, reclaim it, and build highways on it.[64]

Workers reclaimed 1,200 acres (485 ha) in a round-the clock effort from July 1936 to April 1937. The site's massive ash heaps were spread over marshy ground to create open meadows. Moses routed the Grand Central Parkway, the Triborough Expressway, and the Van Wyck Expressway to border or pass through the site. "Great under and over passes were constructed to carry the main arteries across the fair, so as to separate through traffic from local and to make the meadow safe for pedestrians," he reported. Thus the Fair's infrastructure itself demonstrated some of the ideas presented in the Fair's planning-related exhibits.

Like the other Fair organizers, Moses believed the Fair would show "the conditions under which people will live in the next century." He predicted astonishing yet evolutionary changes, rather than the revolutionary transformations envisioned by RPAA and Norman Bel Geddes. The cost of revolutionary transformation was too high, said Moses, and "an immense number of people like city life much as it is."[65]

RPAA and Democracity

RPAA's planning perspective occupied the figural and literal center of the Fair. Inside a giant sphere (called the Perisphere) was Democracity, a model of the metropolis of the future. The exhibit was supervised by Robert Kohn and designed by Henry Dreyfuss, an industrial designer. Dreyfuss had studied theater-set design under Norman Bel Geddes and was known for his designs of vehicles and consumer items.[66]

Figure 7.6: Democracity center, ca. 1939. Freeways, boulevards, and pedestrian plazas and bridges are interwoven on multiple levels. From New York World's Fair (1939–1940) records, Manuscripts and Archives Division, New York Public Library.

Democracity's commercial core was traversed by a modified grid of grade-separated expressways. In many other respects, it closely resembled Greenbelt, Maryland. It had residential superblocks with common greens, large landscaped setbacks, grade-separated pedestrian crossings, single-use zoning, and an outer greenbelt. The city's cleanly rationalized plan was reflected in its social order. "Playtime will not be dissipated in idleness or carousing," said Dreyfuss. "There will be much less drinking of intoxicants, because there will be no need for escape from reality." Instead, residents would be involved with self-improvement. Themes of behavioral control and ideal social arrangements permeated Democracity, Futurama, and the Fair's other planning-related exhibits.[67]

The Democracity exhibit was moderately successful. Fairgoers made some 12 million visits, including repeat visits. But its message was incoherent and confusing, and it seemed plain and static in comparison to the flashier, better-funded corporate exhibits.

Futurama

Norman Bel Geddes tried to interest Shell Oil in an expansion of his City of Tomorrow model. It would have moving vehicles and would address national highway planning; he hoped to exhibit it at the upcoming Fair. He also pitched the idea to Chrysler and General Motors (GM), both of whom turned it down. GM was wary of undermining

BPR chief Thomas MacDonald's planning authority. One GM executive said that MacDonald would "have a fit" if the company appeared to be advocating a highway plan in cooperation with Miller McClintock.

Bel Geddes retooled and expanded his proposal for Goodyear, then brought it back to GM. He procured a meeting with GM president Alfred P. Sloan in April 1938 and won Sloan's interest. He promised that the exhibit would mobilize public opinion in favor of government highway spending. In a subsequent meeting, Bel Geddes gave a four-hour pitch to forty GM department heads. He signed a contract that afternoon.[68]

Futurama was an indoor ride similar to a Coney Island amusement ride. Fairgoers boarded moving cars for a fifteen-minute narrated show. They saw the United States of 1960—21 years in the future—depicted on 35,000 square feet (3,250 sq m) of dioramas on three levels. The toy-scale landscapes contained 500,000 buildings, 40,000 stationary vehicles, and 10,000 vehicles moving at different speeds. The godlike view, theatrical lighting, and plush seats with integrated speakers created an otherworldly effect, as if the viewer was flying over a dream landscape.[69]

Futurama combined the two philosophies of decentralization and hyperurbanism in its main theme of roadway transportation. Much of the presentation was devoted to rural superhighways, but it climaxed with close-up views of a future metropolis. The models featured traffic separation throughout and highlighted both horizontal and vertical methods.

In suburban residential neighborhoods, dendritic street layouts appeared very much like Radburn's. Houses were placed on cul-de-sacs that terminated at linear parks. Bel Geddes endorsed the Radburn Idea; he believed that progressive neighborhood planning meant privacy. The only vehicles that should travel on a residential street were those used in connection with the residents of that street.[70]

To enter the central city, commuters and other travelers would head to the nearest transfer depot. Their "high-speed rural" vehicles would be swapped for a separate fleet of "city" vehicles. These were smaller, lighter, more maneuverable city cars, city taxis, city buses, and city trucks.[71]

The central district was an unforgettable representation of a mid-size American downtown transformed into a motor-vehicle utopia. It was reserved for business, civic, and entertainment uses. Streamlined skyscrapers were set ten blocks apart, and one-third of the surface area was converted to parks. The city retained its grid of small blocks because "it was not financially possible to rebuild the city completely, scrapping its original layout." Otherwise, the streets were completely revamped. Limited-access expressways were spaced every ten blocks. They were about 28 lanes wide (with their side roads) and operated at 50 mph (80 kmh). The local streets were six to eight lanes wide. The lanes occupied the entire right-of-way between the building facades.

Pedestrians were comprehensively separated on an upper level that was utilitarian in character. They walked past long, impermeable facades, suspended over the noise and pollution of rushing traffic; their primary visual gratification was retail display windows. Bicycles were simply absent. Futurama was wholeheartedly devoted to the driving experience.[72]

Futurama's downtown was a stunning representation of the multilevel visions developed by Harriss, Corbett, Ferriss, and other visionaries of the 1900s to 1920s. A brief animation of 120-mph (190-kmh) "torpedo cars" zipping along future elevated

Figure 7.7: Futurama cul-de-sac suburb, ca. 1939. Superblocks were designed on the Radburn model, with cul-de-sacs pointing inward to park space. From Harry Ransom Center, University of Texas at Austin. Image © The Edith Lutyens and Norman Bel Geddes Foundation, Inc.

urban highways had appeared in GM's 1936 promotional film *Streamlines*, but Futurama was incomparably more comprehensive and detailed. Bel Geddes was an autodidact and his 1940 book *Magic Motorways* discussed many of his influences. The "forward-looking men" of highway construction who "realized what had to be done" included Jay Downer, John A. Harriss, and Robert Moses. Bel Geddes cited the traffic separation of Central Park, the Long Island Motor Parkway, Bronx River Parkway, West Side Elevated Highway, other limited-access urban expressways, and Ernest Flagg's 1927 scheme.[73]

Lewis Mumford quite accurately observed that most of the ideas presented in

Figure 7.8: Futurama typical freeway intersection, ca. 1939. The freeways were about 28 lanes wide and crossed over and under each other in a basket-weave pattern. From Harry Ransom Center, University of Texas at Austin. Image © The Edith Lutyens and Norman Bel Geddes Foundation, Inc.

Figure 7.9: Frame from the General Motors film *Streamlines*, 1936. The cartoon science-fictional view of multilevel transportation contrasts to Futurama's supposed realism.

Futurama had originated decades or generations in the past:

> Mr. Geddes is a great magician, and he makes the carrot in the gold-
> fish bowl look like a real goldfish. One has to rub one's eyes before
> one remembers that the future, as presented here, is old enough to
> be somebody's grandfather. . . . The closer Mr. Geddes gets to the city,
> the more old-fashioned his imagination becomes. By the time one
> reaches his remodelled towns, one enters the tinny world of a Jules
> Verne romance, or one of those brittle nightmares Mr. Welles used
> to picture in the early nineteen-hundreds.[74]

Futurama was called the "smash hit" of the Fair. Nearly 45 million visits were made to the Fair and 27 million to Futurama, although many were repeat visits. Futurama's size, detail, and photogenic quality made it an icon of transportation futurism. In its particulars, Futurama was merely one more zany, technocratic transportation-planning scheme. But most people ignored the particulars and remembered the imagery: the omniscient views, the stupefying complication of superhighway facilities, the multilevel downtown organized for ceaseless traffic streams. Futurama helped popularize urban freeways for a generation.[75]

During World War II, Bel Geddes built models of Pacific naval battles for newspapers, magazines, and the military. Meanwhile, Futurama and its imagery were carried forward by GM and Robert Moses.[76]

From 1936 to 1939, GM operated the Parade of Progress, a roadshow that Alfred Sloan called "a world's fair on wheels." It traveled to small cities and towns across America, promoting the general idea of progress and, in one exhibit, limited-access urban expressways. After the New York World's Fair ended, GM revived the roadshow and reassembled selected portions of Futurama into a *Futurama Highlights* exhibit. Some four million people attended the 1941 Parade of Progress tour, and *Futurama Highlights* was one of the most popular attractions. It was dropped from the tour in autumn 1941 in preference to war-themed exhibits.[77]

Robert Moses was both admiring and critical of Futurama. In 1939, he and a small party of notables were personally guided by Bel Geddes on a tour of the exhibit. Moses remained "discreetly silent" while Bel Geddes spoke. Afterward, Moses remarked, "It is all very beautiful, but I don't think it would be very practical. Think of the bond issue that would be necessary for a project like that." The next year, Moses opined that Futurama was "interesting and stimulating, but hardly scientific." He said that "the old theory that you must bypass every city is just plain bunk," pointing to his Belt Parkway in Brooklyn as a counterexample. For denser districts like Midtown Manhattan, Moses recommended elevated highways that ran through buildings at the second or third story.[78]

In 1953, Moses won an essay competition held by GM on the topic of planning and funding the "highways we need." Moses praised Futurama's imagination and drama and recommended it as a public-relations model. "Similar imaginative exhibits should be shown around the country" to promote an interstate freeway program, he said. GM took the recommendation to heart and added an exhibit titled *Out of the Muddle* to its 1954 Parade of Progress tour.[79]

Out of the Muddle told the story of Lake City, a generic small town overwhelmed by traffic congestion. Residents fled to a congestion-free suburb, but the town's engineers had bigger dreams. Their "city of tomorrow" flipped into view like an automaton clock. It comprised a large freeway, blanketing lawns, and randomly strewn modernist slab buildings connected by skywalks. It was a fully car-oriented landscape from which any hint of traditional street frontages and lively sidewalks had been eliminated. The bland, artless layout and aesthetic resembled proposals made in Manhattan during the 1940s for modernist superblock-and-highway developments.

In July 1956 the Parade of Progress was cancelled. Eight million people had attended its final three-year run. GM's official reason was the distraction of television, but the more likely reason was that the tour had outlived its usefulness. The Federal-Aid Highway Act of 1956 created policies and a funding mechanism to build a national freeway system, which would include urban and suburban freeways very much like those portrayed by GM.[80]

H. Alker Tripp

Herbert Alker Tripp (1883–1954) was born in London and worked on the civilian staff of the London Metropolitan Police Force for his whole career. Outside of his stable work life, he was a well-rounded man. He was an avid yachtsman and wrote several books about his sailing adventures. He was also a talented painter and made posters for the London Transport and other rail systems.

Said by his superior to have "a natural flair for traffic," Tripp was appointed as head of the force's traffic department in 1932. He felt he needed a better understanding of the field, so he undertook an extensive study of traffic engineering and town planning. He familiarized himself with the Institute of Traffic Engineers, Raymond Unwin, and garden cities. He studied books by Thomas Adams that covered Radburn, the neighborhood unit, and the Regional Plan of New York.[81]

In 1934 Tripp visited North America to research traffic and policing conditions in New York, Chicago, Boston, Detroit, Toronto, and Montreal. With respect to roadway planning, he was particularly impressed by the parkways and expressways that "refuse to connect with the minor roads at all . . . Access is thus only obtained to the main road at long intervals and then by means of a properly designed roundabout or fly-over." This was a feature that England "might well emulate if we can possibly afford it." Tripp also praised the West Side Elevated Highway and Park Avenue at Grand Central Terminal as being "of vast importance and value to traffic circulation in New York generally." He concluded that "It is necessary to pay high tribute to the way Americans have exploited their layouts (especially in New York)."[82]

Tripp was deeply concerned about pedestrian traffic fatalities, but also wanted to ensure that fast traffic was unimpeded. He had long advocated guard rails and fences to separate pedestrians from traffic. In his view, railways were an exemplary model. They barred public access so that trains could move at great speed, excluding pedestrians by means of fences or grade separation. Tripp believed that major urban roads must do the same; ideally, no pedestrian would ever set foot on one. In his lectures and articles of the mid-1930s, he began to meld his very strict, no-compromise vision of traffic separation with recent town planning ideas.[83]

Tripp's book *Road Traffic and Its Control* (1938) was a textbook for police students and a guidebook for engineers and city officials. Its comprehensive coverage of traffic topics included town planning. Tripp presented a universal traffic-planning vision that applied to big cities, small towns, and new suburbs alike. His vision employed a three-part roadway classification of main arteries, semi-main or distributive roads, and minor roads.

On main arteries, motor traffic moved at high speed and all vehicular access to lots and frontages was strictly prohibited. Fences and guard rails prevented pedestrians from entering the vehicular lanes. Crosswalks at signalized intersections were acceptable on low-volume arteries, but in dense areas pedestrians were required to cross using pedestrian tunnels or bridges.

Distributive roads also carried high-speed traffic. They were limited-access like main arteries, but had intersections with minor roads. They connected minor roads to arteries, serving what later came to be known as the collector function. Pedestrians were fenced from the vehicular lanes and crossed via tunnels or bridges.

Minor roads carried lower-speed local traffic only. Minor roads could cross main arteries only via underpasses or overpasses. Certain "sequestered" minor roads could be free of vehicles. An existing layout could be retrofitted by using "deliberately obstructive designs" to inconvenience and discourage cut-through traffic.[84]

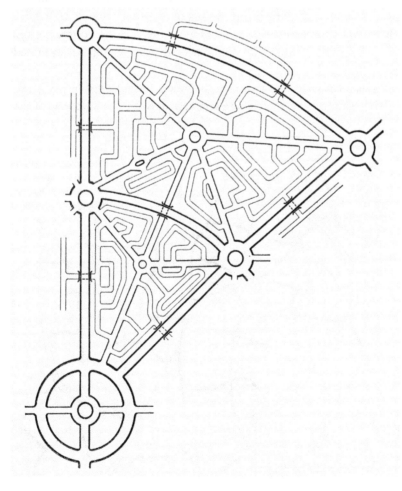

Figure 7.10: Tripp, model town section, 1938. Four years after this diagram was published, Tripp named the concept *precinct*. The diagram appeared to be modeled on Unwin's ideal layout (see figure 4.14).

The layout formed by Tripp's classification resembled a standard neighborhood-unit layout, except that it was walled on all sides by limited-access arterial roads (compare to figures 4.14 and 5.12). In addition, shopping and business uses were located on interior local streets, where motor traffic was slow or prohibited. That contrasted to standard neighborhood-unit layouts, which had shopping and business uses fronting on main arterials.[85]

Tripp strongly endorsed the comprehensive vertical separation of pedestrians in configurations like those of Corbett and Flagg. Ideally, pedestrians always traveled on a separate level one story above the street. Any roadway, even a minor one, could be designed with elevated walkways, retail facades, and house entrances.[86]

In 1942 Tripp published *Town Planning and Road Traffic*, which extracted and revised the town-planning and street-design sections of his previous book. He clarified and augmented his policy recommendations, writing in a lively prose style that conveyed a more personal sense of his opinions. For example, he declared that "the heavy streams of arterial traffic must be regarded as sheer poison, never to be touched, because contact is deadly." Tripp said he preferred physical solutions to abstract rules because it was human nature to circumvent rules. The police officer understood this because, unlike planners and engineers, "he has been well schooled in human perversity. He approaches his whole problem largely, and indeed mainly, from that angle."[87]

Tripp introduced the term *precinct* to describe each area of local streets bounded by traffic arteries. Precincts had a maximum radius of one-quarter mile (0.4 km). Unlike neighborhood units, precincts could be composed entirely of nonresidential uses. All land uses and activities, other than high-speed driving, would be contained within precincts.

Tripp's precincts had a character of abounding wonderfulness tinged by pre-automobile nostalgia. They would be centers of life and activity with "town streets of the

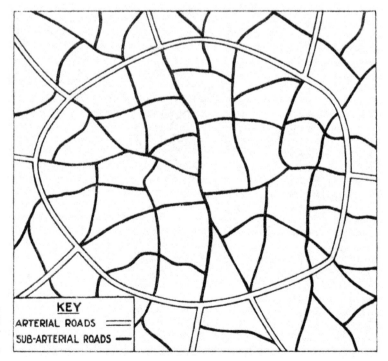

Figure 7.11: Tripp, schematic diagram of regional cellular roadway layout, 1942.

KEY
ARTERIAL ROADS ════
SUB-ARTERIAL ROADS ────

old-fashioned type." In Tripp's imagining, local streets would become "companionable places, with an air of leisure and repose; such streets will provide a real promenade for the town dweller and a rest for jaded nerves. We shall be getting back to Merrie England."[88]

On the other hand, the aim of arterials must be "to develop and encourage speed." Existing intersections with local streets must be blocked off. The newly created dead ends should allow foot traffic to pass through, provided that the arteries they connected to were retrofitted with fenced footways. Vehicular connectivity between local roads and arteries was "grossly overdone, there being too much of it for safety or order." Tripp's planning schema would produce a regional-scale cellular layout composed of major arteries and interstitial precincts.[89]

Tripp tempered his earlier support for elevated pedestrian arcades, noting that connections between buildings were difficult to coordinate, and that ramps and escalators were difficult to install. As for double-deck streets, they were "definitely unsound" because of noise, vibration, and pollution. He professed a neutral stance on the question of centralization versus decentralization; he argued that road systems needed to be rebuilt in either case. But his recommendations tended to favor deconcentration, and he felt that the greatest opportunities for "really modern layouts" would be found in new suburbs.[90]

The precinct concept was rapidly absorbed by Britain's planning and architectural establishments. The County of London Plan (1943) and Greater London Plan (1944) were led by Patrick Abercrombie, who had written the forward to Tripp's 1942 book. Abercrombie's plans fully developed the precinct approach, specifying that no building access was to be permitted on main roads. Abercrombie and Tripp were knighted for their planning work in 1945. The Ministry of Transport's guidebook *Design and Layout of Roads in Built-up Areas* (1946) endorsed Tripp's limited-access and traffic-segregation principles with only minor modifications, and promulgated them throughout the country. By the 1950s, the precinct concept was well established and had become an essential component of many New Town and redevelopment plans in the United Kingdom.[91]

Guidebooks of the 1940s

In the United States during the 1940s, a variety of planning and development guidebooks were released that attempted to systematize roadway planning. The guidebooks were made by interest groups that had overlapping but somewhat different beliefs about which standards were desirable and which were not. Each interest group pursued standards that supported its own work or goals. Planners wanted standards suited for neighborhood-scale and regional-scale planning. Developers wanted standards that matched market preferences. Engineers wanted standards keyed to engineering requirements.

That created tension. Each interest group wanted to have the greatest influence on development patterns, but the groups also understood that their lack of agreement on principles and details hampered their political efficacy. Therefore, some sought external contributors, and some positioned their guidebooks as statements of expert consensus.[92]

A common device used in these guidebooks was the roadway classification, which was a list of roadway types (generally three to five) along with their design or planning standards. By specifying how roadway types were laid out and how they related to each other, interest groups could influence the form and function of individual developments, as well as neighborhoods, districts, and regions.

Public Control of Highway Access, 1943

Chief Thomas H. MacDonald's federal road agency published *Public Control of Highway Access and Roadside Development* in 1943. The report staked out an extreme position in favor of limited access on all new and many existing through roads. It was written by David R. Levin, a young attorney who had recently joined the agency as a transportation analyst. Levin boldly proposed a legal framework to implement limited access on all thoroughfares.

The framework began with a street classification. "In the absence of an established classification of urban streets, the author has fashioned his own, patterned after the sound rural classification," wrote Levin. His street classification comprised primary streets, secondary streets, and land-service streets. Primary streets were main arteries that connected the districts of a city. Secondary streets distributed traffic within districts and performed a connecting function between primary and land-service streets. Land-service streets provided abutter access. Primary streets always had limited access; secondary streets had limited access wherever traffic justified it; and even some land-service streets could have protected roadsides. Existing through roads should be converted to limited access wherever the expense was justified by the resulting traffic improvement.[93]

Levin described limited-access thoroughfares as a panacea for urban traffic problems. They would allow motor vehicles to operate "almost as perfectly as a modern, streamlined train." In cities, they would enhance the value of abutting property and eliminate the "blighting effects of congestion and traffic noise and fumes." They would encourage orderly land-use patterns and outlaw the "metropolitan invasion" that typically followed highways on the urban fringe. They would make communities better, cleaner, and safer.[94]

Levin revised the publication and continued to promote the scheme through 1950 in magazines and professional symposiums. But many officials, businesspeople, and highway engineers considered the strict application of limited access on all high-volume streets to be undesirable or impractical. The American Association of State Highway Officials formally expressed that perspective in its 1957 guidebook *A Policy on Arterial Highways in Urban Areas*.[95]

Building New Neighborhoods, 1943

The Chicago Plan Commission was originally formed to promote Daniel Burnham's Plan of Chicago. It was incorporated into the city's government in 1939. In anticipation of a postwar housing boom, the commission published *Building New Neighborhoods* (1943) to propose new standards for subdivision development. Commission director Harry Evert Kincaid was the primary author. Kincaid had worked as an FHA

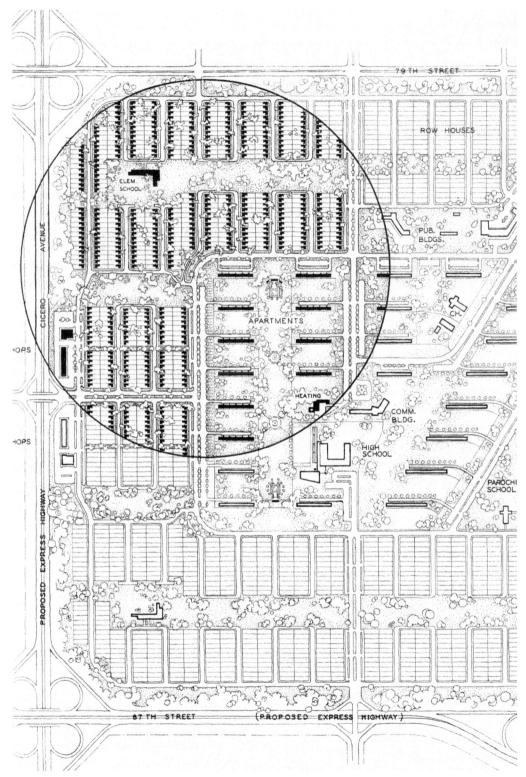

Figure 7.12: In mid-1943, Harry Evert Kincaid collaborated with the architecture firm Skidmore, Owings & Merrill on this proposal for a site near Chicago Municipal (now Midway) Airport. The cellular, dendritic neighborhood unit used the Chicago Plan Commission's subdivision design standards, which had been formulated by Kincaid. Image © SOM.

land planning consultant from 1937 to 1941, and the booklet firmly endorsed FHA design principles.[96]

Kincaid proposed a five-part street classification: express highways, major streets, secondary streets, minor residential streets, and cul-de-sac and loop streets. Major streets were spaced 1 mile (1.6 km) apart and had partially limited access; they collected traffic from the secondary streets and fed it to the expressways and other city districts. Secondary streets were spaced a half-mile (0.8 km) apart; they collected traffic from the residential streets and fed it to the major streets. Residential streets served the abutting properties "almost exclusively." Cul-de-sac and loop streets were "the most private and the safest of all streets."[97]

Kincaid's street classification thus had a strong emphasis on the collector function of major and secondary streets. That, combined with the recommendations for access control and roadway spacing, ensured cellular, dendritic roadway layouts at both the neighborhood and regional scales. The city council approved the report's subdivision design standards. Over the next several years, dozens of project layouts were voluntarily submitted to the Chicago Plan Commission for review. Other city planners and engineers took note and cited the Chicago standards as a model.[98]

Dynamics of Street Layout, 1945

The American Public Works Association represented city engineers who built streets and highways, and other workers who dealt with infrastructure and maintenance. Its booklet *The Dynamics of Street Layout and Design for Urban Traffic* (1945) was written in part by Burton W. Marsh, a civil engineer who led a distinguished career in traffic safety. Marsh was the director of the American Automobile Association's traffic engineering and safety division; he also was a founding member of the Institute of Traffic Engineers and served as ITE's president from 1932 to 1934.

The booklet did not offer a street classification, but it did cite as references *Toll Roads and Free Roads*, *Interregional Highways*, and the Chicago Plan Commission's booklet. It advanced the idea that traffic experts and engineers had arrived at a consensus (a "rapprochement of strong forces for the good") about the fundamental principles of successful traffic planning. Its recommendations, such as urban freeways, cellular layouts, and curtailing or eliminating intersections on arterials, were presented as urgent and unavoidable. It warned of "serious dangers to cities" unless the smooth flow of "traffic 'life-blood'" was assured by "really progressive traffic planning."[99]

Community Builder's Handbook, 1947

The Urban Land Institute, the nation's leading association of land developers, published *The Community Builders Handbook* in 1947. It was edited by ULI's executive director Seward H. Mott and his assistant director Max S. Wehrly. Before taking leadership of ULI, Mott had served from 1935 to 1944 as director of FHA's Land Planning Division. He was largely responsible for the booklets, lectures, and other educational efforts that did so much to promote FHA's neighborhood-design principles, including insular street layouts with large blocks. Mott's position as head of ULI illustrated just how important FHA was to the development industry.[100]

The *Handbook* took a relatively moderate approach to land-development methods, advising readers that "the ultra-modernist and the seeker for radical, unorthodox, or socialized departures in this field will not find them here." The *Handbook* reflected FHA standards, but made notable exceptions because developers believed that some standards conflicted with market demand and profitability.[101]

Gridirons were "highly undesirable" in residential areas, but the Radburn-type superblock also was not recommended. According to ULI, "Careful analysis and comparison of all development costs show that the much heralded economies of the super block plan have not been borne out, and that there is a very definite resistance to such communal schemes in the part of the American home buyer." The *Handbook* advised against excessive use of cul-de-sacs because they caused problems in infrastructure and service delivery. Loop streets were more efficient and prevented through traffic equally well. Long blocks up to 1,800–2,000 feet (550–610 m) in length were recommended as a cheaper pattern. Unlike FHA and most other planning authorities, the *Handbook* did not recommend cut-through footpaths across long blocks. They were infrequently used, expensive to maintain, and adjoining homeowners feared the crime they might bring.[102]

The *Handbook* discussed street types in relatively vague terms, eschewing a formal classification for a more casual, overlapping, and sometimes contradictory review. Major streets should be routed around developments; the presence of through traffic was said to be one of the most important causes of blight. But the regional street plan should also be respected, so that major streets might bisect projects in some cases. A generic street-layout plan showed internal collector streets continuing beyond the

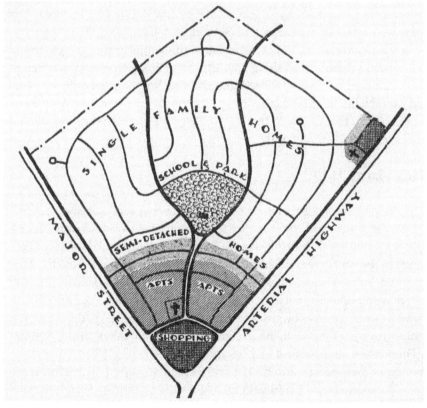

Figure 7.13: ULI's neighborhood unit street-layout diagram showing through-connectors, 1947.

project's boundaries to connect to future developments.[103]

The *Handbook* was the authoritative publication for developers of large subdivisions. It went through five revisions over the next 21 years, and its street-layout recommendations remained generally similar with certain exceptions. In the later editions, the case-study street layouts were more dendritic. Also, cul-de-sacs were recommended as "one of the best street types" because they offered privacy and stimulated premium house prices.[104]

Planning the Neighborhood, 1948

The American Public Health Association's guidebook *Planning the Neighborhood* (1948) asserted that the primary objective of housing was health. It strongly supported neighborhood-unit planning because the neighborhood "constitutes the basis for healthful housing." Burton W. Marsh was the major contributor of the street-planning standards.[105]

The guidebook proposed a four-part street classification: major-traffic, minor-traffic, neighborhood-feeder, and residential-service streets. It put an emphasis on the connecting function of roadways. Neighborhood-feeder streets connected to minor-traffic streets; minor-traffic streets connected to major-traffic streets. The guidebook made several statements about traffic-planning principles that were memorably succinct. In regard to dendritic layouts, it said that "Each class of street should normally lead into a street carrying the next greater volume of traffic." And in regard to intersection frequency, it said that "The frequency of intersections on a street should decrease as the traffic volume increases." Those principles in combination ensured that new developments would be bounded by arterials and have few external connections. New developments were virtually guaranteed to be built as isolated pods.[106]

Planning the Neighborhood was extraordinarily influential as the only guidebook to claim that certain neighborhood-design patterns were linked to good public health. Many of its recommendations were based more on opinion than scientific research, yet it gained widespread, long-lasting acceptance among urban planners. A 1969 survey of 258 members of the American Institute of Planners found that more than half used *Planning the Neighborhood* in their practice.[107]

Building Traffic Safety, 1950

In 1946, Burton W. Marsh organized a committee to bring together and reconcile the viewpoints of planners and traffic engineers. That apparently was a difficult task. The committee's publication *Building Traffic Safety into Residential Developments* was four years in the making, even though it was just a slim 40-page booklet. Most of the organizations that were involved in street-planning policy participated, as well as planners, housing officials, authors of traffic-planning guidebooks, and others. The final draft was written by committee members representing the Federal Housing Administration, Bureau of Public Roads, American Automobile Association, Automotive Safety Foundation, and Urban Land Institute.[108]

The committee generally repeated FHA and BPR street-layout principles. It recommended a four-part street classification: local residential streets (single-family), local residential streets (multifamily), feeder streets, and main highways (arterials, highways, and expressways). The only difference between the two types of local streets was that those for multifamily were wider. Both local and feeder streets provided access to abutting properties, while on arterials, access to abutting properties was limited. Intersections on arterials were spaced a minimum of 800 feet (244 m) apart, and no upper limit was given. Construction standards were assigned to each street type; thus the booklet translated its street classification into a format that roadway engineers could work with readily. *Building Traffic Safety* represented the largest consensus yet assembled on American residential traffic-layout principles.[109]

AASHO

The roadway classifications published by AASHO during the 1930s and 1940s served engineering purposes primarily. They gave little attention to planning topics such as access control and network layout. In 1941 AASHO classified highways, meaning all primary and secondary roads, according to traffic volume, design speed, and vehicle type. Topography was added to the 1945 classification for interstate freeways. These classifications gave engineers guidance about pavement thickness, number of lanes, and other geometric design factors.

During this period, AASHO's stance on limited access was constrained and conservative. In the 1930s several prominent AASHO members advocated freeways, and in 1938 the organization formally supported an "arterial trans-continental highway" from Washington, DC, to Boston. But state highway administrators were generally slow to limit access. In 1945 only a minority had legal authority to limit access. The 1945 AASHO standards for interstate freeways strongly recommended but did not require limited access. When AASHO finally issued a policy on urban roadways in 1957, it advised against excessive or inflexible access control on major urban arterials.[110]

Most of AASHO's standards were issued as voluntary guidelines, but because of the organization's power and prestige, its standards were, in effect, the national standards. AASHO's standards also had a broad influence on roadway design internationally, especially in Western Hemisphere nations.[111]

Chapter 7 Summary

As the automobile became a mass phenomenon, the different types of traffic separation became more blended in the work of leading designers. Visionaries such as Daniel Burnham, Ernest P. Goodrich, and Eliel Saarinen demonstrated that trend in the early twentieth century. Their work encompassed multilevel avenues, functionally divided roadways, and moderately cellular residential layouts. Projects such as the Plan of Chicago hinted at the regional pattern that was fully elaborated by RPNY in the late 1920s.

RPNY's 1929 final plan preached moderation, pragmatism, and diverse methods. It envisioned a bifurcated regional pattern. The dense city center would have towers, grade-separated streets and expressways, and elevated walkways. The suburbs would have lower-density job centers and cellular neighborhood units, all structured by surface expressways. The RPNY plan was the first comprehensive regional plan to bring together hyperurban and deconcentration proposals.

Several visionaries were exceptionally influential in blending different types of traffic separation. Miller McClintock educated a generation of traffic planners at Harvard and Yale from the late 1920s to early 1940s. As a teacher, consultant, and advocate, he called for both elevated pedestrian networks and limited-access expressways. In the early 1930s, he envisioned a citywide system of fully elevated expressways for Chicago.

The organizers of the 1939 New York World's Fair hoped to change American culture. The Fair's most popular and transporting exhibit, Futurama, simulated an aerial view of the metropolis of the future. It had many types of traffic separation, including elevated pedestrian networks and surface expressways in downtowns, and Radburn-style layouts in suburbs.

H. Alker Tripp, in his books of 1938 and 1942, advocated an extremely strict, no-compromise vision of cellular layouts structured by high-speed through roads. Vehicular access to abutting properties was prohibited on all the through roads. Guard rails and fences corralled pedestrians to keep them out of the through roads. Each cell, or precinct, was surrounded on all sides by these fences, and all pedestrian movement in or out would go via bridges and tunnels.

In the United States during the 1940s, various interest groups that were involved in residential development attempted to systematize roadway planning and influence development patterns. Their guidebooks commonly featured a roadway classification, which was a list of roadway types along with planning and design standards for each type. By the end of the decade, the interest groups had reached a partial consensus. The guidebooks agreed that the neighborhood unit, cellular street layouts, and large blocks were desirable. The guidebooks agreed that some kind of roadway classification should encourage dendritic layouts to some extent. But beyond that, the guidebooks differed on details and goals.

The disarray of classification schemes would only be resolved when a broad coalition of interest groups determined that a uniform scheme was needed. The contending classification systems of the 1940s prepared the way for a national consensus classification system in the 1950s.

CHAPTER 8
Establishment of
Functional Classification

In the mid- to late-twentieth century, functional classification became the dominant traffic-planning principle in the United States, and was very influential in other countries. It was a system that classified roadways into a few types to manage roadway design, construction, and funding. Its general purpose was to concentrate the bulk of traffic onto a relative few large, fast roadways. It also served as an administrative framework that arterial spacing standards were attached to. That helped propagate the cellular and dendritic roadway layouts that were so characteristic of America's automobile-dependent suburbs.

Functional classification was invented and championed by the automobile and highway interests, and allied planners and highway engineers. Those groups formed a well-organized and coordinated lobby that effectively propelled the idea to a position of national dominance.

Automotive Safety Foundation

Starting immediately after World War II and continuing for several decades, the Automotive Safety Foundation (ASF) took a leading role in state and metropolitan transportation planning. Often it worked in close cooperation with the Bureau of Public Roads and the American Association of State Highway Officials. During those years, it remained wholly a creation of the motor-vehicle companies and allied industries. Its membership grew steadily, as did the amount of grant money it distributed. By 1960 it was supported by 600 firms associated with motor-vehicle manufacturing, road construction, advertising, insurance, and finance, and was distributing hundreds of thousands of dollars in grants each year.[1]

During those years, ASF helped more than a dozen of the largest US cities reorganize their transportation planning departments. It consulted for 28 states, helping many to create new roadway classification schemes and plan new highway system expansions. Through its consulting work, ASF became the nation's foremost purveyor of state and metropolitan traffic-classification schemes and traffic plans.[2]

ASF's highway-planning program was initially led by the traffic engineer G. Donald Kennedy. Before joining ASF in 1943, Kennedy had served as head of the Michigan State Highway Department and president of AASHO. He was the vice-chair of the Interregional Highway committee, which had established the basic plan of the US Interstate Freeway System. At ASF, his title was vice-president for highways. The historian Bruce Seely noted that Kennedy's position allowed him to work "in effect, as a full-time lobbyist" for the freeway system.[3]

ASF's first highway report was written for California in 1946. It was instrumental in convincing the public, press, and legislators to launch a massive, ten-year program of major roadway construction. The program's first priority was a "key network" of more than 650 miles (1,050 km) of urban freeways and expressways, while over 3,700 miles (6,000 km) of urban arterials were scheduled for capacity expansion. Spending on California highways would increase by 50 percent, and spending on urban arterials would more than triple. At the 1947 annual AASHO meeting, Kennedy told the

Figure 8.1: ASF's vision of an urban freeway in California, 1946.

assembled engineers that each ASF highway report was not merely informative; it was a public-relations tool. An ASF public-relations advisor affirmed that ASF's reports were the "basis of the most impressive public relations contacts that can be had."[4]

Kennedy departed ASF in 1949 for the Portland Cement Association, and became that organization's president in 1955. He remained on ASF's executive committee until 1965 as a representative of the cement industry. In his stead, the traffic engineer D. Grant Mickle directed ASF's planning program. Mickle had achieved an unusually swift rise to leadership positions during his short career. He had graduated from the Erskine Bureau of Street Traffic Research in 1931; over the following years he worked in the public and private sectors and contributed to several city traffic plans. In the early 1940s he served as Detroit's chief traffic engineer and was president of the Institute of Traffic Engineers (taking office at age 33). He became the director of ASF's Traffic Engineering Division in 1943.[5]

Although ASF customized the details of its plans for each city or state, it had standard policies that it applied generally. One policy was to strengthen the authority of traffic engineers. According to a 1949 review, 42 of the 48 states lacked complete authority to acquire land for, finance, build, and maintain urban highways. That was a legacy of state rural-highway programs that had prohibited activity inside city boundaries. ASF usually recommended that state highway departments be given authority over the engineering and administration of all state highways and major arterials. For large cities, ASF usually recommended that non-state roadway planning and construction be consolidated under a single city agency. That agency would then be required to cooperate with the state highway department.[6]

A second policy was to classify all major roadways. By 1950 most states had some form of classification for state and federal highways, but few states had classification schemes that encompassed all other major roadways. The various states' methods of roadway financing and management were bewilderingly complicated and uncoordinated. Often the result was a scattered patchwork of improvements. In addition, despite federal laws that earmarked money for urban highways, some states directed federal funds to the undeveloped city fringes, or ignored large cities altogether. ASF's policy had several important ramifications. Classification determined which level of government was in charge of a roadway and which funding sources paid for it. Classification underpinned roadway plans that that determined where new highways were built and which arterials were widened. Classification determined roadway-design standards such as the number of lanes, one-way operation, grade separation, and access control.[7]

A third policy was to give priority to urban highways and major arterials. State highway engineers had long complained that cronyism and pork-barrel politics caused exasperating inefficiency and dissipation in their systems. Since the 1910s, highway advocates and interest groups had called for traffic plans to concentrate funding and work effort on a smaller number of more elaborate, expensive facilities. ASF often found that rural highway and major-arterial mileage was excessive, while not enough urban roadways were designated as major. It usually recommended a reduction of rural highway and arterial mileage, and a large increase (in the range of 70–180 percent) of urban highway and arterial mileage.[8]

ASF followed the template prescribed by the *Interregional Highways* report as it designed urban freeway networks. It also planned or recommended arterial networks for existing towns and cities. It advised that selected streets should be converted to major arterials by street widening, one-way operation, turning restrictions, parking bans, and other design changes. In some cases, it recommended a very broad application of access control measures. For example, its Michigan report stated that "access can be controlled on any type of roadway—if action is taken at the time right-of-way is acquired." It urged Michigan's traffic planners to consider full use of that power "in locations where traffic volumes are high and in developing areas where roadside encroachments are probable."[9]

Thomas MacDonald, chief of the US Bureau of Public Roads, spoke about highway planning studies at the 1952 AASHO annual meeting. He said the states' inventories of highway needs "have not been uniform or continuous, and thus do not carry the weight of conviction they should" for the drafters of federal-aid highway legislation in Congress. In MacDonald's opinion, the money that Congress had allocated for street and highway construction fell far short of actual long-term needs.

MacDonald singled out ASF for high praise, saying it was responsible for "many of the best state reports." Those reports had "pioneered the development of an essential administrative tool which now should be accepted and used continuously." To accomplish that, MacDonald called on ASF to develop a standard manual based on the procedures and methods of its state reports. ASF agreed to take on that assignment and soon began to organize it.[10]

Meanwhile, the planning and roadway classification work that ASF had already performed was important in the campaign to fund the Interstate Freeway System. To develop a funding scheme, President Eisenhower appointed a working group known as the Clay Committee. A panel of experts advising the committee was headed by the former ASF president Pyke Johnson, who had left ASF in 1954. According to an Institute of Transportation Engineers history, "In selling the [freeway funding] program, the committee relied heavily on the set of state highway needs studies that had been conducted by the engineering staff of the Automotive Safety Foundation." The Interstate System's funding was boosted in 1956, and floods of money soon reached the state highway departments. Cities came under greater pressure than ever to make plans, yet were often unprepared to do so.[11]

Detroit and Chicago Studies

Several innovative studies during the 1950s helped nudge the functional classification concept toward formal systemization. One was the Detroit Metropolitan Area Traffic Study that ran from 1953 to 1955. It was the first study to thoroughly quantify traffic forecasting and the evaluation of expressway proposals at the metropolitan scale. It was organized by the Michigan State Highway Department and directed by the city planner J. Douglas Carroll. When Carroll had been a doctoral student at Harvard, his advisor was the modernist architect Walter Gropius.[12]

The Detroit study was published from 1955 to 1956 and was immediately recognized as the state-of-the-art in traffic planning. Its methodology seemed so comprehensive and systematic, its results so objective and precise, that Carroll was considered the top transportation planner in the United States. He was hired to lead a similar study for the Chicago region, which ran from 1955 to 1962 and was published in three volumes. Carroll and his team of planners extended the methods of the Detroit study and also incorporated land-use forecasting and public transit. These studies were among the largest planning efforts of their time.[13]

Carroll observed that traffic on each urban roadway affected the traffic on nearby roadways. He was convinced that the only way to account for that complexity was to plan the roadway network as a unified system. Modeling all the traffic in a metropolitan area was an enormous computational task; it was made feasible by punch-card tabulating machines and primitive computers. The machines helped model traffic movement, forecast future needs, and calculate the costs of various proposals.[14]

To translate the roadway network into neatly encoded stacks of punch cards, the planners had to classify every roadway. The roadways were classified as either traffic facilities (meaning expressways and major arterials) or land-access facilities (meaning local streets). The latter were removed from the planning process. The planners worked with state and local traffic agencies to make the classifications.[15]

The planners portrayed the process as logical and objective, but it sometimes involved educated guesswork and subjective judgment. As one participant in the Chicago study recalled, "some of the decisions were hard to make (for example, it is difficult to decide whether a street carrying 2,500 vehicles is a heavily loaded local street or a lightly loaded arterial)." In Detroit the planners strove to create or reinforce neighborhood-unit cellular layouts as they designated arterials, citing the "obviously deleterious effect on property values of putting large traffic volumes on local streets." In Chicago the planners asserted that urban freeways were necessary for the neighborhood-unit concept to work at all. Suburban neighborhood units would be defined by arterials spaced one mile (1.6 km) apart, and freeways were necessary to "drain long distance traffic from arterials."[16]

In the Chicago study, the planners discussed the abstract aspects of roadway classification. They noted that the mobility-access relationship could, in theory, be conceived as a continuous function. They concluded that doing so would introduce unnecessary complexity. "Theoretically, there might be an infinite range of street types, varying from the drive way of a single family house to the expressway, yet, practically, there are only three or four basic types of streets," they said. Yet they also noted that many roadways served overlapping functions: "Collector and arterial streets have the dual function of carrying traffic and of providing access to abutting properties. As traffic volumes increase, traffic and land use come into greater and greater conflict. This is a major planning problem." The planners suggested that parallel service drives should be added to the arterials with the highest traffic volumes. For lower-volume thoroughfares, the problem was left unresolved.[17]

The planners believed that they could adequately measure certain costs and benefits as they planned urban freeway and arterial systems. Specifically, they calculated the costs of construction and operation, and the benefits of crash reduction and time savings. But they were baffled when they considered livability factors such as efficient land development patterns, economic productivity, pollution, transit access, comfort, noise, visual appearance, and nuisance effects. Those factors were too thorny and difficult to measure, and so, "rightly or wrongly, were set aside but not without regret."[18]

The Detroit and Chicago studies were models for the urban transportation plans made in the United States over the next several decades. The studies boosted demand for the universal classification of roadways based on standardized roadway types. The Chicago study was also a primary influence on the 1962 Federal Aid Highway bill, which required all US metropolitan areas to engage in transportation planning. Transportation planning was becoming ever more systematized, standardized, and mandated at all levels of government.

National Committee on Urban Transportation

Thomas MacDonald had called on ASF to create a standard manual for traffic planning. To accomplish that, ASF and the Bureau of Public Roads established the National Committee on Urban Transportation (NCUT) in May 1954. At the time, momentum was building for a great expansion of funding for the Interstate Freeway System, but cities were unprepared to handle such a deluge of money. They lacked the data and expertise needed to plan freeways and freeway-oriented roadway networks. Furthermore, many metropolitan areas contained independent and sometimes competing localities that had never before cooperated on regional planning. NCUT aimed to meet those needs by writing and testing a manual of methods and procedures.[19]

NCUT was financed primarily by ASF and the Bureau of Public Roads. D. Grant Mickle, director of ASF's traffic engineering division, and Edward H. Holmes, director of the Office of Planning at the Bureau of Public Roads, were the lead organizers. They recruited a broad representation of the transportation and land-development sectors to help write and promote NCUT's manuals. The roster of 175 consultants and advisors included highway engineers, traffic engineers, city planners, transit managers, city and county officials, finance officers, lawyers, and academics, as well as seven ASF staff members and eighteen BPR staff members. A wide variety of professional associations was represented. Among the participants were David R. Levin of the Bureau of Public Roads; J. Douglas Carroll Jr. of the Chicago Area Transportation Study; Burton W. Marsh of the American Automobile Association; Max S. Wehrly, head of the Urban Land Institute; and Ralph R. Bartelsmeyer, who would become AASHO's president in 1959 (and head of BPR in 1969).[20]

Over the next four years, NCUT's eleven subcommittees produced seventeen manuals and one summary book. The manuals presented NCUT's standardized traffic-planning system, which was "adaptable to communities of all sizes." They gave instruction on all aspects of the system.[21]

NCUT systematized many of the methods that ASF had employed over the previous decade. It reiterated ASF's principles and design recommendations. It generalized some of ASF's operating strategies. The manuals had new elements as well, and one of those was the roadway classification scheme. Previously, ASF had created slightly different classification schemes for each of its clients. Many of the states and cities had legal and administrative contexts that were slightly different from each other, and ASF had adapted its classification schemes to each.

Now NCUT's staff was charged with developing a standard classification that was both universal and acceptable to its many participants. The classification was produced after several years of consultation. It was similar, but not identical, to earlier classifications such as those in the manuals of the 1940s and ASF's own reports.

NCUT's classification formalized the relationship of traffic and abutter access.

Element	System			
	Expressway	Major Arterial	Collector	Local
Service Function				
movement	primary	primary	equal	secondary
access	none	secondary	equal	primary
principal trip length	over 3 miles	over 1 mile	under 1 mile	under 1/2 mile
use by transit	express	regular	regular	none, except C.B.D.
Linkage				
Land Uses	major generators & C.B.D.	secondary generators & C.B.D.	local areas	individual sites
Rural Highways	interstate & state primary	state primary & secondary	county roads	none
Spacing	1-3 miles	1 mile	1/2 mile	----
Percentage of System	0 - 8		20 - 35	65 - 80

Figure 8.2: NCUT's street classification table, 1958. The first formal codification of the movement-access inverse relationship.

Movement described the priority given to high volumes of fast, unimpeded traffic. *Access* described the priority given to abutter access. Movement and access were inversely related: roadways that served the most movement had the least access, and roadways that served the least movement had the most access. The classification had four roadway types, each serving movement and access to a different degree. *Expressways* were freeways or other limited-access roadways that provided no abutter access. *Arterials* served movement primarily. Secondarily, they served the access needs of abutting properties by providing space for loading and unloading people and goods, and parking. *Collectors* served movement and access equally. *Local streets* served access primarily; they served movement secondarily, while discouraging through traffic.[22]

NCUT's classification marked the emergence of functional classification as a codified policy. It was the first complete formulation of the idea—an important but unheralded development in traffic planning. Functional classification exerted a tremendously powerful influence over the following decades. Its impact on the development patterns of the United States and other countries was fundamental and wide-ranging. To those who were unfamiliar with its origin, functional classification was received wisdom: unsourced, unclaimed, and nearly canonized with the status of a natural law, like pi or the golden ratio.

NCUT and the Red Book

Functional classification's greatest effect on development patterns was the shaping of roadway layouts. Two standards were particularly important to that shaping effect: the spacing of arterials and the spacing of intersections on arterials.

As NCUT was underway, the American Association of State Highway Engineers released *A Policy on Arterial Highways in Urban Areas* (1957), popularly known as the Red Book because of its red cover. It quickly became the standard reference for highway and arterial design in American cities (it was reprinted six times through 1966). Many of its standards worked in concert with NCUT's program.

The Red Book recommended widely spaced intersections on suburban arterials to enable continuous, relatively fast (40 mph or 64 kmh) traffic flow. According to the Red Book, "desirable" traffic flow required intersections to be spaced 1,000 feet (330 m) or more apart. The NCUT summary book, which was published a year later, specified that transportation planners should use the Red Book's design standards, including the intersection-spacing standard.[23]

NCUT recommended that collectors should link adjacent neighborhoods and form a continuous network, but in practice that provision tended to be ignored. Notably, the Red Book said nothing about collector networks. Therefore, arterials were often the sole through routes in American suburbs, and their configurations were critical to the way that those suburbs functioned. NCUT recommended that arterials should be spaced one mile (1,600 m) apart so that neighborhoods one mile in diameter could be built in the interstices. By comparison, main streets in traditional city layouts were commonly spaced a quarter-mile (400 m) apart, or four times more frequently.[24]

The combination of infrequently spaced arterials and infrequent intersections on arterials strongly reinforced the cellular principle. The Red Book fully endorsed cellular roadway layouts that enclosed neighborhood units. And, as the Red Book recognized, highways and major arterials "exert a powerful force tending to shape the future development of the city." NCUT's classification system, together with the standards promulgated by AASHO and other organizations, produced disconnected roadway networks and insular neighborhoods. These guidelines and standards were essential strands in the DNA of American sprawl.[25]

Promotional Techniques

NCUT recommended an administrative protocol typical of the era: a top-down process led by a central authority of bureaucrat-engineers. That central authority would create the street classification plan, which would be the basis of "the ultimate plan for street use."[26]

NCUT also recommended a role for lay citizens. It said that a citizens' advisory committee should be formed, composed of "top executives of business, industry, labor, service and professional groups, broadcasting, advertising, and the press." Those citizens would serve as "ambassadors" who could enlist their own organizations and public-relations experts to sell the transportation plan. Committee members should be "properly indoctrinated" and given tasks "so that they can feel they are making a useful contribution," such as unpaid staff work. In short, the role of leading citizens was to mobilize public opinion and support the traffic experts. The same technique had been used to brilliant effect by Paul G. Hoffman in Los Angeles three decades earlier, and had also been used by ASF and other auto-safety initiatives.[27]

Few deployed those promotional techniques more assiduously than NCUT itself. NCUT was widely influential, and that outcome was partly owed to the organization's prominent, well-connected membership. Furthermore, NCUT's name itself was a promotional technique. The strategy of assigning anodyne, generic, quasi-governmental names to private interest groups was used repeatedly by the auto industry in the decades after World War II. It represented the industry's desire to confer upon itself an image of authority and rational impartiality. It gave an impression of service to the public interest, which the industry viewed as identical to its own interests.

NCUT's manuals were field tested in seven cities; by 1960 another five cities had adopted the program and more than 150 communities were considering adoption. Thousands of NCUT manuals were purchased by communities across the nation. As NCUT completed its assignment and dissolved itself in 1960, it boasted that "the Committee's work has been an unqualified success." The NCUT manuals were endorsed by the Bureau of Public Roads, AASHO, and other leading organizations. NCUT's roadway classification scheme was widely cited as an authoritative framework. It was the major source for the AASHO-NACO-NACE publication *A Guide for Functional Highway Classification* (1966) and the federal government's publications on functional classification from 1969 onward.[28]

D. Grant Mickle departed ASF in 1961 to take the newly created position of deputy federal highway administrator at the Bureau of Public Roads. From 1964 to 1966 he was the director of the Highway Research Board. He rejoined ASF in 1966 and became its president in 1969. ASF merged with several organizations to form the Highway Users Federation for Safety and Mobility, and Mickle served as its president from 1970 to 1975. In all those positions, Mickle continued to exert a leading influence on traffic policy and legislation.[29]

Guidebooks of the 1960s

ASF's initiatives added momentum to the effort to establish a national standardized roadway classification. In 1956 ASF helped organize the National Association of County Engineers (NACE). According to a NACE history, ASF representative Howard Bussard "preached to the engineers the benefits of more uniform standards" and, once the organization was established, lent ongoing administrative and research support. In 1961 NACE published a functional classification manual that had been "spearheaded" by Bussard. ASF provided grants and administrative support through the mid-1960s, particularly to help produce NACE's manuals.[30]

NACE had been spun off from the National Association of Counties (NACO), which also received grants from ASF. NACE and NACO partnered with the American Association of State Highway Officials to publish *A Guide for Functional Highway Classification* in 1966. The guide was funded by ASF and the Bureau of Public Roads. It aimed to explain "the process to obtain cooperation" from all road and street agencies in a state, and how to make a roadway plan that would serve as a "firm basis" for estimating highway needs.[31]

The *Guide* listed the problems of nonstandardized roadway classification systems. Classifications could be irrational, meaning that they assigned overlapping responsibilities and vague lines of authority to various agencies. Classifications could be complicated or ambiguous, which created interagency confusion. And classifications could be unstable, meaning that they assigned responsibility for roadways to agencies that lacked the resources to build and maintain them. The *Guide* said these problems were quite common, and claimed that a proper classification system would resolve them.[32]

Conditions that the *Guide* viewed as disordered may have simply been the proper working of democracy in the view of certain city governments. By the mid-1960s, resistance to urban freeways was organized and growing. Freeway construction was stalled in at least a dozen large cities, a dissatisfying situation indeed for the pro-freeway forces. The *Guide* explained that urban freeways that followed circumferential and "penetrating" routes should be under state control. That would allow effective planning and administration, and would respond properly to the public interest as the *Guide* defined it. When planning other urban highways and arterials, the *Guide* said cooperation with city officials was preferable to total state control.[33]

The *Guide* copied NCUT's language and recommended NCUT's classification manual as a source of greater detail. But it also made a few departures. It did not present a standardized or quantified formulation of the movement-to-access relationship; instead, it relied on vague descriptive categories. It emphasized trip length as a determinant of roadway classification. High-volume streets could therefore be classified as local streets: "Some local streets having commercial frontage may serve fairly substantial volumes of traffic but it will be of a terminal, rather than of a through, nature," said the *Guide*. That advice could be problematic in practice, because distinguishing local from through traffic on high-volume roadways could be difficult. To address the danger and conflicts caused by commercial centers and abutter access on arterials, the *Guide* brusquely stated that "limited-access facilities should be developed."[34]

According to NACO, the *Guide* was intended as a manual for a nationwide roadway classification study. BPR and AASHO partnered to execute that study, and submitted the results to the US Congress in 1968. As part of the study, AASHO surveyed its members about future federal-aid highway legislation. The survey found that 46 of the nation's 51 highway departments wanted federal-aid categories to be based on functional classification. That overwhelming response affirmed AASHO's goal of making functional classification a mandated national standard.[35]

ASF also helped prepare the ground for a national functional classification by supplementing the work of AASHO and other organizations. It released a slickly produced booklet, *Functional Highway Classification in Urban Areas* (1967), which was based on various ASF plans and publications, the AASHO-NACO-NACE *Guide*, and the NCUT classification manual.[36]

The booklet offered a notably abstract definition of functional classification: it was the classification of roadways based on "their importance to the general welfare, the motorist, and the land-use structure." The importance of each roadway was determined by the number and length of vehicle trips it carried, as well as subjective judgments about the economic and cultural value of the destinations it served. The purpose of functional classification was to funnel traffic (and government funding) to the most socially important, "higher class," high-speed, high-capacity freeways and arterials.[37]

The resulting roadway classification was similar to the earlier classifications by NCUT and AASHO. The ASF booklet expanded the number of roadway classes from four to five and renamed them (the authors apparently worried that collectors might not receive federal funding unless they were called arterials).[38]

The booklet also featured a chart that showed the relationship of roadway-class importance to through traffic as a nearly continuous function. As roadway-class importance decreased, the percentage of through traffic smoothly decreased to near zero. The chart was a direct precursor to the important functional-classification diagram

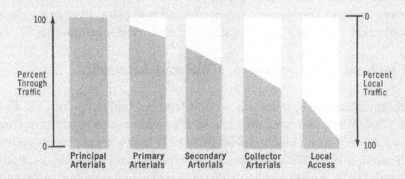

Figure 2—TRAFFIC COMPOSITION AND FUNCTIONAL CLASSIFICATION

Percent Through Traffic

Percent Local Traffic

Principal Arterials — Primary Arterials — Secondary Arterials — Collector Arterials — Local Access

The predominant traffic service determines the functional classification of a street or highway.

Figure 8.3: ASF's prototypical functional classification chart, 1967.

that the US Department of Transportation created two years later.

The booklet made a few noteworthy departures from earlier texts. It specified that the arterials that bounded and defined neighborhoods should be spaced 1 mile (1.6 km) apart in existing urban areas. In suburbs, they typically would be spaced 2 miles (3.2 km) apart and could be as much as 3 miles (4.8 km) apart. In regard to collectors, ASF revoked NCUT's advice of a decade earlier and said that collectors should not link adjacent neighborhoods.[39]

The booklet expressed confidence that functional classification would have a positive effect over the long term. It displayed an emblem that represented the history and desirable future of city roadway patterns. In the old, outmoded city center, gridirons of small blocks and frequently spaced arterials formed dense and highly connected roadway networks. As time went on and development expanded outward, roadway networks became sparser, arterials more widely spaced, and local streets less connected.

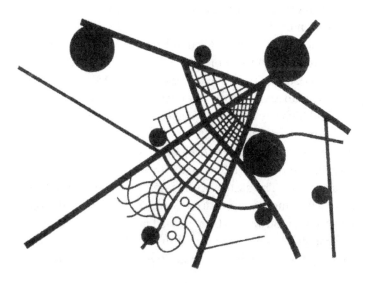

Figure 8.4: ASF's emblem of historical roadway development, 1967. In each successive era, the roadway network becomes more sprawling and disconnected. Cul-de-sacs appear in the outermost areas.

The booklet declared that functional classification was vital to city planning and would produce logical and efficient roadway networks. Roadway plans should respond to changes in land use, it said; but at the same time, functional classification would promote land uses that were consistent with roadway plans. In other words, functional classification would be a powerful shaper of future land-use patterns.[40]

US Federal-Aid Roadways, 1968 and Afterward

Criticism of automobile-dominated development had never entirely disappeared after World War II. Rather, it manifested as a steady undercurrent of discontent. The opposition grew into a highly visible and voluble wave after the Interstate System was authorized in 1956. The criticisms were numerous and the critics passionate. They protested traffic crashes, pollution, disruption of urban neighborhoods, falling property values, displacement of residents, and ever-expanding suburban sprawl. Rather than saving downtown businesses, urban freeways were hastening the loss of customers and the growth of suburban competitors. Any attractive walkable places were degraded if they were in the immediate vicinity of urban freeways. Witnesses at the 1967 Senate hearings on urban highways complained that knowledge from outside the highway engineering profession was poorly integrated into the planning process, which gave short shrift to social, aesthetic, and ecological issues. In reaction to the multifarious criticisms, the auto and highway interests were by turns defensive, defiant, or conciliatory.[41]

Safety was prominent in the public mind because the vehicular fatality rate was spiraling upward. The rate of fatalities per capita reached near-record levels in the 1960s (figure 7.4). During the same period, the rate of fatalities per mile traveled declined. The public-interest lawyer Ralph Nader described the phenomenon in his 1965 book *Unsafe at Any Speed*, saying, "What this means is that a motorist can expect to drive farther in any given year without being killed, but he is just as likely as in previous years to be killed within that year." Nader spotlighted ASF (and the ASF-supported President's Committee on Traffic Safety) as a tool of the auto industry. Over the long term, said Nader, ASF had helped deflect blame away from the vehicles themselves.[42]

Concerns about safety and natural beauty, and a desire for a more multimodal approach, led to a reorganization of the federal transportation bureaucracy. The US Department of Transportation (DOT) and its Federal Highway Administration (FHWA) were established in 1967. The Bureau of Public Roads was folded into the Federal Highway Administration that year (its moniker was retired in 1970). Relations between the new agency and the auto and highway interests were not always friendly. From 1966 to 1968, the auto and highway interests engaged in heated battle with the administration over cuts to highway spending.[43]

That was the context in which the first *National Highway Needs Report* was written. The report, released in early 1968, was written by BPR with the help of AASHO and the state highway departments. The states' anticipated needs amounted to a staggering increase in roadway funding. They needed freeway mileage to be doubled and annual spending on federal-aid roadways to be increased more than fifty percent. Federal-aid system needs through 1985 were projected to be $128 billion. Perhaps recognizing the contemporary political tenor, the *Needs Report* did not endorse an expansion of the Interstate Freeway System. But it did recommend a new federal-aid system dedicated exclusively to urban arterials.[44]

The *Needs Report* was based on a tentative, approximate nationwide functional classification that BPR had performed in partnership with AASHO. The report recommended a more thorough functional classification study, saying it would be "essential for an efficient allocation of resources." Translated from the bureaucratic phrasing, that meant removing underused rural mileage from the federal-aid systems and increasing urban mileage where traffic was congested. The auto and highway interests anticipated that a new functional classification study would lay the foundation for a huge expansion of federal-aid highway and arterial systems.[45]

The pro-auto and highway forces geared up and were well prepared to testify in the congressional hearings for the 1968 Federal-Aid Highway Act. Testimony was given by representatives of the American Association of State Highway Officials, National League of Cities, US Conference of Mayors, National Association of Counties, Institute of Traffic Engineers, American Automobile Association, and others. They marched in lockstep and spoke with a unified message. Functional classification must be standardized and mandated nationwide. It should be used to plan a twenty-year expansion of the nation's highway and major arterial systems. Any city or state that failed to classify its roadways should not receive federal funds.[46]

The lobbyists also advocated a new federal-aid Urban System. This would be a system of urban arterials in the nation's 233 metropolitan areas, augmented by federal funding. The lobbyists expected that federal funds would be spent on new expressways and arterials in developing suburbs, as well as the reconstruction of existing urban roadways to increase traffic speed and capacity. AASHO, which had drafted much of the proposed law, expected that existing arterials would receive design interventions to speed traffic, such as one-way operation, removal of curb parking, added turn lanes, barriers to restrict turns, separation of pedestrian and vehicular traffic in congested areas, and so on.[47]

While the expansion of the Interstate Freeway System and continued construction of urban freeways were very contentious issues, the nationally mandated functional classification system met with no apparent opposition—neither in 1968 nor in later years. The Federal-Aid Highway Act of 1968 was signed into law in August 1968. It required a nationwide functional classification study that would serve as one of the bases for "realigning" federal highway programs.[48]

The next year, BPR issued a functional classification manual to guide its nationwide study. It used the formulations that had been developed since the 1950s, and presented functional classification as a mobility-access relationship. Mobility was defined generally by speed and travel distance; traffic volume and route directness were additional factors. Access was defined as access to land property. A diagram explained the mobility-access relationship. It adapted the 1967 ASF diagram and showed the relationship as a continuous S-shaped curve. The curve magnified the dichotomy of the roadway classes: the mobility function of higher-class roadways was exaggerated and the access function of lower-class roadways was exaggerated. The diagram appeared in Federal Highway Administration manuals for forty years (until it was discontinued in 2013) and was reproduced in countless state manuals, guidebooks, and textbooks. The diagram, and variations based upon it, became the single most identifiable visual

Figure 8.5: US
Bureau of Public
Roads, functional
classification
chart, 1969. The
illustration became
the most well-
known symbol
of functional
classification.

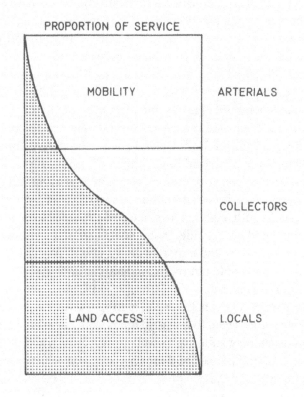

RELATIONSHIP OF FUNCTIONALLY CLASSIFIED SYSTEMS IN SERVING
TRAFFIC MOBILITY AND LAND ACCESS

PROPORTION OF SERVICE

MOBILITY   ARTERIALS

COLLECTORS

LAND ACCESS   LOCALS

symbol of the functional classification idea.[49]

According to the manual, arterials that bounded neighborhoods should be spaced 1 mile (1.6 km) apart in developed areas and 2–3 miles (3.2–4.8 km) apart in new suburbs. Arterials could be more closely spaced in areas of very high traffic density, but the manual's charts showed that only a tiny percentage of a city's traffic traveled in such areas. Identical language appeared in subsequent federal manuals and AASHTO's design manuals into the 2000s. Over time, this and similar standards influenced American suburbs and increased the insularity of their inhabited districts.[50]

The states went to work during 1969–1970 to functionally classify all the nation's roadways. The work was performed by state highway departments with the cooperation of local governments. As sources of advice, BPR suggested groups that had supported or lobbied for the study: local chapters of the National Association of Counties, the National League of Cities, and the National Association of County Engineers.[51]

The US DOT's *1970 National Highway Needs Report* used the results to analyze the nation's roadways. It found notable mismatches between existing roadway classes and traffic volumes. Some high-volume urban streets were not in any federal-aid system, while some local streets were. The report concluded that a realignment was necessary, especially in large urban areas where the mismatches were greatest. *Realignment*—a term that also appeared in legislation—meant adding urban arterials to federal-aid systems and removing underused rural roadways.[52]

Congress adopted the recommendations with little alteration. The Federal Aid Highway Act of 1970 required the US DOT to use functional classification to recommend 20-year plans for federal-aid roadways. BPR interpreted that to mean the construction of new freeways, arterials and collectors, and the widening or reconstruction of existing ones, to ensure uncongested traffic flow. The 1970 Act also established and funded a federal-aid Urban System that comprised urban roadways not already in a federal-aid system. Its routes would serve major activity centers, and would be designed to carry the highest traffic volumes and longest trips. The routes were to be selected by state highway departments and local officials in cooperation.[53]

The early 1970s was a time of widespread cultural turmoil that strongly affected transportation planning. Public concern about the destruction of urban and natural environments swelled into a mass movement. The first Earth Day was held in 1970 and attracted millions of participants nationwide. President Nixon established the Environmental Protection Agency later that year. The National Environmental Policy Act was enacted in 1970; it required environmental impact statements for federal projects, and created opportunities for highway opponents to block or delay highway construction through legal or administrative action. The Arab oil embargo of 1973 roused concerns about the nation's inefficient, auto-dominated transportation system.

The highway lobby grew increasingly worried about the integrity of the Highway Trust Fund. It strenuously opposed calls to divert funding to mass transit. The Highway Users Federation for Safety and Mobility (HUFSAM, the successor to ASF) and its president D. Grant Mickle went on the offensive against highway opponents, not only issuing factual rebuttals but attacking the loudest critics and belittling their knowledge and expertise. HUFSAM's rebuttals became the widely used "script" for the highway lobby. Opponents said HUFSAM was misrepresenting its own public-interest motives. In reality, the opponents charged, it was a lobbying group created to save the Highway Trust Fund.[54]

Meanwhile, efforts to institute functional classification nationwide proceeded with relative unanimity. Witnesses at the hearings for the Federal-Aid Highway Act of 1973 included representatives of the American Automobile Association, Asphalt Institute, National Association of Counties, American Road Builders Association, HUFSAM, and American Association of State Highway Officials. Again they advocated a nationwide functional classification to replan the federally funded roadway systems. They testified that functional classification helped policymakers guide funds to locations that had the greatest congestion and safety needs.[55]

The requirement was duly signed into law. The 1973 Act required each state to use functional classification to re-designate its roadways by 1976. It would be the fourth nationwide functional classification study performed since 1966. The 1973 Act also modified the federal-aid Urban System, allowing any high-volume arterial or collector to be included. Every federal surface-transportation law since then has included a functional classification requirement. The Federal Highway Administration initiated the Highway Performance Monitoring System in 1978, and since 1980 it has reported the states' functional classifications on an annual schedule.[56]

The results were very much as the lobbyists and road advocates had hoped. Growth in the federal-aid system was reoriented from rural to urban roadways, and the mileage of those roadways increased dramatically. Between 1970 and 1990 the mileage

US National Functional Classification Studies 1966-1976

Years	Title	Required By	Manual Used	Reported In	Description
1966-1968	Not applicable	Public Law 89-139 (1965), amendment to Federal-Aid Highway Act of 1956 (1)	AASHO-NACO-NACE Guide (1966)	1968 National Highway Needs Report (2)	An approximate, tentative review of existing roadways and future needs
1969-1970	1968 National Highway Functional Classification Study	Federal-Aid Highway Act of 1968	1968 National Highway Functional Classification Study Manual (1969)	1970 National Highway Needs Report	A nationwide functional classification of existing roadways
1970-1973	1970-1990 National Highway Functional Classification and Needs Study	Federal-Aid Highway Act of 1970	National Highway Functional Classification and Needs Study Manual (1970 to 1990) (1970)	1972 National Highway Needs Report (3)	Preliminary classification of existing and future roadways based on anticipated usage in 1990
1975-1976	1976 National Highway Inventory and Performance Study	Federal-Aid Highway Act of 1973	National Highway Inventory and Performance Study Manual 1976 (1975)	National Functional System Mileage and Travel Summary (1977)	Re-designation of existing and future roadways based on anticipated usage in 1980

(1) The 1966-1968 functional classsification study was motivated by legislation, but not specifically required.
(2) A preliminary version was "Preliminary Report of AASHO on Federal Aid Highway Needs After 1972," US House Committee on Public Works, 7 June 1967.
(3) The 1972 study was updated for the 1974 National Highway Needs Report .

Figure 8.6: US functional classification studies performed from 1966 to 1976. After 1979, such studies were systematized and performed annually.

A HISTORY OF STREET NETWORKS • CHAPTER 8

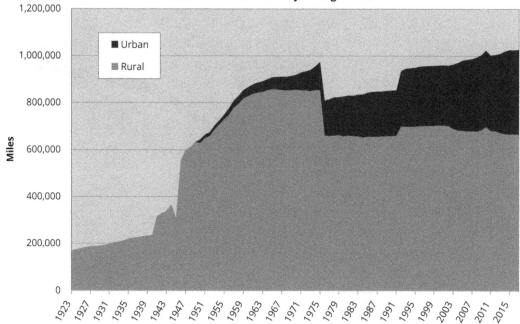

US Federal-Aid Roadway Mileage 1923–2017

Figure 8.7: The urban share of federal-aid roadways grew from zero in 1949 to 35 percent in 2017. The greatest increase occurred after 1975. Data: FHWA.

of federal-aid urban roadways more than tripled. In 1991 the Intermodal Surface Transportation Efficiency Act swept all urban roadways (other than local streets) into the federal-aid program. Urban federal-aid mileage took an abrupt jump, then continued to expand at a steadier pace.[57]

Over that entire period, from 1970 to 2017, urban federal-aid mileage increased nearly 470 percent. By comparison, over the same period, the United States' urban population increased 78 percent. From 1980 to 2017, the mileage of each functional class of the urban federal-aid roadways expanded substantially; growth ranged from 60 to over 200 percent. Minor arterials and collectors constituted three-quarters of the mileage expansion. Urban interstate-freeway mileage grew from 9,200 to 19,300 (14,800 to 31,100 km), an increase of 110 percent. That increase was huge compared to the "freeway revolts" that stopped a few hundred miles at most.

During the 1970s and 1980s, many states formally incorporated the new functional classifications into their roadway planning. Several studies about arterial spacing were issued by the Federal Highway Administration, Institute of Traffic Engineers, and Motor Vehicle Manufacturers' Association. Many states adopted the standards of those studies in addition to functional classification. For most suburban areas, the standards specified widely spaced arterials (typically 1–2 miles or 1.6–3.2 km apart) and widely spaced signalized intersections (typically 0.25–0.5 mile or 0.4–0.8 km apart). As a result, a sprawling version of the cellular roadway pattern became commonplace in most American suburbs.[58]

Furthermore, the design standards issued by AASHTO and other organizations ensured that urban-arterial design was dominated by motor-vehicle requirements, particularly high speed. The resulting arterials were unsafe and uncomfortable for

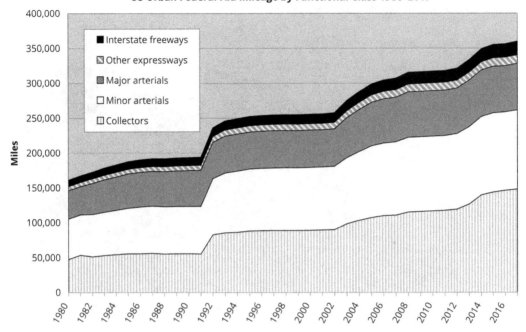

US Urban Federal-Aid Mileage by Functional Class 1980–2017

Figure 8.8: Minor arterials and collectors constituted the majority of urban federal-aid mileage expansion. Note: 2009 and 2010 figures are not available; interpolated estimates are used. Data: FHWA.

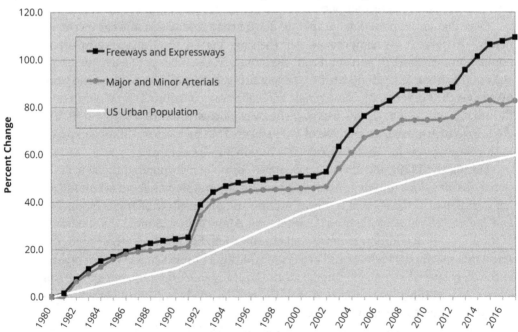

US Urban Federal-Aid Freeway and Arterial Mileage 1980–2017

Figure 8.9: In the United States, urban freeway, expressway, and arterial growth substantially outpaced urban population growth. Data: FHWA and US Census.

pedestrians and bicyclists, and their character contributed to the physical isolation of the neighborhoods they bordered. The design standards induced a sameness of appearance that heightened the image of new suburbs as generic, anonymous places. Technically the manuals did allow flexibility in application, but because of institutional inertia, lack of ready alternatives, and concerns about legal liability, engineers generally hewed to uniform, auto-oriented designs.[59]

Changes were also occurring in the layouts of local streets. As functional classification channeled ever-greater volumes of traffic onto arterials, house lots became more valuable when they offered retreat and disconnection within the bounded residential pods. Homeowners sought increased privacy, security, and safety for children. Local governments abdicated their responsibility for street-layout planning to developers, who believed that cul-de-sacs yielded the biggest profits. During the 1970s the "loops and lollipops" pattern became common: a disconnected, maze-like layout of short loops and cul-de-sacs. During the 1980s the degree of disconnection increased, and the "lollipops on a stick" pattern became common. It was a strongly dendritic roadway layout that branched, sub-branched, and ended in cul-de-sacs. The roadway layouts envisioned by modernist architects in the 1930s had become the American standard, but usually without the pedestrian paths, convenient transit, and commercial centers within walking distance that they had recommended.

These disconnected layouts had major disadvantages. The maze-like patterns were disorienting and especially inconvenient for walking. Driving trips were concentrated on arterials, which consequently became clogged by traffic. The disconnected layouts could be well-suited to specific markets in specific time periods, but they were

	Gridiron (c. 1900)	Fragmented Parallel (c. 1950)	Warped Parallel (c. 1960)	Loops and Lollipops (c. 1970)	Lollipops on a Stick (c. 1980)
Street Patterns	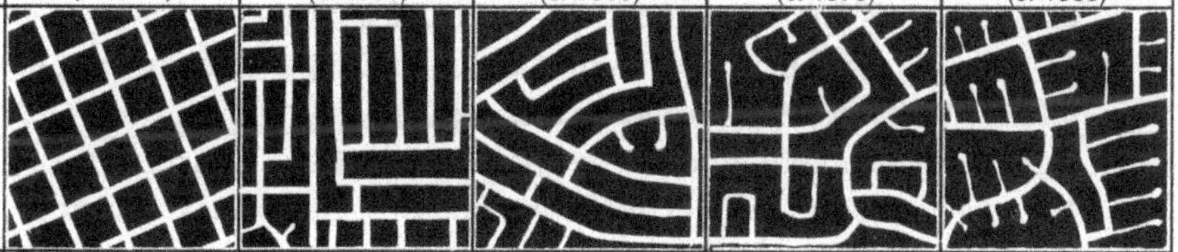				
Intersections	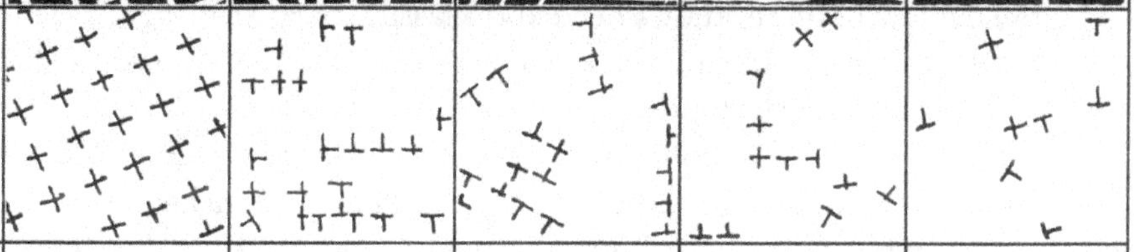				
Lineal Feet of Streets	20,800	19,000	16,500	15,300	15,600
# of Blocks	28	19	14	12	8
# of Intersections	26	22	14	12	8
# of Access Points	19	10	7	6	4
# of Loops & Cul-de-Sacs	0	1	2	8	24

Figure 8.10: Table by Southworth and Owens, 1993, analyzing historical changes in American roadway patterns. After World War II, new suburban layouts became successively more dendritic and disconnected. Image © Michael Southworth and Peter M. Owens.

inflexible and had little ability to handle growth or adapt to changing conditions and preferences.[60]

The concepts and methods of functional classification spread internationally. In 2002 the planning professor Stephen Marshall reviewed fourteen roadway classification systems in nine European countries. He found that all used the mobility-access relationship and trip length as classification factors. Some systems included additional factors to recognize pedestrian-oriented local streets, but only in limited or minor ways. None of the systems promoted pedestrian-oriented major thoroughfares or mass transit, and few recognized the role of streets as lively public spaces (Germany's system was one that did). Marshall observed that "The act of classification is to some extent a 'political' act. A classification reveals the priorities and biases (intentional or unintentional) of those making the classification."[61]

Chapter 8 Summary

From the late 1950s to the early 1970s in the United States, functional classification emerged as a systematized concept, was promoted resolutely, and finally was mandated nationwide.

The primary organizer and funder of that effort was the Automotive Safety Foundation, which had an extensive background in the field. From the late 1940s to early 1960s, ASF was the leading supplier of state and metropolitan traffic-classification schemes and traffic plans. Its policy was to classify all major roadways and give priority to urban highways and arterials. Its classifications helped determine where new highways would go, which arterials would be widened, and which design standards were applied (such as one-way operation, grade separation, and access control). Many cities followed ASF's guidance. They reorganized their roadway systems and planning procedures for faster, larger streams of traffic.

Several large, highly systematized traffic studies performed during the 1950s helped nudge the functional classification concept toward codification. They included the Detroit Metropolitan Area Traffic Study and the Chicago Area Transportation Study. In order to process their plans with tabulating machines and primitive computers, the authors of those studies needed to classify every roadway. The studies strengthened the demand for a universal classification based on standardized roadway types.

Shortly before he retired, Bureau of Public Roads chief Thomas MacDonald called for a standardized national traffic-planning manual based on ASF's methods. The National Committee on Urban Transportation was launched in 1954 to accomplish that. It generally reiterated ASF's principles and strategies, but one of the new elements was its roadway classification scheme. It marked the first appearance of functional classification as a codified policy.

Through the 1960s, a series of traffic-classification manuals was produced by tightly linked, ideologically allied organizations that cited each other as authorities. ASF was a key promoter and funder of those initiatives. One of the manuals, the AASHO-NACO-NACE *Guide*, was written for a nationwide roadway-classification study. The results of that study informed the federal government's 1968 Highway Needs Report. Another of the manuals, a booklet by ASF, stated that the purpose of functional classification was to funnel traffic and funding to the most socially important, high-speed, high-capacity freeways and arterials. It predicted that functional classification would be a powerful shaper of future land-use patterns.

From the late 1960s to early 1970s, the pro-auto and highway forces, and allied planners and engineers, lobbied the US Congress to mandate the use of functional classification. The effort went through several cycles of writing legislation, producing federal roadway classification manuals, and classifying roadways at the state level. At a time when urban freeway construction was extremely contentious, the functional-classification initiative moved forward without public protest, or even much public notice.

Finally in 1973, the use of functional classification was mandated nationwide. Over the following decades, functional classification directed funding to an enormous and growing number of urban roadways. The extent of urban federal-aid roadways grew nearly 470 percent from 1970 to 2017. Most of that expansion took the form of minor arterials and collectors. Interstate freeway mileage in urban areas also expanded greatly, more than doubling from 1980 to 2017.

Functional classification was also used to assign uniform design standards at the state level. States adopted government- and industry-recommended standards for widely spaced arterials and infrequent intersections on arterials. Over time, these and similar standards increased the insularity of developments in new suburban districts. A sprawling version of the cellular, dendritic roadway layout became commonplace in most American suburbs.

Functional classification had a number of disadvantages that were never fully resolved. For instance, roadway classes that combined higher speed with abutter access had greater crash danger. Commonly recommended solutions, such as limited-access arterials and side access lanes, were expensive or made development more sprawling and less convenient. Another disadvantage was that functional classification recognized only a limited set of roadway types. Slow, relatively narrow thoroughfares with civic-social functions, such as traditional main streets or high streets, were banned or discouraged. A third disadvantage was that people who lived along arterials suffered the harms of excessive traffic. The preferred solutions of large setbacks, berms, and noise walls wasted land, were inconvenient, and severed communities.

The invention and adoption of functional classification in the United States represented a large, well-coordinated effort by motordom and state and federal highway departments. The industry organized on multiple fronts and coordinated with multiple levels of government. Remarkably, functional classification remained a relatively obscure policy even as it exerted powerful effects on metropolitan areas. ASF's prediction was correct: functional classification helped make American built environments—especially the thousands of square miles of new suburbs—firmly and almost permanently oriented to automobiles. The concepts of functional classification also spread abroad and exerted similar influences in many cities around the world.

CHAPTER 9
Mid-Twentieth Century to Early Twenty-First

The period from the mid-twentieth century to early twenty-first was a time of both consolidation and challenge in urban traffic planning. Even as dendritic and super-block traffic planning gained a virtual hegemony in urban development worldwide, new trends arose in opposition. Some challengers sought to reverse or moderate extreme cellularity by designing better-connected roadway layouts. Some revived older traffic-separation practices or invented new ones, wanting to foster more humane and livable urban environments. The challengers were motivated by the flaws of mainstream traffic planning. As it was applied to ever larger territories, its negative effects were becoming ever more obvious.

Buchanan Report: *Traffic In Towns*

Colin Buchanan (1907–2001) was a civil engineer who spent part of his career as a road and highway planner in the UK government. From 1946 to 1960 he served in the Ministry of Town and Country Planning, working on planning and transport in the London area. During his years there, he wrote several articles and a book about the mixed nature of the automobile—its unmistakable benefits and attractions as well as its costs and excruciating harms. Buchanan's forthright views on topics beyond the boundaries of engineering earned him a measure of disapproval within the bureaucratic hierarchy.

But others appreciated Buchanan's blend of ethics, aesthetics, and hard-nosed engineering. In 1960 Ernest Marples, head of the Ministry of Transport, appointed Buchanan as an urban road-planning adviser. Buchanan's assignment was to lead a wide-ranging report on motor traffic in British towns and cities. He selected his own team of assistants, but was overseen by a steering committee that may have worked to moderate his most extreme anti-car opinions.[1]

Buchanan's report was published in 1963 as *Traffic in Towns*. It was the first government publication to analyze in detail the conflicts and tradeoffs between motor traffic and street livability. It began by presenting the country's long-term traffic situation.

The number of vehicles was forecast to double within ten years, and peak urban traffic flows were forecast to triple within twenty years. The report said a governmental response was critical, and it had to accommodate the automobile's essential role in the country's economic and social life. Automobile dominance seemed to be inevitable and permanent. The report stated that "there cannot be any going back on it."[2]

Traffic in Towns used specific, idiosyncratic definitions to outline the fundamental traffic problem. It defined good *accessibility* as convenient, fast, and pleasant conditions for driving and parking. It defined a good *environment* as one "free from the dangers and nuisances of motor traffic," or in other words, a place where motor-traffic speed and volume were low. Providing both in an urban district was difficult because they tended to conflict with each other: good accessibility tended to destroy good environments, and good environments tended to impede good accessibility. Most of the report was devoted to ideas and projects that tried to resolve that conflict.[3]

Throughout the country, observed the report, the traffic issues that received the most attention were congestion, collisions, and parking difficulties. But negative environmental impacts—the "deterioration of our urban surroundings"—were also very serious matters that deserved equal consideration. Some of the sensory impacts were (1) the perception of traffic danger, which caused fear and anxiety, particularly in residential areas; (2) noise, including roaring engines and transmissions, honking horns, squealing brakes, slamming doors, rattling loads or vehicle bodies, and tires on surfaces; (3) fumes, including toxic emissions, smells, and smog; and (4) visual consequences, including the clutter of traffic signs and markings, dirt and litter, and highways that were "violently out of scale" with their surroundings.[4]

The coming automobile boom threatened to exacerbate those impacts and overwhelm the nation's cities:

> . . . we know now, by bitter experience, that the motor vehicle is in conflict with the present structure of towns. By it, and because of it, grievous damage has been done to many of the things we have previously cherished. All the indications are that given its head the motor vehicle would wreck our towns within a decade.[5]

Nevertheless, the report counseled an optimistic view. In the future, Britain's cities would surely have the resources to "remould our environment to our liking." To resolve the fundamental conflict between traffic and livability, the report built upon the cellular layout principles that H. Alker Tripp had elucidated in the 1930s. Cities would be fragmented into zones of good environment known as *environmental areas*. Those areas would be bounded by limited-access roadways, which would ensure fast, convenient intra-city traffic movement. Internally, they could be busy with traffic, but only local traffic traveling on local access roads.

The authors created several case-study schemes to illustrate how these ideas might be applied to existing towns and cities, as well as new town extensions. The smaller towns had lighter traffic loads, so environmental areas could be created using only horizontal traffic-separation methods. For example, an urban motorway (the British equivalent of a freeway) could border an environmental area that had consolidated garages and pedestrian-only streets and plazas. The report was strongly in

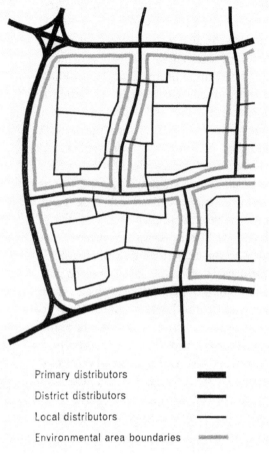

Primary distributors ▬▬▬

District distributors ━━━

Local distributors ───

Environmental area boundaries ▬▬▬

Figure 9.1: Buchanan et al., layout of distributors (limited-access arterials and highways) in cellular pattern, 1963. UK public sector information licensed under the Open Government Licence v3.0.

favor of Radburn-type layouts for new development.

Big cities had heavier traffic loads, which required greater numbers of large motorways and other limited-access arterials. As the number and size of those roadways increased, their impacts became more disruptive and disturbing. The impacts included displacement of people and property, land consumption and increased competition for scarce space, and the "severing effect" of wide roads, big intersections, and heavy traffic flows. In those situations, the only way to ensure both good accessibility and good environments was the comprehensive use of vertical traffic separation. Elaborate multilevel schemes would feature skybridges and pedestrian decks atop high-speed motorways, access roads, and parking lots. The designs could not be implemented in small increments; they had to be coordinated over large areas, requiring powerful authorities and big budgets. Multilevel schemes could secure good environmental standards, but the costs were extravagant.[6]

In the final analysis, cities had three options for dealing with traffic. One was to adopt the American path, meaning total auto dominance and general indifference to environmental effects. The report scorned that path as "the easy way based on the open parking lot," which produced "unrelieved ugliness on a great scale." The second option was to reduce traffic volumes, which would "sacrifice" motor-vehicle accessibility. The report discussed four traffic-reduction policies: entry permits, congestion pricing, decreasing on-site parking requirements for buildings, and subsidizing public transit to decrease fares. The third option was to build the elaborate, expensive multilevel infrastructure that would "accommodate the vehicle in a civilized way."[7]

The report's overall guidance was curiously ambiguous, even self-contradictory in spots. It issued resounding declarations about the harms caused by traffic and the disadvantages of auto-dominated cities. It repeatedly cited Los Angeles's freeway sprawl as a condition to avoid; it called the American disregard for urban environmental quality "almost ruthless." But the report also gave full-throated support to greatly increased automobility in British cities. It purported to lay out the options and leave the choices to the populace, but most of its case studies depicted massive urban motorway and arterial insertions.[8]

Perhaps one intent was to frighten readers and thus build popular support for traffic-reduction policies. The report's conclusion suggested that intent:

> A striking result of our studies is the demonstration of the great scale of the primary networks and interchanges that are required. . . . it has to be admitted that the scale is somewhat frightening, and it may be thought that what we have illustrated is about as much as British cities could possibly stand in the way of being dissected by major roads. . . . The general lesson is unavoidable—if the scale of road works and reconstruction seems frightening, then a lesser scale will suffice *provided there is less traffic.*[9]

Traffic in Towns was exceptionally influential and made Colin Buchanan an international planning celebrity. He took a professorship at Imperial College in London and opened a consulting firm, which was inundated with requests for studies. Meanwhile, *Traffic in Towns* generated much controversy. Its ambiguities allowed readers to draw different conclusions depending on their predilections. Officials, highway engineers, and critics alike saw it as a manifesto for motorization, one that bolstered the national program of urban motorways and urban renewal that was already underway. Conservationists found hope in the report's attention to urban environmental quality and livability. The report inspired a few localities to designate pedestrian streets and establish traffic-restricted environmental areas. In Germany, the report was considered an affirmation of the pedestrianization movement, and Buchanan was called the father of traffic calming.[10]

Fifty years after its publication, *Traffic in Towns* was recognized as one of the planning field's most important books. No other book explained the fundamental conflict between automobility and livability so systematically and in such detail. The book made clear why that conflict is a basic, ineluctable condition of modern cities. Technological trends such as driverless electric cars may ameliorate some aspects of the conflict, but they will not eliminate it. That is because the underlying factors—such as urban spatial geometry, automobile physics, and construction costs—are relatively fixed. They will not change significantly in the foreseeable future.

Donald Appleyard and Cellular-Layout Ethics

The architect and planning professor Donald Appleyard (1928–1982) was powerfully impressed by Buchanan's report, calling it a "salvo in the battle for livable streets." One of the most interesting parts of the report, said Appleyard, was its attempt to define and quantify traffic's effects on street environments. In 1970 he performed a similar exercise for a study of San Francisco's streets.[11]

Appleyard studied three streets that varied in terms of traffic volume but were otherwise similar. The heavy-traffic street carried 15,750 vehicles per day at speeds of 35–45 mph (56–72 kmh). The medium-traffic street carried 8,700 vehicles per day at 25 mph (40 kmh). The light-traffic street carried 2,000 vehicles per day at 15–20 mph (24–32 kmh). The heavy street had traffic signals and was one-way; the medium and light streets had stop signs and were two-way.[12]

As expected, as traffic volumes increased, residents reported more fear of traffic danger and more suffering from traffic noise, stress, and pollution. Appleyard also studied impacts on social relationships and feelings of community. As traffic volumes increased, residents had fewer friends and acquaintances among their neighbors; felt less sense of belonging, seclusion, and privacy; spent less time in their streets' front-ages; and were less aware of their streets' environments. The contrast between heavy and light streets was striking: "On the one hand alienation, on the other friendliness and involvement."[13]

Appleyard continued to study traffic's effects on street environments through-out the 1970s. He also advocated the conversion of existing street grids into traffic-restricting neighborhood layouts. The concept had accumulated a body of practical experience by that time. In the early 1930s, Henry Wright's team wanted to discon-nect existing street layouts to form neighborhood cells. Later that decade, some of the housing projects funded by the US government implemented street closures. More street-layout retrofits were executed in the United States during the 1950s and 1960s, and the Buchanan report motivated another wave in Britain after the mid-1960s. By the 1970s, retrofitting neighborhoods with "traffic restraint" schemes was a global movement, and was implemented in numerous cities using a variety of techniques.[14]

Certain traffic-altering techniques were the most determinative. Barriers and cul-de-sac installations closed streets. Diverters placed diagonally across four-way intersections formed detours and loops. One-way streets and turn restrictions were coordinated in systems that barred through traffic. In 1981 Appleyard found that at least 73 cities in North America had put one or more of those techniques into use. They were deployed in retrofitted neighborhood layouts that either barred entrance to the neighborhood, or created internal mazes that directed traffic back to arterials,

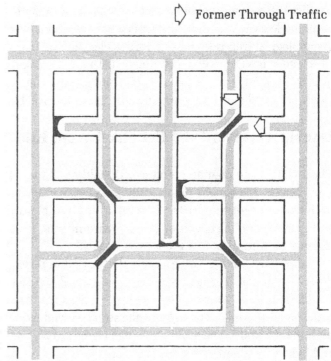

Former Through Traffic

Figure 9.2: Smith and Appleyard, retrofit diagram, 1980. Diverters and cul-de-sacs block through traffic and create internal mazes.

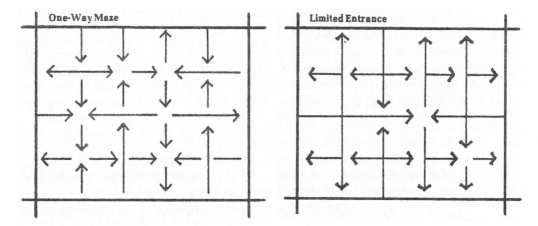

Figure 9.3: Smith and Appleyard, retrofit diagrams, 1981. One-way mazes and a limited number of entrances create cellular traffic-flow patterns.

or combined both methods.[15]

Appleyard believed that an especially important aspect of cellular-layout retrofits was fairness—that is, whether their effects were socially equitable. "The primary question that will arise in each case is, Who gains and who loses, and by how much, from a change in traffic patterns?" he said. "This was never considered when many of these schemes were initiated." He wrote about the fairness of cellular-layout retrofits in the London and San Francisco regions.[16]

London's Barnsbury neighborhood was retrofitted in 1970. It used barriers and one-way streets to form a cellular layout. It caused a substantial traffic-volume decrease within the neighborhood, and a traffic-volume increase on the perimeter streets. Environmental quality was improved for 4,400 residents and worsened for 7,600 residents (Appleyard argued that few of the negative impacts were significant). Traffic noise, pollution, and dirt were more noticeable for longer periods each day on the perimeter streets. Pedestrians, including school children, had more difficulty crossing those busy arterials. The scheme sparked a political backlash, and in 1975 several streets were reopened to "spread the traffic load more evenly." Nighttime traffic was banned on most streets as a compensating measure.[17]

Two neighborhoods in London's Camden borough (Primrose Hill and Camden Square) installed traffic-restraint systems in the early 1970s. Citizen opposition forced those schemes to be scaled back, and the borough government decided that a more comprehensive plan was needed to restrain traffic within neighborhoods. A cellular-layout plan for the whole borough and its population of 230,000 was debated from 1973 to 1974. Thousands of residents opposed the scheme, arguing that it caused "disadvantages to those already disadvantaged and benefits to those already privileged." The borough-wide scheme was ultimately abandoned.[18]

The traffic-restriction program in Berkeley, California, was one of the most extensive. In 1975 the city installed 41 diverters along with other traffic-calming devices, converting the residential grid into an automobile maze. The program was extremely controversial. The diverters were repeatedly vandalized, and opponents forced several citywide votes in an effort to repeal the plan. The repeal initiatives lost and the diverters have remained in place ever since.

A major complaint in the Berkeley controversy was the increased inequality of traffic impacts. Appleyard analyzed the traffic data to measure the equity effects. He found that a majority of the arterials that remained open experienced significant traffic-volume increases. He estimated that most residents experienced traffic-volume reductions, probably because a small percentage of the population lived on the arterials. He was able to find statistics for children in public schools; 21 percent experienced noticeable traffic decreases, while 13 percent experienced traffic increases.[19]

In summary, cellular traffic-restraint retrofits usually increased traffic volumes on perimeter roadways. They often worsened living conditions for at least a portion of the neighborhood's populace. As a result, retrofit schemes were usually controversial, and in some cases were rejected by a groundswell of irate residents.[20]

Because much of the political debate centered on fairness, moral philosophy played an important role. Appleyard believed that each traffic-planning scheme should seek the greatest good for the greatest number of people. If the number that benefited was larger than the number harmed, he believed that the scheme was justified. A different philosophy was put forward during the Camden debate by the planning researchers Mayer Hillman and Irwin Henderson. Although they supported cellular-layout retrofits, they argued that an ethically superior policy would benefit all residents. The only way to achieve that ideal was to reduce traffic volumes throughout the retrofitted district. Hillman and Henderson said planners should first establish as many through routes as possible so that traffic impacts were well distributed. Then, traffic on the through routes should be reduced enough to guarantee good environmental quality on all of them. On local streets, measures like traffic humps should be used instead of hard barriers, because they were more convenient and easier to navigate.

Appleyard flatly rejected Hillman and Henderson's argument. "This is certainly an extreme and idealistic position," he said, "which would thwart any improvement in residential areas for a long time. It ignores the numbers who would benefit, or the degrees of betterment or worsening of conditions."[21]

Appleyard looked for evidence that poorer households suffered disproportionately from the unequal effects of traffic restriction schemes. He did not find such evidence, but he warned that cities must be vigilant. Otherwise, exclusive traffic-restricted enclaves might become "warring fiefdoms" controlled by the wealthier, more powerful social classes.[22]

Neotraditionalism and New Urbanism

Neotraditional urban design can be defined as the adaptation of traditional urban design to contemporary conditions. It arose during the 1960s and 1970s, a time when the dogma of superblocks and cellular roadway layouts informed every aspect of urban-design and traffic-planning practice. The pioneers of neotraditionalism therefore had to devote great effort to rediscovering forgotten or ignored patterns of urban fabric. They explored the ways that historical patterns could be adapted to contemporary contexts, and how the resulting designs could function better than mainstream status-quo practices. They began to reverse the trends of superblocks, cul-de-sacs, and dendritic layouts that had dominated the traffic-planning field for decades.

Jane Jacobs

Jane Jacobs (1916–2006) decided at an early age that she wanted to be a writer. From 1933 to 1943 she worked variously as a newspaper editor, secretary, freelance journalist, and managing editor of a technical trade magazine. She studied journalism, science, geography, and politics at universities, and published her first book in 1941.[23]

In 1943 Jacobs was hired by the News and Features Bureau of the US Office of War Information. She worked as a propaganda writer for the Overseas Division, where she developed military-grade abilities in rhetoric, persuasion, and public relations. After the war she took a similar job as a staff writer for the State Department's magazine *Amerika Illustrated*. The lavish magazine promoted American culture and lifestyles to Russian audiences and "reportedly generated long lines at Soviet newsstands and black-market prices," as the historian Peter Laurence described. Jacobs worked for the magazine for six years, rising to the position of chief of the agency's Pamphlets and Graphics Unit.[24]

Jacobs was a seasoned professional when she joined *Architectural Forum* magazine in 1952. She had previously written (in approving terms) about contemporary architecture, slum clearance, and urban redevelopment. Her husband, the architect Robert H. Jacobs, had given her an understanding of architectural practice. Her initial assignment was to cover hospitals and schools; that soon expanded to include shopping centers and urban redevelopment.[25]

During her early years with *Architectural Forum*, Jacobs expressed an idealized view of contemporary urban planning. She praised urban renewal and its large-scale demolitions and superblocks; praised suburban malls; and even lauded Radburn as a classic of residential planning. Yet her advocacy became more nuanced as she worked with some of the leading urban designers and developers of the era. Many of them were critical of grandiose automobile-focused schemes and sought a more humanized approach. For example, the Philadelphia redevelopment plan by Louis Kahn and Christopher Tunnard closed segments of the street grid, forming loops and superblocks, and inserted small parks and linear landscaped pedestrian "greenways," in an effort to control and mitigate automobile impacts.[26]

Jacobs gave high praise to Kahn and Tunnard's plan in a 1955 article, but also spotlighted the concurrent rehabilitation of Philadelphia's historical housing and city blocks. The latter was immensely healthy, she wrote. It was worth far more than street widening or urban highways that bisected neighborhoods, which, "in ignorance or in ruthlessness," helped perpetuate racial and economic ghettoes. Jacobs was already linking contemporary traffic planning to negative social and economic outcomes, and criticizing its dominance. "Now we are struggling, sometimes it seems at the expense of everything else, to improvise the City Traversible," she wrote.[27]

For a time she implicitly endorsed the cellular planning model. In one article, she noted that a reason for the success of the Georgetown neighborhood in Washington, DC, was its surrounding ring of park and institutional land, which formed "a true innercity green belt of the type recommended by Sir Patrick Abercrombie for London."[28]

Jacobs's 1956 profile of the Fort Worth, Texas, plan was a paean to Victor Gruen's style of precinct planning. She said it was "brilliant as a sheer planning solution." It brought successful suburban-mall design to the heart of the city and represented "the long-dreamed-of pedestrian-island downtown." She praised its pedestrian focus, retention of existing street grid, elaborate traffic-separation techniques, and belt freeway. Other precinct-type plans such as Rotterdam's Lijnbaan and Philadelphia's Penn Center received her approval. She endorsed traffic separation as a general principle, saying that auto, freight, pedestrian, and transit traffic needed to be specialized and sorted to defeat congestion.[29]

Two events were key to her eventual rejection of mainstream city planning. In 1956 Jacobs toured East Harlem, where ten superblock housing projects had replaced fifty-seven city blocks. The community had suffered a devastating loss of small businesses, jobs, and local institutions as a result of urban renewal. Similar problems were appearing in other US cities. Jacobs became convinced that traditional streets and frontages were essential for the creation and continuance of a rich, intricate urban social order. She turned decisively against the type of urban renewal projects she had promoted earlier. She became directly involved in East Harlem reform efforts and helped create alternative proposals for public housing there.[30]

She also got involved in battles over development in Greenwich Village, where she and her husband had purchased a three-story building and raised their family. In 1955 Jacobs joined a local activist group that opposed Robert Moses's plans. Moses wanted to drive an expressway through Washington Square Park and replace the nearby city blocks with superblock towers. Within a few years she had become a leader in the fight.[31]

Moses predicted a crippling mess "as bad as any in the city" if his prescriptions were not followed. But when his plan was defeated and vehicles were banned from the park, the predicted congestion did not appear. Instead, overall traffic appeared to lessen. The experience helped convince Jacobs that in dense, mixed-use, walkable cities the threat of congestion was overblown, and usually did not warrant new highways or the conversion of narrow streets into wide arterials.[32]

Jacobs's article "Downtown is for People" appeared in the April 1958 issue of *Fortune* magazine. Among its many themes, it attacked abstract, non-empirical planning. "The best way to plan for downtown is to see how people use it today," Jacobs wrote. "You've got to get out and walk." She argued that cities needed more streets, not fewer. Cities especially needed streets for pedestrians, because a system of busy walking streets was the nervous system of a downtown. Closing streets to cars was worthwhile only if it helped make the streets busier and more variegated. She criticized the Philadelphia greenway as pretty but empty of walkers, a "promenade minus promenaders."[33]

The article made a big splash and was the first sign of her celebrity status. She spent the next three years writing *The Death and Life of Great American Cities* (1961), a bold defense of the traditional American city and its intensely active street life. The book expanded many themes that she had touched on in her articles, including the superiority of traditional street and block patterns.

As its title stated, *Death and Life* was about big cities. The main hypothesis was that four conditions generated a flourishing diversity of social and economic activities: mixed use, small blocks, a variety of building ages, and population density. The four conditions were synergistic and had to exist in combination. They provided less or no benefit in isolation. Jacobs also gave a caveat with her hypothesis: "But I hope no reader will try to transfer my observations into guides as to what goes on in towns, or little cities, or in suburbs which still are suburban."[34]

Jacobs criticized modernist planning sharply and at length, saying it was a dogmatic pseudoscience and a product of intellectual vacuum. She cited Ebenezer Howard, RPAA, Le Corbusier, and Futurama, and amalgamated their anti-city visions as "the Radiant Garden City Beautiful." The urban and traffic planning professions were stagnant, she charged, and merely recycled those static, simplistic visions.[35]

Uniquely for the time, her criticism was centered on social and economic outcomes. She likened superblock redevelopment projects to gang-dominated territories that impaired safety and free movement. Their streets and private grounds required policing and fences to keep out unwanted classes of people. Modernist superblock plans lacked the public contact and public safety that busy sidewalks provided, and that exacerbated the problems of segregation and racial discrimination.[36]

Jacobs said that oversize blocks channeled walkers onto a limited number of through streets, which consequently grew over-commercialized and monotonous. The inconvenient walking routes reduced business experimentation and overall economic activity. Superblock projects created socially isolated internal streets that were prone to be politically helpless. The projects might be laced with pedestrian promenades, but those routes were seldom busy with a great variety of people, and so were meaningless. "The whole idea of doing away with city streets, insofar as that is possible, and downgrading and minimizing their social and their economic part in city life is the most mischievous and destructive idea in orthodox city planning," she wrote.

Therefore, small blocks were an essential component of great cities: not an end in themselves, but a means of generating diversity and catalyzing economic opportunity. Small blocks increased the amount of street frontage and the multiplicity of pedestrian routes, allowing commerce to be distributed more widely and conveniently. Small blocks helped relieve the oppressive aesthetics of big monolithic buildings. Small blocks also helped slow and reduce the flow of automobiles, which Jacobs saw as an advantage.[37]

Throughout her career, Jacobs had been appalled at the destructive effects of automobiles and traffic arteries. They eroded the very qualities that made cities attractive and useful. "Too much dependence on private automobiles and city concentration of use are incompatible," she declared. "One or the other has to give." Automobile orientation was a positive feedback loop: the more that urban environments were oriented to automobiles, the more that traffic volumes increased. That endless cycle never solved congestion in any city, but it could siphon away incredible, unjustifiable amounts of money and eliminate the possibility of walkable environments.[38]

Jacobs's solution reached back to the traffic-control era of the 1910s and even earlier to more laissez-faire eras. Automobiles and cities were potential allies if only the number of autos could be limited and their dominance reduced. Jacobs's vision of traffic reduction was one of gradual, steady evolution toward more vital city districts. As the diversity and intensity of city uses increased, the need for cars would decrease, car use would become less convenient, and better public transit would be stimulated. The effect of that strategy on congestion should simply be ignored, said Jacobs, with the important exceptions of bus and freight traffic. Dedicated facilities for buses and freight trucks might be merited in some cases.[39]

Even if automobile traffic was greatly reduced, Jacobs knew that through traffic could seriously degrade the livability and safety of local streets. And so, despite her strong defense of city streets and her calls to add new streets, she advocated strategic blockages in street grids. Barriers or small parks could be laid across certain streets to form dead ends. Pedestrians, bicycles, and emergency vehicles could pass through, but vehicular through traffic would be barred. Jacobs's position reflected an ambivalence about traditional street layouts, which persisted among her followers and gave rise to varying degrees of cellularity in later urban plans.[40]

Death and Life was less ambivalent about pedestrian separation. The separation of pedestrians and vehicles was the wrong goal if it created more gaps in the urban fabric and diminished street life. Pedestrian precincts required "a spectacular decline in the absolute numbers of automobiles using a city," and a huge shift to mass transit. "Otherwise," she argued, "the necessary parking, garaging and access arteries around the pedestrian preserves reach such unwieldy and deadening proportions that they become arrangements capable only of city disintegration, not of city saving." Vertically separated pedestrian levels had similar effects. In general, said Jacobs, the advantages of comprehensive pedestrian separation schemes were not great. They often caused more problems than they solved, and anyhow were justified only in the most intensive downtown areas.[41]

Jacobs was fond of carfree precincts when they had the necessary planning elements. In 1969 the government of Ontario, Canada, commissioned a development plan for the Toronto waterfront called Harbour City. Jacobs was one of the project's consultants. Its 510 acres (206 ha) of landfill would have formed an archipelago of midrise mixed-use districts embroidered with canals and lagoons. Most vehicular traffic was restricted to a ring road with parking lots; inside the ring, pedestrian passages and plazas formed a fabric of small blocks. Travel within the community would be on foot or transit. "This may well be the most important advance in city planning that's been made this century," said Jacobs as she praised its walkable, mostly carfree design. The project was defeated by a grassroots citizens' movement upset about traffic and environmental impacts.[42]

Upon its publication, *Death and Life* was roundly criticized by those it attacked most directly: the American urban planning establishment, transportation planners, city officials, and academic thinkers. The director of the leading planners' association warned the book would be used by "screwballs and reactionaries" to block urban renewal. The more serious critics contended that Jacobs's prescriptions would not solve problems such as substandard housing, gentrification, overcrowding, and traffic congestion.[43]

The book was a great popular success, and its commonsense, empirical stance was praised across the political spectrum. By the late 1960s it was a must-read text in design schools; by the 1970s it had entered the urban-planning canon. It was one of the most admired and influential books about city planning. *Death and Life* inspired many activists to fight urban renewal and freeways, and to advocate more pedestrian-friendly streets and sidewalks. It was a foundational text for urban-planning reform movements organized in the 1970s and later decades, particularly historic preservation, neotraditionalism, new urbanism, and smart growth. Perhaps its most important contribution was to elevate the public's esteem of intensive urbanity and vital street life.

Christopher Alexander

The architecture professor Christopher Alexander published his groundbreaking article "A City is Not a Tree" in 1965. Unusually for an architect, Alexander had a master's degree in mathematics, and that informed his critique of contemporary urban-design methods. He argued that modernist urban design produced devitalized urban environments. To achieve better results, designers needed to understand the abstract underlying principles of natural living cities.[44]

Alexander proposed two conceptual patterns to explain how a collection of small systems could combine into a large, complex system. One pattern, named the semi-lattice, was composed of richly connected, overlapping parts. The antithetical pattern, named the tree, was composed of sparsely connected parts that never overlapped. He showed that semi-lattice systems could have a vastly greater variety of elements than tree-like systems.

Alexander argued that tree-like patterns underlay modernist urban plans. He used dendritic roadway layouts to illustrate his thesis. His examples included Ludwig Hilberseimer's settlement unit (ca. 1931–1933); Greenbelt, Maryland (1935); Patrick Abercrombie's London plan (1943); Le Corbusier's plan of Chandigarh, India (1951); Brasília, the federal capital of Brazil (1957); and the New Town of Columbia, Maryland (1964). Alexander concluded that tree-like urban plans did not correspond to modern social networks and were incapable of supporting abundant city life. The tree-like separation of systems disassociated, compartmentalized, and eventually destroyed urban vitality.

Alexander acknowledged Jane Jacobs's brilliance and the excellence of her criticisms. But he thought her urban ideal was too specific and rooted in the past. The ways that people used and inhabited cities had changed since historical times, he said, and urban systems had to keep current.

"A City is Not a Tree" influenced a number of designers to view cities as complex environments that comprised overlapping interconnected systems, such as their streets. But the article's main impact was in academia, where it sparked an animated multiyear debate. In that setting, the article was a theoretical counterweight to dendritic street layouts and other planning doctrines that promoted compartmentalization and insularity.[45]

St. Lawrence Neighborhood

Toronto in the mid-1960s, like many cities in North America, had experienced the negative impacts of modernist urban renewal. Local anger, protests against further depredations, and the rise of New Left politics fueled a wave of planning reform in the city. Jane Jacobs's book *The Death and Life of Great American Cities* was a perennial source of inspiration and guidance for reformers. Some carried the book as they went from door to door to organize opposition to renewal plans. Most reform-minded officials and city staff agreed with the book's prescriptions. The reformist mayor David Crombie had used it in city politics courses when he was a college instructor.[46]

In 1973 Toronto adopted a new housing policy. It said the form and layout of residential development should harmonize with existing traditional neighborhoods.

And it said housing should engage with streets rather than being buffered or walled off. To demonstrate the new policy, a redevelopment site was chosen in a languishing industrial area near the core of the city. The 18-hectare (44-acre) site was occupied by junkyards, parking lots, city equipment yards, and unused rail tracks. It was contaminated by more than a century of industrial activity. Railways and a major freeway ran along the site's southern border, forming a barrier that was punctuated by roadway underpasses.[47]

The project was named St. Lawrence after the nearby historic St. Lawrence Market building. It would have 3,500 dwellings, making it one of the largest central-city redevelopment projects in North America. Its watchword was *mix*. It would have a mix of land uses, housing types, household incomes, and building designs. It would be an extension of the existing city fabric; therefore, the street grid would be "respected" and the site's through routes would be retained.[48]

The city hired a prominent architectural firm that completed an initial site plan in spring 1975. It featured some modernist planning techniques such as cul-de-sacs, elevated pedestrian ways, and housing turned away from adjoining streets. It was rejected by the city staff and politicians who espoused neotraditional planning. City councilor John Sewell represented the St. Lawrence area and headed the citizens' committee that oversaw site planning. "We were not happy with it," remembered Sewell. "It did not give us the road map we were looking for."[49]

Jane Jacobs had moved to Toronto in 1968. Although she preferred writing to activism, she was friends with most of the reformist city councilors and quite willing to dispense advice. She lived across the street from the city housing director Michael Dennis, who was now seeking a replacement planner for St. Lawrence. One day Dennis met Jacobs on the street and asked if she could recommend someone to plan the development. Jacobs was close to Alan Littlewood, a young architect who worked with her husband, and suggested him for the job. Dennis asked, "Does he know anything about planning?" Jacobs replied, "I hope not!"[50]

It was so. Littlewood had grown up in Ireland and trained at the Architectural Association in London, but had no experience in urban design and no familiarity with *Death and Life*. To research his new assignment, he visited the British New Towns. He found them lifeless, and resolved to avoid anything similar for St. Lawrence. He also read *Death and Life* (on the recommendation of Frank Lewinberg, the architect who was coordinating the project in the city planning department), was inspired by it, and wanted to apply its ideas in St. Lawrence.[51]

Jacobs gave design guidance to Littlewood:

> A few weeks after he was hired, Alan says he was talking to Jane and told her all of the studies he was commissioning to get the plan underway. Jane looked askance. "They aren't the right studies," she said. "What you want to do is just replicate the parts of the city that you know work well—take their characteristics and copy them into St. Lawrence. Start by creating a regular street system in the area and go from there." Alan says he was at first taken aback, but then realized that was exactly what he should do, so he set out on a new course. He studied blocks in various neighborhoods that he thought

worked well, and measured their width and depth and how the buildings were placed on the land.[52]

Littlewood created a site plan in late 1975 with the help of Lewinberg and the architecture professor George Baird. The through streets were retained, and the new streets formed small interior blocks. Mid-rise apartments, commercial uses, and civic uses lined the through streets while single-family row houses occupied the protected interior blocks. The plan consciously avoided the form and appearance of the modernist housing projects that had been mainstream practice in Canada since the 1950s. The Housing Department believed that insularity was a major flaw of such projects. It said insularity was partly caused by roadway layouts, particularly external ring roads. The St. Lawrence street layout was intended to improve linkages and engagement, match existing context, and encourage variety by increasing the number of development parcels and mix of housing types.[53]

Construction began in September 1977 and the first building opened in June 1979. The first phase of 1,600 dwellings was completed in 1982; the second phase of 1,300 dwellings in the mid-1980s. Completion of the final phase was delayed until the 2000s. Almost 60 percent of the housing was nonprofit dwellings for low- and medium-income households. City regulations ensured that they would be permanently affordable.[54]

Although St. Lawrence was intended to be a traditional neighborhood, its layout was noticeably different from Toronto's historical street grid. The main east-west route did not continue through to the site's eastern border. Most of the new streets were interior loops that formed extra-small blocks (as small as 0.4 hectare or 1 acre), and

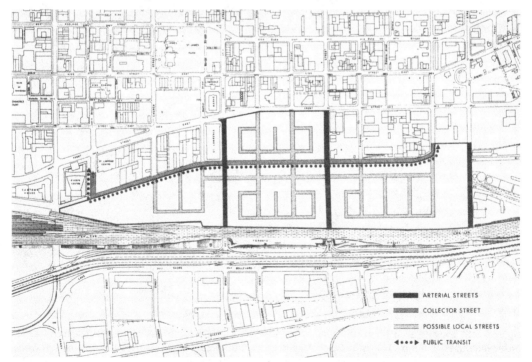

Figure 9.4: St. Lawrence neighborhood street plan, 1976. Three through routes continue south, under the rail tracks and expressway, toward the lakefront. City of Toronto Archives, fonds 388, series 1653, file 249.

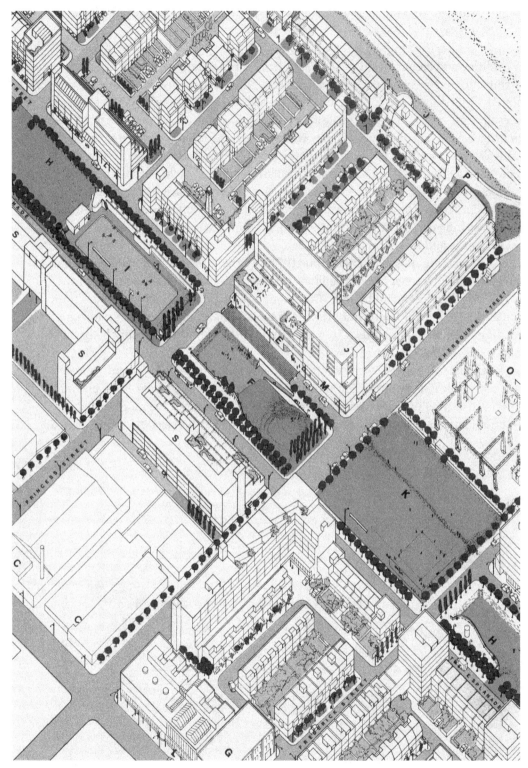

Figure 9.5: St. Lawrence neighborhood built form poster, detail, 1976. Illustrates proposed design character, mixed land uses, and mixed housing types. A central corridor of park blocks is lined by apartment towers. Behind the towers, townhouses occupy small blocks. City of Toronto Archives, fonds 2, series 236, file 133.

Figure 9.6: St. Lawrence neighborhood street layout as built, 2018. Also visible is the extensive redevelopment that has taken place in adjacent areas. Map tiles by Stamen Design, under CC BY 3.0. Data © OpenStreetMap contributors, under ODbL.

none carried through traffic. The southern border was lined with long, narrow housing slabs to buffer the noise and pollution of the adjacent railways. Overall, the layout was moderately cellular, partly owing to planning goals and partly to site conditions.

Those who were familiar with St. Lawrence admired its community-based planning process, physical form, wide variety of land uses, and high proportion of affordable housing. But it was not internationally famous. Indeed, Councilor Sewell's attitude during construction was, "We're trying to build something that looks so ordinary you would have sworn it has always been there." The project catalyzed new development in the surrounding Old Town district, so that by the 2010s the urban fabric was much more continuous and the project was better integrated with the rest of the city. St. Lawrence was a pioneering example of neotraditional brownfield redevelopment; moreover, its planning achievements were seldom exceeded during the late twentieth and early twenty-first centuries.[55]

Léon Krier and Rob Krier

Léon Krier (b. 1946) and Rob Krier (b. 1938) were brothers who grew up in Luxembourg City, Luxembourg. It was a small capital city that retained much of its traditional architecture and urbanism in the years after World War II. The brothers also lived part-time with their grandparents in Echternach, a medieval town 30 km (19 miles) northwest of the capital. Their family enjoyed trips to nearby cities.

The beauty and quality of life of those places greatly affected the brothers. Léon remembered Luxembourg as "a miracle of traditional architecture." Echternach was equally so. Echternach had been partially destroyed by German and US army artillery exchanges in 1945. Over the next nine years it was fully rebuilt in its traditional style, using traditional methods. Rob remembered the "enthralling reconstruction works" that were like "an open textbook." Léon remembered the craftsmen who took great pleasure in their work. Echternach left a powerful impression on the brothers that was at first subconscious, but later became explicit.[56]

Both brothers chose to become architects. As children of the postwar era they absorbed the prevailing ideas on modernity and modern architecture. From 1963 to 1970, Rob designed a variety of modernist circulation layouts in his projects, experimenting with different types of traffic separation both horizontal and vertical. Léon often assisted as modelmaker.

Rediscovering Traditional Urbanism

When he took a job with the London architect James Stirling in 1968, Léon was still working in a modernist idiom according to contemporary trends. His University of Bielefeld project (1968) proposed to house a university of ten thousand people in one megastructure, with dramatic ramps, bridges, and concourses for vertical traffic separation. But Léon's perspective was undergoing a thorough conversion.

The grounds of his discontent had been formed earlier. In 1955 the highway authority cut down the street trees in front of the Kriers' house, which caused his "first doubts on the value of progress." A few years later, the city of Brussels executed a huge program of road expansion and highway building to support the Expo 58 world's fair. The city was mangled by invasive engineering works, a program that Léon rejected absolutely. A 1963 visit to Le Corbusier's Unité d'Habitation in Marseille was deeply disillusioning. And throughout the 1960s, he saw parts of Luxembourg City redeveloped according to modernist precepts.[57]

After settling in London, Léon explored the magnificent collection of the Royal Institute of British Architects library. The work of Camillo Sitte was a revelation, in particular the conceptualization of urban space as something much greater than a conduit for traffic. "Sitte gave the key to deciphering town plans, both geometrically and semantically," Krier recalled. "I realized how little I or anyone alive knew about this." That and his travels in northern Italy led to a "Damascus experience." He embarked on a years-long effort to "get back to basics," wishing to learn the craft of traditional urban design and stop the depredations of contemporary planning.[58]

Little guidance or theory about neotraditional urban design was available in the late 1960s and early 1970s. Léon studied a wide range of German, French, and Italian architectural and planning scholars and designers from the eighteenth century through the 1960s. He reinvented those older ideas for contemporary conditions and developed his own critique of the dominant modernist approach. That personal journey gave his theoretical stance in the late 1970s and afterward an unusual clarity and force.[59]

A constant lodestar was his experience of traditional urbanism, especially the town of Echternach and similar postwar reconstructions. They were tangible proof that traditional forms and methods were "superior on all levels, demonstrably functional and loved by the inhabitants." They were not obsolete or impractical as the critics charged. On the contrary, their construction was faster, more efficient, and produced high-quality buildings of great charm.[60]

Rob Krier too was dismayed by new modernist districts throughout Europe. He felt they were degrading, stifling, ugly, and basically anti-urban. Persuaded by Léon's arguments about the critical importance of urban space, Rob decided to dedicate his life to the creation of better city environments. In 1970 Rob began a dissertation about the loss of urban space in twentieth-century urban design. Also in the early 1970s, both brothers began teaching, exhibiting at major venues, and traveling on lecture tours, including a tour of twenty-five US architectural schools in 1973.[61]

Rob's dissertation was published in 1975 as *Stadtraum in Theorie und Praxis*, and was possibly the first book about neotraditional urban-design methods. It rejected planning ideas by architectural modernists such as Le Corbusier, Hilberseimer, and Mies van der Rohe. It cast a skeptical eye on pedestrian-separation schemes as a long-term solution to motor traffic impacts. It called for the recovery of urban space, particularly small streets and squares keyed to the size of the human body. The book was a success and was translated into four languages; the English version was *Urban Space* (1979).[62]

Urban Design at the Neighborhood and Metropolitan Scales

Léon felt that his home city of Luxembourg was one of the most beautiful in the world, but contemporary planning was destroying its traditional character and historic buildings. A 1972 proposal to replace a city park with a massive parking structure was, for him, the breaking point. Realizing that intermittent protest was insufficient, he began to develop global alternatives that would challenge contemporary planning concepts. "I looked desperately to find a modern and living author who could express a viable theory of a modern metropole," he recalled. The only "serious precedents" he found were the urban plans of the German architect Otto Wagner and Finnish architect Eliel Saarinen.[63]

Wagner's 1911 plan for Vienna proposed urban extensions in the form of complete, mixed-use districts, which Wagner described as "miniature cities." Each district had a central spine of plazas and promenades interspersed with public buildings, schools, churches, theaters, and the like. The district's street pattern was a grid of small blocks with public squares, plazas, and playgrounds distributed throughout. Krier highlighted the "almost intimate size of the blocks (40 x 60 meters) which is the key to any really urban structure." Major through routes ran along the district's edges and were lined with retail uses, markets, and hotels.[64]

Saarinen was active in large-scale city and regional planning throughout the 1910s. Like Wagner, Saarinen proposed growth in the form of compact, self-contained mixed-use districts, but unlike Wagner, he set them in an exploded arrangement, with parkland strips or green belts surrounding each district. Some of Saarinen's city-center plans had a sophisticated, nested arrangement of street types that blended monumental and picturesque qualities, which reflected the influences of Haussmann and Burnham on one hand, and Sitte on the other. That blending fascinated Saarinen throughout his life and was the overall aim of all his town planning.

In his plans of the 1910s, Saarinen routed traffic arteries through urban districts rather than bypassing them. His major thoroughfares were either Haussmann-like boulevards or quasi-parkways. The latter had buffers of green space a few blocks wide and moderately infrequent spacing of intersections (approximately 230 meters or 750 feet apart) in order to speed through traffic.[65]

Saarinen moved to the United States in 1923 and encountered the nation's large and burgeoning automobile culture. He soon incorporated the American mindset into his regional planning model. He said fast traffic must be removed from the districts and concentrated on arterials in interstitial green belts. The districts were compact, mixed-use, walkable environments where auto use was optional, not compulsory. Therefore, he claimed, most commuting trips would be internal and on foot, and the traffic problem would be solved.[66]

Wagner's and Saarinen's plans were models for Léon's urban planning from the mid-1970s onward. From Wagner, Saarinen, Stübben, and other historical sources and examples, he developed his approaches to planning and roadway layout at the neighborhood and metropolitan scales.

La Villette

In 1976 Léon entered the La Villette competition in Paris. It was the first competition after World War II to dispense with monofunctional zoning and specify a full range of land uses for a single development. The 55-hectare (136-acre) site was located in the northeastern section of the city, just inside the Périphérique circumferential highway. Léon proposed a compact, walkable neighborhood, and called it a *quartier* to highlight the influence of Paris's historical districts.[67]

Léon's La Villlette plan was laid out as a grid. It had a hierarchy of roadway types keyed to width, monumentality, adjacent land use, and community role. Boulevards and a bypass road bounded the quartier and carried faster through traffic. They were lined with warehouses, light industry, a hospital, and similar uses that screened the residential areas. A monumental boulevard on the central axis was lined with important civic buildings. Avenues were lined with local retail shops, schools, workshops, and similar uses. Secondary streets and passages were narrow and gave access to residential buildings. A few passages allowed vehicles on a restricted basis; most were pedestrian-only. The grid of travelways formed tiny blocks approximately 30 by 60 meters (98 by 197 feet), similar to Otto Wagner's blocks.[68]

La Villette would house 15,000 people, many of whom would work within the quartier. Its diverse land-use mix put jobs within easy walking distance of residences. That would eliminate most commuting traffic and drastically reduce other public and private traffic. Therefore, local auto traffic "would not only be possible, but even desirable." The mix of activities and travel modes, and the narrowness of the thoroughfares, would help maintain low speeds. Léon recommended no unusual traffic controls beyond the traffic plan. In general, "local traffic would be left to sort itself out." He argued that the reorganization of cities along these lines—into compact, mixed-use neighborhoods—was the only solution to urban traffic problems.[69]

Several other competition entries departed from the 1960s modernist model, but Léon's plan was the most firmly rooted in the traditional mode. It was the first neotraditional neighborhood plan to gain international press coverage and widespread recognition from urban designers. The architect Jaquelin Robertson was in Iran working on the Shahestan Phalavi project when he saw the La Villette plan. With a shock he

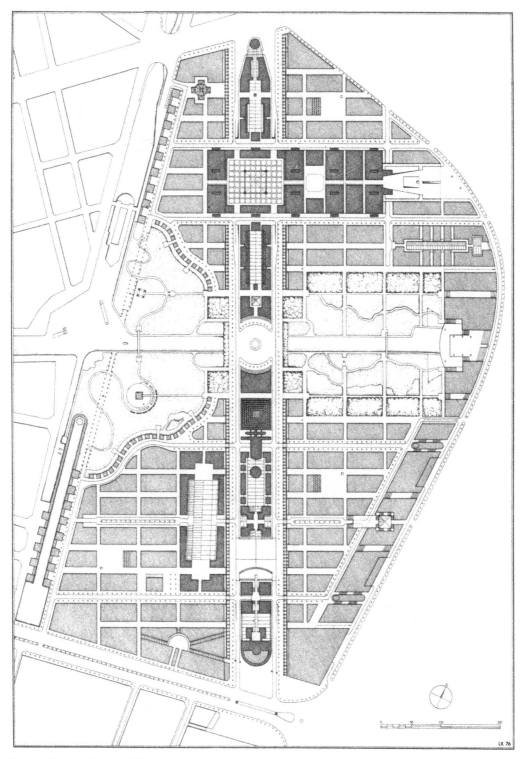

Figure 9.7: Léon Krier, La Villette plan, 1976. Courtesy of Léon Krier.

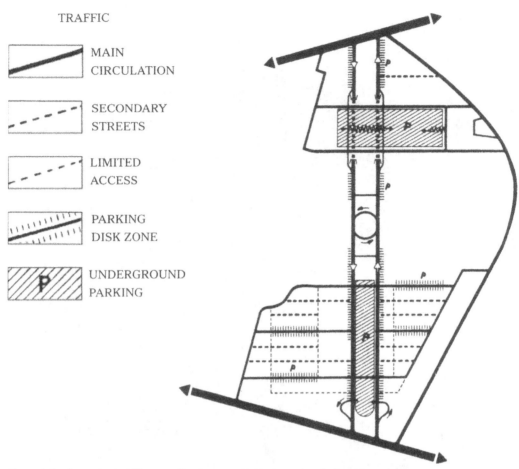

TRAFFIC

MAIN CIRCULATION

SECONDARY STREETS

LIMITED ACCESS

PARKING DISK ZONE

UNDERGROUND PARKING

Figure 9.8: Léon Krier, La Villette traffic diagram, 1976. Courtesy of Léon Krier.

realized that Léon was "the first and best modern designer of cities" and, after studying the plan, felt "renewed courage and strength in my own hard-earned convictions."[70]

Refining Principles

Leon's Luxembourg City plan (1973–1978) illustrated one solution to excessive through traffic in districts with grid layouts. The city had a geography of small plateaus separated by deep ravines. Working with that geography, Léon depicted the city as 23 small compact quartiers, which were arranged in an exploded plan in the Saarinen manner. New quartiers were placed on a plateau at the city's edge and, being so isolated, had few links to other quartiers. Main avenues bridged the ravines and ran along the edges of the new quartiers. The new quartiers would experience little demand for through traffic apart from the main avenues. Protection from through traffic was inherent.[71]

During the 1970s and early 1980s, Léon was quite influential in the fight to end intolerance of traditional architecture. His ideas were disseminated throughout Europe and the United States through his counterprojects, witty polemical cartoons, teaching, writing, lecture tours, and so on. "Ten years ago when you talked about streets and squares you were considered a bit of a nostalgic, or 'out of touch with your time.' This is no longer so," he said in 1981. Léon and Rob Krier were not the only advocates

Figure 9.9: Léon Krier, Luxembourg City as a federation of 23 quartiers, detail, 1978. Proposed quartiers (Quartiers de l'Europe) at top right of plan. Courtesy of Léon Krier.

of neotraditional plans and street layouts during this period, but they were the most famous and prolific.[72]

In 1984 Léon bolstered his arguments for small blocks. Small blocks maximized the potential amount of commercial facades, and thus maximized economic return on urban land. Small blocks were "the basis of urban character, of intense *social*, *cultural*, and *economic* exchange." Therefore, each urban block should be made the smallest size that was viable for its type. Urban blocks should form as many streets and squares as possible in an extensive urban fabric. And the most important, lively streets should have as many intersections as possible.[73]

Poundbury

In 1988 Prince Charles (HRH The Prince of Wales) appointed Léon to plan a 400-acre (162-hectare) model development called Poundbury. It was located at the edge of the

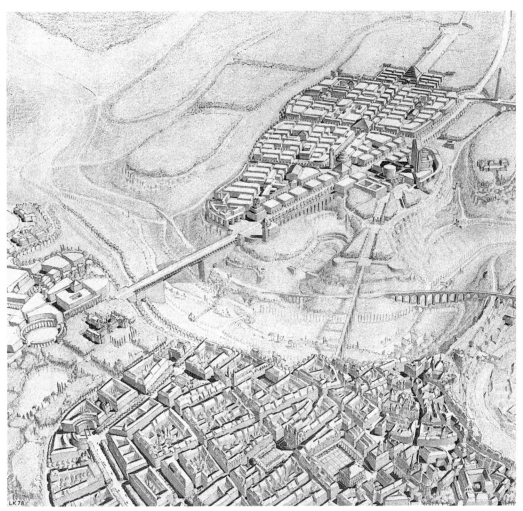

Figure 9.10: Léon Krier, Quartiers de l'Europe, 1978. Steep ravines separate plateaus, forming a natural basis for compact neighborhoods (quartiers). Courtesy of Léon Krier.

town of Dorchester in southwest England. Léon's plan employed many of his previous street-planning methods and added certain new ones. Poundbury's four quartiers, or "urban villages," were delimited by avenues and civic spaces in the project's interior, and a highway, parkway, parkland, and buffer space at its exterior. Within each quartier, a mixed-use high street (main street) and civic squares formed a central spine. Streets were pedestrian-friendly. Most were designed for 20-mph (32-kmh) traffic, and the irregular layout helped keep speeds low. Poundbury did not have a comprehensive pedestrian-only network as some of Léon's earlier plans did; instead, a scattering of pedestrian routes provided strategic links.

The site lay between Dorchester and an interregional highway. An arrow-straight road (Bridport Road), which dated from the ancient Roman occupation of England, ran through the site and carried a high volume of traffic to the highway. Léon created a bypass parkway to redirect traffic around Poundbury. It was not strictly access-limited; its original plan had connections to the development spaced an average of 670 feet (204 m) apart, and thus created moderate cellularity. The formerly straight thoroughfare was redesigned as a walkable street with abrupt bends and deflections

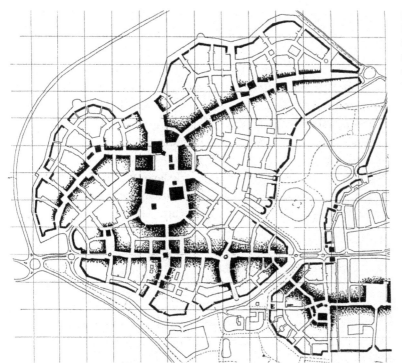

Figure 9.11: Léon Krier, Poundbury plan of high streets (main streets) and major civic spaces, 1988. Courtesy of Léon Krier.

Figure 9.12: Léon Krier, Poundbury traffic plan, 1988. Courtesy of Léon Krier.

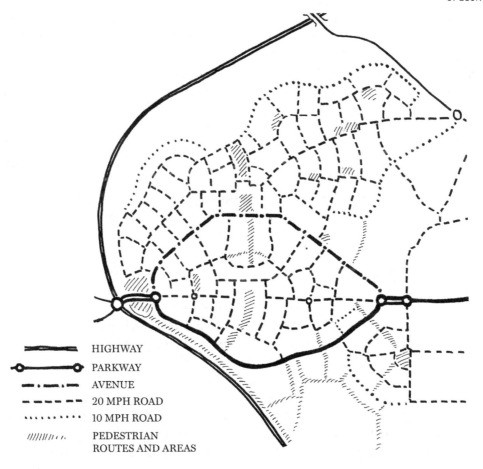

HIGHWAY

PARKWAY

AVENUE

20 MPH ROAD

10 MPH ROAD

PEDESTRIAN
ROUTES AND AREAS

to calm traffic. Implementing the redesign was a long-term effort. "For fifteen years I was told to give up the idea," Léon said in 2016. "Now it is done and no one remembers it was a straight Roman road."[74]

By 1990, Léon had expanded his written typology of roadways to include parkways, thereby embracing regional patterns of greater cellularity. The boundary of a quartier should be "an important landscaped feature; a promenade, boulevard, avenue and parkway articulating natural or artificial incidents," he wrote. That prescription was sufficiently general and flexible to encompass a wide variety of regional thoroughfare layouts. At one end of the spectrum, it could include layouts of slight cellularity such as Otto Wagner's; at the other end, it could include layouts of moderately strong cellularity such as Saarinen's 1943 model. "There is no single correct model, particularly if one has to integrate existing settlements and complicated topography," Léon commented.[75]

New York City's Urban Design Group

From 1959 to 1965 John V. Lindsay was the US congressman from New York's East Side. His district included Greenwich Village, and he was a friend and close ally of Jane Jacobs. During his time in Congress, he actively supported her campaigns against Robert Moses's expressway and urban-renewal proposals. Lindsay was elected mayor of New York City in 1966 and served until 1973.[76]

Lindsay had exceptional confidence that planning and design could improve the quality of life for New Yorkers. His administration established urban design initiatives and policies, and backed them vigorously. Lindsay's planners and advisors were familiar with the precepts of *The Death and Life of Great American Cities*. They believed in the importance of street life, and that the existing fabric of streets and blocks should be protected. The administration supported historic preservation, mixed use, pedestrian zones, and building facades that helped enliven sidewalks.

A number of young, progressive, Ivy-League-educated architects joined, and in some cases led, the administration's urban-design initiatives. Among those who participated from the mid-1960s to early 1970s were Robert A. M. Stern, Jonathan Barnett, Jaquelin Robertson, Alexander Cooper, and Stanton Eckstut. Those designers went on to become practitioners and professors in the budding neotraditional urban-design movement.[77]

Battery Park City

In the early 1950s, the Port Authority of New York expanded Port Newark–Elizabeth in New Jersey to accommodate the largest ships sailing the freight lanes. The freight industry began to convert to containerized-cargo shipping a few years later. Those developments sealed the fate of the region's historical shipping facilities. By the early 1960s, the docks of lower Manhattan were defunct.[78]

Various groups vied for control of the waterfront immediately north of Battery Park. Through the 1960s, at least five serious plans were proposed to landfill the dock area and develop it. All the plans were modernist and featured towers, superblocks and complete vertical separation of pedestrians on elevated decks or skybridges. The plan advanced by Mayor Lindsay envisioned a megastructure occupying the site. The megastructure had a seven-story atrium extending through its full length (about 0.9 mile or 1.4 kilometers) that contained retail, civic uses, and a monorail. Along the atrium, seven superblock pods of development were situated above multilevel circulation podiums. That plan was approved in 1969, and illustrations of the project, which looked science-fictional, became popular in the mass media.[79]

But the megastructure remained a grand fantasy. Economic recessions during the 1970s inhibited developers. The city was sliding into a financial crisis. The megastructure plan itself was problematic. Its elevated pedestrian system was expensive and cumbersome; it would work well only as a complete system. It was not suitable for incremental construction over a period of decades. A 1973 plan proposed to break up the megastructure, but each of the resulting multilevel superblock pods still represented an enormous risky investment. People began to refer to the large vacant site as "the beach."[80]

Meanwhile, the Battery Park City Authority issued $200 million in bonds to landfill the 92-acre (37-ha) site and fund operations. By 1979 BPCA was nearing default, having generated no development income. The governor decided that an overhaul was necessary and appointed new leadership. When the new BPCA president arrived at the office, he found that many of the old plan models had been installed around the boardroom. It was, he said, like viewing the "Hall of Dinosaurs at a museum." He hired the architects Alexander Cooper and Stanton Eckstut to make a more feasible and resilient plan.[81]

Cooper had worked in the Lindsay administration's Urban Design Group, becoming director in 1971. He also had been involved in Lower Manhattan planning issues for six years as a city planning commissioner. Eckstut too had worked in the city's Urban Design Group. The architects said that professional views and methods in New York City had changed fundamentally since the 1960s. They believed that the emphasis on megastructures and superblocks had been replaced by more traditional, flexible, and successful forms.[82]

Their 1979 plan was neotraditional. Instead of seven development pods, it had 36 blocks. The general pattern and orientation of the nearby street grid was extended into the site. Street connections were made where possible. The number of external street connections was limited by the viaduct and vehicular ramps on West Street, but the plan was designed to permit more street connections when future conditions changed. Most of the project's streets were one-way (only a few streets around the commercial center were two-way); the resulting circulation pattern was a collection of local loops that limited through traffic. Pedestrian circulation was generally placed at ground level. Vertical pedestrian separation was recommended only for the spots where vehicular traffic was heaviest.[83]

Many advantages of the neotraditional street layout were identified in the plan. They can be categorized generally as access, development flexibility, and aesthetics. In regard to access, the street grid would knit the urban fabric to adjacent neighborhoods and overcome "a potential sense of isolation." It would support active, multipurpose streets, and make parks, promenades, and other amenities easier to reach. In regard to flexibility, a traditional street grid was best for enabling urban districts to develop in increments, adapt to changing demands, and gain value over time. Battery Park City's

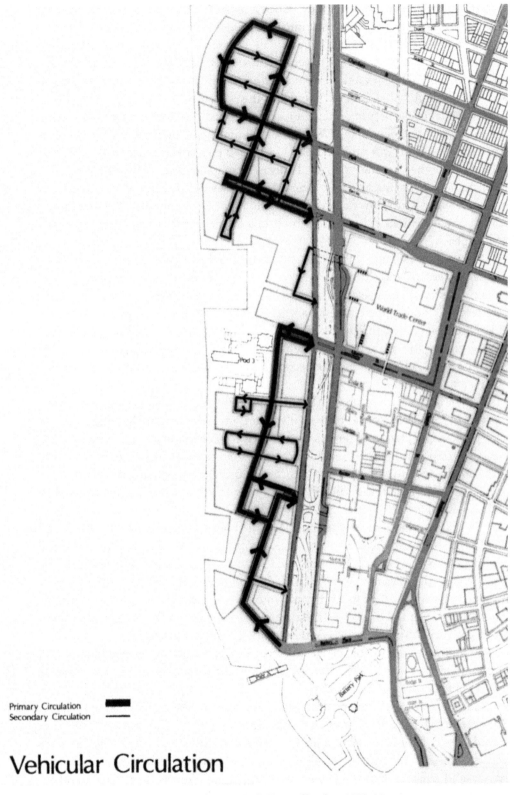

Primary Circulation
Secondary Circulation

Vehicular Circulation

Figure 9.13: Alexander Cooper Associates, Battery Park City traffic plan, 1979. Most streets were one-way; the segments adjacent to the central commercial area were two-way. Courtesy of Cooper Robertson.

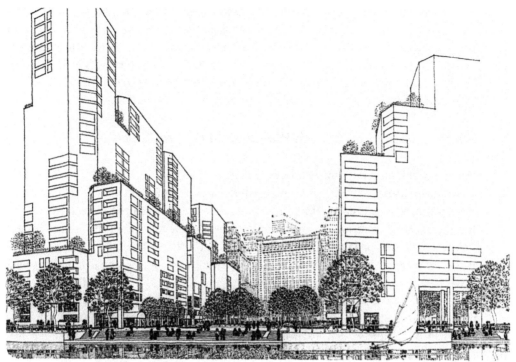

Figure 9.14: Alexander Cooper Associates, proposal for Rector Place in Battery Park City, 1979. An example of urban design that emphasized water views. Rector Place would have a broad central green encircled by a one-way lane. Courtesy of Cooper Robertson.

grid followed the typical block size in that part of Manhattan (200 by 400 feet or 60 by 120 meters), which allowed greater flexibility when drawing lot lines. Lots could be more diverse in size and available to a wider range of developers, who could build a wider range of building types and sizes. Development processes would be easier and more familiar. In regard to aesthetics, the grid fostered a finer, more intimate texture of small spaces that was "vital to the livability of the city." Also, the grid's orientation provided outstanding river views from both streets and buildings.[84]

The plan was approved in November-December 1979 and the first buildings were occupied in June 1982. Construction continued through the 2010s. The street layout as built was more like a traditional Manhattan grid than the original plan had envisioned—which, in the planning field, was an unusual and remarkable outcome. Because the viaduct on West Street was demolished in 1981, Battery Park City was able to make eight connections to the Financial District rather than the four originally planned. The layout was composed mostly of two-way streets, and had a few one-way minor streets, in contrast to the original plan. A planned pedestrian bridge over North End Avenue was not built. However, much of Battery Park City's retail activity was located within internal galleries and passages, so the building facades tended to be less active and engaging than traditional Manhattan facades.[85]

The plan did achieve its hoped-for success. As of 2016, Battery Park City had 15,000 residents in 30 buildings; 40,000 workers in 10 million square feet (929,000 sq m) of commercial space; and a full range of civic and recreational facilities. It was the most profitable large-scale development in the region during the 1980s and 1990s. Developers and officials across the country sought to emulate its achievement. Battery

Park City was critically acclaimed: *Progressive Architecture* magazine said it was a "landmark in American urbanism" in 1984, and *Time* magazine named it one of the best designs of the 1980s. As perhaps the most visible example of neotraditional urban design, it influenced the redevelopment of downtowns and waterfronts in other cities. Its popularity and profitability helped make neotraditional street layouts an acceptable, and in many cases preferred, pattern for urban redevelopment.[86]

Andrés Duany, Elizabeth Plater-Zyberk, and Seaside

The husband-and-wife team of Andrés Duany (b. 1949) and Elizabeth Plater-Zyberk (b. 1950) formed an illustrious partnership in the architecture and planning fields. They were prominent advocates of neotraditional urban design in the United States and leaders in the international movement to reform modernist planning. Their designs and codes called for layouts of small blocks and well-connected streets, and drew inspiration from historical towns and cities where walking was the original primary travel mode.

Duany's father and grandfather, both land developers in Cuba, were major influences on his planning thought, as was living in Barcelona as a teen and studying at the École des Beaux-Arts in Paris in 1971. Plater-Zyberk grew up in Paoli, Pennsylvania, a walkable railroad suburb, and was most influenced by her architect father. He taught her building design and imparted a passion for construction; she worked at his Philadelphia firm during summers. Duany and Plater-Zyberk attended the Yale School of Architecture in New Haven and became enamored of the city's vernacular houses, porches, and walkable streets. In 1974 Duany began teaching at the University of Miami in Coral Gables, Florida. Plater-Zyberk soon joined him to help with a detailed survey of historic Key West, Florida.[87]

The Key West Naval Station had been declared surplus property in 1974. Duany and the visiting lecturer Bernardo Fort-Brescia led a team of architectural students in the creation of a redevelopment plan, which was published in 1977. The plan articulated many of the principles that Duany and Plater-Zyberk would advocate throughout their careers. It stated that the redevelopment of American cities in the 1960s had been a failure, partly because of a reliance on reductive social statistics. In contrast, the Key West plan was based on the town's architectural vernacular, which better reflected people's realities and aspirations. One element of that vernacular was the definition of streets as spatial entities akin to outdoor rooms. Well-designed streets formed "the bonds rather than the barriers of the city."[88]

Duany made an initial master plan that the students used as a base for individual site designs. A main goal of the street layout was seamless continuity with the adjacent urban fabric. It extended existing streets in order to open dead ends and create new blocks, and it added new streets to split oversize blocks. That mended the layout's breaks and allowed greater building variety and density. Another goal was lively streets that supported community identity. The streets' narrow dimensions and frequent traffic signals would moderate speed and protect pedestrians. Although a mix of land uses was encouraged wherever possible, the industrial zone was sited so that heavy trucks would not travel through the historic and redevelopment areas.[89]

In 1978 the Florida developer Robert Davis (b. 1943) inherited an 80-acre (32-ha) beachfront property on the Gulf Coast of the Florida Panhandle. Acquiring the land free of debt allowed Davis to proceed slowly and deliberately. He envisioned the property as a gated community and solicited plans from several architects. The first plan featured housing clusters and was mostly carfree. Its rudimentary street layout comprised two dead-end drives leading to parking lots, while boardwalks throughout the

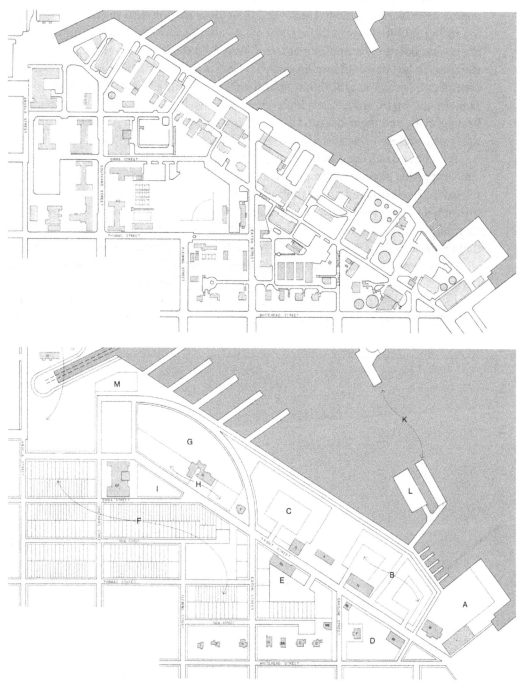

Figure 9.15: Duany et al., Key West existing conditions (above) and proposed plan (below), details, 1977. The proposed plan extended the adjacent grid to create more through streets, as well as two new cul-de-sacs. Note: water areas have been tinted for legibility. Courtesy of Andrés Duany.

site formed a separate pedestrian network. The second plan was a crescent shape made of superblocks that recalled the Royal Crescent in Bath, England. An existing two-lane highway, State Route 30-A, traversed the property along the beach. The crescent plan proposed to deflect the highway on a giant semicircle around the development.[90]

Davis met Duany and Plater-Zyberk and asked them to refine the crescent plan. The architects completed drawings in early 1979, attempting to make the project appear more like a real town. Davis liked their ideas and pursued the concept through the spring of 1980. He won the support of neighboring landowners, got approval from the county board of commissioners, and promoted the plan in newspapers. He said the crescent layout would give homeowners direct views and access to an uncluttered beachfront. Davis was still thinking of the development as a gated community. The semicircular highway formed a high-speed buffered barrier between the project and its neighbors, and the residential area had one controlled entrance. The character of the layout was exclusive and insulated.[91]

As it turned out, the cost of moving Route 30-A was prohibitive, and the required state approvals were complicated. Also, the nation was mired in a tough economic recession. Davis decided not to move the highway. During this period, Davis and his future wife Daryl Rose, and Duany and Plater-Zyberk, toured small towns across Florida, Georgia, and Alabama. They studied the vernacular patterns and considered them as models for a new town. Davis began to question the conventional real-estate wisdom that gated communities extracted the maximum value from residential land. He wondered if that was correct, considering that real-estate values were higher in America's streetcar suburbs. In addition, his reading of Jane Jacobs around this time was influential. When Duany evolved a neotraditional street layout later in 1980, Davis

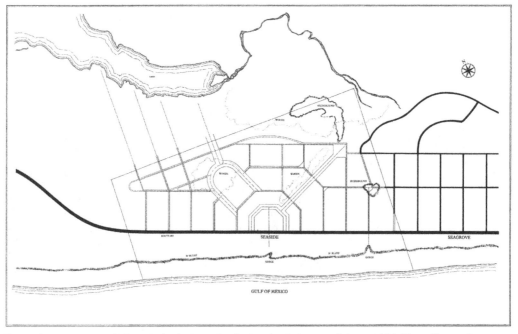

Figure 9.16: Duany and Plater-Zyberk, Seaside plan and existing conditions, 1984. The adjacent Seagrove grid was extended through the site and deflected in an echo of the previous crescent plan. To the north, four street connections were proposed. Courtesy © DPZ CoDESIGN.

A HISTORY OF STREET NETWORKS • CHAPTER 9

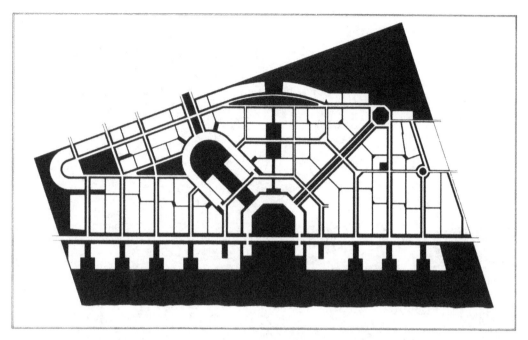

Figure 9.17: Duany and Plater-Zyberk, Seaside pedestrian plan, 1984. Pedestrian facilities shown in black. A comprehensive network of pedestrian paths ran through every block. Also, a pedestrian street was created on the central axis. Courtesy © DPZ CoDESIGN.

decided to adopt it. His decision involved more than a simple change of geometry. It changed the character of the development to one that was connected, open to neighbors, and welcoming to travelers on the highway.[92]

The neotraditional plan was a hybrid of grid and crescent. The street grid of neighboring Seagrove Beach was extended across the property "to provide multiple access points and social continuity"—similar to how the Key West studio had extended the nearby grid. The plan also indicated future street connections to the northwest. The central commercial area and its surrounding blocks were adapted from the crescent plan. Around the central green, attached mixed-use buildings formed a continuous facade that was consciously adapted from traditional Southern main streets and town squares. Radial elements from the crescent plan reappeared as diagonal streets and a civic green. Construction of the first few buildings started in 1981, and the project was officially named Seaside.[93]

Duany had heard Léon Krier speak in Miami in the late 1970s. He was profoundly affected by Krier's fiery, uncompromising defense of traditional urbanism and his sophisticated plans. On Duany's recommendation, Krier visited Seaside as a consultant in the fall of 1982. Krier critiqued the plan by creating his own version. It retained Duany and Plater-Zyberk's layout, and added extra-small "point blocks" and a comprehensive pedestrian network.[94]

Duany and Plater-Zyberk incorporated Krier's ideas by adding a major pedestrian street and laying pedestrian paths through every block. The paths came to be known as "Krier walks." In the 1984 master plan, Duany and Plater-Zyberk declared that the plan represented a "turning away from the methods of contemporary real estate development toward those of traditional American urbanism." Davis quipped, "Our motto

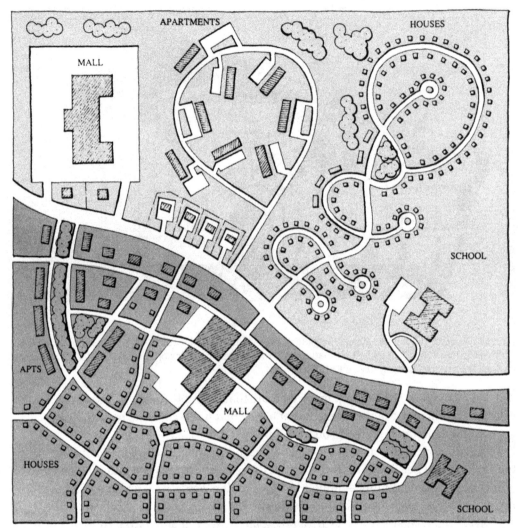

Figure 9.18: Duany and Plater-Zyberk, conventional and neotraditional layouts, 1989. A layout of insular single-use pods contrasts with a well-connected mixed-use plan. The former funnels all inter-pod traffic onto the main arterial; the latter provides many alternative routes for local traffic. Courtesy © DPZ CoDESIGN.

is, 'Don't invent anything.'" Yet the designers and Davis also considered Seaside to be a village of ideas and a model for reform. Many architects and planners were inspired by the combination of design ideals and reformist zeal.[95]

Seaside achieved a swift and unexpected fame. *Progressive Architecture* magazine gave it an award (along with the Battery Park City plan), calling it "a veritable small-town alchemy" with "a clarity that is superbly convincing." *Time* magazine called it a "splendid and improbable little utopia." By the late 1980s, Seaside's land prices exceeded those of comparable gated developments. Grid layouts were not uncommon in urban redevelopment by that time, but Seaside demonstrated that neotraditional street layouts could succeed in newly developing areas too.[96]

Duany Plater-Zyberk and Company (DPZ) was launched into prominence as a town planning firm. It planned more than twenty new towns and urban projects by 1989. The firm's principals embraced neotraditional planning as a mission and spread their message through projects, teaching, lecturing, and writing. Plater-Zyberk, who had begun teaching at the University of Miami's School of Architecture in 1979, created the graduate program in Suburb and Town Design in 1988 and became dean in 1995.[97]

Duany, while on the lecture and teaching circuit, sharpened his criticism of conventional street-network planning. "The different parts of suburbia have been walled and separated. The planners have not provided internal connections from one place to the other . . . the consequences are enormous," he explained at a 1988 symposium held in Seaside. "The right amount of asphalt is always provided by the planners, but it is designed to lead all of the trips on to very, very few streets. This is why all the new suburbs from California to Florida have the densities of towns but the traffic of a metropolis." The problem was greater than congestion alone; the social culture of suburbs was affected. "There's no public realm, there's no street life," Duany observed. "Everything in suburbia built since the 1960s suffers from that disconnection, and that disconnection often is legislated."[98]

DPZ developed relationships with allied architects, planners, and developers, and the members of that network began to contemplate organizing formally. Léon Krier, who was perennially interested in associations and manifestoes as reform vehicles, advised them to use CIAM (International Congresses of Modern Architecture) and its annual congresses as an organizational model. The movement was re-branded *new urbanism*, and the Congress for the New Urbanism (CNU) was established in 1993. Its Charter document was a founding manifesto that called for compact, diverse, mixed-use development. Its transportation principles included interconnected street networks and streets that were safe, open, and accessible.[99]

New Urbanism and Traffic Planning

The work of DPZ and other neotraditionalists filtered into the traffic-planning profession by stages. The civil engineer Richard A. Hall was hired in 1984 to perform the required traffic analysis of Seaside's plan. "I had never seen such a fine-grained network of streets in a proposed development plan," remembered Hall. "They were proposing twelve intersections, within a half-mile, connecting with an arterial highway. This was unheard of and certainly not part of conventional engineering practice at the time." The Seaside assignment was a turning point in his career. His preferred practice became transportation design for walkable, compact, mixed-use communities.[100]

The civil engineer Chester E. Chellman encountered DPZ at a project design session in Bedford, New Hampshire in 1987. Chellman was immediately enthused about DPZ's ideas and led the creation of a Traditional Neighborhood Development (TND) ordinance for the project. DPZ and Chellman soon developed a generic version that aimed to legalize all elements of neotraditional planning. In his usual audacious style, Duany called it "an ordinance to save America." The transportation elements included well-connected street networks, small blocks, and pedestrian-friendly streets; specific parameters were customized for various communities. For example, the proposed ordinance for Palm Beach County, Florida (1990), stated that no more than 5 percent of streets could be dead ends; the average perimeter of blocks could not exceed 1,300 feet (400 m); and no block could exceed 300 feet (91 m) in length unless an alley provided through access.[101]

Similar codes were used in scores of DPZ projects, and over the years they evolved into DPZ's free, open-source SmartCode (2003). By 2017 the SmartCode had been adopted in some 380 locations in the United States and Canada, applying to approximately 7,700 square miles (19,900 sq km) and 4.7 million inhabitants.[102]

The civil engineer Frank Spielberg, and Chellman as well, attended the 1988 Seaside Symposium. Spielberg had grown up in central Philadelphia, and was drawn by his sense that finally people were doing urban design the way it ought to be done. On the trip home he wrote an article about the principles that had been discussed. It became one of the first articles to cover neotraditional traffic-planning principles in a professional engineering publication. Spielberg began speaking and writing about those principles to professional audiences, sometimes teamed with Chellman.[103]

In 1992 an Institute of Transportation Engineers committee chaired by Spielberg started work on a TND guidebook. Chellman eventually became the guidebook's lead author. *Traditional Neighborhood Development: Street Design Guidelines* was approved as an ITE recommended practice and published in 1999. With regard to street layouts, it stated flatly that "TND streets are interconnected. This principle is central to TND design. Cul-de-sacs and other dead-end streets are not a part of a TND."

The guidebook endorsed a moderately cellular model for street networks. Large, high-volume arterials should not penetrate a TND; they should be located at the edges. They were hostile to pedestrians and, like a river, required elaborate pedestrian crossings. One of the challenges of TND design was to moderate the dispersed flow carried by internal streets, so that cut-through traffic never became excessive or endangering. Cut-through traffic could be impeded by three-way intersections, narrow street widths, and other land-planning and network-design methods.[104]

Walter Kulash

Until 1990, advocates of neotraditional planning justified interconnected street layouts by referring to the evident good performance of historical layouts. But many other planners and engineers were skeptical. They believed that historical layouts were obsolete, and that mainstream traffic planning was essential to an auto-oriented society. So when the civil engineer Walter Kulash rebutted some of those beliefs using the language and analysis techniques of traffic engineering, it caused a considerable stir.

In late 1989, Kulash attended a Duany lecture in Orlando, Florida. He was "dumbstruck" and felt the presentation was one of the most interesting and exciting things he had heard. Returning to his office, he performed a comparative analysis of TND and conventional dendritic street layouts. They were modeled in otherwise identical development projects.[105]

Kulash found that the TND layout generated less than half the vehicle-miles of travel, because internal trips could use internal routes that were more direct. The TND generated more travel on local streets but less on arterials and collectors, and thus had less congestion and delay. Speeds were lower in the TND, but the overall time spent traveling was about the same. That was because the routes were more direct, the narrower streets permitted shorter traffic-signal cycles, and more travel went through unsignalized intersections (where there was no waiting for a light to change). Also, a TND could provide a more appealing driving environment, which reduced perceived travel time. The TND's traffic capacity could be adequate well into the foreseeable future, and as a result, it might never need multiphase traffic signals. In summary, the well-connected street network performed equally well or better in terms of travel time, capacity, congestion, and delay.[106]

Kulash and his colleagues wrote a report and Kulash presented the findings at several conferences during 1990–1991. Although the report was unpublished, it was widely circulated and influential among pedestrian advocates. From then on, Kulash specialized in livable traffic design. Other engineers began to test the performance of well-connected street layouts and often found significant benefits.[107]

In 2001 Kulash wrote the third edition of *Residential Streets* for the Urban Land Institute. He expanded his arguments against dendritic layouts while noting that inter-neighborhood connections faced tough opposition in local politics. "Connecting the entire network of local streets from one subdivision to the next, even where mandated by local regulations, has proved to be a near impossibility, politically," he wrote. He suggested that local governments could establish collector-street networks before development started in order to ensure that linkages were made between neighborhoods.[108]

Indeed, the town of Seaside experienced such disagreements. Seaside's well-connected street layout generated no disputes as long as tourism and development in the region was minimal. Then in 2000, the Watercolor development (planned by Jaquelin Robertson and Alexander Cooper's firm) began construction along the north and west boundaries of Seaside. Although the 1984 Seaside plan had projected several street connections to the northwest, Seaside's residents were concerned about construction vehicles driving through the neighborhoods. Robert Davis reluctantly acceded to their request to barricade the sole connecting street. The barrier fence blocked vehicles while allowing pedestrians to pass through.[109]

The surrounding coastal area continued to develop and traffic increased concomitantly. In 2006 Seaside residents barricaded a street on the eastern border in an effort to reduce cut-through traffic. After a few weeks, the county planning director ordered the barrier removed because it decreased connectivity and forced more cars onto the already congested Route 30-A. Cut-through traffic remained a contentious issue. To address future traffic, Davis organized the 30A Mobility Project in 2015 to plan transit, off-site parking, and regional traffic-demand management.[110]

Into the 21st Century

A variety of initiatives were organized during the 1990s and early 2000s that were allied with new urbanism and advocated well-connected streets and small blocks. The smart-growth movement, which emerged in the mid-1990s, was mainly concerned with policy and legislation at all levels of government. New urbanism was a consistent theme in smart-growth recommendations. Interconnected street networks were advocated because they benefited walking, bicycling, transit, and overall efficiency. The plans, programs, and guidebooks produced by smart-growth advocates helped advance street connectivity in built projects and policies across the United States.[111]

In 2002 the American Planning Association formally endorsed planning practices that gave high priority to street connectivity. The APA's smart-growth policy guide explained that well-connected streets enhanced transportation efficiency, unlike "gated communities, private road systems, and the introduction of disconnected cul-de-sac systems." The APA publication *Planning for Street Connectivity* (2003) found that at least twenty jurisdictions in the United States had adopted street-connectivity standards since the early 1990s. The standards sometimes faced political challenges, but the results led to more accepting attitudes. For instance, in Eugene, Oregon, opposition faded after residents discovered that connectivity reduced congestion and that they liked to use the new connections themselves.[112]

From the mid-2000s onward, several state transportation agencies promoted street connectivity for specific contexts. Agencies in Virginia, New Jersey, Pennsylvania, and Florida encouraged connectivity by methods such as subdivision regulations, recommended-practice guidebooks, and design flexibility for walkable urban areas.[113]

But in most jurisdictions, high-speed, high-volume arterials continued to act as major impediments to livable urban places. New urbanists decided to create standards for more humane urban thoroughfares. They identified functional classification as part of the problem because it produced generic, auto-dominated roadways. Those roadways often did not match their adjacent environments, particularly walkable urban environments.

In 2002, CNU members outlined a street-design manual that would systematize the neotraditional and context-sensitive concepts. The following year, CNU partnered with ITE and obtained support from the Federal Highway Administration and Environmental Protection Agency. A draft version was released in 2006; the manual was approved as an ITE recommended practice, and was published as *Designing Walkable Urban Thoroughfares* in 2010. Whereas the 1999 ITE guidebook by Chester Chellman had covered local and collector streets that were inside neotraditional developments, the 2010 manual covered major thoroughfares in areas that were walkable or aspired to be walkable.[114]

Designing Walkable Urban Thoroughfares reiterated the principle that walkable urban areas should have a high level of street and thoroughfare connectivity. The manual gave guidance for the spacing of arterials: in urban areas, one half mile (0.8 km) or less; in denser and core areas, one quarter mile (0.4 km) or less. It said that local streets should be connected to thoroughfares at many points, while curb cuts and driveways should be minimized. In general, blocks should not be longer than 600 feet (183 m), and 200–400 feet (61–122 m) was preferable. In the densest urban centers and core areas, blocks should not be longer than 400 feet (122 m), and 200–300 feet (61–91 m) was preferable.[115]

The manual was disseminated widely and was used by planners, public works departments, city officials, and local advocates. Many municipalities and several state agencies adopted it, and the US Federal Highway Administration endorsed it for use by transportation agencies.[116]

A related ITE publication was *Planning Urban Roadway Systems*. It was the strongest, most definite endorsement of well-connected roadway networks yet issued by a professional organization. It was published as a draft proposal in 2011 and as an approved practice in 2014.

ITE had first issued a guidebook on planning arterial networks in 1969, and issued updates in 1988 and 1997. ITE's guidance had changed remarkably little over 42 years. Its guidebooks shared a reliance on functional classification, had similar arterial spacing standards, and even used the same arterial-spacing graph. In contrast, *Planning Urban Roadway Systems* was a rewrite—a new document in many respects. It reflected major changes in the professional field and ITE's greater emphasis on planning for walking, bicycling, and transit. An additional stimulus for the rewrite was *Designing Walkable Urban Thoroughfares*; several of the authors worked on both ITE guidebooks and other CNU street-planning documents.[117]

Planning Urban Roadway Systems encouraged planners and engineers to think of roadway networks as a collection of coordinated sub-networks, each optimized for different travel modes. Some examples were bicycle networks, transit networks, and truck networks. Dense, well-connected roadway layouts had an abundance of alternative routes that permitted such optimization. Well-connected networks helped produce roadways that were more efficient, flexible, and good for walking, bicycling, and transit. Well-connected networks were part of the solution to many issues including regional pollution, congestion, crashes, maintenance costs, economic development, and community livability. The guidebook gave extra attention to the issues that arose when a roadway system was transformed from rural to suburban, or from suburban to urban.[118]

In 2013 the US Federal Highway Administration released a new functional-classification guidebook. It represented the agency's first reconsideration of basic principles since the original 1969 *Functional Classification Study Manual*. The guidebook endorsed functional classification in broad outline, but recognized that strict adherence to the conventional access-mobility relationship could produce roadways that were poorly fitted to their surroundings. It said that reformers had altered mainstream transportation thought:

> With the institutionalization of new concepts such as sustainability, smart growth, new urbanism and complete streets comes a different perspective on transportation as a whole and on roadways in particular. These movements have shifted the dialogue from the movement of automobiles to the mobility of persons.

The federal guidebook cited the ITE-CNU manual and the British *Manual for Streets* (2007) as initiatives that broadened the design options for functional classification. "Gone are the days of simply verifying a roadway's functional classification and applying a 'one-size-fits-all' approach," it announced. To illustrate the new functional-classification relationships, the guidebook presented an access-mobility diagram in the shape of clouds. Although it was meant to suggest flexibility, the diagram actually communicated vagueness and uncertainty. State DOTs were likely to ignore it.[119]

American neotraditional policies and practices had mixed results at the national scale. A study of US urbanized areas found that between 1920 and 1994, street connectivity decreased and the proportion of cul-de-sacs increased. Then around 1994 the trend reversed. Over the next twenty years, street connectivity increased and the proportion of cul-de-sacs decreased (returning approximately to 1960s levels). The findings suggested that the largest increases in connectivity occurred in places with pro-connectivity policies. On the other hand, a study of 51 US metropolitan areas found that street networks became slightly more circuitous (that is, less direct and

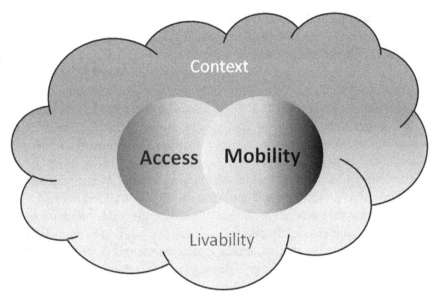

Figure 9.19: US Federal Highway Administration, access-mobility cloud diagram, 2013.

efficient) between 1990 and 2010. The authors speculated that the growth of dendritic road networks in suburban areas caused the trend. Together, these studies suggested that, from the 1990s to the 2010s, connectivity *within* neighborhoods increased but connectivity *between* neighborhoods decreased.[120]

The Federal Highway Administration's cloud diagram reflected the reality that the United States in the 2010s remained a predominately auto-oriented nation. A minority of its people lived in walkable areas. Many state engineers and officials were skeptical of neotraditional layouts and continued to specify the cellular model for new development. That said, most transportation engineers readily acknowledged that well-connected layouts of small blocks facilitated walkable urban neighborhoods and districts.

Such layouts appear to be gaining ground at present, but future outcomes are uncertain. If connections between neighborhoods become sparser—if the built environment becomes more cellular—then regional accessibility will likely worsen, and the mode share of walking, bicycling, and transit will likely decline.

British Street Design Manuals

As new urbanism and parallel movements arose in the United States, similar reform efforts developed in Great Britain. During the late 1990s and 2000s, a series of guidebooks were written by private consultants for various government agencies, including *Places, Streets and Movement* (1998), *Urban Design Compendium* (2000), and *Better Places to Live: By Design* (2001). That activity culminated in *Manual for Streets* (2007), which was the official street-design guidance for England and Wales. It was extended in *Manual for Streets 2* (2010), which gave recommendations for main thoroughfares, and in *Designing Streets* (2010), which was Scotland's street-design guidance. Those documents represented a major governmental shift from auto-oriented design to pedestrian-oriented design.[121]

In regard to roadway networks, the guidebooks recommended well-connected layouts of small blocks. Well-connected layouts created more convenient and efficient routes for walkers, bicyclists, and transit; they dispersed traffic and reduced congestion; and they supported long-term adaptability. The guidebooks said that main streets should be safe and comfortable for pedestrians, and should be routed through development areas instead of bypassing them. Maximizing the number of direct connections to main streets increased the potential for mixed use. The guidebooks advised against suburban, dendritic cul-de-sac layouts because they made travel routes inconvenient and required residents to use cars for all travel. Cul-de-sacs were useful in certain situations, but were to be used with caution because of their negative effects.

The 1998–2001 guidebooks were primarily authored by the consulting firms Alan Baxter & Associates and Llewelyn-Davies. The Baxter firm had been responsible for the civil engineering of Poundbury since 1993. David Taylor, who led Baxter's guidebook-writing team, was a staunch proponent of new urbanism. The *Manual for Streets* and later guidebooks were written by a team led by the engineer Alan Young of the consulting firm WSP. The traffic engineer Andrew Cameron contributed to all these guidebooks while working for the Baxter firm and WSP in succession, and he worked concurrently on Poundbury's street layouts.[122]

Poundbury certainly influenced Britain's guidance on street-network connectivity. Yet many other groups and trends did also, such as urban-regeneration practice, the pedestrianization movement, and urban-sustainability advocacy. The main authors of *Manual for Streets* were in complete agreement on street connectivity. The previous official guidebook had promoted dendritic cul-de-sac layouts for thirty years, and all the authors understood the damage it had done.[123]

Cellularity in Neotraditionalism and New Urbanism

By the 1970s the planning, engineering, and design fields had absorbed fifty years of traffic-planning dogma, and were keenly aware of the cellularity issue. Most of the pioneering neotraditional designers believed that standard gridirons had to be modified or protected to be suitable for residential use. All the early neotraditional projects addressed the issue of cut-through traffic in some fashion. Indeed, that was one of the main differences between traditional and neotraditional urban design.

Different solutions were used depending on project context. Some projects, like the St. Lawrence neighborhood, were located next to natural or built features that blocked traffic from one or more directions. Some, like La Villette, had bypass roadways that handled fast through traffic, internal layouts that inconvenienced cut-through traffic, and policies that restricted traffic entry. Some, like Seaside, converted the bordering arterial to a pedestrian-friendly main street and controlled cut-through traffic with slow, narrow internal streets.

That diversity of design approaches and philosophies continued over the subsequent decades. No perfect consensus about cellularity emerged within the neotraditional and new-urbanism fields. No universally supported guidance helped designers understand what degree of cellularity was desirable, or which types of cellularity had positive or negative impacts, or which types were best applied to which situations. Disagreements between designers occasionally flared into quarrels. They agreed that different types of cellularity should be matched to different conditions, but disagreed about which patterns (if any) represented an ideal to strive for.[124]

Notwithstanding such divided opinions, neotraditional designers, planners, and engineers achieved significant successes in the traffic-planning field. In the United States, Great Britain, and other countries, they revived and disseminated the principle of well-connected street layouts composed of small blocks. They effected that resurgence despite professional skepticism and institutional inertia, and their work paved the way for more walkable, vital, and adaptable urban environments.

Other Trends

From the mid-twentieth century to the early twenty-first, several traffic-separation trends gained tremendous momentum and expanded to affect entire global regions. They were implemented in many of the world's cities and achieved various degrees of popular support and success. Three major traffic-separation trends are covered in the following sections: gated communities, dedicated rail and bus lanes, and carfree and car-limited districts.

Gated Communities in Recent Decades

Gated communities represented the opposite of neotraditional layouts, inasmuch as they aimed to be disconnected and insular. Gated communities were a relatively minor phenomenon in America until a growth boom started in the 1980s. From 1980 to 2000 the number exploded from about 1,000 to more than 25,000. The fast growth continued until the Great Recession of 2008. In 2015 the American Housing Survey found that 9 million dwellings were in communities "gated or surrounded by walls or fences that prevent access by persons other than residents." (The AHS figures included military housing for civilian family members.) That represented about 6.7 percent of the US population, although in some regions, especially the southwestern states, the percentages were appreciably higher. For example, a 1999 survey of Phoenix, Arizona, found 641 gated communities that housed about 12 percent of the population.[125]

Gated communities became a global phenomenon in the 1990s; most metropolitan areas had at least a few. They were especially numerous in Mexico, Brazil, and Argentina; in African cities such as Lagos, Nigeria, and Johannesburg, South Africa; and in major Chinese cities. China had a legacy of enclosed residential-industrial compounds built by the Communist government from the 1960s onward. Those compounds were the predominant living arrangement in a number of Chinese cities. During the 1990s and 2000s, residential developments with gates and guards were widely encouraged in Chinese cities. Some places even required them, as Beijing did in the early 2000s. China's policies were partly driven by local officials who wanted a greater ability to classify, monitor, and manage the populace.[126]

The global boom had a number of causes. One, developers in many countries imported the American model. Two, many regions had their own historical traditions of enclosed, restricted-access territories. Three, similar motivating conditions appeared concurrently in many parts of the world, which was an outcome of expanding globalization. Those conditions included increased personal wealth; general economic inequality; weakened governments and inadequate policing capability; and social stress or disruption, which was often associated with high rates of migration and immigration.[127]

Gated communities that are large enough to have internal street networks affect traffic circulation like ungated dendritic layouts. Both eliminate through traffic and discourage nonresidential traffic. Gated communities make explicit what ungated dendritic layouts strongly imply: territoriality and exclusion. Both may form large barriers in the regional roadway network, and may create inconvenient, inefficient regional circulation patterns. The main circulatory difference between the two patterns is the delay caused by the gates themselves. Gates sometimes delay critical emergency-response services, and slow other services such as deliveries, taxis, and repair and maintenance operations. As the number of gated communities in a jurisdiction increases, the task of managing the proliferating entry protocols becomes more complicated for public agencies and private firms.

From a traffic-flow perspective, gated communities have no need of dendritic street layouts. Gates and sealed perimeters can ensure that through traffic will be nonexistent in any type of layout, even gridirons. And yet, many privately developed gated communities have dendritic layouts. The goal seems to be not only isolation from the outside world, but unequal status and traffic impacts for the residents within. Some gated communities have multiple smaller gated zones inside their walls, which create additional layers of exclusion.[128]

Gated-community residents have different reasons for wanting to live behind gates. Some residents are most concerned about crime, social disruption, and civil strife. Because those conditions have the potential to improve over time, gated communities that are motivated by those conditions could use more flexible and hopeful planning methods. Well-connected street layouts of small blocks could be enclosed by gates and walls to reduce the fear of crime and disruption. When conditions are perceived to improve and residents desire more involvement with the surrounding community, the gates and walls could be modified to allow free pedestrian and bicycle access. If the residents are interested in starting businesses and redeveloping their properties, they may even wish to add external roadway connections and allow public vehicular traffic into the community. Over the long term, the community could be integrated into the public urban fabric.

Other motivations are less amenable to change. Some gated-community residents are most concerned about maintaining certain appearances and behaviors by excluding and controlling others. Some desire the prestige of a gated enclave, like an aristocratic estate, and the high housing valuations associated with that prestige. For some, being apart from the city—physically, mentally, financially, and politically—is the main point. Gated communities that serve those desires are unlikely to be retrofitted. They are anti-urban in every respect. They fragment developed areas, increase class segregation, and contribute to the dissolution of civic society and identity.[129]

The challenge of retrofitting automobile-oriented gated communities may be tested in China. In 2016, the central government issued a national directive on urban design that promoted neotraditional and sustainable practices. New gated communities would be banned "in principle," and existing ones would be gradually opened. Some existing superblocks would be broken up, and denser street networks would be created. The central government said the main reasons for these rules were to improve traffic circulation, increase openness and accessibility, and make land use less wasteful.

But the difficulties are legion. Many residents like their gates and walls, and fear their removal will allow more crime, traffic, and unwanted visitors such as peddlers. The cost of retrofitting is high and developers do not know how to profit from it. Property owners may object on legal grounds. Local officials may believe that the new policies will increase social disorder. If Chinese cities can negotiate these challenges and satisfy the affected citizens too, it will be an important and instructive achievement.[130]

Dedicated Rail and Bus Lanes

Professional interest in divided roadways faded as automobility dominated urban transportation planning from the 1920s to 1950s. During that period, most of the extant divided roadways were legacies of the tram-trolley-streetcar era. The first inklings of a revival appeared in the mid-1950s. The number of facilities steadily increased over the following decades, reflecting growing concerns about urban livability, fuel efficiency, mass transit, and environmental quality. Heavy-rail metro systems (which did not use divided roadways) began to multiply at accelerated rates in the 1970s. Light-rail transit systems, which generally traveled in dedicated street lanes or separate limited-access rail corridors, began to multiply at faster rates in the early 1980s. Bus rapid transit systems with dedicated lanes began to multiply at accelerated rates in the 1990s.[131]

Light Rail and Tram Lanes

Trams (also called trolleys or streetcars) operated in many cities of the developed world until the 1920s and 1930s. Because they usually ran in mixed-traffic lanes, they were liable to be blocked. That happened more frequently as auto traffic increased. In the United States, United Kingdom, France, and other countries, most tram systems were scrapped before and after World War II. Trams were viewed as obsolete, while automobile-dominated roadways represented progressive modernity. But some cities in Germany, Switzerland, Belgium, the Netherlands, and a few other countries followed a different path. They gradually upgraded their old tram systems by placing rail tracks in dedicated lanes or carfree streets.[132]

The light-rail revival that got underway in the early 1980s took its inspiration from European systems. The new systems operated mostly in dedicated right-of-ways, which could be lanes in city streets, limited-access rail corridors, tunnels, or elevated structures. Light-rail systems opened in 42 cities from 1985 to 2000, and another 78 systems opened from 2000 to 2015.

In 2015, light-rail and tram systems operated on 9,700 miles (15,600 km) of tracks in 388 cities worldwide. The large majority of those systems (77 percent) were located in Europe and Russia. The most active builders of new systems were the United States, France, Spain, and Turkey. The fastest growth was being planned in South America, the Middle East, North Africa, and India.[133]

The 2001 Millennium Cities Database for Sustainable Transport sampled 100 cities worldwide to obtain transit statistics. It found that Eastern European cities had the highest density of dedicated routes for trams and light rail: 4.7 meters per urban hectare. Western European cities had 1.5, Middle Eastern cities had 0.7, and wealthy Asian cities had 0.7. Cities in all other global regions had very low densities of dedicated routes, even though light rail was growing quickly in some of those regions.[134]

Bus Lanes

The first dedicated bus lanes on city streets were installed in Nashville, Tennessee, in 1956. They were designated by yellow-painted lines and overhead neon signs, and were in effect only during morning and evening rush hours. Nashville's example immediately convinced engineers and officials in other cities to take similar actions. By the end of the year, bus lanes were operating in Chicago; Philadelphia; Harrisburg, Pennsylvania; and Newark, New Jersey.

Other North American cities soon followed those examples, and the idea spread to Europe. Paris installed bus lanes in 1964 and Brussels in 1966. Most of the early European bus lanes were short and intended as temporary measures, usually created to relieve spot congestion in historic city cores. But they gradually led to more comprehensive systems.

Some American cities abandoned their bus lanes during the 1960s and 1970s, while others retained theirs. The key conditions for retention were high congestion and high bus demand; the latter was usually supported by high density, mixed land uses, and walkable urban design. Also, a number of American cities installed bus lanes on freeways to serve commuter travel from suburbs to central business districts.[135]

A 1976 international review listed 96 miles (155 km) of on-street bus lanes in cities throughout Europe, America, and Asia. In some cases buses and taxis shared the lane; in some cases buses and trams shared the lane. The review also listed 59 miles (95 km) of bus lanes on US freeways.[136]

In Curitiba, Brazil, plans since 1965 had envisioned a predominantly transit-oriented city. Instead of undifferentiated automobile-oriented growth, the city would develop along radial high-density transit corridors. The first dedicated bus lanes opened in 1974. Bus lanes were used because they could be built quickly and at low cost; compared to rail transit, they were more suitable for a midsize city in a developing nation. By 1982 Curitiba had 34 miles (54 km) of dedicated lanes on five radial routes.

The system was so successful that the buses became overcrowded. In response, the city introduced advanced features to speed operations. It started fare prepayment in 1980 and also deployed three-door buses. In 1991 the city launched another system of express routes that had more advanced features (but did not run in dedicated lanes). These routes had stations in the form of glass tubes, bus doors level with station floors, and double-length articulated buses able to carry 270 passengers. In essence, the city was attempting to provide rail-system comfort and capacity at bus-system cost. By the early 1990s, those advanced features were in use on dedicated bus lanes in the Boqueirao district, creating the first example of what later became known as bus rapid transit (BRT).[137]

Curitiba's system was extraordinarily influential, and inspired BRT systems throughout Latin America and around the world. By 2018 there were 22,700 miles (36,500 km) of dedicated bus lanes on the streets of 116 cities worldwide. Latin America, Asia, and Europe had the most BRT systems and the most BRT system-kilometers. Latin America was the clear leader among global regions, and had the highest levels of BRT ridership.[138]

Carfree and Car-Limited Districts

In centuries past, vehicular traffic was occasionally excluded from city roadways so that more sociable activities could take place. Ordinary traffic was excluded during events such as holiday festivals, fairs, markets, parades, and ceremonies. Permanent informal traffic restrictions probably existed in many towns and cities where streets were too narrow for wheeled traffic.[139]

From the mid-twentieth century through the 2010s, the number of traffic-restricted areas grew rapidly, and a dizzying variety of schemes were developed. They aimed to reduce congestion, or improve air quality, or make urban environments more livable. Many schemes focused on private cars, because they caused the great majority of roadway congestion and pollution problems.

A typology of carfree and car-limited schemes can be organized according to the policies by which cars are filtered:[140]

1. Open to all cars
2. Open to a subset of cars
      a. Open to all trip functions
      b. Open to a subset of trip functions
3. Closed to all cars
      a. Historically carfree
      b. Retrofitted carfree
      c. Newly built carfree

Any of these schemes can be modified or combined to create locally unique policies. They can be combined with other vehicle restrictions such as truck restrictions and limits on vehicle size or weight. They can be applied full time, or during part of each day, on certain days of the week, during certain seasons of the year, or in any combination of schedules.

Category 1 consists of traffic-restraint schemes like those promoted by Donald Appleyard. Any car driver can enter the controlled zone, and through traffic is controlled or eliminated by barriers, dead ends, diverters, one-way street systems, and so on. Walkers and bicycles can move through freely. In the acclaimed examples, such as the Vauban district in Freiburg, Germany, car use is greatly reduced by parking limits, frequent transit service, and good bicycle facilities. Equity continues to be an important issue for this category. In the United States, for instance, lower-income households and racial and ethnic minorities are disproportionately exposed to high traffic volumes. Traffic-restraint schemes should benefit all residents—and that ethical position is more needed than ever. But it has not yet become conventional wisdom for this category.[141]

Under category 2a schemes, only a subset of car drivers are allowed in the controlled zone, and the restrictions are not related to trip function. This category comprises several scheme types. One, congestion charging allows entry to drivers who pay tolls. It was first implemented in Singapore in 1975, and has been adopted by a relatively small number of cities worldwide. Pitched political battles have been fought over congestion-charging proposals; they often were defeated on equity grounds. Two, low-emission zones allow entry to efficient or alternative-fuel vehicles. They were first instituted in the 1990s in large Swedish cities, and the number swelled after the mid-2000s. About 230 were in operation across Europe in 2018. Three, alternating-assignment schemes select groups of license-plate numbers (such as even and odd) on an alternating basis. Selected plate numbers are allowed entry on alternating days or during specified time periods. These schemes are most common in Latin American cities. They have been most successful as temporary measures because, over time, drivers find ways to circumvent the system.[142]

Under category 2b schemes, only a subset of car drivers are allowed in the controlled zone, and the restrictions are related to trip function—specifically, trips that serve the needs of residents and businesses inside the zone. More than 250 of these schemes are in operation in Europe. Nearly all are in Italy, where they are called *zona traffico limitato* (ZTL), or traffic-limited zones. Their main goal is livability. Only the residents and businesses in each zone are allowed to bring their vehicles in. Exemptions are granted to public transit, taxis, vehicles for disabled people, and certain services. ZTLs were first set up in the 1980s in Bologna and Milan, and were formally authorized by the Italian highway code in 1989. They spread throughout the country in the 1990s and proliferated in the 2000s. They were established in settlements of all sizes, from villages to large metropolises, as well as residential suburbs. ZTLs existed at the discretion of each city's leadership and proved to be popular; very few were discontinued. Much of their success was enabled by technological advances. The early schemes depended on gates and guards for enforcement, and cheating was rampant. Later schemes used cameras or electronic detection, which greatly reduced cheating, lowered enforcement costs, and made the systems more adaptable.[143]

Category 3a comprises the oldest carfree zones. The largest and most famous examples are Venice, Italy, which is 725 hectares (1,800 acres) in area, and the Medina of Fez in Morocco, which is 280 hectares (690 acres) in area. Portions of many other historical towns and villages have always been free of large vehicles because their streets were too narrow, bent, steep, stepped, or otherwise impassable.

Category 3b consists of street networks and districts that were retrofitted to be free of private cars. The roadways could be simply barricaded or thoroughly redesigned, while the existing urban fabric of buildings and blocks was retained. In the early twentieth century, a number of part-time schemes were begun in spots around the world. After World War II, Germany became the international leader. German cities created a few permanent schemes in the 1940s, 60 by the 1960s, and 800 by the 1980s. The trend spread around the world during the 1960s and 1970s and continues to expand today in many historical centers in Europe, Asia, and South America. Retrofitted carfree areas usually allow freight vehicles during specified hours, and often have bus or tram lines running through them.[144]

Category 3c consists of newly built carfree districts located in city centers or, more commonly, in suburban centers. Of the six categories of carfree and car-limited districts, this category has received the lion's share of attention in architecture and planning histories, but probably occupies the smallest total land area. Some early influential examples were Coventry city center, England (1953); the Lijnbaan in Rotterdam, the Netherlands (1953); and Vällingby in suburban Stockholm (1954).

In summary, carfree and car-limited districts were initially enforced by physical barriers or clumsy analog technologies. Since the 1990s, electronic technologies have enabled more precise filtering of certain vehicles according to each city's transportation goals. The new-generation schemes spread very quickly and, in some regions such as Western Europe, are now the dominant methods of car limitation. As the technology continues to improve, cities will have more options available for reducing traffic volumes to the amounts desired by the citizenry.

Chapter 9 Summary

A broad variety of traffic-separation trends developed in the late twentieth and early twenty-first centuries. All were intended to improve the quality of life in urban and suburban areas, but their philosophies and methods differed significantly, and in some cases were diametrically opposed.

The UK Ministry of Transport's 1963 report *Traffic in Towns* was the first book devoted to the tradeoff between urban motor traffic and street livability. It explained that good vehicular mobility tended to destroy good built environments, and good built environments tended to impede good vehicular mobility. It found three basic options for dealing with the conflict: total auto dominance and indifference to environmental effects, reduced traffic volumes, and elaborate multilevel infrastructure.

During the 1970s, Donald Appleyard researched and advocated retrofits of existing city neighborhoods to create cellular traffic layouts. He believed that fairness was the primary concern that arose from those schemes. Cellular traffic-restraint retrofits often worsened living conditions for a portion of the neighborhood's populace. Appleyard felt that if the number helped was greater than the number harmed, then a scheme was ethically justified. Others argued that an ethically superior policy would ensure that all residents benefited; achieving that goal required major traffic-volume reductions.

One can fairly say that the writer and theorist Jane Jacobs started the neotraditional urban design movement. In the late 1950s she rejected mainstream urban planning as out of touch and harmful to true urban vitality and prosperity. Her 1961 book *The Death and Life of Great American Cities* was an unapologetic defense of intensively urban places. It argued that well-connected street layouts composed of small blocks offered numerous social and economic advantages. Automobiles could have a positive role in cities if their numbers were limited and their dominance lessened. Although it was not without controversy, *Death and Life* became one of the most admired and influential books ever written about city planning.

In Europe, the brothers Léon Krier and Rob Krier led a parallel movement for neotraditional conceptions of urban streets and blocks. They were the best-known neotraditional urban designers during the 1970s and early 1980s, and their influence was international. Being architects, they attended to urban space and methods by which small blocks could humanize urban streets. Léon addressed through traffic in his highly connected street layouts by a variety of design techniques, such as bypass boulevards and three-way intersections.

Neotraditional projects and roadway layouts began appear in North America in the 1970s. The St. Lawrence neighborhood in Toronto was the first neighborhood-size, fully neotraditional project to be built (designed 1975–1976, opened 1979). Battery Park City in New York was the first neotraditional project built in the United States (designed 1979, opened 1982). Seaside, Florida, demonstrated that neotraditional development could succeed in a newly developing location as well as in an existing city (designed 1980–1984, opened 1982).

None of these neotraditional projects had undifferentiated street grids. All featured techniques to impede through traffic—and that was one of the characteristics that distinguished traditional layouts from neotraditional layouts. The techniques included (1) a location next to natural or built features that blocked traffic from one or more directions, (2) bypass roadways that handled fast through traffic, (3) internal layouts that inconvenienced cut-through traffic, (4) policies that restricted traffic entry, and (5) slow and narrow street design.

Andrés Duany and Elizabeth Plater-Zyberk, the designers of Seaside and many other neotraditional projects, were widely influential and inspirational in the urban design field. In the early 1990s they helped found the Congress for the New Urbanism, an education and advocacy group for architects, planners, developers, and others who supported neotraditional urban design. The organization's transportation principles included interconnected street networks that were safe and convenient for walking, bicycling, and transit. A growing number of designers, planners, and engineers engaged in reform of the dominant street-layout ethos.

Neotraditional traffic planning gradually filtered into the engineering field during the 1990s. A few traffic engineers researched the performance of neotraditional developments using professional analysis techniques, and reported the benefits and advantages in professional engineering language. Advocates also organized in fields such as planning, policy, and environmental activism. In the 1990s and early 2000s, neotraditional traffic-planning principles appeared in zoning ordinances, planning documents, and industry standards and manuals.

Neotraditional traffic-planning principles also appeared in governmental guidebooks. A series of British neotraditional urban-design guidebooks culminated in official advisory manuals for England and Wales (2007) and Scotland (2010). In 2013 the US Federal Highway Administration restated functional-classification principles to reject absolute uniformity and instead recommend flexibility and responsiveness to context.

Neotraditional principles affected market preferences and development practices in the United States. From 1994 to 2013, street connectivity inside developments increased, reversing the trend of the previous fifty years and returning approximately to 1960s levels. But connectivity between and outside developments may have decreased, creating more obstacles to walking, bicycling, and transit.

Concurrent with the rise of neotraditional roadway layouts, three other trends gained popularity: gated communities, divided roadways for transit, and carfree and car-limited districts. Those three trends increased traffic separation in different ways, and had very different effects on urban form.

Gated communities were an extreme form of insular development—the epitome of territoriality and exclusion. They affected traffic circulation like ungated dendritic layouts. That is, they tended to form large barriers in the regional roadway network and create inefficient regional circulation patterns. The number of private gated developments boomed in the United States after 1980, and in Latin America, Africa, and China after 1990. In the United States they housed almost 7 percent of the US population in 2015. In China, government-built and private gated developments were common; about two-thirds of urban residential neighborhoods restricted nonresidents' entry in 2006.[145]

Divided roadways reappeared, after a hiatus of 30–40 years, in the form of dedicated lanes for light-rail and bus transit. Light-rail systems began to multiply at faster rates in the early 1980s. They were most prevalent in Europe and Russia, but grew more quickly in other world regions. Bus rapid transit systems began to multiply at accelerated rates in the 1990s, and were most prevalent in Latin America. Light rail and BRT systems generally served walkable urban districts and performed best in well-connected layouts of small blocks.

Another traffic-separation trend was carfree and car-limited districts. They appeared in a great variety of types but shared the goal of reducing automobile traffic. They were instituted in cities all around the world, and were especially popular in Europe after 1990. Some schemes aimed to solve roadway congestion and pollution problems. Others aimed to improve the livability and sociability of urban environments. Many were intended to protect historical urban centers.

The overall diverse and complicated history of this period can be interpreted according to the strategies identified in *Traffic in Towns*. The strategy of automobile dominance manifested in suburban gated communities and dendritic layouts. The strategy of elaborate multilevel infrastructure was so expensive and difficult that it could be justified only in a very small percentage of any city's land area. The strategy of reduced traffic volumes was realized in carfree and car-limited schemes, and by dedicated transit lanes. Cellular traffic-restraint schemes (such as those advocated by Appleyard) had variable traffic effects, depending on many factors. Neotraditional developments generated less traffic than their mainstream equivalents; the degree of reduction depended on many factors such as location, density, mixed use, transit service, and good walking and biking facilities.

CHAPTER 10
Conclusion:
Evaluating Traffic Separation

The history of urban roadway layouts encompasses many contending visions for the modern metropolis. Throughout the extensive and complicated history, a basic condition motivated a perennial search for alternative physical forms. That condition was the fundamental conflict between excessive traffic volume and velocity on one hand, and livable roadway environments on the other.

The desire to resolve that conflict persisted and grew after 1800, in response to the burgeoning of mechanized metropolises. Visionaries, designers, engineers, administrators, and businesspeople wanted to remake cities' physical patterns. Often, they advocated solutions that were radically nontraditional, conjectural, and unproven. Some sought piecemeal change at the corridor or district scale, while others sought wholesale change at the national or global scale. Certain individuals and coalitions were incredibly successful at achieving those goals, such as Frederick Law Olmsted and his emulators; Raymond Unwin and the garden-city movement; the combination of Henry Wright, Clarence Perry, RPAA, RPNY, the US real-estate industry, and associated federal agencies; Robert Moses; and the combination of Thomas MacDonald, his federal agencies, state highway engineers, road builders, and automakers. During the latter half of the twentieth century, the US automobile industry's efforts had extraordinary repercussions that exceeded by far all previous achievements.

A key solution common to the reformers' efforts was functional traffic separation; that is, the separation of different traffic types according to role or purpose. By the mid-nineteenth century, that idea was developing in several concurrent trends. It evolved into the generic cellular-dendritic pattern, which emerged in the mid-twentieth century. Functional traffic separation was the foundation of roadway-planning policies and roadway patterns used in most American suburbs after World War II. Those policies and patterns fostered automobile-dependent built environments throughout the United States and in many metropolises worldwide.

Justifications of Functional Traffic Separation

Functional traffic separation initially developed in four distinct ways. In the vertical dimension, there was vertical separation; and in the horizontal dimension, there were divided roadways, insular roadways, and fast roadways.

Vertical separation. Vertical traffic separation gained currency during the 1830s and 1840s, in parallel with the early passenger railways. Hyperurbanism was a type of vertical separation that envisioned mixes of powered vehicles, abutter access, and sidewalk activities on multiple stacked levels. The main justifications offered for these methods were increased speed and convenience of travel, as well as congestion reduction, physical order, and the stimulation of business in adjoining spaces. Secondary justifications included civic pride and the spectacle of modernity.

Divided roadways. Early divided roadways in Europe grew from the leisure pursuits of the elite, and were associated with the separation of social classes. European multiway boulevards often became the spines of new affluent city districts. In America, multiway boulevards were built to activate and structure new suburbs. Olmsted and Vaux invented the term *parkway*, saying the goals were urban deconcentration, elegant low-density residential development, and carefree driving. By the late nineteenth century, advocates had added the justifications of traffic efficiency and order. Multiway roadways were one response (albeit relatively minor) to the chaotic urban street scene of the period; they were implemented to sort traffic streams by travel mode and trip purpose, improve safety, and minimize disturbance.

Insular roadways. Insular roadways of the nineteenth century typically had the goals of social exclusion, privacy, high status, and protection from noise and bothersome activities. A number of additional justifications were given over the years. Frederick Law Olmsted designed indirect, inconvenient roadway layouts to ensure that affluent residential neighborhoods would never change or support business activity. Raymond Unwin initially advocated dead ends to promote communal life and reduce development costs. As cities grew more motorized and dense, the justifications became more focused on traffic impacts and green space. German modernist architects after the mid-1920s designed superblocks and cul-de-sac developments to maximize uniformity and construction speed, minimize construction costs, and provide generous lawns and gardens. Clarence Perry's neighborhood unit was intended to promote cohesive and homogeneous social groupings, support local schools, and guarantee traffic safety, especially for children.

By the 1930s advocates had accumulated a full suite of justifications. Insular roadways planned at the neighborhood and metropolitan scales would form cellular patterns. Those patterns were supposed to eliminate traffic danger, noise, and pollution on local streets while enabling speedy traffic on the bordering arterials. Cellular patterns would help deconcentrate cities and increase open green space. In addition to reducing development costs, they would guarantee neighborhood stability and protect from "inharmonious" land uses. The exclusion of certain social classes and races likely remained a significant motive, but insular-roadway advocates of the time tended not to speak of it.

Fast roadways. Fast city roadways were originally established for racing, which provided thrills, social status, and spectator entertainment. As the motor-vehicle era progressed into the 1920s, fast roadways were more often advocated by engineers than racers, and the justifications tended to reflect engineering values. High-speed expressways would improve travel efficiency and convenience, and would reduce or eliminate congestion. They would solve the exploding traffic-safety problem by eliminating all crossing conflicts and by strictly separating fast vehicles from other travel modes. Expressways that orbited cities and penetrated downtowns were necessary for metropolitan prosperity. The psychological and sensual appeals of fast driving were not often discussed by engineers, but were certainly recognized and exploited by salespeople, advertisers, and artists.

Downtown business interests hoped that urban expressways and freeways would counteract the suburbanization trend and reinvigorate downtowns. The auto industry hoped that urban expressways would cause city dwellers to buy more cars; at the same time, it expected that urban expressways would accelerate the suburbanization trend and thus expand the market of suburban drivers.

The combination of rational-seeming engineering and economic arguments, support from business interests, and psychological appeal proved convincing. By the late 1940s, high-speed motor-vehicle travel had become the top priority in US urban roadway planning. That orientation was exported worldwide, and had the greatest influence on Latin American and Asian cities, and in some European suburbs.

Overarching Themes

This review shows that several of the justifications given for functional traffic separation were overarching. All the traffic-separation methods were claimed to improve the quality of urban life. They would impose order and efficiency on chaotic city traffic. They would provide built environments that were more convenient and aesthetically pleasing. Some were associated with feelings of personal power and control, such as the social superiority that derived from exclusivity, or the psychological exhilaration of high speed.

Increased speed and reduced congestion were primary justifications for the vertical and fast methods, and secondary justifications for the divided and insular methods. Advocates assumed that those effects would boost metropolitan prosperity. All the traffic-separation methods were claimed to facilitate real-estate development, and that was supposed to increase metropolitan prosperity too. Traffic safety was another overarching justification. It was a primary justification for the vertical, insular and fast methods, and a secondary justification for the divided method.

Although the traffic-separation methods had justifications in common, they generally differed in terms of their advocates' motives and urban-development goals. But the unprecedented impacts and demands of mass automobile usage spurred efforts to reconcile those differences. Having justifications in common may have allowed certain traffic-separation methods to be more easily blended.

Consolidation

In the late nineteenth and early twentieth centuries, functional traffic separation was typically implemented in individual, local instances, not in regional or national systems. Thus it was a relatively minor phenomenon. After the advent of mass automobile usage, some strands of functional traffic separation were blended into new combinations as other strands faded or disappeared. The promoters of certain combinations achieved tremendous political victories, and the methods they favored became the default roadway-planning patterns in the United States and internationally.

Elevated and depressed freeways. Fast roadways were blended with vertical separation to became elevated and depressed urban freeways, expressways, and major arterials. They were promoted by engineers, designers, government officials, and business interests, especially the auto industry. The advocates generally recycled the justifications of the past, blending the gee-whiz futurism of vertical separation with the psychological attraction of high-speed driving.

Early built examples, such as the Route 1 extension in New Jersey, adapted the engineering principles of utilitarian trunk railways. They were designed to maximize efficiency and speed, and to minimize engagement with the surrounding city. Later advocates forthrightly acknowledged the disruptive effect of such facilities and called for them to "gash" through cities and "trample" urban-design tradition. The US government supported that program in its 1944 national freeway system proposal, with the caveat that freeways through existing residential areas should be depressed or placed underground because elevated facilities caused too much disturbance. (Engineers in subsequent decades did not always follow that advice.) Those visions and justifications played a major role in determining freeway-planning principles in the United States and many cities worldwide.

Skywalk and tunnelwalk networks. Vertical separation also survived in relatively small central-city districts as semipublic skywalk and tunnelwalk networks. Popular in North America and East Asia from the 1950s–1960s onward, they were claimed to improve pedestrian safety, furnish weather protection, and reduce congestion. But a host of disadvantages soon became apparent. The systems were not inclusive; they sometimes banned certain types of people or activities other than shopping, and generally catered to daytime office workers. Street-facing businesses were harmed because the networks diminished surface pedestrian activity and retail vitality. Also, the extra construction and security expenses required to join the networks excluded small or low-rent commercial buildings. The global verdict was mixed. From the 1990s to 2010s, some cities dismantled their networks while others expanded theirs.

Functional classification. Cellular layouts were blended with expressways and freeways to become the omnipresent functional-classification policy. Functional classification was established in the United States primarily by the federal government, state highway engineers, and business interests working in close coordination. The automobile industry played a maximal role in the policy's creation and promotion.

Previous justifications for cellular layouts and expressways were generally reused by functional classification's advocates. The themes of increased speed and capacity, reduced congestion, and improved safety were cited continually and relentlessly. Advocates also added numerous justifications to the basic drumbeat. The cellular pattern would preserve property values, and the dendritic type maximized the number of cul-de-sacs, which would yield the largest profits for developers. Freeways were necessary to make all types of cellular roadway patterns operate properly. Functional classification would strengthen highway engineers' authority, and rationalize and coordinate roadway administration. It would make traffic-demand forecasts uniform and continuous in order to secure government funding. It would funnel money and traffic to the most socially important, high-speed freeways and arterials. It would produce logical and efficient roadway networks. It would be a powerful shaper of urban land-use patterns.

In the United States, functional-classification policy was codified in the 1950s and mandated in the 1970s. It led to enormous increases in federally funded major roadways in metropolitan areas. Functional classification, in combination with arterial-spacing and intersection-spacing standards, molded vast areas of suburbs as sprawling, auto-dependent zones. Its influence subsequently spread and ascended internationally until it became the world's paramount roadway-planning principle.

Hyperurbanism. Full-fledged hyperurbanism was abandoned like an unsuccessful exotic species in a ruthless evolutionary competition. After the 1920s it existed almost entirely in hypothetical (and increasingly fantastical) architectural visions and science-fiction imagery. Although its boosters promised only benefits, serious investigators found critical disadvantages. Weather-protected public space drew homeless persons and vandals, and had considerable public-safety needs. Pedestrians, bicyclists, and people with disabilities were inconvenienced or hindered by the need to change levels. Construction costs were extremely high, and schemes had to be built in large increments, or all at once, to function. Retrofitting downtowns and linking existing buildings on multiple levels was exceedingly difficult. Large-scale coordination and standardization required authoritarian power and exorbitant building-construction rules.

Divided roadways. The strand of divided roadways took a different course. Divided roadways faded during the mid-twentieth century because traffic engineers believed they were unsafe and inefficient, and that limited-access expressways made them obsolete. Also, non-automobile modes were in decline generally, and the widespread belief among planners and engineers was that future cities would be completely dominated by motor vehicles.

But by the 1960s and 1970s, attitudes were swinging back. Cities worldwide established transportation systems that were more multimodal. Dedicated travelways gained in popularity once again, and the reasons for the revival were much the same as in the late 1800s: to bring order, efficiency, and safety to roadways that served diverse travel modes and trip purposes. Dedicated lanes sped light rail, buses, and carpooling cars, and they protected and encouraged bicycling.

Throughout the rises and falls, and advances and retreats described above, declarations about performance were ubiquitous. Advocates touted extreme traffic separation as wholly beneficial for cities. They confidently declared many claims and promises, but gave minimal evidence. The two most common justifications were congestion relief and improved safety. After the neotraditional reformers began to advocate alternative patterns, questions of evidence and proof came to the fore. Researchers began to test performance outcomes, and an active debate opened about the benefits of traditional and neotraditional development patterns in comparison to modernist and auto-oriented development patterns. The next sections summarize research findings about roadway-layout performance, specifically in regard to traffic congestion and traffic safety.

Economic Effects of Congestion

Officials, engineers, and reformers have been obsessed with the "evil" and "disease" of urban traffic congestion for centuries. Throughout the history of traffic planning, congestion was assumed to cause enormous harm to urban economies. Congestion costs were used to justify new roadway construction, widening of existing roadways, and the separation of different types of traffic.[1]

According to William Haywood, Londoners were measuring congestion costs by the 1840s. He reported that "many ingenious calculations" had been made of "the loss of time consequent upon the inadequacy of the thoroughfares." In 1899 John Wolfe Barry described his process for estimating congestion costs. First he counted the vehicles and people moving along a street. Then he measured the travel time under free-flow and congested conditions, and said the difference was time lost to delay. Finally, he multiplied the time lost by the typical wages of the affected travelers to produce a total congestion cost. Applying his method to four London thoroughfares, Barry concluded that "many more millions of expenditures" on roadways were justified.[2]

That procedure became conventional wisdom and was used in essentially unchanged form through the twentieth and early twenty-first centuries. Leading officials, traffic engineers, and the motoring public were convinced that traffic congestion caused immense harm to urban economies, and that huge sums of money and effort were justified to solve it.

Cellular roadway layouts were widely promoted as one solution. Traffic planners knew that disconnected roadway networks within subdivisions had inefficient traffic movement. They tried to compensate by designing adjacent arterials that carried large volumes of traffic at higher speeds. But that strategy generally had inferior traffic performance. Superblocks and disconnected, dendritic layouts combined with wide arterials had less overall capacity and were more liable to become congested than well-connected networks of smaller blocks and narrower roadways.[3]

Vast suburban expanses were developed with cellular, disconnected roadway networks, and by the late twentieth century those patterns dominated US metropolitan areas. In terms of traffic capacity, the advantages of high-speed arterials were overwhelmed by the disadvantages of spreading out and disconnecting. Metropolitan-area roadway patterns that were more sparse, circuitous, and disconnected were associated with more congestion. Higher levels of congestion were also associated with roadway networks in which local streets predominated and through streets were relatively scarce. In short, the roadways patterns advocated by some traffic planners to relieve congestion probably increased congestion instead.[4]

Critics have challenged both the accuracy and importance of congestion-cost estimates. In regard to accuracy, the cost estimates used by US state and federal governments are hugely overstated. That is mainly because they assume an ideal of perfectly free-flowing traffic during peak hours. But from the economic perspective, that ideal is a preposterous fantasy. No city in the world can afford to build enough roadway space to ensure unlimited free flow during peak hours. Any city that tried would have a gigantic oversupply of roadway space during off-peak hours; the waste would be staggering and budget-busting.[5]

Instead, economists argue for maximum efficiency. They identify "optimal" peak-hour speeds that maximize traffic flow and make the most efficient use of the roadway infrastructure. Australia used that method and found that congestion costs were half the size of those produced by the "free-flow" calculation. In the United States, the economist Joe Cortright asserted that a realistic congestion-cost estimate was 70 percent lower than the mainstream estimate. A study that used the "optimal" speed method in Bogotá, Columbia, found that congestion costs were quite small—probably equivalent to less than 0.5 percent of the time spent traveling, or about 20 seconds per day for a typical traveler.[6]

In regard to the importance of congestion costs, researchers have asked a fundamental question: does traffic congestion harm urban economies? The question is difficult to answer because congestion is an extremely complicated phenomenon. It has multiple, sometimes opposite, relationships with economic performance. It has different economic implications at different scales. Congestion associated with urban density has different economic implications than congestion associated with sparse, disconnected roadway patterns. Some congestion remedies are very pro-urban and others are profoundly anti-urban.

At the scale of local neighborhoods and districts, the perspective held by officials and the motoring public is generally correct. Reducing congestion allows drivers to reach more destinations in the same amount of time, and that helps improve economic performance. Policies that reduce traffic volumes are most economically justified in dense, pedestrian-oriented, mixed-use districts. In such districts, small congestion reductions make relatively large improvements in the ability to reach destinations. In addition, reduced traffic volumes complement pedestrian-oriented street designs.[7]

At the scale of US metropolitan areas, the relationship of congestion and economic performance is reversed. Denser metropolitan areas have greater economic productivity, and to the degree that traffic congestion is caused by density in those areas, more congestion is associated with more economic productivity. Put simply, congestion in those areas is a byproduct of prosperity. In denser metropolitan areas the economic drag of congestion is outweighed by the economic benefits of access to many destinations in close proximity.[8]

In parallel with those findings, research in the United States found that denser, more mixed-use metropolitan areas with smaller blocks had more upward mobility. In other words, workers were more likely to move from low to high income brackets. The researchers attributed that result to the fact that compact metropolitan areas provided better access to workplace destinations.[9]

Overall, congestion is not the overriding economic threat that it has been painted as over the past 180 years. Its costs and importance to urban economies are less than commonly claimed. Building cities and suburbs with sparse, dendritic, disconnected roadway networks in order to reduce congestion is neither effective nor economically justified. Nor do congestion costs justify extremely expensive transportation investments that disperse urban development and diminish the benefits of compactness. Traffic planning should not aggrandize congestion relief to the exclusion of other urban livability values.

Traffic-Safety Effects of Roadway Layouts

The chart of US traffic fatalities per capita (figure 7.4) gives a long view of the nation's traffic-safety record. After seventy years of rebuilding American cities and suburbs according to engineers' specifications, and making the vehicles themselves safer, the traffic-fatality rate in 2017 was reduced to the 1920 level. But in 1920, the traffic-fatality rate was considered so outrageous and unacceptable that it spurred a national protest movement. Advocates have long claimed that cellular, disconnected roadway layouts are important for traffic safety, so detailed evaluations of that claim are crucial.

In 1889 Camillo Sitte criticized 4-way intersections in gridirons. They had an excessive number of "intersecting traffic trajectories" that slowed vehicles. In addition, he said, intersections that connected more than four street segments were "truly hazardous" for pedestrians.[10]

Sitte's line of thought was reprised by the designers of Radburn, who wanted to make traffic safety the first priority. Radburn was designed to eliminate all 4-way crossings by means of medians, roundabouts, and cul-de-sacs. Similar intuitive reasoning was used to justify cellular roadway layouts throughout the United States. Planners and officials believed that if through traffic was barred from subdivisions, then crash rates would plummet. And if whole regions were filled with cellular layouts, then the traffic-safety problem would be solved. Simple intuition and "common sense" were sufficient to justify policies that helped change the country.[11]

But by the 1950s, American society had become more professionalized and statistics-oriented. In Los Angeles, public agencies were said to be handicapped by the lack of statistics verifying the safety of cellular layouts. So the county traffic engineer Harold Marks made a study of crashes in subdivisions. He compared FHA-style cellular layouts to grid layouts, and found that grids had almost eight times more crashes. He believed that cellular layouts were safer because they discouraged through traffic and had a higher proportion of 3-way intersections. Three-way intersections in grid layouts, he discovered, were as safe as those in cellular subdivisions. Marks's explanation essentially repeated Sitte's argument, and he even duplicated Sitte's diagram of intersection conflict points.[12]

Marks's research was the "guiding study" on the subject of urban form and traffic safety at least until the 1990s. During that time, a few more studies confirmed that 4-way intersections were more dangerous, and they supported the mainstream recommendations for long cul-de-sacs, oversize blocks, and ever-more dendritic and disconnected subdivision layouts. But the studies were seriously flawed—limited and reductive. They ignored a wide range of roadway, roadway-network, and community-design elements that might affect traffic safety.

By the early 2000s, some researchers were determined to gain a more comprehensive view. They realized that urban environments had a complex mix of elements that worked in concert and produced important synergies. So, in addition to 4-way intersections, they considered block size, roadway width, frontage or roadside design, roadway layout, land use, speed, and crash severity. They included major arterials, which were the most dangerous urban roadways of all. They looked at multiple scales, as well as regional planning factors that influenced whether built environments were auto dependent or multimodal.[13]

Surprising findings appeared when researchers took a more comprehensive view. Four-way intersections were generally confirmed as more dangerous, but smaller blocks were safer. That was probably because short street segments kept traffic from reaching higher speeds, which reduced crash severity. Narrower streets, bike lanes, pedestrian-oriented frontages, and small shops were also associated with a lower risk of severe crashes, probably because those elements caused drivers to drive more cautiously and be more alert. Conversely, a higher risk of severe crashes was associated with faster, wider, more auto-oriented major arterials, and auto-oriented land uses such as big-box stores.[14]

Differences also appeared at different scales. At the street and block scales, 4-way intersections were more dangerous. But at the city and regional scales, greater roadway connectivity dispersed traffic more evenly, allowing roadways to be narrower, which was safer. Greater connectivity enabled more direct transit routing and more extensive transit coverage; as people rode transit more, they had less risk from traveling in cars. Greater connectivity also permitted faster emergency response to both medical and fire emergencies. The general result was that cities and counties had lower traffic-fatality rates if they were more dense and transit-oriented, and had better-connected roadway networks, more clustering of workplaces and housing, and more jobs-housing balance. However, some research found that more compact, connected cities also had higher non-fatal crash rates; that is, minor and non-injury crashes were more likely.[15]

By the late 2010s, a convincing body of literature had confirmed that the safest cities had a synergistic blend of roadway design and planning elements. Those elements were usually built within well-connected roadway layouts. One outcome of that condition was seen in a study of California cities, which found that "in terms of how these networks are built in practice, the safest street patterns of all were those that had fully connected street networks." At the regional scale, the risk of being killed or severely injured in traffic crashes was substantially less in denser, more compact urban areas, and that finding seemed to hold true in many parts of the world.[16]

Car-limited schemes such as Vauban in Freiburg, Germany, also may have promise as safer urban patterns. They have small blocks, pedestrian-oriented streets, and highly connected walking and bicycling networks, but prohibit through travel by motor vehicles. Such patterns have not been tested at large scales in cities that travel primarily by automobile. Their safety performance may depend on greatly reduced car use and nearby thoroughfares that are relatively narrow, slow, and pedestrian oriented.[17]

In sprawling suburbs, traffic danger is partly related to roadway design and partly to the amount of car travel. Design issues include wider, faster roadways; auto-oriented frontages associated with less-cautious driving; and sparse, disconnected layouts that lengthen emergency response times. Car-travel issues arise from low-density, single-use development patterns where destinations are spread far apart. In those patterns, residents drive more and spend more time exposed to the risks of traveling in cars. The former effect causes about two-thirds of the total traffic risk, and the latter about one-third.[18]

Questionable Assumptions

The congestion and safety justifications for cellular and dendritic roadway layouts started in similar ways. Initially (in the 1920s and during most of the twentieth century), they were based on simplistic reasoning and limited anecdotal evidence. They seemed to make intuitive sense, and more importantly, they supported the desired goal of suburban cellular layouts that served fast traffic. The justifications went virtually unexamined over the course of several generations. That was understandable, because the topics were complicated and difficult to study, and few challengers were clamoring to overturn the mainstream consensus.

Only in the 1990s and 2000s did researchers begin to re-examine and test the justifications. They found that the underlying assumptions were incorrect in numerous ways. Sparsely built cellular and dendritic roadway layouts did not reduce traffic congestion and were not associated with greater metropolitan prosperity. The case for auto-oriented cellular and dendritic roadway layouts as safety panaceas had been overstated.

Over and over again during the twentieth century, the public was promised permanent solutions to traffic problems. Vast areas were planned and built under the approbation of questionable assumptions, causing excessive and unnecessary harms to urban economies and human bodies. The results of traffic "improvements" were short-lived or subpar in many instances. The permanent solutions did not materialize as promised.

Fortunately, better-performing development patterns—walkable, lively, mixed use, and multimodal—have been gaining popularity and market share in many parts of America and in cities around the world. The situation in the 2010s is definitely better than it was just a few decades earlier. But at this stage, reforms must be constantly defended or else risk backsliding to what is still the status quo of automobile domination and alienating spaces.

Future Trends

The history of functional traffic separation reveals many of the ways that individuals, organizations, and governments attempted to resolve the fundamental conflict between traffic and livable roadway environments. That conflict is likely to intensify in the foreseeable future. Thus, the history of functional traffic separation can help inform responses to future urban-transportation trends.

In regard to forecasts, the most determinative condition is that motor vehicles and motor-vehicle traffic are increasing almost everywhere in the world. At present, the number of motor vehicles in use worldwide is at an all-time high. The growth rate during the early twenty-first century has been extremely constant. Markets are saturated (or nearly so) in the wealthy nations of Western Europe, North America, and Japan, and so they had lowest growth rates. Moderate-income nations had highest growth rates, such as those in Central and South America, the Near and Middle East, most of Asia, and Russia. The number of cars grew fastest in China, increasing an astonishing 415 percent from 2005 to 2015.[19]

Looking to the future, we can expect that cities worldwide will face ever-intensifying traffic pressures based on the global trends of increasing urbanization, economic production, and median incomes. Automobile growth rates will likely increase in low-income nations as they move to middle-income tiers. In addition, the automobile is perceived in most parts of the world as the most comfortable and convenient travel mode, and if that perception continues, it will also increase demand. All signs point to a future in which the fundamental conflict between traffic and urban-roadway livability will become more acute in more of the world's cities.[20]

Numerous trends have the potential to significantly affect the quality of future urban roadway environments. Several involve traffic separation, and have important implications for roadway networks. What are their benefits and drawbacks? Will they improve or worsen the traffic-livability conflict?

Electric vehicles. Electric vehicles have the potential to reduce some, but not all, of the air and noise pollution caused by traffic. They eliminate engine exhaust in city streets, and that is sufficient reason to promote them. But engine exhaust is only a portion of the car-pollution problem. In the United Kingdom, for instance, 60 to 73 percent of road-transport particulates are from brake, tire, and pavement wear. Electric vehicles will continue to have that problem, especially from tire and pavement wear. In addition, electric vehicles reduce drivetrain noise but not tire noise. Tire noise increases linearly with speed, and at 30 mph, it is loud enough to interfere with conversational speech. Therefore, electric vehicles may not be a panacea for the air and noise pollution of traffic.[21]

Electric vehicles could aid experiments in hyperurbanism. At the turn of the nineteenth century, electric locomotion enabled subways and multilevel constructs such as Grand Central Terminal. Similarly, electric vehicles could help make the multilevel roadways of hyperurbanism more viable. Compared to internal-combustion vehicles, they pollute less, require less ventilation in enclosed spaces, and can coexist with pedestrians more comfortably.

Autonomous vehicles. Autonomous-vehicle advocates claim that AVs will improve traffic safety, reduce congestion, and provide robot-chauffeur service to people who are unable to drive or prefer not to drive. Today's cars have driver-assist technologies such as collision avoidance, lane-keeping, and speed control; the optimistic advocates predict that fully autonomous vehicles will have even better safety performance. In their ultimate scenario, all vehicles will operate under networked computer control, and human drivers will be prohibited. That would allow vehicles to travel in fast, tightly packed platoons and weave through intersections with barely a handbreadth of clearance. In theory, traffic congestion would be reduced or eliminated.

To obtain the promised safety and capacity benefits during the transition period, some transportation engineers have recommended dedicated AV lanes on limited-access roadways. Engineers have also sought to develop supporting policies. For example, a universal classification scheme would classify roadways with dedicated AV lanes as higher class, and roadways that serve electronically connected AVs exclusively would be the highest class. Dedicated lanes might also be established on busy arterials. The most likely candidates would be high-speed arterials with widely spaced or grade-separated intersections.[22]

AV operation is much more difficult in existing city districts where pedestrian and bicycle activity is abundant. Self-driving autos may need many decades of maturation before they are able to perform safely on complicated city streets. Even then, pedestrians may be emboldened to cross anywhere along the street, secure in the knowledge that AVs will always yield. To prevent that from happening, some in the auto industry have called for pedestrians to be corralled with guardrails and fences. Pedestrians would be able to cross thoroughfares only at specified points.[23]

Many city streets cannot be fenced along the curb because the abutting lots and buildings have vehicular access only at the front. In addition, fencing along the curb blocks the pickup and drop-off of car, bus, and taxi passengers; fire-emergency response; and utility-company work on roadside infrastructure. An alternative configuration is fencing along the roadway centerline. That can control pedestrian crossings while allowing buildings to be accessed from the street. But both fencing configurations share a large set of disadvantages.

Pedestrian fences give roadways the character of a traffic-dominated speedway. They induce a false sense of protection for both drivers and pedestrians; as a result, everyone pays less attention and collisions generally increase. Fences restrict pedestrians' freedom of movement. They funnel pedestrians through a small number of openings, and lines can form in the roadway when groups of pedestrians try to squeeze through the narrow gaps. That creates obvious safety hazards and traffic delays.

Fences with mid-block crossings bunch pedestrians at the crossing points. That increases the need for pedestrian signals that stop the traffic flow. By contrast, if traffic is slow and sparse, and pedestrians can spread out and cross informally, there is less need to stop the traffic flow. Fences can channel pedestrians into inconvenient or bothersome routes, which discourages shopping and business activity. Annoyed pedestrians may attempt to circumvent the fences, placing themselves in greater danger. Overall, pedestrian fences create environments that are cluttered and oppressive.[24]

To deploy fenced roadways and, at the same time, minimize their costs and disadvantages, city authorities might decide to fence only selected major thoroughfares. That could reinforce cellular roadway patterns of superblocks and precincts. If traffic evolves as many engineers and automakers anticipate—into high-speed platoons of electronically connected AVs—cities will have to make radical changes in response. Clearly, high-speed platoons would be thoroughly incompatible with walking and bicycling. Pedestrians, bicycles, and other ultralight conveyances would have to be absolutely, comprehensively separated from the robotic traffic streams.

The result could be extremely strict, no-compromise cellular layouts devoted to auto speed and convenience. Historical visions such as Le Corbusier's grid of Radiant-City superblocks and H. Alker Tripp's fenced precincts are idealized examples. The major-arterial networks of Moscow and Warsaw are examples in built reality. In such strict cellular layouts, pedestrians are forced to use bridges or tunnels to cross arterials, and bicycling on thoroughfares is difficult and dangerous. Another possible response to high-speed AV platoons is comprehensive vertical separation. Elevated decks, podiums, and skywalk and tunnelwalk networks could be designed to carry pedestrians, bicycles, and other ultralight conveyances.

The history of functional traffic separation teaches us to be skeptical of proposals to comprehensively remake roadway systems when they are untested and based on limited analyses. Studies that consider roadway-network effects have found that self-driving private autos may greatly increase vehicle travel, congestion, and pollution on urban and suburban roadways. They would likely create demand for more freeways and wider arterials.[25]

Better AV scenarios have been proposed to counter the dystopian, anti-pedestrian, anti-bicycling scenarios. For example, the National Association of City Transportation Officials proposed that the key principle of an AV future should be that "people walking, biking, rolling, and resting get first priority for street space and resource investments." Pedestrians could make mid-block crossings anywhere along a block, which would allow them to choose the most convenient and attractive routes. Vehicles would travel no faster than 25 mph (40 kmh) and would always yield to pedestrians. The next priority would go to spatially efficient heavy modes. Dedicated AV lanes would be open only to autonomous buses and rail transit. Multiple-passenger automobiles would be encouraged in general-purpose lanes. Travel by solo automobile drivers and empty AVs would have a low priority. Those policies would maximize the spatial, fiscal, and energy efficiencies of urban roadways, and could help make them more equitable and livable.[26]

Connected Vehicles. Connected vehicles are able to communicate electronically with other vehicles, roadside infrastructure, and public or private data networks. The technology is spreading quickly, and many groups are working toward standardized communication protocols. Universal deployment could enable traffic separation schemes that are more complex, precise, and able to respond quickly to changing demands and conditions. Motor-vehicle traffic volumes could be more easily reduced to the levels that communities desire. Traffic-limitation schemes could be implemented with flexible boundaries, time periods, toll amounts, and other quick-response factors. Manual or automatic systems could reduce speed limits in response to unusually large numbers of pedestrians and bicyclists.

Personal Transporters. Personal transporters are very small, ultralight conveyances that operate at low to moderate speeds. In addition to standard bicycles, this category consists of low-speed electric bicycles, seated scooters, and standing scooters; self-balancing electric scooters and boards; unpowered scooters, skateboards, and skates; and more.[27]

Because these devices typically travel three to six times faster than an average pedestrian, they can be dangerous and frightening to people on foot. They are incompatible with sidewalk activities such as conversing, resting, shopping, dining, playing, spectating, and so on. Numerous cities have banned personal transporters from sidewalks, and some have regulated additional zones. For example, in 2019 the mayor of Paris proposed an 8 kmh (5 mph) speed limit for carfree streets and other public gathering spaces.[28]

A related category is microcars, also known as neighborhood electric vehicles or quadricycles. Their weight and speed lie in a middle range between personal transporters and conventional automobiles. In some countries, their top speed is limited by law to 25 or 28 mph (40 or 45 kmh) and they are prohibited from highways and high-speed arterials. A few localities have established dedicated lanes for microcars.

These three categories—standard motor vehicles, microcars, and personal transporters—are generally incompatible. They are significantly different in terms of size, weight, and typical speed, and those differences increase the frequency and severity of crashes. The forecasted profusion of incompatible modes may be similar to the chaotic diversity of city traffic around 1900. As was the case then, one solution is multiway boulevards that separate vehicle types according to vehicular speed and weight. Some transportation planners have suggested that all existing streets be dedicated to single vehicle types (similar to Etienne Cabet's Icara City), or that separate, comprehensive networks be created for low-speed vehicles. The historical record suggests that those ideas could entail major costs and difficulties. The easiest and least costly solution is to reduce traffic volume and velocity on selected roadways to the point at which standard motor vehicles, microcars, and personal transporters can coexist safely. That solution, however, requires a mobility culture in which all roadway users treat each other with basic care and respect.[29]

Recommendations

The above review argues that various potential trends could have severely negative consequences for walkable, livable roadways. To guide those trends toward more positive outcomes, broadly based reform efforts will be needed. The history of street networks offers a number of lessons about past reform efforts and future desirable solutions. Reformers should keep several principles in mind as they work to improve urban transportation systems.

One, historical knowledge can provide a strategic advantage. Understanding how roadway patterns were envisioned and instituted in the past can alert reformers to similar processes operating in the present. This book covers in detail three initiatives to achieve policy dominance (promoting cellular layouts, envisioning urban freeways, and establishing functional classification) and mentions others, such as planning the 1920s US highway system.

The initiatives followed similar trajectories. Powerful industries organized coalitions with professionals, administrators, and nongovernmental groups such as associations and nonprofits. They co-opted existing reform initiatives, or launched organizations that they controlled or influenced. Those initiatives and organizations developed policies that supported the coalition members' goals. The coalitions often gained extraordinary sway within the halls of government. They installed leaders from their own ranks into positions of government power. They lobbied legislators and administrators, and got industry-friendly laws and administrative policies adopted at all levels of government.

The most consequential changes were achieved by the automobile industry and its allies as they undertook tightly coordinated policy campaigns. Through such processes, automakers exerted an enormous influence on roadway layouts and networks, especially in the developing suburbs of American metropolises. Highway engineers were key allies; they adopted policies and standards that augmented functional classification and enforced cellular roadway patterns throughout suburban areas. Similar processes operating in the present can stymie reformers' best efforts. To overcome that, reformers may need to organize, form coalitions, gather intelligence, campaign, and persuade.[30]

Two, beware of an undue focus on urban freeways that draws attention away from other major roadways. Policymakers, reformers, historians, and others in the roadway-planning realm have long devoted the majority of their concern to freeways. Freeways certainly deserve much attention, but other thoroughfares as a group have a greater impact on the shape and function of metropolises. In many jurisdictions, arterials and collectors receive more funding than freeways and cover a larger land area. They have a more determinative effect on built-environment patterns, travel behaviors, and the related quality of life.

Three, reformers should give greater consideration to cellularity issues. Roadway connectivity is vitally important to the creation of healthy, satisfying, and prosperous cities. Cellularity determines much of how neighborhood and districts function, the character of their roadways and frontages, and the pressures they exert on nearby arterials (in the worst cases, to become wider, more dangerous, and hostile to pedestrians). As a general rule, cellularity in walkable and transit-oriented places should be low to moderate. A good principle is to seek a happy medium between local protection and livability on one hand, and community-wide convenience, fairness, and adaptability on the other. Strictly cellular and dendritic layouts are generally detrimental to walkable and transit-oriented places, yet entirely undifferentiated layouts, such as uniform grids, can also produce inferior results in certain contexts.

The traffic-planning and urban-design fields should generate more and better guidance about cellularity. A salient question is how to determine whether a given degree of cellularity is too much or too little in specific situations. Ideally, professional guidance would explain how cellularity should relate to context. The body of knowledge would encompass a wide variety of possibilities, and be well-tested and based on long-term evidence.

Four, past experiments and visions may inspire the designers of future urban forms and roadway patterns. For example, hyperurbanism has proved too costly and impractical to execute at large scales, but perhaps new ideas or construction techniques could solve those problems. New permutations of civic space may be inspired by unsuccessful historical ideas, such as the Arcade Railway's local trains that could stop anywhere along a continuous underground frontage, or Alfred Speer's Endless Sidewalk that provided civic and social space on a traveling platform. Many ideas disappeared because autos and trucks were so much easier and cheaper, but if that changes, some could become viable again, such as freight subways and pneumatic-tube networks.

Finally, historical memory is crucial for progress. The traffic-planning field has witnessed several cycles in which practices were advocated and implemented, then opposed, removed, and forgotten. Decades or generations later, similar ideas were rediscovered or reinvented, and the cycle began anew, reviving many of the same arguments. An example is the debate between the traffic-regulation and market-supply responses to roadway congestion. The arguments put forward in the 1970s and 2000s were at times identical to the arguments that raged during the 1920s.

These cycles generated much conflict—after all, fortunes and reputations were at stake—but produced little long-term progress for society. Without a good understanding of history, practitioners, officials, and the public are liable to remain stuck in wasteful ruts of ignorance. The recollection of past debates and actions is important for progress in this field. A broad and firmly grounded understanding of traffic-separation history can help produce better urban roadway layouts and transportation systems, which can help produce better cities. And building better cities is a worthy goal indeed. Urban places are home to the majority of humankind, and will likely house an even greater share in the foreseeable future.

Notes

HMSO: His/Her Majesty's Stationery Office
USGPO: United States Government Printing Office

Chapter 1. Vertical Traffic Separation: Early Schemes

1. Lisa Massimiliano, Mario Taddei and Edoardo Zanon, *Da Vinci's Workshop in the Ideal City: Codices, Machines and Drawings*, exhibition catalog (Milan: Leonardo3, 2009), pp. 34, 48–49.

2. Leonardo da Vinci, *Manuscript B*, folio 16r.

3. "Like goats": Leonardo da Vinci, *Codex Atlanticus*, folio 184v ; Massimiliano et al., *Da Vinci's Workshop*, p. 38.

4. Leonardo da Vinci, *Manuscript B*, folios 12v, 48r; Jean Guillaume, "Leonardo and Architecture," in Paolo Galluzzi, ed., *Leonardo da Vinci: Engineer and Architect* (Montreal: Montreal Museum of Fine Arts, 1987), p. 262.

5. Leonardo da Vinci, *Codex Atlanticus*, folio 184v; Luigi Firpo, "Leonardo as Urban Planner," in *Leonardo da Vinci: Engineer and Architect*, pp. 291–292.

6. Howard S. Merritt, "The Anthony J. and Frances A. Guzzetta Collection of Vinciana," *University of Rochester Library Bulletin*, vol. 17, no. 3 (Spring 1963), http://www.lib.rochester.edu/index.cfm?PAGE=3376.

7. Joseph Kirwan, *A Descriptive and Historical Account of the Liverpool and Manchester Railway . . .* (Glasgow: W. R. McPhun, 1831), pp. 18–20, 30–32; James Scott Walker, *An Accurate Description of the Liverpool and Manchester Railway . . .*, 3rd ed. (Liverpool: J. F. Cannell, 1832), pp. 8–15; "Sankey Viaduct," *Our Transport Heritage*, Transport Trust Transport Heritage Site, accessed 7 June 2013, http://www.transporttrust.com/heritage-sites/heritage-detail/sankey-viaduct.

8. "The London and Greenwich Railway," *The Mirror*, vol. 28, no. 810 (17 December 1836), pp. 402–405; Ronald H. G. Thomas, *London's First Railway – the London & Greenwich* (London: B. T. Batsford, 1972), pp. 32–34; Christian Wolmar, *Fire and Steam: A New History of the Railways in Britain* (London: Atlantic Books, 2007), pp. 58–59, 322.

9. Wolmar, *Fire and Steam*, pp. 59, 87–89.

10. Fl. de Kérizouët, "Économie sociale: rues de fer, ou locomotion dans les grandes villes," *La Revue Independante*, 2nd series, vol. 11 (25 October 1847), pp. 328–329, 339, 353–354.

11. Fl. de Kérizouët, *Projet d'etablissement d'un chemin de fer dan l'intérieur de la ville de Paris* (Paris: Librairie Scientifique-Industrielle de L. Mathias, 1845), pp. 5–6.

12. Nicholas Papayanis, *Planning Paris Before Haussmann* (Baltimore, MD: Johns Hopkins University Press, 2004), pp. 210–212; Kérizouët, *Projet d'etablissement*, pp. 11–12, fig. 4 caption; Fl. de Kérizouët, *Rues de fer, ou examen de la question suivante: supprimer les octrois de Paris sans surtaxer l'impôt et sans réduire les recettes municipale* [Paris: 1847], p. 8.

13. Kérizouët, *Rues de fer*, p. 8; Kérizouët, "Économie sociale," pp. 357–359.

14. Kérizouët, "Économie sociale," pp. 351, 357; Kérizouët, *Projet d'etablissement*, pp. 11–12; Kérizouët, *Rues de fer*, pp. 1–2, 8.

15. Kérizouët , *Rues de fer*, pp. 1–2; Papayanis, *Planning Paris*, pp. 213, 229, 299.

16. Susan Ryley Hoyle, "The First Battle for London: A Case Study of the Royal Commission on Metropolitan Termini 1846," *London Journal*, vol. 8, no. 2 (Winter 1982), pp. 140–143.

17. Great Britain, Parliament, House of Commons, *Journals of the House of Commons*, vol. 101, part 1 (1846), p. 710.

18. Howard Colvin, *A Biographical Dictionary of British Architects 1600-1840*, 3rd ed. (New Haven, CT: Yale University Press, 1995), pp. 253–254; *Mechanics' Magazine*, vol. 29, no. 790 (29 September 1838), p. 479; "List of New Patents," *Repertory of Patent Inventions . . .*, vol. 8, no. 46 (October 1837), p. 256.

19. Metropolitan Railway Commission, *Minutes of Evidence Taken before the Commissioners Appointed to Investigate the Various Projects for Establishing Railway Termini . . .* (London: HMSO, 1846), pp. 234–236; Great Britain, Parliament, House of Commons, *Journals of the House of Commons*, vol. 101, part 1 (1846), p. 710.

20. Metropolitan Railway Commission, *Minutes of Evidence*, appendix ("Maps, Plans and Evidence"), exhibit no. 24.

21. Metropolitan Railway Commission, *Report of the Commissioners . . . for Establishing Railway Termini* (London: HMSO, 1846), p. 16.

22. Metropolitan Railway Commission, *Report of the Commissioners*, pp. 5–9.

23. Metropolitan Railway Commission, *Report of the Commissioners*, p. 21; Hoyle, "The First Battle for London," pp. 144, 151.

24. Archibald Douglas Turnbull, *John Stevens: An American Record* (New York: Century, 1928), pp. 477–480, 494–498; John Stevens, "Proposed Improvements," letter to New York City officials, and an additional fragment, [ca. 1829–1834], box 1, folder 18, pp. 830–831, 839–840, John Stevens Collection, no. 333, National Museum of American History Archives, Washington, DC.

25. "Elevated Railway and Prominade," *American Railroad Journal*, vol. 20, no. 579, 24 July 1847, p. 465; Margaret Holloway, *The Measure of Manhattan* (New York: W. W. Norton, 2013), pp. 284–285.

26. John Randel Jr., *The Elevated Railway and its Appendages for Broadway, in the City of New York* (New York: J. M. Elliot, 1848), pp. 7–11.

27. I. N. Phelps Stokes, *The Iconography of Manhattan Island 1498–1909*, vol. 5 (New York: Robert H. Dodd, 1926), p. 1806. Randel's concept predated the screw-type elevator patented by Otis Tufts in 1859. Tufts's elevator was installed in the seven-story Fifth Avenue Hotel in Manhattan. It remained in service for fifteen years and helped popularize elevators in America.

28. City of New York, *Proceedings of the Board of Aldermen*, vol. 34, part 1, 6 December 1847, p. 78.

29. Holloway, *Measure of Manhattan*, p. 291. Competing proposals included those by John B. Wickersham, Elisha G. Otis, J. R. Orton, and Patrick O'Neil.

30. The only exceptions were crossings. By 1881 Manhattan had four north-south elevated railway lines; two of them, the Sixth and Ninth Avenue lines, crossed over Broadway. See Manhattan Railway, *Map and Guide of the Elevated Railroads of New York City* (New York: H. I. Latimer, 1881), http://www.loc.gov/item/98688705.

31. Holloway, *Measure of Manhattan*, pp. 289–290.

32. Great Britain, Parliament, House of Commons, Sessional Papers, 1854–1855, *Reports from Committees*, vol. 4, "Report from the Select Committee on Metropolitan Communications," 23 July 1855, pp. 78–96.

33. Greater London Council, "The Changing Population of the London Boroughs," 2nd ed., by C. M. Morrey, research memorandum no. 413, March 1978, http://data.london.gov.uk/dataset/historic-census-population; Tertius Chandler, *Four Thousand Years of Urban Growth: An Historical Census*, 2nd ed. (Lampter, Wales: Edwin Mellen, 1987), pp. 526–527; James Winter, *London's Teeming Streets, 1830–1914* (Abingdon, Oxon, UK: Routledge, 1993), pp. 2–8.

34. House of Commons, "Metropolitan Communications," pp. iii–vi, 86.

35. Kate Colquhoun, *"The Busiest Man in England"* (Boston: David R. Godine, 2006), pp. 65–67, 96–100, 122–124, 164–187, 213–214, 252.

36. House of Commons, "Metropolitan Communications," p. 81

37. Georg Kohlmaier and Barna von Sartory, *Houses of Glass*, trans. John C. Harvey (Cambridge, MA: MIT Press, 1986), pp. 5, 14–15, 55.

38. As the streets of Paris were improved and cleaned, the popularity of arcades waned. None were built after 1840. See Papayanis, *Planning Paris*, p. 43.

39. House of Commons, "Metropolitan Communications," pp. 52–57.

40. House of Commons, "Metropolitan Communications," pp. iv–vi, 134–137.

41. House of Commons, "Metropolitan Communications," testimony of Thomas Henry Hall, pp. 63–64.

42. City of London, Holborn Valley Improvement Committee, *Report of Proceedings in Connection with the Holborn Valley Improvements* (London: City of London, 1872), pp. 4–16.

43. "The Peabody Fund," *The Builder*, vol. 21, no. 1059 (23 May 1863), p. 369; William Haywood, "Report . . . in Relation to the Traffic of the City, and the Improvements Needed in the Public Ways," in Special Improvement Committee of the Corporation of the City of London, *Report to the Court of Common Council . . .* (London: 1869), pp. 15–16, 41, 47–48; Select Committee on Coal Duties (London) Abolition Bill, "Report . . .," 1889 session, no. 228, pp. 67, 77–80, in Great Britain, Parliament, House of Commons, Parliamentary Papers, *Reports from Committees*, vol. 9, 1889.

44.   City of London, *Report of Proceedings in Connection with the Holborn Valley Improvements*, pp. 17, 64–66; "Vaults of the Holborn Viaduct," *Mechanics' Magazine*, vol. 22 (17 September 1869), p. 207.

45.   "The Queen's Visit to the City," *The Illustrated London News*, vol. 55, no. 1566, 13 November 1869, p. 495; Walter Thornbury, *Old and New London*, vol. 2 (London: Cassell, Petter & Galpin, 1878), pp. 500, 502.

46.   Jack Harris, "The Electricity of Holborn," *New Scientist*, 14 January 1982, pp. 88–90; Frank L. Dyer and Thomas C. Martin, *Edison, His Life and Inventions* (New York: Harper & Brothers, 1910), p. 336. Edison's Holborn system was also the world's second public electricity system. A small public system serving 47 lights had been installed in Godalming, Surrey, UK, in October 1881, three months before Edison's system went online. See Brian Bowers, "Britain Lights Up – A Century Ago," *New Scientist*, 17 September 1981, pp. 730–732.

47.   Carlton Reid, *Roads Were Not Built for Cars* (Washington, DC: Island Press, 2015), pp. 117, 220–221.

48.   Robert C. Reed, *The New York Elevated* (Cransbury, NJ: A. S. Barnes and Co., 1978), p. 22.

49.   Reed, *New York Elevated*, pp. 24, 27, 31–32, 37.

50.   New York State, Senate, *Report of a Special Commission Designated by the Senate to Ascertain the Best Means for the Transportation of Passengers in the City of New York*, no. 28, 31 January 1867, pp. 11–14, 56–59; Egbert L. Viele, *The Arcade Under-Ground Railway* (New York, [1868?]), pp. 9–15.

51.   Rebecca Read Shanor, *The City That Never Was: Two Hundred Years of Fantastic and Fascinating Plans That Might Have Changed the Face of New York City* (New York: Viking, 1988), pp. 86–90; Joseph Brennan, *Beach Pneumatic* (online publication), chapter 23, May 2005, http://www.columbia.edu/~brennan/beach/chapter23.html. For additional history about Viele, Olmsted, and Central Park, see Shanor, pp. 167–177.

52.   William J. Pape, ed., *The News' History of Passiac* (Passiac, NJ: News Publishing, 1899), p. 182; W. Woodford Clayton, ed., *History of Bergen and Passiac Counties . . .* (Philadelphia: Everts and Peck, 1882), pp. 396–399.

53.   Alfred Speer, Improvement in Endless-Traveling Sidewalks, US Patent 119,796, issued 10 October 1871; "Endless Traveling or Railway Sidewalk," *Scientific American*, vol. 26, no. 17 (20 April 1872), pp. 255–256; [Alfred Speer?], *Speer's Endless Railway Train: Solving the Problem of Rapid Transit* ([1875?]), pp. 4, 5, 8.

54.   Alfred Speer, *Treatise on City Travel with a True Solution of Rapid Transit* (Passiac, NJ: 1875), p. 23–24, 26.

55.   Speer, *Treatise on City Travel*, pp. 24–25; "The Stepped Platform Railway," *Scientific American*, vol. 62, no. 17 (26 April 1890), p. 265.

56.   Speer, *Treatise on City Travel*, p. 24; State of New York, Legislature, *Annual Report of the State Engineer and Surveyor on the Railroads . . .* (Albany, NY: 1880), p. 21; State of New York, Legislature, *Annual Report of the State Engineer and Surveyor on the Railroads . . .* (Albany, NY: 1882), p. 717; "Methods of Rapid Transit," *New York Times*, 13 February 1884, p. 8; "Many Plans Presented," *New York Times*, 16 January 1891, p. 8; William Nelson, *History of the County of Passiac, New Jersey* (Paterson, NJ: Press Printing and Publishing, 1901), p. 206. In 1886 Speer patented an electric streamlined suspended monorail. The "pointed or cigar-shaped" railcars were projected to travel at 120 mph (193 kmh) and had lateral stabilizing wheels to reduce high-speed sway. See Alfred Speer, Elevated-Railway Track and Car, US Patent 339,494, issued 6 April 1886.

57.   Robert M. Fogelson, *Downtown: Its Rise and Fall, 1880–1950* (New Haven, CT: Yale University Press, 2001), pp. 120, 143–144, 151–152.

58.   Lee Edward Gray, *From Ascending Rooms to Express Elevators: A History of the Passenger Elevator in the 19th Century* (Mobile, AL: Elevator World, 2002), p. 242; G. R. Strakosch, ed., *The Vertical Transportation Handbook*, 3rd ed. (Hoboken, NJ: John Wiley & Sons, 1998), pp. 5, 9–10.

59.   Jon A. Peterson, *The Birth of City Planning in the United States, 1840–1917* (Baltimore, MD: Johns Hopkins University Press, 2003), pp. 38–39.

60.   However, the sanitary-reform agenda remained important to housing reformers in the Progressive Era and through the mid-twentieth century. Suburbanization as sanitary reform persisted in a modified form on the basis of psychological health, protection from air pollution, safety from traffic, and increased exercise.

61.   An article by the famed inventor Hudson Maxim typified the millennial rhetoric: "There will be homes in sky-hung parks and gardens up in the clear, cool, pure air, and from their commercial work

down near the earth business men will take express elevators to their homes in a veritable 'airy, fairy dreamland of nightingales,' where the clouds hover and smile in the evening sun long after the ink of night has engulfed the lower floors." Hudson Maxim, "Man's Machine Made Millennium," *Cosmopolitan*, vol. 45, no. 6 (November 1908), p. 576.

62. *The Encyclopedia of Science Fiction* (website), s.vv. "Dime-Novel SF," by Everett F. Bleiler, updated 10 February 2016, "Pulp," by Peter Nicholls and Mike Ashley, updated 3 April 2015, http://www. sf-encyclopedia.com.

63. *The Encyclopedia of Science Fiction* (website), s.v. "New York," by John Clute, updated 15 September 2017, http://www.sf-encyclopedia.com/entry/new_york.

64. Justin Kaplan, *When the Astors Owned New York* (New York: Viking, 2006), pp. 57–66; John Jacob Astor, Pneumatic Road Cleaning Machine, US Patent 514,805, filed 31 May 1892 and issued 13 February 1894.

65. John Jacob Astor, *A Journey in Other Worlds: A Romance of the Future* (New York: D. Appleton, 1894), p. 66.

66. Astor, *A Journey in Other Worlds*, p. 68.

67. *The National Cyclopedia of American Biography*, vol. 8 (New York: James T. White, 1907), p. 107.

68. "Automobile Club Plans Vast Roads," *New York Times*, 2 April 1900, p. 1; Albert C. Bostwick, "Automobiles and Automobiling," *The Book of Sport*, vol. 1 (New York: J. F. Taylor, 1903), pp. 267–269. The call for a transcontinental motor highway was a modification of bicycle advocates' call for national cycle-path system. Astor was a leading cycling enthusiast before autos caught his fancy.

69. John Jacob Astor, "A Coast to Coast Highway," *Motor*, vol. 1, no. 2 (November 1903), pp. 1–2. Astor was a cousin to Franklin Delano Roosevelt, who also was an auto enthusiast, and who established the US Interstate Freeway System.

70. Kenneth M. Roemer, *The Obsolete Necessity: America in Utopian Writings 1888-1900* (Kent, OH: Kent State University Press, 1976), p. 3; Jean Pfaelzer, *The Utopian Novel in America* (Pittsburgh, PA: University of Pittsburgh Press, 1984), pp. 3, 8.

71. Roemer, *The Obsolete Necessity*, p. 156; Howard P. Segal, *Technological Utopianism in American Culture* (Chicago: University of Chicago Press, 1985), p. 25. Examples of sensational transportation visions include Alvarado Mortimer Fuller, *AD 2000* (Chicago: Laird and Lee, 1890), pp. 245–248 and Chauncey Thomas, *The Crystal Button: or, The Adventures of Paul Prognosis in the Forty-Ninth Century* (Boston and New York: Houghton and Mifflin, 1891), pp. 49–50, 57.

72. Albert Waldo Howard (writing as M. Auburré Hovorrè), *The Milltillionaire* (Boston: n.p., 1895), p. 7–8.

73. James Gilbert, *Designing the Industrial State: The Intellectual Pursuit of Collectivism in America* (Chicago: Quadrangle Books, 1972), p. 160.

74. King C. Gillette, *The Human Drift* (New York: New Era, 1894), pp. 28, 36, 45, 49, 87, 118–121.

75. Gillette, *Human Drift*, pp. 63, 85, 89, 93, 108.

76. Gillette, *Human Drift*, pp. 90, 95–96, 111–112.

77. Gillette, *Human Drift*, pp. 92–97, 108. Gillette expressed an antipathy to streets spatially defined by building facades, a view shared by architects of the time and succeeding generations. He wrote: "*We can never obtain grand effects in architecture except by ample space and complete conceptions in buildings. . . . A building that is high and broad should have an open space around it, sufficient to allow of its beauty being grasped as a whole . . . Our modern office buildings are the result of necessity; and the architect, instead of being allowed the free play of his imagination in the development of an artistic conception, is obliged to make his ideas conform to a contracted and narrow strip of land.*"

78. Kenneth M. Roemer, "Technology, Corporation, and Utopia: Gillette's Unity Regained," *Technology and Culture*, vol. 26, no. 3 (July 1985), p. 565.

79. "US Business Cycle Expansions and Contractions," National Bureau of Economic Research, 23 April 2012, http://www.nber.org/cycles/cyclesmain.html; "Nativity of the Population and Place of Birth of the Native Population: 1850 to 1990," US Bureau of the Census, 9 March 1999, http://www.census.gov/population/www/documentation/twps0029/tab01.html; Pfaelzer, *Utopian Novel in America*, pp. 113–114.

80. Roemer, *Obsolete Necessity*, pp. 28, 161–162; Segal, *Technological Utopianism*, p. 102.

81. Segal, *Technological Utopianism*, p. 102.

82. Kurt C. Schlichting, *Grand Central's Engineer* (Baltimore, MD: Johns Hopkins University Press, 2012), pp. 74–75; William J. Wilgus, *Proposed New Railway System . . .* (New York: Amsterdam

Corporation, 1908), pp. 6–7.

83. Ann L. Buttenweiser, *Manhattan Water-Bound: Manhattan's Waterfront from the Seventeenth Century to the Present*, 2nd ed. (Syracuse, NY: Syracuse University Press, 1999), pp. 85–86.

84. New York (State), *Report of a Special Commission Designated by the Senate to Ascertain the Best Means for the Transportation of Passengers in the City of New York*, Senate No. 28, 31 January 1867, p. 3; William J. Wilgus, *Proposed New Railway System . . .* (New York: Amsterdam Corporation, 1908), pp. 9–10, 29.

85. "Bridging New York Streets," *Scientific American*, vol. 62, no. 6 (8 February 1890), p. 87.

86. Mosette Broderick, *Triumvirate: McKim, Mead & White* (New York: Alfred A. Knopf, 2010), p. 13; Sarah Bradford Landau and Carl W. Condit, *Rise of the New York Skyscraper: 1865–1913* (New Haven: Yale University Press, 1999), pp. 100–102; J. R. LeMaster and James D. Wilson, eds., *The Mark Twain Encyclopedia* (New York: Garland, 1993), pp. 247–248; Richard O. Reisem, *Historic New York: Architectural Journeys in the Empire State* (Rochester, NY: Landmark Society of Western New York, 2006), p. 201.

87. "Novel Rapid Transit for New York," *New York Herald*, 16 February 1891, p. 3.

88. Alfred H. Thorp, "A Scheme for Rapid Transit for New York City," *Architecture and Building*, vol. 14, no. 9 (28 February 1891), p. 104.

89. "A River-Front Railroad," *New York Times*, 30 May 1895, p. 2; "A Proposed System of Rapid Transit for New York City," *The American Architect and Building News*, vol. 49, no. 1027 (31 August 1895), pp. 90–91.

90. City of New York, Department of Docks, *Twenty-Second Annual Report. . .*, 30 April 1892, pp. 120–122; "The Improvement of the North River Waterfront, New York City," *Scientific American*, vol. 74, no. 23 (6 June 1896), p. 360; "New Water-Front Scheme," *New York Times*, 14 November 1898, p. 3.

91. Charles R. Lamb, *Report of Thoroughfares Committee of Municipal Art Society*, bulletin no. 5 (New York: Municipal Art Society of New York, 1904), pp. 13–14, 18; "A Suggested Improvement of the Water Front of New York," *Engineering Record*, vol. 49 (23 April 1904), p. 525.

92. Calvin Tompkins, *Review of the Work of the Municipal Art Society by the President*, bulletin no. 24½ (New York: Municipal Art Society of New York, 1905), p. 4; David A. Johnson, *Planning the Great Metropolis: The 1929 Regional Plan of New York and Its Environs* (London: E & FN Spon, 1996), pp. 28–31. The mayor's father was a famous Civil War general and also the first chief engineer of New York's Department of Docks.

93. New York City Improvement Commission, *The Report of the New York City Improvement Commission . . .* (New York: 1904), pp. 7–8; New York City Improvement Commission, *The Report of the New York City Improvement Commission. . .* (New York: 1907), p. 11. The 1907 plan expanded Olmsted & Vaux's park and parkway proposals to encompass the New York region. That, plus the elaborations and additions made by the Regional Plan of New York and Its Environs in the 1920s, served as a blueprint for Robert Moses and his agencies as they built parks and parkways throughout the region. See Johnson, *Planning the Great Metropolis*, pp. 28–31.

94. Buttenweiser, *Manhattan Water-Bound*, pp. 100–101.

Chapter 2. Vertical Traffic Separation: 1900s–1930s

1. National Automobile Chamber of Commerce, *Facts and Figures of the Automobile Industry*, 1928 ed. (New York: National Automobile Chamber of Commerce, 1928), pp. 70–71.

2. John Wolfe Barry, "Address on the Streets & Traffic of London" (1898), presented to the Royal Society of Arts, 16 November 1898 (London: 1899), pp. 1, 9, 11, 16–18.

3. Barry, "Address on the Streets & Traffic of London," pp. 5, 11, 14–15, 18.

4. Barry, "Address on the Streets & Traffic of London," pp. 14–16, 25.

5. Barry, "Address on the Streets & Traffic of London," pp. 19–20, 25–26, 28–29.

6. John Wolfe Barry, "Address on the Streets & Traffic of London" (1899), presented to the Royal Society of Arts, 15 November 1899 (London: 1899), pp. 3–6, 14–15.

7. Great Britain, Royal Commission on London Traffic, *Report of the Royal Commission on London Traffic*, vol. 1, *Report . . . upon the Means of Locomotion and Transport in London* (London: HMSO, 1905), p. 2; Charles Scott Meik and Walter Beer, "The Improvement of London Traffic," in Society of Engineers, *Transactions for 1905* (London: E. & F. N. Spon, 1906), p. 117.

8. Great Britain, Royal Commission on London Traffic, *Report of the Royal Commission on London*

Traffic, vol. 2, *Minutes of Evidence* (London: HMSO, 1905), pp. 540–541, 544; Meik and Beer, "Improvement of London Traffic," pp. 125–128.

9. Theo Barker, "Introduction," in Theo Barker, ed., *The Economic and Social Effects of the Spread of Motor Vehicles: An International Centenary Tribute* (London: MacMillan, 1987), p. 46–47; US Census Bureau, *Manufactures: 1905*, part 4 (Washington DC: USGPO, 1908), p. 289. The motor-vehicle statistics for both countries include motorcycles.

10. Commission on London Traffic, *Minutes of Evidence*, pp. 541–543; Meik and Beer, "Improvement of London Traffic," p. 142.

11. Commission on London Traffic, *Minutes of Evidence*, p. 541; Meik and Beer, "Improvement of London Traffic," pp. 120–121.

12. Commission on London Traffic, *Minutes of Evidence*, pp. 543, 610; Meik and Beer, "Improvement of London Traffic," p. 125.

13. Commission on London Traffic, *Minutes of Evidence*, p. 543; Meik and Beer, "Improvement of London Traffic," pp. 123–124, 126.

14. Meik and Beer, "Improvement of London Traffic," pp. 135, 142.

15. Commission on London Traffic, *Report . . . upon the Means of Locomotion and Transport in London*, pp. 35–37; Great Britain, Board of Trade, *Report of the London Traffic Branch of the Board of Trade* (London: HMSO, 1908), p. 20; "Arterial Roads for London, England," *Good Roads*, new series, vol. 5, no. 10 (3 May 1913), p. 275; Great Britain, Board of Trade, *Report of the London Traffic Branch of the Board of Trade, 1915* (London: HMSO, 1916), pp. 8, 26–27.

16. "L. Biedermann, Art Director, 83," *New York Times*, 17 July 1957, p. L27.

17. "New York City as It Will Be in the Year 1999," *New York World*, 30 December 1900, supplement section.

18. Jacques Sadoul, *2000 A.D: Illustrations from the Golden Age of Science Fiction Pulps* (Chicago: Henry Regnery, 1975), pp. 160, 162–163. A prime example of comically exaggerated hyperurbanism is John Kendrick Bangs, "The Spectrophone," illustrated by Winsor McCay, *New York Herald*, 13 November 1904, magazine section, p. 6.

19. Raymond Francis Yates, "Underground Roads and Elevated Speedways May Solve the World's Worst Traffic Tangle," *Popular Science*, vol. 99, no. 2 (August 1921), pp. 42–43; Charles Clifton, "Miracles Made to Order," *Collier's*, vol. 69, no. 1 (7 January 1922), p. 7.

20. "One Campaign Still On," *The Independent Press* [Bloomfield, NJ], 6 November 1914, p. 4; "Charles Mck. Smith Dies at East Orange, *Metuchen* [NJ] *Recorder*, 18 August 1933, p. 1. Smith married and moved to the village of Metuchen, New Jersey, in 1893. His neighbor was the prominent bridge engineer Gustav Lindenthal.

21. *Scientific American* magazine: Williamsburg Bridge: vol. 89, no. 3 (18 July 1903); Sixth Avenue: vol. 95, no. 26 (29 December 1906); three-level street: vol. 96, no. 25 (22 June 1907); Cunard liner: vol. 93, no. 4 (22 July 1905); White Star liner: vol. 100, no. 25 (19 June 1909); Jean-Louis Cohen, *Scenes of the World to Come: European Architecture and the American Challenge 1893–1960*, trans. Kenneth Hylton (Paris: Flammarion, 1995), pp. 29–31; Le Corbusier, *The City of To-Morrow and Its Planning*, trans. Frederick Etchells (London: Architectural Press, 1929), p. 149, originally published as *Urbanisme* (1925); Le Corbusier, *The Radiant City*, trans. Pamela Knight, Eleanor Levieux, and Derek Coltman (New York: Orion Press, 1967), p. 118, originally published as *La Ville Radieuse* (1935).

22. "Harry Pettit," *askART*, accessed 13 October 2017, http://www.askart.com.

23. "Plans for Improving and Beautifying New York," *Harper's Weekly*, vol. 49, no. 2543 (16 September 1905), pp. 1342–1343.

24. Robert Caro, *The Power Broker* (Alfred A. Knopf: New York), 1974, pp. 65–67.

25. Moses King, *King's Views of New York* (New York: Moses King, 1908), p. 1. The image's perspective resembled that of Louis Sullivan's setback-skyscraper city, which had appeared in *The Graphic* in 1891. See Donald Hoffmann, "The Setback Skyscraper City of 1891: An Unknown Essay by Louis H. Sullivan," *Journal of the Society of Architectural Historians*, vol. 29, no. 2 (May 1970), pp. 185–186.

26. "Sees Future New York," *New-York Tribune*, 16 January 1910, part 2, pp. 1, 3; Henry Harrison Suplee, "A Five-Storied Street," *Cassier's Engineering Monthly*, vol. 43, no. 6 (June 1913), pp. 57–60; *Scientific American*, vol. 109, no. 4 (26 July 1913), front cover. The architecture historian Neil Levine observed that the clock towers in Pettit's 1908 King's Dream image and the five-story-street image were set to the same time. See Neil Levine, *The Urbanism of Frank Lloyd Wright* (Princeton, NJ: Princeton University Press, 2016), p. 404, footnote 97. The drawings had additional similarities, such as the imaginary aircraft in

the 1910 image, which were similar to others drawn by Pettit. Furthermore, at least one other Pettit image appeared in the *Tribune* around 1909–1910. The evidence overall suggests that Pettit drew both the 1910 and 1913 versions of the five-story street.

27.   Walter Bernard, "The World's Greatest Railway Terminal," *Scientific American*, vol. 104, no. 24 (17 June 1911), p. 594; Cohen, *Scenes of the World to Come*, pp. 32–33; Esther da Costa Meyer, *The Work of Antonio Sant'Elia: Retreat into the Future* (New Haven: Yale University Press, 1995), pp. 128–133; "May Live to See," *Popular Science*, May 1925, p. 41.

28.   David Walsh, "Pennsylvania Steel Works Mural Restored: Rescuing History from the Dustbin," *World Socialist Web Site*, 18 December 2004, http://www.wsws.org.

29.   Carol Willis, "Skyscraper Utopias: Visionary Urbanism in the 1920s," in Joseph J. Corn, ed., *Imagining Tomorrow: History, Technology, and the American Future* (Cambridge, MA: MIT Press, 1986), pp. 166–169.

30.   Kurt C. Schlichting, *Grand Central's Engineer* (Baltimore, MD: Johns Hopkins University Press, 2012), pp. 246–249.

31.   Schlichting, *Grand Central's Engineer*, pp. 4–5, 42–43.

32.   William J. Wilgus, "Grand Central Terminal in Perspective," *Proceedings of the American Society of Civil Engineers*, October 1940, p. 1418.

33.   William J. Wilgus, letter to William H. Newman, 22 December 1902, in New York Public Library, William J. Wilgus Papers, box 1.

34.   Gale Harris, *Murray Hill Historic District Designation Report*, New York City Landmarks Preservation Commission, 29 January 2002, pp. 4, 9, 24–25, 30, 132.

35.   Schlichting, *Grand Central's Engineer*, p. 49.

36.   Wilgus, "Grand Central Terminal in Perspective," p. 1425; William J. Wilgus , letter to William H. Newman, 22 December 1902, in New York Public Library, William J. Wilgus Papers, box 1.

37.   *Inception and Creation of the Grand Central Terminal* (New York: A. H. Stem and A. Fellheimer, 1913), n.p.; Wilgus probably wrote: Alfred Fellheimer, letter to William Wilgus, 21 April 1913, in New York Public Library, William J. Wilgus Papers, box 1.

38.   *Inception and Creation of the Grand Central Terminal*, n.p.; "No Break in Park-Ave.," *New York Daily Tribune*, 4 June 1903; "Finest of All Terminals," *New York Sun*, 4 June 1903, p. 6.

39.   Forty acres: "Grand Central Development Seen As Great Civic Center," *Engineering News Record*, vol. 85, no. 11 (9 September 1920), p. 496. Property value: Wilgus, "Grand Central Terminal in Perspective," p. 1442. Wilgus defined "local area" as 42nd Street to 96th Street between Madison Avenue and Lexington Avenue.

40.   "Park Av. Traffic to Flow through 35-Story Building," *New York Times*, 18 September 1927, p. 26; "A Great Public Improvement," *New York Times*, 19 September 1927, p. 24; "New Viaduct Thoroughfare Relieves Park Avenue Traffic Congestion," *New York Times*, 2 September 1928, p. RE 1; City of New York, Landmarks Preservation Commission, "New York Central Building," by Janet Adams, designation list no. 188 LP-1297, 31 March 1987, pp. 7–8.

41.   "Grand Central Development Seen As Great Civic Center," p. 500.

42.   Schlichting, *Grand Central's Engineer*, p. 72; New York City Department of City Planning, "Grand Central Subdistrict," DCP #91–17, November 1991, pp. 8–9; Municipal Art Society of New York, *East Midtown: A Bold Vision for the Future*, 27 February 2013, pp. 20–22, http://www.scribd.com/doc/127599215/Municipal-Art-Society-Report-A-Bold-Vision-for-the-Future-in-East-Midtown.

43.   George W. Jackson, "Scope, Extent and Construction of the Underground Conduits. . ." *Journal of the Western Society of Engineers*, vol. 7, no. 5 (October 1902), pp. 482, 500; "Tunnel System of the Illinois Tunnel Company" in appendix 8, *Bulletin of the International Railway Congress*, vol. 19, no 7 (September 1905), page 2099; Bruce G. Moffat, *The Chicago Tunnel Story* (Chicago: Central Electric Railfans' Association, 2002), pp. 18, 28, 35; "Just as Was Thought," *Chicago Eagle*, 27 July 1901, p. 1; "Voice of the People," *Chicago Eagle*, 16 August 1902, p. 2.

44.   Moffat, *Chicago Tunnel Story*, p. 55.

45.   "Banquet Hall a Tunnel," *Chicago Daily Tribune*, 11 February 1904, p. 7; Otto Zimmerman, "Solving the Problem of Traffic Congestion," *Chicago Daily Tribune*, 10 October 1904, p. 10.

46.   Concentration of freight operations: Zimmerman, "Solving the Problem of Traffic Congestion"; George F. Stone, ed., *Annual Report of the Trade and Commerce of Chicago*, vol. 43 (Chicago: Chicago Board of Trade, 1901), pp. 127–130.

47.   US Congress, *Five Per Cent Case: Letters from the Chairman of the Interstate Commerce*

Commission, Senate document no. 466, vol. 3, 63rd Congress, 2nd session (Washington, DC: USGPO, 1915), pp. 2577, 2578.

48.　"Chicago Freight Subway," *Electric Railway Journal*, vol. 40, no. 14 (5 October 1912), pp. 590–591.

49.　Moffat, *Chicago Tunnel Story*, pp. 64–68, 107.

50.　Moffat, *Chicago Tunnel Story*, pp. 64, 68, 123.

51.　Moffat, *Chicago Tunnel Story*, pp. 36–43, 95, 100, 119.

52.　"Double-Deck Streets as a Relief for Traffic Congestion," *Scientific American*, vol. 96, no. 25 (22 June 1907), p. 510.

53.　Occupied 30 percent: William J. Wilgus, *Proposed New Railway System for the Transportation and Distribution of Freight by Improved Methods in the City and Port of New York* (New York: Amsterdam Corporation, 1908), p. 11; Schlichting, *Grand Central's Engineer*, p. 85.

54.　Used only seven percent: Wilgus, *Proposed New Railway System*, p. 11. Short-lived improvement: Schlichting, *Grand Central's Engineer*, p. 191. The three tunnels were the Hudson and Manhattan Railroad's uptown tunnels at Christopher Street, opened 1908; the Hudson and Manhattan Railroad's downtown tunnels at Cortlandt Street, opened 1909; and the Pennsylvania Railroad's North River Tunnels at 32nd Street, opened 1910.

55.　"Grand Central Terminal–New York," *Construction News*, vol. 36, no. 6 (9 August 1913), pp. 7–15.

56.　Handicaps will be avoided: Wilgus, *Proposed New Railway System*, p. 17; flaws of Chicago system solved: "Gigantic Plan to Relieve Street Congestion," *New York Times*, 4 October 1908, part 5 (magazine), p. 10.

57.　Schlichting, *Grand Central's Engineer*, pp. 92, 95, 102.

58.　"Freight Subway Plan," *New York Tribune*, 27 October 1912, p. 4.

59.　Stronger authority: Schlichting, *Grand Central's Engineer*, pp. 163–164, 179; legislation: Josef W. Konvitz, "William J. Wilgus and Engineering Projects to Improve the Port of New York, 1900–1930," *Technology and Culture*, vol. 30, no. 2 (April 1989), p. 411.

60.　Backed up to Mississippi: William J. Cunningham, "The Railroads Under Government Operation," *The Quarterly Journal of Economics*, vol. 35, no. 2 (February 1921), p. 298; New York freight congestion: Carl W. Condit, *The Port of New York*, vol. 2 (Chicago: University of Chicago Press, 1981), pp. 111–121; changed debate: Keith D. Revell, *Building Gotham: Civic Culture and Public Policy in New York City, 1898–1938* (Baltimore, MD: John Hopkins University Press, 2005), pp. 75–80. President Wilson appointed his secretary of the treasury and son-in-law William G. McAdoo as director of the Railroad Administration to consolidate and rationalize the nation's rail operations. McAdoo was a leading proponent of nationalization and had built two of the rail tunnels under the Hudson River.

61.　New York, New Jersey Port and Harbor Development Commission, *Joint Report with Comprehensive Plan and Recommendations* (Albany, NY: 1920), pp. 233–238, 254.

62.　Schlichting, *Grand Central's Engineer*, pp. 142–151, 163–164; Port of New York Authority, *Report with Plan for the Comprehensive Development of the Port of New York* (Albany, NY: 1921), pp. 19–21, 32, 34–35.

63.　Charles D. Norton, "The Merchants Club and the Plan of Chicago," in *The Merchants Club of Chicago, 1896–1907* (Chicago: Commercial Club of Chicago, 1922), pp. 95–99; David A. Johnson, *Planning the Great Metropolis: The 1929 Regional Plan of New York and Its Environs* (London: E & FN Spon, 1996), p. 51.

64.　Daniel H. Burnham, "Report on Improvement of Manila," in US War Department, *Sixth Annual Report of the Philippine Commission 1905*, part 1 (Washington, DC: USGPO, 1906), p. 628; Daniel H. Burnham, *Report on a Plan for San Francisco* (San Francisco, CA: City of San Francisco, 1905), pp. 53, 80, 85, 181–182.

65.　John W. Stamper, *Chicago's North Michigan Avenue: Planning and Development, 1900–1930* (Chicago: University of Chicago Press, 1991), pp. 1–7; Daniel H. Burnham and Edward H. Bennett, *Plan of Chicago* (Chicago: Commercial Club, 1909), p. 100.

66.　Burnham and Bennett, *Plan of Chicago*, pp. 100–105.

67.　Stamper, *Chicago's North Michigan Avenue*, pp. 9–17.

68.　E. S. Taylor, "The Plan of Chicago in 1924," *Annals of the American Academy of Political and Social Science*, vol. 116, no. 205 (November 1924), p. 227; Burnham and Bennett, *Plan of Chicago*, pp. 14, 96–97, 112, and fig. 121.

69.   Taylor, "The Plan of Chicago in 1924," p. 228; Chicago Plan Commission, *Reclaim South Water Street for All the People* (Chicago: Chicago Plan Commission, 1917), pp. 11–13, 24–31, 40–43.

70.   City Council of Chicago, *Journal of the Proceedings of the City Council . . .*, 18 June 1924, p. 3377.

71.   Wikipedia contributors, "Multilevel Streets in Chicago," *Wikipedia*, 20 July 2015, http://en.wikipedia.org.

72.   New Jersey Interstate Bridge and Tunnel Commission, *Fourth Report . . .* (Trenton, NJ: 1913), pp. 17–21; "The Proposed New York and New Jersey Vehicular Tunnel," *Proceedings of the American Society of Civil Engineers*, vol. 45, no. 5 (May 1919), pp. 249–260.

73.   Schlichting, *Grand Central's Engineer*, pp. 195–218; Jamison W. Doig, *Empire on the Hudson* (New York: Columbia University Press, 2001), pp. 108–112.

74.   US Department of the Interior, National Park Service, *Route 1 Extension*, National Register of Historic Places no. 05000880, by Mary E. McCahon and Sandra G. Johnston, 12 August 2005, item 8, p. 7.

75.   Advisory Board to the New Jersey State Highway Commission, *Report of the Advisory Board to the New Jersey State Highway Commission: Vehicular Tunnel Traffic Study* (Trenton, NJ: 1924), pp. 6, 32, 41.

76.   National Park Service, *Route 1 Extension*, 2005, item 8, pp. 7–9.

77.   US Department of the Interior, National Park Service, *Route 1 Extension, South Street Viaduct*, Historic American Engineering Record no. NJ-81, by TAMS Consultants, 1992, pp. 11, 14.

78.   National Park Service, *Route 1 Extension*, 2005, item 8, pp. 17–18.

79.   National Park Service, *Route 1 Extension*, 1992, pp. 15–17.

80.   "Traffic Situation in New York Grave Says Police Official," *Motor Truck*, vol. 13, no. 11 (November 1922), p. 617; Johnson, *Planning the Great Metropolis*, pp. 63, 109–110.

81.   "Central Offers City $24,000,000 Highway Along the West Side," *New York Times*, 2 February 1925, p. 1; "Argue on Removal of West Side Tracks," *New York Times*, 8 March 1925, p. 16.

82.   "Fears Rail Project Imperils Port Plan," *New York Times*, 19 February 1925, p. 1; "Argue on Removal of West Side Tracks," p. 16; "Censure Port Heads in 'Death Av.' Delay," *New York Times*, 4 December 1925, p. 25; Doig, *Empire on the Hudson*, pp. 102–103.

83.   "Miller Proposes Biggest Boulevard to Ease West Side," *New York Times*, 21 January 1926, p. 1; "New River Highway is Assured to City," *New York Times*, 11 November 1926, p. 3.

84.   "Walker Beats Move by Miller to Push Express Highway," *New York Times*, 5 April 1927, p. 1; "Strongly Opposes Elevated Highway," *New York Times*, 12 May 1927, p. 20.

85.   "Elevated Highway along Hudson Shore is Ordered by City," *New York Times*, 17 August 1928, p. 1; "Express Highway Wins Final Vote," *New York Times*, 11 January 1929, p. 28; "Julius Miller Dies at 75," *Newsday*, 4 February 1955, p. 101.

86.   "Elevated Speedway on East Side in View," *New York Times*, 21 October 1928, section 2, p. N1; "Manhattan to Pay for Express Highway," *New York Times*, 16 March 1929, p. 27; "Hudson Highway Officially Started to Cheers Of 5,000," *New York Times*, 25 May 1929, p. 1; "Express Road Unit Opened by Miller," *New York Times*, 14 November 1930, p. 3; "Act to Name Express Road," *New York Times*, 27 May 1931, p. 4; "Mayor Wins 'Auto Race' With Levy As Elevated Highway Link Opens," *New York Times*, 10 February 1937, p. 25.

87.   "New York to Build Elevated Highway," *New York Times*, 25 April 1926, section 9, p. XX1; "Elevated Speedway on East Side in View," *New York Times*, 21 October 1928, section 2, p. N1; Thomas Adams, *Regional Plan of New York and Its Environs*, vol. 2, *The Building of the City* (New York: Committee on Regional Plan of New York and Its Environs, 1931), pp. 357–358; Raymond J. Harrington, "The Elevated Public Highway along the Hudson River Waterfront . . .," *Municipal Engineers Journal*, vol. 20, no. 3 (1934), p. 118.

88.   Adams, *The Building of the City*, pp. 337–339, 358; Johnson, *Planning the Great Metropolis*, p. 111.

89.   Robert Caro, *The Power Broker* (New York: Alfred A. Knopf, 1974), pp. 526, 573, 796; *New York Times* (photographic feature), 3 August 1977, p. B3; *New York Times* (photographic feature), 26 May 1989, p. B2.

90.   Benjamin W. Levitan, "A Unique Institutional Building," *The American Architect*, vol. 67, no. 2310 (31 March 1920), pp. 415–423; "'Mitchel' on Tablet Replaced by 'Hylan,'" *The Sun*, 13 July 1919, p. 9. Vehicular service ended in 1956 but pedestrian service continued until 1973. The building was replaced by

the Roosevelt Island aerial tramway station around 1974–1975. See Anthony Bailey, "Manhattan's Other Island," *New York Times*, 1 December 1974, magazine, p. 33; Tom Buckley, "Roosevelt Island: Town in Making," *New York Times*, 22 August 1973, p. 39.

91. J. Bernard Walker, "A Study in Magnitude," *Scientific American*, vol. 124, no. 23 (4 June 1921), pp. 450–451; "Proposes Suspended Railways to Bridge Cities!" *Popular Science*, vol. 102, no. 3 (March 1923), pp. 46–47; Orrick Johns, "Bridge Homes—A New Vision of the City," *New York Times*, 22 February 1925, magazine section, p. 3.

92. David Gissen, "Exhaust and Territorialisation at the Washington Bridge Apartments, New York City, 1963–1973," *Journal of Architecture*, vol. 12, no. 4 (2007), pp. 449–461; David W. Chen, "Life on the Road," *New York Times*, 18 June 2004, p. B1.

93. David A. Johnson, *Planning the Great Metropolis*, pp. 108–109.

94. Regional Plan staff minutes, 20 March 1923, Regional Plan Papers, quoted in Johnson, *Planning the Great Metropolis*, p. 109.

95. Harvey Wiley Corbett, "Different Levels for Foot, Wheel and Rail," *American City*, vol. 31, no. 1 (July 1924), pp. 2–6; Gregory F. Gilmartin, *Shaping the City: New York and the Municipal Art Society* (New York: Clarkson Potter, 1995), pp. 88, 495.

96. Carol Willis, "Drawing Toward Metropolis," in Hugh Ferriss, *The Metropolis of Tomorrow*, reprint ed. (Princeton, NJ: Princeton Architectural Press, 1986), p. 160; Adams, *The Building of the City*, pp. 306–313, 411–417.

97. Harvey Wiley Corbett, "New Stones for Old," *The Saturday Evening Post*, 8 May 1926, p. 189; "The Wonder City You May Live to See," *Popular Science Monthly*, vol. 107, no. 2 (August 1925), pp. 40–41. Corbett's advocacy was bolstered by his status in the profession. He taught at Columbia University, and served as an officer of the Architectural League, American Institute of Architects, and other organizations. See Willis, "Drawing Toward Metropolis," p. 159.

98. "Hugh Ferriss," *Pencil Points*, vol. 1, no. 7 (December 1920), p. 25; Carol Willis, "Zoning and Zeigeist," *Journal of the Society of Architectural Historians*, vol. 45, no. 1 (March 1986), pp. 54–55; Willis, "Drawing Toward Metropolis," pp. 156–160.

99. Joseph J. Corn and Brian Horrigan, *Yesterday's Tomorrows: Past Visions of the American Future* (Washington, DC: Smithsonian Institution, 1984), p. 43; Jean Ferriss Leich, *Architectural Visions* (New York: Whitney Library of Design, 1980), pp. 16, 132; Willis, "Drawing Toward Metropolis," pp. 161, 163, 187.

100. Hugh Ferriss, *The Metropolis of Tomorrow* (New York: Ives Washburn, 1929), pp. 18, 59, 66.

101. Ferriss, *The Metropolis of Tomorrow*, pp. 26, 64, 130; Leich, *Architectural Visions*, p. 69; Eliel Saarinen, "Project for the Lake Front Development of the City of Chicago," *The American Architect - The Architectural Review*, vol. 124, no. 2434 (5 December 1923), pp. 487–514.

102. Leich, *Architectural Visions*, pp. 24–26, 36–37; Willis, "Drawing Toward Metropolis," pp. 176–178.

103. H. Allen Brooks, *Le Corbusier's Formative Years* (Chicago: University of Chicago Press, 1997), pp. 200, 368–370; H. Allen Brooks, "Jenneret and Sitte: Le Corbusier's Earliest Ideas on Urban Design," in Helen Searing, ed., *In Search of Modern Architecture: A Tribute to Henry Russell Hitchcock* (New York: Architectural History Foundation, 1982), pp. 282–285, 291, 295; George Benoit Levy, "A French Garden-Hamlet," *The Survey*, 2 February 1918, pp. 488–489; Mervyn Miller, *Raymond Unwin*, pp. 101–102. Le Corbusier's garden-suburb proposals were Cité-Jardin aux Crétets, La Chaux-de-Fonds, Switzerland (1914) and Cité Ouvrière, Saint-Nicolas d'Aliermont, France (1917).

104. Nicholas Fox Weber, *Le Corbusier: A Life* (New York: Alfred A. Knopf, 2008), pp. 169–186; Brooks, *Le Corbusier's Formative Years*, p. 207; Le Corbusier, *The City of To-Morrow and Its Planning*, trans. Frederick Etchells (London: Architectural Press, 1929), p. 12.

105. Le Corbusier and Saugnier, "Trois rappels a MM. LES ARCHITECTS," *L'esprit nouveau*, no. 4 (January 1921), p. 468; Henri-Jules Borie, *Aérodomes: essai sur un nouveau mode de maisons d'habitation ...* (Paris: Typographie Morris, 1865), pp. 14, 15; Le Corbusier, *Toward an Architecture*, trans. John Goodman (Los Angeles: Getty Research Institute, 2007), pp. 126–129, 314.

106. Le Corbusier, *City of To-morrow*, pp. 168–170.

107. Le Corbusier and Pierre Jeanneret, *Oeuvre complète de 1910–1929*, nouvelle ed. (Zurich: H. Girsberger, 1937), pp. 92, 94.

108. Le Corbusier, *The Radiant City: Elements of a Doctrine of Urbanism to be Used as the Basis for Machine-Age Civilization*, trans. Pamela Knight, Eleanor Levieux, and Derek Coltman (New York:

Orion Press, 1967), pp. 92, 125–126.

109. Le Corbusier, *The Radiant City*, p. 124; originally published as Le Corbusier, "Vivre! (habiter)," *Plans*, no. 4 (April 1931). The corridor street is a roadway lined with buildings that spatially define a continuous, linear civic realm.

110. Le Corbusier, *When the Cathedrals Were White: A Journey to the Country of the Timid People*, trans. Francis E. Hyslop Jr. (New York: Reynal and Hitchcock, 1947), pp. 80, 153–155, 174; Mardges Bacon, *Le Corbusier in America: Travels in the Land of the Timid* (Cambridge, MA: MIT Press, 2001), pp. 67, 70, 94, 118.

111. Bacon, *Le Corbusier in America*, pp. 176–181, 238.

112. James Dunnett, "Le Corbusier and the City without Streets," in Thomas Deckker, ed., *The Modern City Revisited* (London: Spon, 2000), pp. 68–70.

113. Auke van der Woud, *Het Nieuwe Bouwen Internationaal/International* (Delft: Delft University Press, 1983), pp. 134–152; John R. Gold, "Creating the Charter of Athens: CIAM and the Functional City, 1933–43," *Town Planning Review*, vol. 69, no. 3 (July 1998), pp. 225–247.

114. "Dr. J. A. Harriss Named Special Police Deputy," *New York Times*, 16 February 1918, p. 3.

115. John F. Hylan, "Keeping the Wheels Moving," *Motor*, vol. 36, no. 5 (October 1921), p. 74; Herbert Asbury and Joseph Brinker, "Speeding Up Traffic on the World's Busiest Corner," *Popular Science Monthly*, vol. 98, no. 1 (January 1921), pp. 40–43.

116. "Enright's Entourage of Millionaires Has Enviable Record of Service, But People Wonder How He Signs Them On," *Brooklyn Daily Eagle*, 4 November 1923, p. C6; City of New York Police Department, *Annual Report for the Year 1919* (1920), pp. 28–29; Louis S. Levy, *Yesterdays* (New York: Library Publishers, 1954), pp. 173–175.

117. "Burdensome Traffic Regulations Are Modified," *Greater New York*, vol. 8, no. 7 (17 February 1919), p. 7; John A. Harriss, "Street Traffic Segregation in New York," *Motor Travel*, vol. 10, no. 10 (March 1919), pp. 19–20.

118. Asbury and Brinker, "Speeding Up Traffic on the World's Busiest Corner," p. 40; Hylan, "Keeping the Wheels Moving," p. 76.

119. "For Sixth Avenue Viaduct," *New York Times*, 1 March 1918, p. 9; "Novel Automobile Roadway Proposed for New York City," *Good Roads*, vol. 15, no. 10 (9 March 1918), p. 142; "Double and Triple-Decking Busy City Thoroughfares," *Science and Invention*, vol. 9, no. 1 (May 1921), p. 1.

120. John A. Harriss, "Arcades to Relieve City Traffic," *Popular Science*, vol. 100, no. 5 (May 1922), p. 26.

121. "Plan to Drain a New York River," *Popular Science*, vol. 105, no. 6 (December 1924), p. 47. The engineer T. Kennard Thompson had been proposing to fill the East River for more than a decade, and he said the idea dated from the Civil War era. See "Fill Up the East River to Solve Port Problems," *New York Times*, 31 August 1913, part 5, p. 1.

122. "Dr. John A. Harriss Proposes Six-Deck Streets," *American City*, vol. 36, no. 6 (June 1927), pp. 803–805; "Sees Traffic Aid in 6-Level Street," *New York Times*, 29 April 1927, p. 24.

123. "Harriss Taking Traffic Towers to Berlin To Show Fifth Avenue Signal System," *New York Times*, 25 May 1922, p. 1; "Future of Elevated Ways," *New York Times*, 17 May 1928, p. 24.

124. "Multiple Highways for City Traffic," *New York Times*, 29 June 1930, section 11, p. RE1.

125. Levy, *Yesterdays*, pp. 176–181; "Dr. John Harriss, Expert on Traffic," *New York Times*, 13 October 1938, p. 23.

Chapter 3. Horizontal Traffic Separation: Divided Roadways

1. Mogens Trolle Larsen, *Ancient Kanesh: A Merchant Colony in Bronze Age Anatolia* (New York: Cambridge University Press, 2015), pp. 9–10, 49; William L. MacDonald, *The Architecture of the Roman Empire*, vol. 1 (New Haven, CT: Yale University Press, 1965), pp. 27–30; Spiro Kostof, *The City Assembled: The Elements of Urban Form through History* (Boston: Little, Brown, 1992), pp. 209, 216–217; Francesca Bocchi, *Bologna e i suoi portici* (Bologna: Grafis Edizioni.1995), pp.18–21; Paul Zucker, *Town and Square* (New York: Columbia University Press, 1959), p. 92.

2. Nancy Shatzman Steinhardt, *Chinese Imperial City Planning* (Honolulu, HI: University of Hawaii Press, 1990), pp. 66, 69, 94; Pierre Patte, *Mémoires sur les objects les plus importants de l'architecture* (Paris: Rozet, 1769), pp. 19–21.

3. Henry W. Lawrence, *City Trees: A Historical Geography from the Renaissance through the Nineteenth Century* (Charlottesville, VA: University of Virginia Press, 2006), pp. 14–19.

4. Henry W. Lawrence, "Origins of the Tree-Lined Boulevard," *Geographical Review*, vol. 78, no. 4 (October 1988), p. 360; Lawrence, *City Trees*, pp. 33–34, 279; A. E. J. Morris, *History of Urban Form*, 3rd ed. (Essex, UK: Pearson Education, 1994), p. 231; Olmsted, Vaux & Company, "Report of the Landscape Architects and Superintendents," in *Eighth Annual Report of the Board of Commissioners of Prospect Park, Brooklyn* (Brooklyn, NY: 1868), p. 51.

5. Lawrence, *City Trees*, p. 32–33.

6. Lawrence, *City Trees*, pp. 34–37, 63–64; Mark Girouard, *Cities and People: A Social and Architectural History* (New Haven, CT: Yale University Press, 1985), pp. 124, 166–167, 186.

7. A. E. J. Morris, *History of Urban Form*, pp. 201–202; Allan B. Jacobs, Elizabeth Macdonald, and Yodan Rofé, *The Boulevard Book: History, Evolution, Design of Multiway Boulevards* (Cambridge, MA: MIT Press, 2002), pp. 75–76; Les Musées de la Ville de Paris, *Les grands boulevards* (Paris: Paris-Musées, 1985), pp. 6–7, 22–23; Lawrence, *City Trees*, pp. 38–39, 139–140.

8. Patte, *Mémoires sur les objects les plus importants de l'architecture*, pp. 11–13, 19–21; Robert Sutton, introduction to Etienne Cabet, *Travels in Icaria*, trans. Leslie J. Roberts (Syracuse, NY: Syracuse University Press, 2003), pp. vii–xi.

9. J. C. Loudon, "Hints for Breathing Places for the Metropolis, and for Country Towns and Villages on Fixed Principles," *The Gardener's Magazine*, vol. 5 (December 1829), pp. 686–690; Patrice Bouche, "Transport Planning as Suggested in John Claudius Loudon's 1829 Plan for London," *Planning Perspectives*, vol. 32, no. 2 (2017), pp. 273–274.

10. Cabet, *Travels in Icaria*, pp. 19–22, 36–39.

11. Michel Carmona, *Haussmann: His Life and Times, and the Making of a Modern Paris*, trans. Patrick Camiller (Chicago: Ivan R. Dee, 2002), pp. 34, 147; Robert P. Sutton, *Les Icariens* (Urbana, IL: University of Illinois Press, 1994), pp. 31–38; Albert Shaw, *Icaria: A Chapter in the History of Communism* (New York: G. P. Putnam's Sons, 1884), pp. 16–18.

12. Sutton, *Les Icariens*, p. 145.

13. Stephane Kirkland, "A Napoleon III-Eye View of London," *stephanekirkland.com* (blog), 17 January 2012, http://stephanekirkland.com/a-napoleon-iii-eye-view-of-london; Stephane Kirkland, *Paris Reborn: Napoléon III, Baron Haussmann, and the Quest to Build a Modern City* (New York: St. Martin's, 2013), p. 68.

14. Etienne Cabet, *Curieuse Lettre du Cit. Cabet a Louis-Napoleon* (Paris: Bureau du Republicain, 1851), p. 3; Etienne Cabet, *Toute la Vérité au Peuple* (Paris: Prévôt, 1842), p. 16.

15. Carmona, *Haussmann*, p. 6.

16. Carmona, *Haussmann*, p. 9.

17. Carmona, *Haussmann*, pp. 147, 153, 393; Nicholas Papayanis, *Planning Paris Before Haussmann* (Baltimore, MD: Johns Hopkins University Press, 2004), p. 118.

18. The avenue's name translates as Avenue of the Empress. It was renamed Avenue du Général-Uhrich in 1870 after the emperor was deposed, then Avenue du Bois de Boulogne in 1875, then Avenue Foch in 1929.

19. Georges-Eugène Haussmann, *Memoires du Baron Haussmann*, vol. 3, *Grands travaux de Paris* (Paris: Victor-Havard, 1893), p. 497, quoted in Carmona, *Haussmann*, p. 242.

20. Haussmann, *Memoires*, vol. 3, p. 496; Adolphe Alphand, *Les promenades de Paris*, vol. 1 (Paris: J. Rothschild, 1868), p. 237.

21. Haussmann, *Memoires* vol. 3, p. 76; Ville de Paris, *Recueil d'actes administratifs et de conventions relatifs aux servitudes spéciales d'architecture* . . . (Paris: Ville de Paris, 1905), pp. 21–22.

22. Richard S. Hopkins, "From *Place* to *Espace*: Napoleon III's Transformation of the Bois de Boulogne," *Proceedings of the Western Society for French History*, vol. 31 (2003), pp. 201–202.

23. Baron Haussmann, presentation to the Commission Departementale, 24 November 1853, quoted in David Van Zanten, "Paris Space: What Might Have Constituted Haussmanization," in Christian Herman Cordura, ed., *Manifestoes and Transformations in the Early Modernist City* (Farnham, UK: Ashgate, 2010), p. 203; Hopkins, "From *Place* to *Espace*," pp. 205–206.

24. David P. Jordan, *Transforming Paris: The Life and Labors of Baron Haussman* (New York: Simon & Schuster, 1995), p. 281.

25. Frederick Law Olmsted, letter to A. J. Downing, 23 November 1850, in Frederick Law Olmsted Jr. and Theodora Kimball Hubbard, eds., *Frederick Law Olmsted, Landscape Architect, 1822–1903: Early*

Years and Experiences (New York: G. P. Putnam's Sons, 1922), p. 90; Witold Rybczynski, *A Clearing in the Distance: Frederick Law Olmsted and America in the 19th Century* (New York: Scribner, 1999), pp. 142–144.

26. Rybczynski, *A Clearing in the Distance*, p. 163.

27. Olmsted and Vaux, *Description of a Plan for the Improvement of the Central Park "GREEN-SWARD,"* (New York: Sutton, Brown, 1858, reprinted 1868), pp. 9–10.

28. Olmsted and Vaux, *Central Park "GREENSWARD,"* pp. 12–13.

29. Charles E. Beveridge and David Schuyler, eds., *The Papers of Frederick Law Olmsted*, vol. 3, *Creating Central Park 1857–1861* (Baltimore, MD: Johns Hopkins University Press, 1983), pp. 23–26.

30. Olmsted and Vaux, *Central Park "GREENSWARD,"* pp. 10–11; Frederick Law Olmsted to Mariana Griswold Van Rensseleaer, September 1893, quoted in Beveridge and Schuyler, *Creating Central Park*, pp. 180–181.

31. George F. Chadwick, *The Works of Sir Joseph Paxton* (London: Architectural Press, 1961) p. 53; George F. Chadwick, *The Park and the Town* (New York: F. A. Praeger, 1966), pp. 184–185.

32. Frederick Law Olmsted and Calvert Vaux, "Description of the Central Park," in Board of Commissioners of the Central Park, *Second Annual Report . . .* (New York: 1859), p. 66; Mere consciousness: Frederick Law Olmsted, *Public Parks and the Enlargement of Towns* (Cambridge, MA: American Social Science Association, 1870), p. 32; Least possible anxiety: Olmsted, Vaux & Company, "Report of the Landscape Architects," in Board of Commissioners of Prospect Park, *Sixth Annual Report of the Commissioners of Prospect Park, Brooklyn* (Brooklyn, NY: 1866), p. 17; Beveridge and Schuyler, *Creating Central Park*, pp. 22–23.

33. Eric Dumbaugh, "Safe Streets, Livable Streets," *Journal of the American Planning Association*, vol. 71, no. 3 (Summer 2005), pp. 283–288.

34. Frederick Law Olmsted, "Letter to Board of Commissioners of Central Park," 28 December 1859, in Beveridge and Schuyler, *Creating Central Park*, pp. 234–235.

35. Rybczynski, *A Clearing in the Distance*, pp. 192, 237; David Schuyler et al., eds., *The Papers of Frederick Law Olmsted*, vol. 9, *The Last Great Projects, 1890–1895* (Baltimore, MD: John Hopkins University Press, 2015), p. 340.

36. Calvert Vaux, letters to Frederick Law Olmsted, 1865, in Victoria Post Ranney et al., eds., *The Papers of Frederick Law Olmsted*, vol. 5, *The California Frontier, 1863–1865* (Baltimore, MD: Johns Hopkins University Press, 1990), pp. 358–364, 372–378, 383–390, 402–406.

37. Frederick Law Olmsted, *Preliminary Report in Regard to a Plan of Public Pleasure Grounds for the City of San Francisco* (New York: 1866), in Ranney, *California Frontier*, pp. 536–543.

38. Olmsted, Vaux & Company, "Report of the Landscape Architects," in *Sixth Annual Report of the Commissioners of Prospect Park*, pp. 37–38.

39. Frederick Law Olmsted, "Park," in Beveridge and Schuyler, *Creating Central Park 1857–1861*, pp. 348, 352. Originally published in *New American Cyclopaedia* (1861).

40. Olmsted, Vaux & Company, "Report of the Landscape Architects and Superintendents," in Board of Commissioners of Prospect Park, *Eighth Annual Report of the Board of Commissioners of Prospect Park* (Brooklyn, 1868), pp. 33–40, 46, 51–52; Elizabeth Macdonald, *Pleasure Drives and Promenades: A History of Frederick Law Olmsted's Brooklyn Parkways* (Chicago: Columbia College Chicago Press, 2012), pp. 42–44; John C. Olmsted, "Classes of Parkways," *Landscape Architecture*, vol. 6, no. 1 (October 1915), pp. 43, 45.

41. Olmsted, Vaux & Company, "Report," *Eighth Annual Report of the Board of Commissioners of Prospect Park*, pp. 43–54; Macdonald, *Pleasure Drives and Promenades*, pp. 35, 44.

42. Macdonald, *Pleasure Drives and Promenades*, pp. 48, 111–112, 191, 206, 210.

43. William McMillan, "Superintendent's Report," in *Fourth Annual Report of the Buffalo Park Commissioners* (Buffalo, NY: Warren, Johnson, 1874), p. 22; Charles Beveridge, "Buffalo's Park and Parkway System," in Francis R. Kowsky et al., *Buffalo Architecture: A Guide* (Cambridge, MA: MIT Press, 1981), p. 19.

44. Olmsted, Vaux & Company, *Preliminary Report upon the Proposed Suburban Village at Riverside, near Chicago* (New York: Sutton, Browne, 1868), pp. 9–13.

45. David Schuyler and Jane Turner Censer, eds., *The Papers of Frederick Law Olmsted*, vol. 6, *The Years of Olmsted, Vaux & Company, 1865–1874* (Baltimore, MD: Johns Hopkins University Press, 1992), pp. 19–20, 290, 343–347; "The Riverside Boulevard," *The Land Owner*, vol. 1, no. 3 (September 1869), p. 60.

46. City of Chicago, "Chicago Park Boulevard System Historic District," draft National Register of Historic Places nomination form, July 2011, pp. 72–73, 77, 84–92, http://www.cityofchicago.org; Daniel Bluestone, *Constructing Chicago* (New Haven, CT: Yale University Press, 1991), pp. 20–32.

47. City of Chicago, "Chicago Park Boulevard System," pp. 93–94; Olmsted, Vaux & Co., *Report Accompanying Plan For Laying Out The South Park* (Chicago: Chicago South Park Commission, 1871), p. 5.

48. Chicago City Council, *Laws and Ordinances Governing the City of Chicago*, Murray Floyd Tuley, ed. (Chicago: Bulletin Printing, 1873), p. 89; South Park Commission, *South Park: Acts of the General Assembly Relating to the Same*... (Chicago: Beach, Barnard & Co., 1875), pp. 5–6, 72; "Operation of Vehicles Restricted," *Municipal Code of Chicago*, section 9–72–020 (Cincinnati, OH: American Legal Publishing, 1990). Commercial vehicles were allowed to travel one block on a boulevard's side lanes to reach abutting houses. The South Park district in Hyde Park was annexed by Chicago in 1889.

49. City of Chicago, "Chicago Park Boulevard System," pp. 28, 98, 110, 112; Bluestone, *Constructing Chicago*, p. 55.

50. Horace Cleveland, letter to Frederick Law Olmsted, 11 July 1874, quoted in Bluestone, *Constructing Chicago*, p. 57.

51. Charles E. Beveridge et al., eds., *The Papers of Frederick Law Olmsted*, vol. 8, *The Early Boston Years, 1882–1890* (Baltimore, MD: Johns Hopkins University Press, 2013), pp. 15–16, 362–363; Robert L. McCullough, *Old Wheelways: Traces of Bicycle History on the Land* (Cambridge, MA: MIT Press, 2015), pp. 194, 214–216; Charles Mulford Robinson, *Modern Civic Art* (New York: G. P. Putnam's Sons, 1903), p. 209. In 1888 Whitney decided to use the new electric streetcar technology invented by Frank J. Sprague instead of cable cars, and Boston became the first major city to have electric streetcar service.

52. Macdonald, *Pleasure Drives and Promenades*, pp. 110–128; McCullough, *Old Wheelways*, pp. 220–232.

53. Clay McShane, *Down the Asphalt Path: The Automobile and the American City* (New York: Columbia University Press, 1995), p. 35; US Department of Commerce, Bureau of the Census, *General Statistics of Cities: 1916* (Washington, DC: USGPO, 1917), p. 53; McCullough, *Old Wheelways*, pp. 232–244.

54. Macdonald, *Pleasure Drives and Promenades*, pp. 133–140; Allan B. Jacobs, Elizabeth Macdonald, and Yodan Rofé, *The Boulevard Book: History, Evolution, Design of Multiway Boulevards* (Cambridge, MA: MIT Press, 2002), p. 89; Detroit Rapid Transit Commission, *Proposed Super-Highway Plan for Greater Detroit* (Detroit, MI: 1924), pp. 16–17.

Chapter 4. Horizontal Traffic Separation: Insular Roadways to 1910s

1. Cornelis van Tilburg, *Traffic and Congestion in the Roman Empire* (London: Routledge, 2007), pp. 74, 136–146, 160, 165–166, 170.

2. Besim Selim Hakim, *Arabic-Islamic Cities: Building and Planning Principles* (London: KPI, 1986), pp. 15–19, 24–27, 45–54, 64.

3. James D. Tracy, "Introduction," and "To Wall or Not to Wall: Evidence from Medieval Germany," in James D. Tracy, ed., *City Walls: The Urban Enceinte in Global Perspective* (Cambridge, UK: Cambridge University Press, 2000), pp. 1–7, 71–73.

4. Henry W. Lawrence, *City Trees: A Historical Geography from the Renaissance through the Nineteenth Century* (Charlottesville, VA: University of Virginia Press, 2006), pp. 5, 47.

5. Spiro Kostof, *The City Assembled: The Elements of Urban Form through History* (Boston: Little, Brown, 1992), pp. 104–105; Tracy, *City Walls*, p. 3.

6. Nancy Shatzman Steinhardt, *Chinese Imperial City Planning* (Honolulu, HI: University of Hawaii Press, 1990), pp. 9–11, 67–68, 85, 94–97, 115–117, 138.

7. Riaz Hassan, "Islam and Urbanization in the Medieval Middle-East," *Ekistics*, vol. 33, no. 195 (February 1972), pp. 108–112; Ira M. Lapidus, *Muslim Cities in the Late Middle Ages*, student ed. (Cambridge, UK: Cambridge University Press, 1984), pp. 85–95; Jamel Akbar, *Crisis in the Built Environment: The Case of the Muslim City* (Singapore: Concept Media, 1988), pp. 164–172.

8. Great Britain, House of Commons, *Fourth Report of the Surveyor General of His Majesty's Land Revenue*, by John Fordyce (London: 1809), pp. 28–31, 89–91; John Summerson, *The Life and Work of John Nash, Architect* (Cambridge, MA: MIT Press, 1980), pp. 56–63.

9. Summerson, *Life and Work of John Nash*, pp. 66–69. Regent's Park was originally called Marylebone Park.

10. John Nash, "Report . . ." and "Further Report . . ." (appendix 12G), in Great Britain, Commissioners of His Majesty's Woods, Forests, and Land Revenues, *First Report of the Commissioners . . .* (London: 1812), pp. 100, 131.

11. James Elmes, *Metropolitan Improvements; or, London in the Nineteenth Century . . .* (London: James & Co., 1829), p. 21; Ann Saunders, *Regent's Park: A Study of the Development of the Area from 1086 to the Present Day* (Newton Abbot, Devon: David & Charles, 1969), pp. 146–147.

12. Donald J. Olsen, *Town Planning in London: the Eighteenth & Nineteenth Centuries*, 2nd ed. (New Haven, CT: Yale University Press, 1982), pp. xxii, 5–6.

13. Olsen, *Town Planning in London*, p. 146.

14. Henry W. Lawrence, "The Greening of the Squares of London," *Annals of the Association of American Geographers*, vol. 83, no. 1 (March 1993), p. 108.

15. Olsen, *Town Planning in London*, pp. 58, 146–147, 152.

16. More than 187: London County Council, Statistical Department, *London Statistics 1892-93*, vol. 3 (London: London County Council, 1893), pp. 622–626; P. J. Atkins, "How the West End was Won: The Struggle to Remove Street Barriers in Victorian London," *Journal of Historical Geography*, vol. 19, no. 3 (July 1993), pp. 266–269.

17. Olsen, *Town Planning in London*, pp. 147–149; Atkins, "How the West End was Won," pp. 266, 274; "Mudlordism in London," *Punch*, vol. 82 (17 June 1882), p. 286.

18. Olsen, *Town Planning in London*, pp. 149–150; Atkins, "How the West End was Won," pp. 269–272.

19. Saunders, *Regent's Park*, p. 104; John Britton, *Descriptive Sketches of Tunbridge Wells and the Calverley Estate* (London: 1832), pp. 53–55; John Archer, "Country and City in the American Romantic Suburb," *Journal of the Society of Architectural Historians*, vol. 42, no. 2 (May 1983), pp. 142–143; Tunbridge Wells Borough Council, *Royal Tunbridge Wells and Rusthall: Conservation Areas Appraisal* (Royal Tunbridge Wells, Kent: 2000), pp. 47–48, http://www.tunbridgewells.gov.uk.

20. Renaud Le Goix and Delphine Callen, "Production and Social Sustainability of Private Enclaves in Suburban Landscapes," in Samer Bagaeen and Ola Uduku, eds., *Gated Communities: Social Sustainability in Contemporary and Historical Gated Developments* (London: Easthscan, 2010), pp. 95–96.

21. Robert Fishman, *Bourgeois Utopias: The Rise and Fall of Suburbia* (New York: Basic Books, 1987), p. 82–84.

22. Fishman, *Bourgeois Utopias*, pp. 93–94; Maurice Spiers, *Victoria Park, Manchester: A Nineteenth Century Suburb in its Social and Administrative Context* (Manchester: Chetham Society, 1976), p. 14.

23. Spiers, *Victoria Park*, p. 19; Fishman, *Bourgeois Utopias*, p. 92.

24. Nathaniel Hawthorne, *Passages from the English Note-Books*, vol. 1 (Boston: Fields, Osgood, 1870), pp. 30–31.

25. Lawrence, *City Trees*, pp. 186–189.

26. Kate Colquhoun, *"The Busiest Man in England"* (Boston: David R. Godine, 2006), pp. 108–115; Howard Daniels, "European Parks, no. I," *The Magazine of Horticulture . . .* , vol. 21, no. 9 (September 1855), pp. 415–417; Allan Smith, "Paxton's Park," *Architects' Journal*, vol. 178, nos. 51/52 (21 & 28 December 1983), p. 50.

27. Alan C. B. Urwin, *Twickenham Parke: An Outline of the History . . .* (Hounslow, UK: Thomasons, 1965), pp. 37, 116–120; John Archer, *Architecture and Suburbia: From English Villa to American Dream House, 1690-2000* (Minneapolis, MN: University of Minnesota Press, 2005), p. 219.

28. Jane B. Davies, "Llewellyn Park in West Orange, New Jersey," *Antiques*, vol. 107, no. 1 (January 1975), pp. 142–145; John R. Stilgoe, *Borderlands: Origins of the American Suburb, 1820-1939* (New Haven, CT: Yale University Press, 1988), pp. 52–55. The entire development was not known as Llewellyn Park until 1860.

29. Daniels, "European Parks, no. I," pp. 411–417; Howard Daniels, "European Parks, no. II," *The Magazine of Horticulture . . .* , vol. 21, no. 10 (October 1855), pp. 472–473.

30. Henry Winthrop Sergeant, "Supplement," in A. J. Downing, *A Treatise on the Theory and Practice of Landscape Gardening*, 6th ed. (New York: A. O. Moore, 1859), p. 570; US Department of the Interior, National Park Service, *Llewellyn Park Historic District*, by Robert P. Guter, National Register of Historic Places no. 86000423, 28 Febuary 1986, item 8, pp. 2–3.

31. Archer, "Country and City in the American Romantic Suburb," pp. 154–155; Susan Henderson, "Llewellyn Park, Suburban Idyll," *Journal of Garden History*, vol. 7, no. 3 (July-September 1987), p. 239.

32. Sergeant, "Supplement," pp. 568, 571; National Park Service, *Llewellyn Park Historic District*, item 8, p. 6.

33. National Park Service, *Llewellyn Park Historic District*, item 8, pp. 7, 16; Davies, "Llewellyn Park," pp. 142, 145.

34. Olmsted, Vaux & Company, "Report of the Landscape Architects and Superintendents," in Board of Commissioners of Prospect Park, *Eighth Annual Report of the Board of Commissioners of Prospect Park* (Brooklyn, NY: 1868), pp. 33–45; Frederick Law Olmsted, "History of Streets," lecture to Brookline Club, February 1889, in Charles E. Beveridge et al., eds., *The Early Boston Years, 1882-1890*, Papers of Frederick Law Olmsted, vol. 8 (Baltimore, MD: Johns Hopkins University Press, 2013), pp. 584–593; Robert M. Fogelson, *Bourgeois Nightmares: Suburbia 1870-1930* (New Haven: Yale University Press, 2005), pp. 28–32.

35. Frederick Law Olmsted, letter to Henry H. Elliott, 27 August 1860, in Charles E. Beveridge and David Schuyler, eds., *The Papers of Frederick Law Olmsted*, vol. 3, *Creating Central Park 1857-1861* (Baltimore, MD: Johns Hopkins University Press, 1983), pp. 264–265. The letter also contained the first use of the term *landscape architects*, which was used to describe Olmsted and Vaux's work.

36. Olmsted, Vaux & Company, *Report Upon a Projected Improvement of the Estate of the College of California, at Berkeley near Oakland* (New York: Wm. C. Bryant, 1866), pp. 23–24.

37. Olmsted, Vaux & Co., *Preliminary Report upon the Proposed Suburban Village at Riverside, near Chicago* (New York: Sutton, Browne, 1868), pp 16–17.

38. US Bureau of the Census, "Historical Census Statistics on the Foreign-born Population of the United States: 1850–1990," by Campbell J. Gibson and Emily Lennon, Population Division working paper no. 29, table 21 (Washington DC, 1999); Rob Wilson, "The Disease of Fear and the Fear of Disease: Cholera and Yellow Fever in the Mississippi Valley" (PhD diss., St. Louis University, 2007), pp. 55, 65, 76–90.

39. Disconnected street patterns: Eric Sandweiss, *St. Louis: The Evolution of an American Urban Landscape* (Philadelphia, PA: Temple University Press, 2001); more prevalent: Charles C. Savage, *Architecture of the Private Places of St. Louis* (Columbia, MO: Columbia University Press, 1987), pp. 11, 169, 219; David Beito, "The Formation of Urban Infrastructure through Nongovernmental Planning: The Private Places of St. Louis, 1869-1920," *Journal of Urban History*, vol. 16, no. 3 (May 1990), pp. 269, 297.

40. Savage, *Architecture of the Private Places of St. Louis*, pp. 4, 219.

41. Savage, *Architecture of the Private Places of St. Louis*, pp. 7–9, 13–15, 129–131; David J. Simmons, "Residences of George I. Barnett," *Society of Architectural Historians Missouri Valley Chapter Newsletter*, vol. 18, no. 3B (Fall 2012), p. 5, http://www.stlouisarchitecture.org.

42. Savage, *Private Places of St. Louis*, pp. 18–19; familiar with Parisian: John Noyes, "The 'Places' of St. Louis," *American City*, vol. 12, no. 3 (March 1915), p. 206; US Department of the Interior, National Park Service, *Lafayette Square Historic District* (boundary increase), National Register of Historic Places no. 86002127, by Mary M. Stiritz, 24 July 1986, item 8, pp. 5–6.

43. Simmons, "Residences of George I. Barnett," p. 7–8; Mary M. Stiritz, Lafayette Square NRHP Nomination, Missouri SHPO (1986), item 8, p. 6; Savage, *Private Places of St. Louis*, pp. 22, 32; Robert L. Vickery Jr., *Anthrophysical Form: Two Families and Their Neighborhood Environments* (Charlottesville, VA: University Press of Virginia, 1972), pp. 15–16.

44. More than ninety: Beito, "The Formation of Urban Infrastructure," p. 267; several dozen: John Noyes, "The 'Places' of St. Louis," *The American City*, vol. 12, no. 3 (March 1915), p. 206; more than half: William Hyde and Howard L. Conrad, eds., *Encyclopedia of the History of St. Louis*, vol. 3 (New York: Southern History, 1899), p. 1742.

45. Sandweiss, *St. Louis*, p. 158; Savage, *Private Places of St. Louis*, pp. 44–45.

46. Scot McConachie, "Public Problems and Private Places," *Bulletin of the Missouri Historical Society*, vol. 34, no. 2 (January 1978), pp. 99–101.

47. The Kingshighway was eventually constructed, but not as Kessler had imagined it. In 1916 he complained bitterly that the street was now "nothing . . . but a trafficway." George Kessler, letter to Nelson Cunliff, 6 November 1916, Kessler Papers, box 4, quoted in Sandweiss, *St. Louis*, p. 212.

48. The Civic League of St. Louis, *A City Plan for St. Louis* (1907), p. 11.

49. Sandweiss, *St. Louis*, pp. 18–19.

50. William S. Worley, "A Legacy to a City: Kansas City Architects George Kessler, Henry Wright, and Sid and Herbert Hare," *Kansas History*, vol. 20, no. 3 (Autumn 1997); US Department of the Interior, National Park Service, *Brentmoor Park, Brentmoor and Forest Ridge*, National Register of Historic Places no. 82004716, by Esley Hamilton, 23 September 1982; David E. Tarn, "Co-operative Group Planning,"

Architectural Record, vol. 34, no. 5 (November 1913), pp. 468–471.

51.   Sandweiss, *St. Louis*, pp. 204–219; Harland Bartholomew, "Reduction of Street Traffic Congestion by Proper Street Design," *Annals of the American Academy of Political and Social Science*, vol. 116, no. 205 (November 1924), pp. 244-246; Eldridge Lovelace, *Harland Bartholomew: His Contributions to American Urban Planning* (Chicago: University of Illinois, 1993), pp. 5–8. Bartholomew had begun his career working for Ernest P. Goodrich in the New York City area.

52.   Brian Ladd, *Urban Planning and Civic Order in Germany, 1869-1914* (Cambridge, MA: Harvard University Press, 1990), p. 14.

53.   Ladd, *Urban Planning and Civic Order in Germany*, pp. 187–188; Josef Stübben, *Der Städtebau* (Stuttgart: Alfred Kröner, 1907), trans. Adalbert Albrecht as *City Building*, published by Julia Koschinsky and Emily Talen (2014), part 2, chapter 2, p. 20; appendix A, part 1, p. 92, http://www.design4planning.org.

54.   Ladd, *Urban Planning and Civic Order in Germany*, pp. 85–86, 99–100, 104.

55.   Ladd, *Urban Planning and Civic Order in Germany*, pp. 106–110.

56.   Camillo Sitte, *City Planning According to Artistic Principles*, trans. George R. Collins and Christiane Crasemann Collins (New York: Random House, 1965), pp. 97, 138–140, originally published as *Der Städte-Bau* (Wien: Carl Graeser, 1889).

57.   Sitte, *City Planning According to Artistic Principles*, p. xvi (preface to 3rd ed. of 1900).

58.   Stübben, *City Building*, appendix A, part 1, pp. 98, 128.

59.   Axel R. Schäfer, *American Progressives and German Social Reform, 1875-1920* (Stuttgart: Franz Steiner, 2000), pp. 114–116; Frederic C. Howe, *European Cities at Work* (New York: Charles Scribner's Sons, 1913), pp. 92–94.

60.   Charles Mulford Robinson, *Modern Civic Art* (New York: G.P Putnam's Sons, 1903), pp. 13, 23.

61.   Jon A. Peterson, *The Birth of City Planning in the United States, 1840-1917* (Baltimore, MD: Johns Hopkins University Press, 2003), pp. 120, 191–192.

62.   Robinson, *Modern Civic Art*, pp. 114, 189–193.

63.   Robinson, *Modern Civic Art*, pp. 248–251, 253.

64.   Robinson, *Modern Civic Art*, pp. 189, 198, 228–229, 236, 244.

65.   Robinson, *Modern Civic Art*, p. 121.

66.   Robinson, *The Width and Arrangement of Streets: A Study in Town Planning* (New York: Engineering News Publishing, 1911), pp. 8–10, 41, 113.

67.   Robinson, *Width and Arrangement of Streets*, pp. 9, 13–27.

68.   Robinson, *Width and Arrangement of Streets*, pp. 10, 42, 122–129.

69.   US Department of the Interior, National Park Service, *St. James-Belgravia Historic District*, National Register of Historic Places no. 72000538, by Walter Langsam and Mrs. Harvey Sloan, 5 December 1972; George H. Yater, "Pedestrian Courts," in John E. Kleber, ed., *The Encyclopedia of Louisville* (Lexington, KY: University Press of Kentucky, 2001), p. 696.

70.   H. M. Meinell, "Center Walks Supplemented by Back Alleys in Place of Roadways and Sidewalks in Venice, Cal.," *Engineering News*, vol. 62, no. 23 (2 December 1909), p. 605.

71.   Mervyn Miller, *Raymond Unwin: Garden Cities and Town Planning* (Leicester: Leicester University Press, 1992), pp. 10, 15.

72.   Coal-worker villages designed by Unwin include Poolsbrook and Arkwright Town in Derbyshire; extensions to Brimington and Barlbourough in Derbyshire; Marham Colliery in Norfolk, and Warsop Vale in Nottinghamshire. See Miller, *Raymond Unwin*, p. 20. For Unwin on quadrangles, see Barry Parker and Raymond Unwin, *The Art of Building a Home* (London: Longmans Green & Co., 1901), pp. 103–104.

73.   Miller, *Raymond Unwin*, pp. 23–27.

74.   Miller, *Raymond Unwin*, p. 29.

75.   William Morris, "Art Under Plutocracy," lecture delivered at University College, Oxford, 14 November 1883, in *Collected Works*, vol. 23 (London: Longmans Green & Co., 1915), pp. 170–171.

76.   William Mackenzie and Percy Handford, *Model Byelaws. . .*, vol. 1 (London: Shaw & Sons, 1899), pp. 99, 103, 106; M. J. Daunton, *House and Home in the Victorian City* (London: Edward Arnold, 1983), pp. 7–8, 12–13, 24–31, 37; Raymond Unwin, *Town Planning in Practice* (London: T. Fisher Unwin, 1909), p. 393.

77.   For example, William Morris in *News from Nowhere* (1891) described a future England in which great cities were abolished, suburbs were "melted away," and the population decentralized into small towns and villages "scattered up and down the country, all trim and neat and pretty."

78.   Ebenezer Howard, *To-Morrow: A Peaceful Path to Real Reform* (London: Swan Sonnenschein, 1898), pp. 2–20.

79.   Miller, *Raymond Unwin*, pp. 8, 35–36, 40–42; Joseph Rowntree Village Trust, *One Man's Vision: The Story of the Joseph Rowntree Village Trust* (London: George Allen and Unwin, 1954), pp. 3, 14–17.

80.   First Garden City Ltd., *Letchworth Garden City: General Remarks* (Letchworth, UK: First Garden City, 1909), pp. 4, 5, 21; "Diagram to Scale Showing Area and Relative Size . . . ," *Garden Cities and Town Planning*, new series, vol. 1, no. 1 (February 1911), p. 12.

81.   Miller, *Raymond Unwin*, p. 72; Aileen Reid, *Brentham: A History of the Pioneer Garden Suburb, 1901-2001* (Brentham Heritage Society, 2000), p. 151; United Kingdom, Parliament, "The Birth of Town Planning," 21 April 2010, http://www.parliament.uk/about/living-heritage/transformingsociety/towncountry/towns/overview/townplanning/.

82.   Adams and Unwin were founders of the Town Planning Institute, the UK's first professional association of practicing town planners. Adams served as its first president in 1914, and Unwin as its second in 1915. Adams led the Regional Plan of New York and Its Environs during the 1920s, an effort that had important ramifications for traffic-separation ideas.

83.   Miller, *Raymond Unwin*, p. 46.

84.   Miller, *Raymond Unwin*, p. 85.

85.   UK Parliament, "The Birth of Town Planning"; E. G. Bentley and S. Pointer Taylor, *Practical Guide in the Preparation of Town Planning Schemes* (London: George Philip and Son, 1911), p. 143.

86.   Miller, *Raymond Unwin*, pp. 83, 84.

87.   Miller, *Raymond Unwin*, pp. 47–48; Raymond Unwin, *Town Planning in Practice*, pp. 353–357, 381, 393.

88.   Letter to Henrietta Barnett, 3 June 1911, in Henrietta Barnett, *Canon Barnett – His Life, Work and Friends*, vol. 2 (London: John Murray, 1918), p. 322; Raymond Unwin, "The Town Extension Plan," lecture no. 14, given at Victoria University of Manchester, 29 January 1912 (Manchester: Sherratt & Hughes, 1912).

89.   Raymond Unwin, "Roads and Streets," *The Town Planning Review*, vol. 5, no. 1 (April 1914), p. 33.

90.   Catherine Bauer, *Modern Housing* (Boston: Houghton Mifflin, 1934), pp. 176–178, 261–266; Peter Hall, *Cities of Tomorrow*, 4th ed. (Chichester, UK: Wiley Blackwell, 2014), pp. 70–78; Miller, *Raymond Unwin*, pp. 142, 181–182.

91.   Miller, *Raymond Unwin*, pp. 206, 209, 247.

92.   Carl Feiss, "Unwin's American Journeys," *Town and Country Planning*, vol. 31, no. 11 (November 1963), p. 424 and no. 12 (December 1963), pp. 471–473; Miller, *Raymond Unwin*, pp. 233–237; Raymond Unwin, *Housing and Town Planning: 1936-Lectures-1937* (Washington, DC: Central Housing Committee, 1937), pp. 1, 64, 74.

93.   The financial performance of Forest Hills Gardens was a disappointment. The Sage Foundation sold its interest in the property for $1.9 million in 1922, losing $361,000 on its total investment. Susan L. Klaus, *A Modern Arcadia* (Amherst, MA: University of Massachusetts Press, 2002), pp. 145, 148.

94.   Klaus, *A Modern Arcadia*, pp. 61–62.

95.   Klaus, *A Modern Arcadia*, pp. 70–72.

96.   Frederick Law Olmsted Jr., "The Scope and Results of City Planning in Europe," in *Proceedings of the First National Conference on City Planning* (1910; reprint, Chicago: American Society of Planning Officials, 1967), pp. 64–65, 66.

97.   Klaus, *A Modern Arcadia*, p. 123.

98.   Charles C. May, "Forest Hills Gardens from the Town Planning Standpoint," *Architecture*, vol. 34, no. 2 (August 1916), p. 169.

99.   Daniel H. Burnham and Edward H. Bennett, *Plan of Chicago* (Chicago: Commercial Club, 1909), pp. 82, 84, 88.

100.   Burnham and Bennett, *Plan of Chicago*, pp. 88, 134.

101.   Leslie Coburn, "Considering the People on the Back Streets: Urban Planning at the City Club of Chicago," in David van Zanten et al., *Drawing the Future: Chicago Architecture on the International Stage, 1900-1925* (Evanston, IL: Northwestern University Press, 2013), pp. 84–87; Donald Leslie Johnson, "Origin of the Neighbourhood Unit," *Planning Perspectives*, vol. 17, no. 3 (2002), p. 229; Maureen A. Flanagan, "Gender and Urban Political Reform: The City Club and the Woman's City Club of Chicago in

the Progressive Era," *American Historical Review*, vol. 95, no. 4 (October 1990), pp. 1032–1050.

102. *Proceedings of the Fifth National Conference on City Planning* (Boston: National Conference on City Planning, 1913), p. 189; Johnson, "Origin of the Neighbourhood Unit," p. 231; Raymond Unwin, "Garden Cities in England," *City Club Bulletin*, vol. 4, no. 13 (7 June 1911), pp. 134, 138–139.

103. Alfred B. Yeomans, ed., *City Residential Land Development* (Chicago: University of Chicago Press, 1916), pp. 1, 4–5.

104. Yeomans, *City Residential Land Development*, pp. 2–3.

105. Yeomans, *City Residential Land Development*, pp. 56–60, 66–69, 81–82, 87–89, 93–94.

106. Yeomans, *City Residential Land Development*, pp. 37–44. Competition participants who were associated with the prairie style included Bernhard, Cone, Drummond, Griffin, Lawrence, Tirrell, and Wright.

107. *Fifth National Conference on City Planning*, p. 189; Coburn, "Considering the People on the Back Streets," p. 94; James Dahir, *The Neighborhood Unit Plan: Its Spread and Acceptance* (New York: Russell Sage Foundation, 1947), p. 20.

Chapter 5. Horizontal Traffic Separation: Insular Roadways 1910s–1930s

1. Carmen Hass-Klau, *The Pedestrian and City Traffic* (London: Belhaven, 1990), pp. 66–71; Dirk Schubert, "Theodor Fritsch and the German (völkische) Version of the Garden City," *Planning Perspectives*, vol. 19, no. 1 (January 2004), pp. 25–27.

2. David H. Haney, *When Modern Was Green: Life and Work of Architect Leberecht Migge* (London: Routledge, 2010), pp. 30, 80, 84, 146; Katharina Borsi, "Drawing the Region: Hermann Jansen's Vision of Greater Berlin in 1910," *Journal of Architecture*, vol. 20, no. 1 (2015), p. 52. Ludwig Mies van der Rohe (then Ludwig Mies) took a DGG tour of Britain in 1909; see Haney, p. 102

3. Barry A. Jackisch, "The Nature of Berlin: Green Space and Visions of a New German Capital, 1900–45," *Central European History*, vol. 47, no. 2 (June 2014), p. 312; Martin Wagner, "Das sanitäre Grün der Städte" (PhD. diss., Royal Technical College of Berlin, 1915), frontispiece, figure 8.

4. Iain Boyd White and David Frisby, eds., *Metropolis Berlin: 1880–1940* (Berkeley: University of California Press, 2012), pp. 267–268.

5. David Frisby, *Cityscapes of Modernity* (Cambridge, UK: Polity, 2001), p. 271; "Ein Denkmal, das Baugeschichte(n) schreibt," *Mitglieder-Echo*, publication of GeWoSüd Housing Cooperative, no. 2 (2014), pp. 8–11, http://www.gewosued.net.

6. Hass-Klau, *The Pedestrian and City Traffic*, pp. 77–82.

7. Wolfgang Pehnt, "The New Man and the Old Adam: On the Image of Man and the New Building," in Claudia Quiring et al., eds., *Ernst May 1886–1970* (Munich: Prestel, 2011), pp. 99–105.

8. Peter Blundell Jones, *Hugo Häring: The Organic Versus the Geometric* (Stuttgart: Edition Axel Menges, 1999), pp. 99–101.

9. White and Frisby, *Metropolis Berlin*, pp. 463–467; Mumford, *CIAM Discourse on Urbanism*, p. 29; Auke van der Woud, *Het Nieuwe Bouwen Internationaal/International* (Delft: Delft University Press, 1983), p. 20.

10. Eckhard Herrel, "'Constant Maturing': Student Years, House-Building in Frankfurt and War Memorials on the Front," in Quiring et al., *Ernst May 1886–1970*, pp. 15–18.

11. Herrel, "'Constant Maturing,'" pp. 19, 29; Walter L. Creese, *The Search for Environment* (New Haven, CT: Yale University Press, 1966), p. 316.

12. Claudia Quiring, "From 'Carp Pond' to 'Getting Accustomed to Caviar,'" in Quiring et al., *Ernst May 1886–1970*, pp. 135, 142.

13. Herrel, "'Constant Maturing,'" pp. 22–28; Beate Störtkuhl, "Ernst May and the Schlesische Heimstatte," in Quiring et al., *Ernst May 1886–1970*, pp. 33–36, 46.

14. John Robert Mullin, "City Planning in Frankfurt, Germany 1925–1932," *Journal of Planning History*, vol. 4, no. 1 (November 1977), pp. 7–10; Wolfgang Voigt, "Strategist for the New City: Ernst May on Three Continents," and Claudia Quiring et al., "Catalogue Raisonné," in Quiring et al., *Ernst May 1886–1970*, pp. 220, 270–271.

15. Susan R. Henderson, *Building Culture: Ernst May and the Frankfurt Initiative, 1926–1931* (Bern: Peter Lang, 2013), pp. 398–404.

16. Quiring, "From 'Carp Pond,'" and Wolfgang Voigt, "Strategist for the New City," and Quiring et al., "Catalogue Raisonné," in Quiring et al., *Ernst May 1886–1970*, pp. 134–139, 231, 262–275.

17. Frisby, *Cityscapes of Modernity*, pp. 272–273.

18. Thomas Flierl, "'Possibly the Greatest Task an Architect Ever Faced': Ernst May in the Soviet Union (1930–1933)," in Quiring et al., *Ernst May 1886–1970*, pp. 152, 157–158, 162.

19. Selim Khan-Magomedov, *Arkhitektura sovetskogo avangarda (Architecture of the Soviet avant garde)*, vol. 2 (Moscow: Stroĭizdat, 2001), chapter 2.42.

20. Flierl, "'Possibly the Greatest Task,'" pp. 167–168; El Lissitzky, *Russia: An Architecture for World Revolution*, trans. Eric Dluhosch (Cambridge, MA: MIT Press, 1970), pp. 199, 204.

21. Flierl, "'Possibly the Greatest Task,'" pp. 176–177, 187–188, 190.

22. Flierl, "'Possibly the Greatest Task,'" pp. 158, 162, 170–175, 194.

23. Florian Seidel, "'Making the Best of a Situation,'" and Voigt, "Stategist for the New City," and Quiring et al., "Catalogue Raisonné," in Quiring et al., *Ernst May 1886–1970*, pp. 215–227, 238–239, 295–313.

24. Richard Pommer, "More a Necropolis than a Metropolis," in Richard Pommer et al., *In The Shadow of Mies: Ludwig Hilberseimer; Architect, Educator and Urban Planner* (Chicago: Art Institute of Chicago, 1988), pp. 21–29.

25. Pommer, "More a Necropolis than a Metropolis," pp. 39–41; Ludwig Hilberseimer, *Metropolisarchitecture and Selected Essays*, Richard Anderson, ed. (New York: GSAPP Books, 2012), pp. 43–44.

26. Pommer, "More a Necropolis than a Metropolis," pp. 43–45. According to the Art Institute of Chicago, an undated, unpublished sketch by Hilberseimer titled "The Metropolis as a Garden City" (AIC object no. 184866) was made circa 1927. The sketch showed a partially dendritic precursor of the settlement unit and indicated its role as a repeating module. But in his other work through the early 1930s, Hilberseimer used connected gridirons of large blocks and superblocks. His semi-autobiographical review suggested that he did not begin to develop the settlement-unit idea until 1931. See David Spaeth, "Ludwig Hilberseimer's Settlement Unit," in Pommer et al., *In the Shadow of Mies*, pp. 59–60 and Ludwig Hilberseimer, *Entfaltung einer Planungsidee* (Berlin: Ullstein, 1963), pp. 24–48, 137.

27. Ludwig Hilberseimer, *The New City: Principles of Planning* (Chicago: Paul Theobald, 1944), pp. 104–111, 125–126; Ludwig Hilberseimer, *The Nature of Cities* (Chicago: Paul Theobald, 1955), p. 193.

28. Hilberseimer, *Entfaltung einer Planungsidee*, pp. 48–49; Ludwig Hilberseimer, "The Elements of City Planning," *Armour Engineer and Alumnus*, vol. 6, no. 2 (December 1940), p. 13.

29. Hans M. Wingler, *The Bauhaus: Weimar, Dessau, Berlin, Chicago*, 2nd printing, trans. Wolfgang Jabs and Basil Gilbert (Cambridge, MA: MIT Press, 1976), pp. 10–11, 187–189, 562–565; Pommer, "More a Necropolis than a Metropolis," pp. 45, 53.

30. Alfred Swenson and Pao-Chi Chang, *Architectural Education at IIT 1938–1978* (Chicago: Illinois Institute of Technology, 1980), p. 15.

31. Hilberseimer, *The New City*, pp. 104, 109, 111, 124–125; Hilberseimer, *The Nature of Cities*, pp. 242–256; Hilberseimer, *Entfaltung einer Planungsidee*, p. 96; Pommer, "More a Necropolis than a Metropolis," pp. 35, 43, 52; Kevin Harrington, "Ideas in Action: Hilberseimer and the Redevelopment of the South Side of Chicago," in Pommer et al., *In The Shadow of Mies*, pp. 85–88.

32. Hilberseimer, *The New City*, pp. 133–162; Hilberseimer, *The Nature of Cities*, pp. 254–256.

33. Hilberseimer, *The New City*, p. 113; Spaeth, "Ludwig Hilberseimer's Settlement Unit," pp. 71–72; Harrington, "Ideas in Action," pp. 72, 85.

34. Ludwig Hilberseimer, "The Automobile and the City," *AIA Journal*, vol. 34, no. 6 (December 1960), pp. 30–31; Hilberseimer, *The New City*, pp. 48–54, 100, 113–115; Hilberseimer, *The Nature of Cities*, pp. 110–112, 192–193, 280–284.

35. Hilberseimer, *The New City*, pp. 68–71, 105, 107.

36. George E. Danforth, "Hilberseimer Remembered" and Harrington, "Ideas in Action," in Pommer et al., *In The Shadow of Mies*, pp. 10–14, 73; Swenson and Chang, *Architectural Education at IIT*, pp. 16, 102.

37. Christopher Alexander, "A City Is Not a Tree," *Architectural Forum*, vol. 122, no. 1 (April 1965), p. 62; Pommer, "More a Necropolis than a Metropolis," pp. 43, 45; Spaeth, "Ludwig Hilberseimer's Settlement Unit," pp. 64–65; Michael Southworth and Peter M. Owens, "The Evolving Metropolis: Studies of Community, Neighborhood, and Street Form at the Urban Edge," *Journal of the American Planning Association*, vol. 59, no. 3 (Summer 1993), pp. 280–281; Christopher Barrington-Leigh and Adam Millard-Ball, "A Century of Sprawl in the United States," *PNAS*, vol. 112, no. 27 (7 July 2015), pp. 8244–8246.

38. Álvaro Sevilla-Buitragom, "Martin Wagner in America: Planning and the Political Economy of Capitalist Urbanization," *Planning Perspectives*, vol. 32, no. 4 (2017), p. 485.

39.   "Lineal Cities Declared Need of the Future," *Christian Science Monitor*, 5 April 1940, section 2, p. 13. An accompanying diagram labeled the townships as neighborhood units.

40.   Walter Gropius and Martin Wagner, "A Program for City Reconstruction," *Architectural Forum*, vol. 79, no. 1 (July 1943), pp. 75–86.

41.   "The Town of Willow Run," *Architectural Forum*, vol. 78, no. 3 (March 1943), pp. 37–54; "Planned Neighborhoods for 194X," *Architectural Forum*, vol. 79, no. 4 (October 1943), pp. 79–87, 91–99, 111–122; Andrew M. Shanken, *194X: Architecture, Planning, and Consumer Culture on the American Home Front* (Minneapolis, MN: University of Minnesota Press, 2009), pp. 29–39, 59–69, 123–127.

42.   Sevilla-Buitragom, "Martin Wagner in America," pp. 490, 492.

43.   Frank Rowsome Jr., "Are Big Cities Ugly Monsters?" *Popular Science*, vol. 144, no. 6 (June 1944), pp. 103–106; Sevilla-Buitragom, "Martin Wagner in America," pp. 495–496.

44.   Jeffry Diefendorf, "Skyscrapers and Healthy Cities: Walter Gropius and Martin Wagner between Germany and America," *German Historical Institute Bulletin*, supplement 2 (2005), pp. 40–41; Sevilla-Buitragom, "Martin Wagner in America," p. 483.

45.   Sevilla-Buitragom, "Martin Wagner in America," p. 498.

46.   "Alumni Notes," *Record of Sigma Alpha Epsilon*, vol. 22, no. 2 (May 1902), p. 180; *Sixth General Catalogue of Sigma Alpha Epsilon* (Evanston, IL: Sigma Alpha Epsilon, 1904), p. 248; "Cornell Alumni Notes," *Cornell Alumni News*, vol. 8, no. 14 (11 January 1905), p. 230; "Cornell Alumni Notes," *Cornell Alumni News*, vol. 11, no. 16 (20 January 1909), p. 189; "Clarence A. Perry, Recreation Expert" *New York Times*, 7 September 1944, p. 23.

47.   John M. Glenn, Lilian Brandt, and F. Emerson Andrews, *Russell Sage Foundation, 1907-1946*, vol. 1 (New York: Russell Sage Foundation, 1947), pp. 72, 79, 82–83, 220.

48.   Clarence Arthur Perry, "Ten Years of the Community Center Movement" (New York: Russell Sage Foundation, [1921]), p. 4.

49.   Clarence Arthur Perry, *Wider Use of the School Plant* (New York: Russell Sage Foundation, 1910), pp. 365–371, 391.

50.   Glenn et al., *Russell Sage Foundation, 1907-1946*, vol. 1, pp. 77, 322–323; Clarence Arthur Perry, "A Measure of the Manner of Living," *Publications of the American Statistical Association*, vol. 13, no. 101 (March 1913), pp. 398–403; Clarence Arthur Perry, ed., *Contributions to Community Center Progress* (New York: Russell Sage Foundation, 1920), p. 3.

51.   Glenn et al., *Russell Sage Foundation, 1907-1946*, vol. 1, p. 250.

52.   Clarence Arthur Perry, *Housing for the Machine Age* (New York: Russell Sage Foundation, 1939), pp. 208–209, 214; Robert Whitten, *A Research Into the Economics of Land Subdivision* (Syracuse, NY: Syracuse University, 1927), p. xi.

53.   Donald Leslie Johnson, "Origin of the Neighbourhood Unit," *Planning Perspectives*, vol. 17, no. 3 (2002), pp. 227–245; Clarence Arthur Perry, "The Neighborhood Unit," in *Regional Survey of New York and Its Environs*, vol. 7, *Neighborhood and Community Planning* (New York: Regional Plan of New York and Its Environs, 1929), pp. 25, 50–52, 83.

54.   Perry, "The Neighborhood Unit," pp. 51–52, 84, 87.

55.   Perry, "The Neighborhood Unit," pp. 42–44, 109–110; Clarence Arthur Perry, *The Rebuilding of Blighted Areas* (New York: Regional Plan Association, 1933).

56.   Perry, "The Neighborhood Unit," pp. 30–31.

57.   Perry, "The Neighborhood Unit," p. 85.

58.   Perry, *Housing for the Machine Age*, pp. 209–213.

59.   Perry, "The Neighborhood Unit," p. 98.

60.   James Dahir, *The Neighborhood Unit Plan: Its Spread and Acceptance* (New York: Russell Sage Foundation, 1947); Tridib Banerjee and William C. Baer, *Beyond the Neighborhood Unit: Residential Environments and Public Policy* (New York: Plenum Press, 1984), p. 24; Jason Brody, "Constructing Professional Knowledge: the Neighborhood Unit Concept in the Community Builders Handbook" (PhD diss., University of Illinois at Urbana-Champaign, 2009), pp. 7, 59.

61.   US Shipping Board, Emergency Fleet Corporation, *Housing the Shipbuilders* (Philadelphia, PA: US Shipping Board, 1920), p. 1; US Department of Labor, *Report of the United States Housing Corporation*, vol. 2 (Washington, DC: USGPO, 1919), pp. 77–78.

62.   *Proceedings of the Seventh National Conference on City Planning* (Boston: National Conference on City Planning, 1915), pp. 242–244; Clarence Stein, "Henry Wright, 1878-1936," *American Architect and Architecture*, vol. 149 (August 1936), pp. 23–24.

63.   Lewis Mumford, introduction to Clarence S. Stein, *Toward New Towns for America*, 3rd ed. (Cambridge, MA: MIT Press, 1966), p. 12.

64.   Henry Wright, "Shall We Community Plan?" *Journal of the American Institute of Architects*, vol. 9, no. 10 (October 1921), pp. 320–324. Clarence Stein was an associate editor of *JAIA*. The October 1921 issue read like a manifesto for the future RPAA; it included Benton MacKaye's Appalachian Trail proposal and a proposal for agricultural "wedges" adjacent to garden cities.

65.   Edward K. Spann, *Designing Modern America: The Regional Planning Association of America and Its Members* (Columbus, OH: Ohio University Press, 1996), pp. 139–144; Clarence Stein, letter to Benton MacKaye, 12 October 1967, in Kermit Carlyle Parsons, ed., *The Writings of Clarence Stein: Architect of the Planned Community* (Baltimore, MD: Johns Hopkins University Press, 1998), p. 642.

66.   Stuart Chase, interview by Carl Sussman, 17 June 1975, quoted in Carl Sussman, ed., *Planning the Fourth Migration: The Neglected Vision of the Regional Planning Association of America* (Cambridge, MA: MIT Press, 1976), pp. 22–23.

67.   Sussman, *Planning the Fourth Migration*, p. 38; Spann, *Designing Modern America*, pp. 105, 116; Henry Wright, "The Autobiography of Another Idea," *Western Architect*, vol. 39, no. 9 (September 1930), p. 139.

68.   Clarence Stein, "The Influence of Letchworth in America," 22 June 1953, in Parsons, *Writings of Clarence Stein*, pp. 551–552; Stein, *Toward New Towns for America*, p. 19; Mervyn Miller, "The Origins of the Garden City Residential Neighborhood," in Kermit C. Parsons and David Schuyler, eds., *From Garden City to Green City: The Legacy of Ebenezer Howard* (Baltimore, MD: Johns Hopkins University Press, 2002), p. 125.

69.   Spann, *Designing Modern America*, pp. 111, 115.

70.   Roy Lubove, *Community Planning in the 1920s: The Contribution of the Regional Planning Association of America* (Pittsburgh, PA: University of Pittsburgh Press, 1963), pp. 40, 63–66; Stein, *Toward New Towns for America*, pp. 37–39.

71.   Wright, "Autobiography of Another Idea," pp. 140–141, plate 130.

72.   Carl Feiss, "Unwin's American Journeys," *Town and Country Planning*, vol. 31, no. 11 (November 1963), p. 424; Mervyn Miller, *Raymond Unwin: Garden Cities and Town Planning* (Leicester, UK: Leicester University Press, 1992), p. 226.

73.   Major streets: In 1929, after Radburn's street layout had been determined, the architect Fritz Malcher applied his "steadyflow" method of geometric traffic separation to Radburn's streets. Malcher also classified every street using a nine-part classification based on road width, medians, and one- or two-way operation. Ultimately the method was applied to only one segment of Plaza Road. See Fritz Malcher, "The Economic Value of Laying Out Roadways for Steadyflow Traffic," in American Society of Municipal Engineers, *Proceedings of the Thirty-Sixth Annual Convention* (St. Louis, MO: American Society of Municipal Engineers, 1931), pp. 42–45. Limited-access parkway: The Saddle River Parkway was proposed by RPNY in 1925 as a project of "urgent importance." It appeared in RPNY's recommendations for several years but was never built.

74.   Lewis Mumford, "Wright, Henry," in Robert Livingston Schuyler and Edward T. James, eds., *Dictionary of American Biography*, vol. 11, supplement 2 (New York: Charles Scribner's Sons, 1958), p. 738; Stein, *Toward New Towns for America*, pp. 41–47.

75.   Stein, *Toward New Towns for America*, pp. 48–49; Daniel Schaffer, *Garden Cities for America: The Radburn Experience* (Philadelphia: Temple University Press, 1982), pp. 4, 175, 193; "Bridge Will Benefit Town of Radburn," *New York Times*, 25 October 1931, p. RE6; "New Road Aids Radburn," *New York Times*, 22 November 1931, p. 34.

76.   RPAA members: Examples included Robert Kohn, director of housing for the Public Works Administration; Herbert Emmerich, head of the Federal Public Housing Authority; Frederick Bigger, chief of planning for the greenbelt-town program; J. Henry Klaber, director of rental-housing architecture at the Federal Housing Administration; and Tracy Augur, principal planner of the Tennessee Valley Authority.

77.   Eugenie L. Birch, "Radburn and the American Planning Movement," *Journal of the American Planning Association*, vol. 46, no. 4 (October 1980), pp. 424–431; Stein, *Toward New Towns for America*, p. 72; Kermit C. Parsons, "British and American Community Design," in Parsons and Schuyler, *From Garden City to Green City*, pp. 135–138, 148, 152–157.

78.   Parsons, *Writings of Clarence Stein*, p. xxxii.

79.   Marc A. Weiss, *The Rise of the Community Builders: The American Real Estate Industry and Urban Land Planning* (New York: Columbia University Press, 1987), pp. 1–12, 67, 141–144.

80.   Natasha Porfirenko, "Register of the President's Conference on Home Building and Home Ownership Records," Hoover Institution Archives, 1998, accessed from Online Archive of California, http://oac.cdlib.org/findaid/ark:/13030/tf1w1001jf.

81.   John M. Gries and James Ford, eds., *The President's Conference on Home Building and Home Ownership*, vol. 1, *Planning for Residential Districts* (Washington, DC: National Capital Press, 1932), pp. iii, vii–viii; Henry Wright, *Rehousing Urban America* (New York: Columbia University Press, 1935), p. xi; Weiss, *Rise of the Community Builders*, p. 143. Most committee participants were members of, or consultants to, the National Association of Real Estate Boards. NAREB established the forerunner of the Urban Land Institute in 1936 and spun off the National Association of Homebuilders in 1942. NAREB was renamed the National Association of Realtors in 1974.

82.   "Notes on Convention of National Association Of Real Estate Boards, Boston, June, 1929," *City Planning*, vol. 5, no. 4 (October 1929), p. 262.

83.   Henry Wright, "The Place of the Apartment in the Modern Community," *Architectural Record*, vol. 67, no. 3 (March 1930), pp. 229–238.

84.   Robert Whitten and Thomas Adams, *Neighborhoods of Small Homes* (Cambridge, MA: Harvard University Press, 1931), pp. 47–80.

85.   Gries and Ford, *Planning for Residential Districts*, pp. 85–124.

86.   Gries and Ford, *Planning for Residential Districts*, pp. 55, 74–75.

87.   Gries and Ford, *Planning for Residential Districts*, pp. xiv, 6–11, 42, 66.

88.   John M. Gries and James Ford, eds., *The President's Conference on Home Building and Home Ownership*, vol. 5, *House Design, Construction and Equipment* (Washington, DC: National Capital Press, 1932), pp. 8–11, 22; John M. Gries and James Ford, eds., *The President's Conference on Home Building and Home Ownership*, vol. 11, *Housing Objectives and Programs* (Washington, DC: National Capital Press, 1932), pp. 102, 109–110, 114, 157, 159, 160, 182, 183. The sections in Volume 5 about neighborhood planning, mortgage financing, and "sound design" were likely written by Henry Wright. He was the Committee on Design's research secretary, and an editor of the volume, and those sections reflected his planning interests.

89.   US Federal Emergency Administration of Public Works, *The Purposes, Policies, Functioning and Organization of the Emergency Administration*, circular no. 1 (Washington, DC: USGPO, 1933), p. 18; Richard Pommer, "The Architecture of Urban Housing in the United States during the Early 1930s," *Journal of the Society of Architectural Historians*, vol. 37, no. 4 (December 1978), p. 236.

90.   Pommer, "The Architecture of Urban Housing," pp. 236, 262.

91.   Bernard J. Newman, "Typical Projects Proposed by Philadelphians for Limited Dividend Housing under the Public Works Administration," *Housing in Philadelphia*, 1933 ed. (Philadelphia, PA: Philadelphia Housing Association, 1934), pp. 20–21.

92.   Walter H. Blucher, "Planning a Housing Project," *City Planning*, vol. 10, no. 3 (July 1934), pp. 112–125.

93.   US Federal Emergency Administration of Public Works, *Urban Housing; the Story of the P.W.A. Housing Division, 1933-1936* (Washington, DC: USGPO, 1936), pp. 30–34, 45, 90–91; Pommer, "The Architecture of Urban Housing," p. 236.

94.   Albert Mayer et al., "Realistic Replanning," *Architectural Forum*, vol. 61, no. 1 (July 1934), pp. 49–55; Albert Mayer, "Garden Cities within a City: a Large Scheme of Rehousing," *New York Times*, 6 May 1934, p. XX3.

95.   Gaia Caramellino, *Europe Meets America: William Lescaze, Architect of Modern Housing*, trans. Marella Feltrin-Morris (Newcastle-upon-Tyne, UK: Cambridge Scholars, 2016), pp. 116-129; Pommer, "The Architecture of Urban Housing," p. 256.

96.   Weiss, *Rise of the Community Builders*, pp. 146–147; US Federal Housing Administration, *The FHA Story in Summary 1934–1959* (Washington DC: USGPO, 1959), p. 4.

97.   Federal Housing Administration, *FHA Story*, pp. 7–12. Canaday became chairman of Willys-Overland in 1936 and was later known as "the father of the Jeep."

98.   FHA publications that presented the agency's subdivision design principles included: "Subdivision Development," circular no. 5, 1935; "Planning Neighborhoods for Small Houses," technical bulletin no. 5, 1936; "Subdivision Standards," circular no. 5, 1937; "Planning Profitable Neighborhoods," technical bulletin no. 7, 1938; "Successful Subdivisions," land planning bulletin no. 1, 1940. Did not own a car: US Department of Labor, Bureau of Labor Statistics, *100 Years of U.S. Consumer Spending*, report 991 (Washington, DC: US Department of Labor, 2006), p. 16.

99.   Weiss, *Rise of the Community Builders*, pp. 152–153.

100. Seward H. Mott, "The Benefits of Controlled Neighborhood Planning," *Architectural Record*, vol. 88, no. 5 (November 1940), pp. 36–37; US Department of the Interior, National Park Service, *Historic Residential Suburbs*, National Register bulletin, by David L. Ames and Linda Flint McClelland, September 2002, p. 51; Leo Grebler, *The Role of Federal Credit Aids in Residential Construction* (New York: National Bureau of Economic Research, 1953), p. 17.

101. Homer Hoyt, "The Housing Market in the United States since World War II," *Real Estate Issues*, vol. 8, no. 1 (Spring/Summer 1983), p. 2; US Department of Housing and Urban Development, *HUD 3rd Annual Report* (Washington, DC: USGPO, 1968), pp. 7–13; US Department of Housing and Urban Development, *Annual Report 1968* (Washington DC: USGPO, 1969), pp. 17, 21–22; Walter Kulash, *Residential Streets*, 3rd ed. (Washington, DC: Urban Land Institute, 2001), p. 4; US Department of Housing and Urban Development, *HUD at 50: Creating Pathways to Opportunity*, October 2015, pp. 15–16, 32–33; US Department of Housing and Urban Development, Federal Housing Administration, "Planned-Unit Development with a Homes Association," land planning bulletin no. 6, 1973, pp. 38–41.

102. James W. Loewen, *Sundown Towns: A Hidden Dimension of American Racism* (New York: Touchstone, 2005), pp. 79–80, 109–114, 137–138; Andrew Wiese, *Places of Their Own: African American Suburbanization in the Twentieth Century* (Chicago: University of Chicago Press, 2004), pp. 5, 15, 94–104.

103. Loewen, *Sundown Towns*, pp. 112–113; W. E. B. Du Bois, *Dusk of Dawn: An Essay Toward an Autobiography of a Race Concept* (New York: Harcourt, Brace, 1940), pp. 185–186; letter from Sage Foundation Homes Company to W. E. B. Du Bois, 2 November 1912, W. E. B. Du Bois Papers, University of Massachusetts Amherst, http://credo.library.umass.edu/view/full/mums312-b007-i136; Herbert Aptheker, ed., *The Correspondence of W. E. B. Du Bois*, vol. 1, *Selections, 1877–1934* (Amherst, MA: University of Massachusetts Press, 1973), pp. 401–402.

104. Loewen, *Sundown Towns*, pp. 129–133, 198–213, 254–255, 316–317, 387–390; Wiese, *Places of Their Own*, pp. 101, 129, 138–140; Clarence Arthur Perry, "Local Community as a Unit in the Planning of Urban Residential Areas," in Ernest W. Burgess, ed., *The Urban Community* (Chicago: University of Chicago Press, 1926), pp. 238–241.

Chapter 6. Horizontal Traffic Separation: Fast Roadways

1. An average trot was about 8 mph (13 kmh), a hard trot about 12 mph (19 kmh), and top racers could trot as fast as 24 mph (38 kmh). By the 1880s, bicycles could rival most trotting horses and could travel faster than horse-drawn vehicles. Speed limits between 6 and 12 mph (10–19 kmh) were commonly instituted for cycles. Cable cars typically ran at 8–10 mph (13–16 kmh), but were capable of 15–20 mph (24–32 kmh). Electric streetcars typically ran at similar or slightly higher speeds, even though they were capable of 35–40 mph (56–64 kmh). Typical automobiles of the 1890s and early 1900s could manage 25 mph (40 kmh) under ideal conditions, but often operated under city speed limits of 6–12 mph (10–19 kmh).

2. Melvin L. Adelman, "The First Modern Sport in America: Harness Racing in New York City," *Journal of Sport History*, vol. 8, no. 1 (Spring 1981), pp. 5–32.

3. Olmsted and Vaux, "Report of the Landscape Architects," 24 January 1866, in Board of Commissioners of Prospect Park, *Sixth Annual Report of the Board of Commissioners of Prospect Park, Brooklyn* (Brooklyn, NY: 1866), p. 37; Charles E. Beveridge and Carolyn F. Hoffman, eds., *Writings on Public Parks, Parkways, and Park Systems*, Papers of Frederick Law Olmsted, supplementary series, vol. 1 (Baltimore, MD: Johns Hopkins University Press, 1997), pp. 16, 142, 190–191; Elizabeth Macdonald, "Enduring Complexity: A History of Brooklyn's Parkways" (PhD diss., University of California, Berkeley, 1999), pp. 115–116.

4. Driving enthusiast: Elizabeth Macdonald, *Pleasure Drives and Promenades: A History of Frederick Law Olmsted's Brooklyn Parkways* (Chicago: Columbia College Chicago Press, 2012), p. 38; taste for driving: Brooklyn Park Commission, *Fourteenth Annual Report of the Brooklyn Park Commissioners* (Brooklyn, NY: 1874), p. 13; trolley crossing: Macdonald, "Enduring Complexity," pp. 240–242. Stranahan had hired Olmsted and Vaux to design Prospect Park, and he was the park commissioner who championed the parkway plan and saw it through to completion.

5. Grand Boulevard: "Local Miscellany: On the Boulevard," *Chicago Daily Tribune*, 7 June 1874, p. 13; City of Chicago, *Chicago Park Boulevard System Historic District*, draft National Register nomination, 2011, p. 98, http://www.cityofchicago.org; Delaware Avenue: Willard Glazier, *Peculiarities of American Cities* (Philadelphia, PA: Hubbard Brothers, 1886), p. 64; Beacon Avenue: John W. Linnehan and Edwards E. Cogswell, eds., *The Driving Clubs of Greater Boston* (Boston, MA: Atlantic Printing, 1914), pp. 34, 139;

Commonwealth Avenue: Clay McShane and Joel A. Tarr, *The Horse in the City: Living Machines in the Nineteenth Century* (Baltimore, MD: John Hopkins University Press, 2007), p. 93.

6.   McShane and Tarr, *Horse in the City*, pp. 94–95; Charles Chapin Sargent Jr., "A Horseman's Paradise," *Munsey's Magazine*, vol. 20, no. 2 (November 1898), p. 197.

7.   "Blackest magnitude": Peter B. Sweeny, quoted in "Gotham's Greater Rotten Row," *New York Herald*, 3 August 1890; "educator": Peter B. Sweeny, quoted in "New York's Rising Sun," *Evening Telegram*, 26 May 1890.

8.   Russell Sage, quoted in "New York Must Have that Hudson Driveway," *New York Herald*, 6 August 1890.

9.   McShane and Tarr, *Horse in the City*, p. 95; Clay McShane, *Down the Asphalt Path: The Automobile and the American City* (New York: Columbia University Press, 1995), p. 39.

10.   The law required: Edwin A. Bedell, "Matter of . . . City of New York," *Reports of Cases Decided in the Court of Appeals of the State of New York*, vol. 168 (Albany, NY: J. B. Lyon, 1902), p. 138; "The Harlem River Speedway, New York City," *Scientific American*, vol. 76, no. 6 (6 February 1897), p. 90; "Speedway Bill Passed in the Senate," *New York Times*, 31 March 1900, p. 6.

11.   Louis A. Risse, "History in Brief of the Conception and Establishment of the Grand Boulevard & Concourse in the 23rd and 24th Wards" (1897), and Louis A. Risse, "The True History of the Conception and Planning of the Grand Boulevard & Concourse in the Bronx" (1902), in Antonio Sergio Bessa, ed., *Intersections: The Grand Concourse at 100* (New York: Fordham University Press, 2009), pp. 25, 35, 39, 42; Louis A. Risse, "Public Works," in North Side Board of Trade, *The Great North Side or Borough of the Bronx* (New York: North Side Board of Trade, 1897), p. 187.

12.   Ray Bromley, "Bold Vision: Louis Risse's Grand Plan for the Concourse," and "Chronology," in Bessa, *Intersections*, pp. 59, 63–64, 143–146.

13.   McShane and Tarr, *Horse in the City*, p. 94; Macdonald, "Enduring Complexity," pp. 130–135.

14.   "Bayonne Speedway Opened," *New York Times*, 18 June 1900, p. 8; "Bayonne Fights Railroad," *New York Times*, 1 March 1902, p. 1.

15.   New Jersey State Legislature, "An Act to Provide for Construction and Maintenance of Speedways . . . ," *Acts of the One Hundred and Twenty-Sixth Legislature . . .* (Trenton, NJ: 1902), pp. 44–45.

16.   "New Pleasure Drive," *Washington Post*, 17 June 1903, p. 2; "Park Driveway on River Front Formally Opened," *Washington Times*, 19 October 1903, p. 1; "Permit for Speedway," *Evening Star*, 9 December 1903, p. 10; "The Speedway Ready," *Evening Star*, 11 May 1904, p. 13; "History of Speedway," *Washington Post*, 11 December 1905, p. 8.

17.   William T. Pierce, "The Charles River Speedway of the Boston Metropolitan Park System," *Engineering Record*, vol. 51, no. 17 (29 April 1905), p. 496; "History of Speedway," *Washington Post*, 11 December 1905, p. 8.

18.   "War on Jersey Speedway," *New York Times*, 3 September 1909, p. 6.

19.   "To the Capitalist," *Horseless Age*, vol. 1, no. 6 (April 1896), p. 6; "The Motor Car in England," *Scientific American*, vol. 75, no. 24 (12 December 1896), p. 423; "The Horseless Age," *The Horseless Age*, vol. 1, no. 1 (November 1895), p. 8; William F. Dix, "The Automobile as a Vacation Agent," *Independent*, vol. 56 (2 June 1904), pp. 1259–1260.

20.   Imes Chiu, *The Evolution from Horse to Automobile* (Amherst, NY: Cambria Press, 2008), pp. 57–60; Carlton Reid, *Roads Were Not Built for Cars* (Washington, DC: Island Press, 2015), pp. 5–6, 45–49.

21.   Charles P. Norcross, "Owners of America," *Cosmopolitan*, vol. 45, no. 4 (September 1908), p. 381.

22.   "An Island Speedway for Fast Automobiles," *Brooklyn Daily Eagle*, 14 May 1902, p. 8; "Speeding Unlimited," *Motor World*, vol. 4, no. 7 (15 May 1902), p. 202; *Brooklyn Life*, vol. 25, no. 638 (24 May 1902), p. 4; "Automobile Speedway from L.I. City to Roslyn," *Brooklyn Daily Eagle*, 14 September 1902, p. 6; "Speedway for Motorcars," *New York Times*, 14 June 1903, p. 20.

23.   "To Discourage Automobilists," *New York Times*, 15 May 1902, p. 8.

24.   "The Autophobe Association," *Motor World*, vol. 5, no. 7 (13 November 1902), p. 207.

25.   "Automobile Topics of Interest," *New York Times*, 3 May 1903, p. 14. Some motorists continued to press for access to speedways such as the Harlem River Speedway, but their complaints about unfair treatment were to no avail. See "Motoring on the Speedway of the Metropolis," *Motor*, vol. 1, no. 3 (December 1903), p. 21.

26.   "Six Victims Dead," *Washington Post*, 26 May 1903, p. 1; "Automobile Topics of Interest," *New York Times*, 28 June 1903, p. 14; "Automobile Topics of Interest," *New York Times*, 2 August 1903, p. 13.

27.   Howard Kroplick, "Elsie Janis and The Broadway Show 'The Vanderbilt Cup,'" *Vanderbilt Cup Races* (blog), 10 May 2011, http://www.vanderbiltcupraces.com.

28.   Clay McShane, *The Automobile: A Chronology of Its Antecedents, Development, and Import* (Westport, CT: Greenwood Press, 1997), p. 23.

29.   "The Speedway Across Long Island," *Automobile*, vol. 15, no. 17 (25 October 1906), p. 526; Howard Kroplick, "From the Pardington Papers: Original Parkway Names and Toll Gate Locations," *Vanderbilt Cup Races* (blog), 9 March 2010, http://www.vanderbiltcupraces.com.

30.   Howard Kroplick and Al Velocci, *The Long Island Motor Parkway* (Charleston, SC: Arcadia, 2008), pp. 7–8; A. R. Pardington, "The Modern Appian Way for the Motorist," *Harper's Weekly*, vol. 51, no. 2621 (16 March 1907), p. 390.

31.   "Starting the Construction of Long Island Motor Parkway," *Automobile*, vol. 18, no. 24 (11 June 1908), pp. 805–807.

32.   Howard Kroplick, "Trucks, the Motor Parkway and the Vanderbilt Cup Races" *Vanderbilt Cup Races* (blog), 24 November 2009, http://www.vanderbiltcupraces.com. The western terminus initially was located in Oakland Village/southern Bayside. In 1926 a two-mile (3.2 km) extension relocated the terminus to Fresh Meadows.

33.   "Autoists Amazed at New Speed Bill," *New York Times*, 21 March 1907, p. 11; Seth K. Humphrey, "Automobile Selfishness," *Atlantic Monthly*, vol. 102, no. 5 (November 1908), p. 682; "The Vanderbilt Cup Race Slaughter," *Scientific American*, vol. 103, no. 16 (15 October 1910), p. 293.

34.   Kroplick and Velocci, *Long Island Motor Parkway*, p. 9; "New York Hemmed in with Rich Estates Little Known," *New York Times*, 6 April 1913, Sunday magazine, p. 5; "Auto Cars Have Helped Realty," *Brooklyn Daily Eagle*, 17 July 1915, p. 20.

35.   Kroplick and Velocci, *Long Island Motor Parkway*, pp. 9–10; Howard Kroplick, "The Opening of the Motor Parkway Bike Path - July 9, 1938," *Vanderbilt Cup Races* (blog), 6 February 2009, http://www.vanderbiltcupraces.com.

36.   Jonathan Spiro, *Defending the Master Race: Conservation, Eugenics, and the Legacy of Madison Grant* (Lebanon, NH: University Press of New England, 2009), pp. 31–44; New York Zoological Society, *Seventh Annual Report* (New York: 1903), pp. 41–42; North Side Board of Trade, *The Great North Side or Borough of the Bronx* (New York: North Side Board of Trade, 1897), p. 53; Gilmore D. Clarke, "The Parkway Idea," in W. Brewster Snow, ed., *The Highway and the Landscape* (New Brunswick, NJ: Rutgers University Press, 1959), pp. 34–37.

37.   "Village's Best Citizen Dies," *Scarsdale Inquirer*, 8 July 1916, p. 1; Kroplick and Velocci, *The Long Island Motor Parkway*, p. 14.

38.   Bronx River Parkway Commission, *Report* (New York: Trow, 1907), p. 11; "Quakers Lay Out Park Road Race Course," *Motor Age*, vol. 14, no. 9 (27 August 1908), p. 6; "All Philadelphia Working for Road Race," *Motor Age*, vol. 16, no. 12 (16 September 1909), pp. 16–17; "Robertson Wins Philadelphia Race," *Motor Age*, vol. 16, no. 16 (14 October 1909), p. 7.

39.   Boston Landmarks Commission, "Back Bay Fens," 1983, pp. 14–15, http://www.cityofboston.gov; Bronx Parkway Commission, *Report* (1912), pp. 13 facing, 17 facing, 17–18.

40.   Bronx River Parkway Commission, *Report* (1907), pp. 8–9, 11, 13.

41.   Bronx River Parkway Commission, *Report* (1907), pp. 4, 7–8; US Department of the Interior, National Park Service, *Bronx Parkway Reservation*, Historic American Engineering Record no. NY-327, 2002, pp. 33–34.

42.   Madison Grant, *The Passing of the Great Race* (New York: Charles Scribner's Sons, 1916), pp. 5, 8, 81, 186; National Park Service, *Bronx Parkway Reservation*, pp. 30, 34–35.

43.   *Scarsdale Inquirer*, 5 October 1912, p. 4.

44.   "Alumni Trustee Candidates-at-Large," *Princeton Alumni Weekly*, vol. 35, no. 19 (1 March 1935), p. 1.

45.   National Park Service, *Bronx Parkway Reservation*, pp. 31, 64–65.

46.   National Park Service, *Bronx Parkway Reservation*, pp. 70, 72, 77, 95–99; "Bronx River Parkway Partly in Use," *Scarsdale Inquirer*, 23 July 1921, p. 2.

47.   Jay Downer and James Owen, "Public Parks in Westchester County," in Alvah P. French, ed., *History of Westchester County New York*, vol. 2 (New York: Lewis Historical, 1925), pp. 964, 973–974; National Park Service, *Bronx Parkway Reservation*, pp. 83–88.

48.   National Park Service, *Bronx Parkway Reservation*, pp. 6, 93.

49.   National Park Service, *Bronx Parkway Reservation*, pp. 7–12, 57.

50. "Building Projects in Westchester," *New York Times*, 31 December 1922, p. RE-1; National Park Service, *Bronx Parkway Reservation*, pp. 103–104, 115–116.

51. Stephen Paul DeVillo, *The Bronx River in History & Folklore* (Charleston, SC: History Press, 2015), p. 192.

52. DeVillo, *The Bronx River in History & Folklore*, pp. 180, 185–186, 223.

53. National Park Service, *Bronx Parkway Reservation*, pp. 94, 103–104, 107–111, 116–117.

54. Westchester County Park Commission, *Report of the Westchester County Park Commission* (1924), p. 39, http://collections.westchestergov.com. Some of the regional planning initiatives underway at the time included the Port Authority's freight-transport plan, the Sage Foundation's Regional Plan of New York and Its Environs, and the New York State Association's Committee on the State Park Plan.

55. "Plan $10,000,000 Westchester Park," *New York Times*, 6 February 1922, p. 15; "Offers First Bill for $10,000,000 Park," *New York Times*, 21 February 1922, p. 2; Downer and Owen, "Public Parks in Westchester County," p. 982.

56. W. Delevan Baldwin, "Westchester County Park System," *Bronxville Review*, 13 January 1923, pp. 15, 17.

57. Westchester County Park Commission, *Report* (1926), p. 41.

58. Westchester County Park Commission, *Report* (1925), pp. 11–12.

59. Westchester County Park Commission, *Report* (1925), p. 9; *Report* (1926), pp. 1,8; *Report* (1927), pp. 15, 17, 41; *Report* (1929), pp. 16–17.

60. Jay Downer, "Utilizing Small Stream Valleys for Traffic Routes," *Public Works*, vol. 52, no. 4 (28 January 1922), p. 57.

61. US Department of the Interior, National Park Service, *Taconic State Parkway*, Historic American Engineering Record no. NY-316, 1999, p. 32.

62. American Association of State Highway Officials, *A Story of the Beginning, Purposes, Growth, Activities and Achievements of AASHO, 1914–1964* (Washington, DC: AASHO, 1965), p. 184.

63. National Park Service, *Taconic State Parkway*, pp. 39–40.

64. National Park Service, *Taconic State Parkway*, p. 48.

65. Westchester County Park Commission, *Report* (1932), pp. 7, 9, 41, 47; Regional Plan Association, *From Plan to Reality*, vol. 1 (New York: Regional Plan Association, 1933), p. 54.

66. "Jay Downer, 71, Designer of Parkways, Dies," *Herald Statesman* (of Yonkers, NY), 31 May 1949, pp. 1–2; Winfield Scott Downs, ed., *Encyclopedia of American Biography*, new series, vol. 11 (New York: American Historical, 1940), pp. 579–580; Stanley W. Abbott, interview by S. Herbert Evison (National Park Service, 1958), tape no. 55, pp. 9–10, accessed from University of North Carolina at Chapel Hill, "Driving through Time: The Digital Blue Ridge Parkway in North Carolina," http://www2.lib.unc.edu/dc/brp_media/no_audio/1958_Abbott/1958_Abbott.pdf.

67. Cleveland Rodgers, *Robert Moses: Builder for Democracy* (New York: Henry Holt, 1952), p. 2; Robert Caro, *The Power Broker* (New York: Alfred A. Knopf, 1974), pp. 65–67; Frances Perkins, interview by Dean Albertson, *Reminiscences of Frances Perkins*, Columbia University Oral History Research Office (ca. 1952), part 3, pp. 361–365, http://www.columbia.edu/cu/lweb/digital/collections/nny/perkinsf/audio_transcript.html.

68. New York State, Reconstruction Commission, Committee on Retrenchment, *Report . . . on Retrenchment and Reorganization in the State Government* (Albany, NY: Executive Chamber, 1919), pp. 22, 99–106; Caro, *The Power Broker*, p. 97; Rodgers, *Robert Moses*, p. 20.

69. New York State Association, *State Bulletin*, vol. 1, no. 2 (15 January 1921), p. 2; Caro, *The Power Broker*, p. 166.

70. City of New York, Department of Parks, *20 Years of Progress 1934–1954*, by Robert Moses (New York: City of New York Department of Parks, 1954), p. 38; Caro, *The Power Broker*, p. 218; "Mr. Moses and Governor Miller," *New York Times*, 28 July 1922, p. 12.

71. Caro, *The Power Broker*, pp. 157–171

72. New York State Association, *The State Park Plan for New York*, 2nd ed. (1924); Caro, *The Power Broker*, pp. 221, 230; "Smith Dedicates Nassau Parkway," *New York Times*, 7 November 1927, p. 23.

73. Frederick Boyd Stevenson, "Will Long Island Have a State System of Parks and Parkways or Will Private Owners Prevail?" *Brooklyn Daily Eagle*, 8 March 1925, p. E1; Caro, *The Power Broker*, 899–908.

74. Caro, *The Power Broker*, pp. 181–220, 278–280.

75. Caro, *The Power Broker*, pp. 153–156, 237–238; 308–314; C. L. Grant, ed., *New York State Parks and Highways* (Albany, NY: State Council of Parks, 1928), p. 4.

76. City of New York, Department of Parks, *20 Years of Progress 1934–1954*, by Robert Moses (New York: City of New York Department of Parks, 1954), p. 38; David A. Johnson, *Planning the Great Metropolis: The 1929 Regional Plan of New York and Its Environs* (London: E & FN Spon, 1996), pp. 225–240, 269; Caro, *The Power Broker*, pp. 339–344, 620–622.

77. "Governor Endorses Queens Road Plan," *New York Times*, 17 October 1930, p. 40; "Roosevelt Starts a New Road Project," *New York Times*, 27 July 1931, p. 17.

78. W. A. Warn, "Roosevelt Message Assails Budget Cuts as Blow to the Idle," *New York Times*, 28 February 1932, p. 1.

79. "Queens Parkways Win City Approval," *New York Times*, 6 May 1933, p. 15; "Lehman Dedicates 2 Parkways Here," *New York Times*, 16 July 1933, p. 21.

80. Caro, *The Power Broker*, pp. 540–548, 560–561.

81. Regional Plan Association, *From Plan to Reality*, vol. 2 (New York: Regional Plan Association, 1938), pp. III-11 to III-12; Caro, *The Power Broker*, pp. 520–525

82. US Federal Works Agency, Public Roads Administration, *Public Control of Highway Access and Roadside Development*, by David R. Levin (Washington, DC: USGPO, 1943), p. 34; Caro, *The Power Broker*, pp. 508, 569–573; Rodgers, *Robert Moses*, pp. 288–300, 342.

83. Gilmore D. Clarke, "Modern Motor Arteries," in *Planning Problems of Town, City and Region*, proceedings of 22nd National Conference on City Planning (Philadelphia: William F. Fell, 1930), pp. 73–75; US Department of the Interior, National Park Service, *Rock Creek and Potomac Parkway: History and Description*, by Timothy Davis, Historic American Buildings Survey no. DC-697, 1992, pp. 36–38.

84. Caro, *The Power Broker*, pp. 556–557; National Park Service, *Rock Creek and Potomac Parkway*, pp. 114–115.

85. Public Roads Administration, *Public Control of Highway Access and Roadside Development*, p. 16.

86. "Catalog of Built Work and Projects in New York City, 1934–1968," and Owen D. Gutfreund, "Rebuilding New York in the Auto Age: Robert Moses and His Highways," in Hillary Ballon and Kenneth T. Jackson, eds., *Robert Moses and the Modern City: The Transformation of New York* (New York: W. W. Norton, 2007), pp. 91–93, 217–228.

87. Caro, *The Power Broker*, pp. 11, 706, 838–843, 921, 1131.

88. "Bassett Given Medal for His City Planning," *Brooklyn Daily Eagle*, 14 May 1943, p. 3.

89. Russell Sage Foundation, *Plan of New York and Its Environs: the Meeting of May 10, 1922* (New York: Russell Sage Foundation, 1922); *Regional Plan of New York and Its Environs*, vol. 1, *The Graphic Regional Plan: Atlas and Description* (New York: Committee on Regional Plan of New York and Its Environs, 1929), p. 13.

90. *Regional Plan of New York and Its Environs*, vol. 1, p. 265.

91. Gilmore D. Clarke, "Modern Motor Arteries," in *Planning Problems of Town, City and Region*, proceedings of 22nd National Conference on City Planning (Philadelphia: William F. Fell, 1930), p. 73; Edward M. Bassett, "Laws of Planning Unbuilt Areas," in *Regional Survey of New York and Its Environs*, vol. 7, *Neighborhood and Community Planning* (New York: Regional Plan of New York and Its Environs, 1929), pp. 275–276; *Regional Plan of New York and Its Environs*, vol. 1, pp. 269–272.

92. Edward M. Bassett, "The Freeway—A New Kind of Thoroughfare," *The American City*, vol. 42, no. 2 (February 1930), p. 95.

93. Regional Plan Association, *From Plan to Reality*, vol. 1 (New York: Regional Plan Association, 1933), pp. 94–96, 131–133; Edward M. Bassett, "Zoning and Freeways," *City Planning*, vol. 9, no. 3 (July 1933), pp. 138–139; American Association of State Highway Officials, *A Story of the Beginning, Purposes, Growth, Activities and Achievements of AASHO, 1914–1964* (Washington, DC: AASHO, 1965), p. 114.

94. Tom Lewis, *Divided Highways: Building the Interstate Highways, Transforming American Life* (New York: Viking, 1997), pp. 6–9; "Early History of the Iowa State Highway Commission" ([Ames, IA?]: [Iowa State Highway Commission?], [1921?]), p. 4, http://publications.iowa.gov/22216/.

95. Iowa State Highway Commission, *Report . . . for 1915* (Ames, IA: State Highway Commission, 1916), pp. 5–6; "Motor Vehicle for Every 18 Persons," *Automotive Industries*, vol. 40, no. 3 (16 January 1919), p. 102, 198.

96. Iowa State Highway Commission, *Report . . . to 1914* (Ames, IA: State Highway Commission, 1915), pp. 154–156; Iowa State Highway Commission, *Report . . . for 1915*, p. 123.

97. Bruce E. Seely, *Building the American Highway System: Engineers as Policy Makers* (Philadelphia: Temple University Press, 1987), pp. 41–42.

98. Lewis, *Divided Highways*, pp. 5, 12–14; American Association of State Highway Officials, *A Story . . . of AASHO*, pp. 52–53.

99. US Department of Transportation, Federal Highway Administration, *America's Highways 1776-1976* (Washington, DC: USGPO, 1977), pp. 107–109, 113–115, 123–124; US Department of Agriculture, Bureau of Public Roads, "Report of the Chief of the Bureau of Public Roads," by Thomas H. MacDonald, 1 September 1931, pp. 38, 43; American Association of State Highway Officials, *A Story . . . of AASHO*, p. 156.

100. US Department of Agriculture, Bureau of Public Roads, "Report of the Chief of the Bureau of Public Roads," by Thomas H. MacDonald, 15 October 1925, pp. 32–35. The law that prohibited BPR from spending money on urban highways was changed in 1933.

101. "Parkways for Pleasure and Utility," *The American City*, vol. 31, no. 5 (November 1924), pp. 421–422.

102. US Department of the Interior, National Park Service, *George Washington Memorial Highway*, Historic American Engineering Record no. VA-69, 1994/1998, pp. 82–99, 103–104, 116, 138–140.

103. California State Legislature, Assembly, *Journal of the Assembly*, 50th session, 1933, pp. 730, 1783–1784.

104. New England Regional Planning Commission, "Model State Enabling Act Empowering State Highway Departments to Construct and Maintain Freeways and Parkways," prepared by US Bureau of Public Roads, publication no. 3, July 1934; "The Freeway, a Modern Highway for General Traffic in Metropolitan Areas," Regional Plan Association, *Information Bulletin*, no. 33, 14 December 1936, pp. 8–12.

105. Public Roads Administration, *Public Control of Highway Access and Roadside Development*, pp. 67–70, 99–103; John Sheail, "The Restriction of Ribbon Development Act: The Character and Perception of Land-Use Control in Inter-War Britain," *Regional Studies*, vol. 13, no. 6 (1979), pp. 501–512.

106. Regional Plan Association, *From Plan to Reality*, vol. 2 (New York: Regional Plan Association, 1938), pp. III-9 to III-12.

107. Public Roads Administration, *Public Control of Highway Access and Roadside Development*, pp. 16, 33–35; US Federal Works Agency, Public Roads Administration, *Highway Statistics: Summary to 1945* (Washington, DC: USGPO, 1947), p. 95.

108. US Federal Works Agency, Public Roads Administration, *Public Control of Highway Access and Roadside Development*, by David R. Levin, revised 1947 (Washington, DC: USGPO, 1947), pp. 25–27, 99–101.

109. Seely, *Building the American Highway System*, pp. 156–159; Thomas H. MacDonald, "Tomorrow's Roads," *Engineering News-Record*, vol. 117, no. 25 (17 December 1936), pp. 868–870.

110. Seely, *Building the American Highway System*, pp. 165–168.

111. US Congress, House Committee on Roads, *Toll Roads and Free Roads*, 76th Congress, 1st Session, 1939, House document no. 272, p. 91; Seely, *Building the American Highway*, pp. 169–171.

112. US Congress, *Toll Roads and Free Roads*, pp. 95–97, 103–107.

113. US Congress, *Toll Roads and Free Roads*, pp. 95, 99, 121.

114. Seely, *Building the American Highway System*, p. 172; US Congress, *Toll Roads and Free Roads*, pp. 94, 97.

115. US Congress, *Toll Roads and Free Roads*, pp. 93, 98.

116. Seely, *Building the American Highway System*, p. 172; Paul G. Hoffman, "America Goes to Town," *Saturday Evening Post*, 29 April 1939, p. 35.

117. Seely, *Building the American Highway System*, pp. 177–179.

118. Seely, *Building the American Highway System*, p. 180; US Congress, House Committee on Roads, *Interregional Highways*, 78th Congress, 2nd session, 1944, House document no. 379, pp. 51–52, 126.

119. US Congress, *Interregional Highways*, pp. 62, 69–70.

120. US Congress, *Interregional Highways*, p. 80, plate 13.

121. US Congress, *Interregional Highways*, pp. 89, 92.

122. "Concentrate Postwar Highway Planning on Urban Areas," *Engineering News-Record*, vol. 129, no. 13 (24 September 1942), p. 51; US Department of Transportation, Federal Highway Administration, *America's Highways 1776-1976* (Washington, DC: USGPO, 1977), pp. 159–160; Adolf D. May Jr., "The Permanence of Limited Access Highways," in *Proceedings of the 41st Annual Road School*, extension series no. 88 (Lafayette, Indiana: Purdue University, 1955), pp. 119, 124, http://docs.lib.purdue.edu/roadschool/1955/proceedings/11/. The mileage statistic does not include mileage in New Jersey, freeways in New York, or toll roads.

123. Thomas H. MacDonald, "The Case for Urban Expressways," *The American City*, vol. 62, no. 6 (June 1947), pp. 92–93.

124. Thomas H. MacDonald, "American Inter-Regional Highway System: How it Affects Cities," *Civil Engineering*, vol. 14, no. 5 (May 1944), p. 190.

125. Federal Highway Administration, *America's Highways 1776–1976*, pp. 473, 476.

126. Federal Highway Administration, *America's Highways 1776–1976*, p. 258.

127. Jeffrey Brinkman and Jeffrey Lin, "Freeway Revolts!" Federal Reserve Bank of Philadelphia, working paper WP-19-29, July 2019, https://doi.org/10.21799/frbp.wp.2019.29.

128. Gijs Mom, *Atlantic Automobilism: Emergence and Persistence of the Car, 1895–1940* (New York: Berghahn, 2015) pp. 456–457, 460, 638–650.

129. Mark S. Foster, *From Streetcar to Superhighway: American City Planners and Urban Transportation, 1900–1940* (Philadelphia: Temple University Press, 1981), pp. 112–115; Robert M. Fogelson, *Downtown: Its Rise and Fall, 1880–1950* (New Haven, CT: Yale University Press, 2001), pp. 269, 274–276; Institute for Transportation and Development Policy and EMBARQ, *The Life And Death of Urban Highways* (New York: IDTP, 2012), p. 6; Brian Ladd, *Autophobia* (Chicago: University of Chicago Press, 2008), pp. 126, 137, 208; Miquel-Àngel Garcia-López, "All Roads Lead to Rome . . . and to Sprawl? Evidence from European Cities," *Regional Science and Urban Economics* (2019), https://doi.org/10.1016/j.regsciurbeco.2019.103467; Zhong-Ren Peng, "Urban Transportation Strategies in Chinese Cities and Their Impacts on the Urban Poor," Wilson Center, 7 July 2011, http://www.wilsoncenter.org.

Chapter 7. Blending and Winnowing

1. David A. Johnson, *Planning the Great Metropolis: The 1929 Regional Plan of New York and Its Environs* (London: E & FN Spon, 1996), pp. 55–58, 93.

2. Johnson, *Planning the Great Metropolis*, pp. 59–67.

3. Rose C. Feld, "For a City of 37,000,000," *New York Times*, 21 May 1922, section 7, p. XX3; Raymond Unwin, "New York and Its Environs as a Regional Planning Problem from the European Point of View," in *Plan of New York and Its Environs: Report of Progress* (New York: Plan of New York and Its Environs, 1923), pp. 14–20.

4. Johnson, *Planning the Great Metropolis*, pp. 95, 138–140.

5. Thomas Adams, *Regional Plan of New York and Its Environs*, vol. 2, *The Building of the City* (New York: Committee on Regional Plan of New York and Its Environs, 1931), pp. 274–317, 393–417.

6. *Regional Plan of New York and Its Environs*, vol. 1, *The Graphic Regional Plan: Atlas and Description* (New York: Committee on Regional Plan of New York and Its Environs, 1929), pp. 264–273.

7. "Double-Decked Streets for Lower New York," *New York Times*, 6 August 1911, p. 5; E. P. Goodrich and George B. Ford, *Report of Suggested Plan of Procedure for City Plan Commission . . .* (Jersey City, NJ: City Plan Commission, 1913), pp. 9–10; Ernest P. Goodrich, "The Urban Auto Problem," in *Proceedings of the Twelfth National Conference on City Planning* (National Conference on City Planning, 1920), pp. 87–88.

8. Adams, *The Building of the City*, pp. 5, 145, 203, 219, 568–571; Johnson, *Planning the Great Metropolis*, pp. 141, 143.

9. Adams, *The Building of the City*, pp. 105–108, 577.

10. Johnson, *Planning the Great Metropolis*, p. 268; Robert Fishman, "The Regional Plan and the Transformation of the Industrial Metropolis," in David Ward and Oliver Zunz, eds., *The Landscape of Modernity: New York City 1900–1940* (Baltimore, MD: Johns Hopkins University Press, 1992), p. 106. Between 1929 and 1932, RPNY was detached from the Sage Foundation and was re-established as a private corporation named the Regional Plan Association. Alexander Bing, the developer of Radburn, joined the board of directors in 1929 along with other reform-minded developers, bankers, lawyers, and businessmen. See Johnson, *Planning the Great Metropolis*, pp. 176–177.

11. Franklin D. Roosevelt, "Address on Regional Planning," *The Public Papers and Addresses of Franklin D. Roosevelt*, vol. 1 (New York: Random House, 1938), pp. 495–496, 499.

12. Johnson, *Planning the Great Metropolis*, p. 270.

13. Alan R. Raucher, *Paul G. Hoffman: Architect of Foreign Aid* (Lexington, KY: University Press of Kentucky, 1985), pp. 2–4.

14. Raucher, *Paul G. Hoffman*, pp. 5–7, 15; Alan R. Raucher, "Paul G. Hoffman, Studebaker, and

the Car Culture," *Indiana Magazine of History*, vol. 79, no. 3 (1 September 1983), pp. 212–214.

15.   Raucher, *Paul G. Hoffman*, p. 7; Christopher H. Sterling, ed., *The Concise Encyclopedia of American Radio* (New York: Routledge, 2010), p. 408; Mark S. Foster, "The Model-T, the Hard Sell, and Los Angeles's Urban Growth: The Decentralization of Los Angeles during the 1920s," *Pacific Historical Review*, vol. 44, no. 4 (November 1975), p. 464; National Automobile Chamber of Commerce, *Facts and Figures of the Automobile Industry* (New York: National Automobile Chamber of Commerce, 1923), p. 22.

16.   Peter D. Norton, *Fighting Traffic: The Dawn of the Motor Age in the American City* (Cambridge, MA: MIT Press, 2008), p. 65.

17.   Clay McShane, *Down the Asphalt Path: The Automobile and the American City* (New York: Columbia University Press, 1995), pp. 193–194; Norton, *Fighting Traffic*, pp. 48–49.

18.   Norton, *Fighting Traffic*, pp. 105–128.

19.   Robert M. Fogelson, *Downtown: Its Rise and Fall, 1880–1950* (New Haven, CT: Yale University Press, 2001), p. 254; McShane, *Down the Asphalt Path*, p. 202; Norton, *Fighting Traffic*, pp. 138, 155; Miller McClintock, *Street Traffic Control* (New York: McGraw-Hill, 1925), pp. 95–100, 153.

20.   Norton, *Fighting Traffic*, pp. 22, 25–46, 64; US Department of Transportation, Federal Highway Administration, *Highway Statistics Summary To 1995*, report no. FHWA-PL-97-009 (Washington, DC: USGPO, 1997), table FI-200, p. V-26.

21.   Norton, *Fighting Traffic*, pp. 89–101, 156; Miller McClintock, "How Shall We Separate Walkers and Riders?" *The American City*, vol. 31, no. 2 (August 1924), p. 155.

22.   Norton, *Fighting Traffic*, pp. 149–159, 169–194; Fogelson, *Downtown*, pp. 251–252.

23.   Charles Clifton, "Miracles Made to Order," *Collier's*, vol. 69, no. 1 (7 January 1922), p. 7.

24.   Fogelson, *Downtown*, pp. 256–257.

25.   Matthew William Roth, "Concrete Utopia: The Development of Roads and Freeways in Los Angeles, 1910–1950" (PhD diss., University of Southern California, 2007), pp. 139–143; Marc A. Weiss, *The Rise of the Community Builders: The American Real Estate Industry and Urban Land Planning* (New York: Columbia University Press, 1987), pp. 94–95.

26.   Frederick Law Olmsted, Harland Bartholomew, and Charles Henry Cheney, *A Major Traffic Street Plan for Los Angeles* (Los Angeles: Traffic Commission of the City and County of Los Angeles, 1924), pp. 3–8, 12–24.

27.   Paul G. Hoffman, "The Traffic Commission of Los Angeles: Its Work on the Traffic Problem," *Annals of the American Academy of Political and Social Science*, vol. 116, no. 205 (November 1924), p. 25; Raucher, *Paul G. Hoffman*, p. 8.

28.   Roth, "Concrete Utopia," pp. 152–157, 163, 166–169.

29.   Thomas Sugrue, "Miller McClintock," *Scribner's*, vol. 52, no. 6 (December 1937), p. 12; Norton, *Fighting Traffic*, pp. 163–165

30.   McClintock, *Street Traffic Control*, pp. 37, 77–78, 107, 113, 160; McClintock, "How Shall We Separate Walkers and Riders?" p. 155.

31.   Raucher, *Paul G. Hoffman*, p. 11.

32.   Raucher, *Paul G. Hoffman*, p. 17; Sugrue, "Miller McClintock," pp. 12–13.

33.   Sugrue, "Miller McClintock," p. 12; Institute of Transportation Engineers, *Pioneers of Transportation* (Washington, DC: Institute of Transportation Engineers, 2011), pp. 14, 25.

34.   *Facts and Figures of the Automobile Industry*, 1930 ed. (New York: National Automobile Chamber of Commerce, 1930), p. 15.

35.   Miller McClintock, "Remedies for Traffic Congestion," *S.A.E. Journal*, vol. 23, no. 5 (November 1928), pp. 444–445; Miller McClintock, "Preventive and Palliative Measures for Street Traffic Relief," *City Planning*, vol. 6, no. 2 (April 1930), pp. 99–105.

36.   Chicago Association Of Commerce, *Report and Recommendations of the Metropolitan Street Traffic Survey*, by Miller McClintock (Chicago: 1926), pp. 112, 126; Hugh E. Young, "Ten-Mile $60,000,000 Motor Express Highway Proposed for Chicago," *American City*, vol. 38, no. 3 (March 1928), pp. 91–92; Eugene S. Taylor, "Chicago's Superhighway Plan," *National Municipal Review*, vol. 18, no. 6 (June 1929), pp. 371–376.

37.   City Council of the City of Chicago, *Limited Ways: A Plan for the Greater Chicago Traffic Area*, vol. 3 (Chicago: City Council of the City of Chicago, 1933), pp. 32, 42–43, 61–64, 100.

38.   Paul G. Hoffman, "Congestion of Traffic Retards Motor Buying," *New York Times*, 7 January 1934, p. A4.

39.   Fogelson, *Downtown*, pp. 228–229, 260, 271, 273, 316.

40. "The Early Years: Establishing an Identity," *ITE Journal*, vol. 50, no. 8 (August 1980), pp. 10–14; "Unfit for Modern Motor Traffic," *Fortune*, vol. 14, no. 2 (August 1936), p. 89.

41. Harry Lewis Bird, *This Fascinating Advertising Business* (Indianapolis, IN: Bobbs-Merrill, 1947), p. 245; Sugrue, "Miller McClintock," p. 99; "Dr. Miller McClintock Dies at 65," *New York Times*, 11 January 1960, p. 45.

42. "Both Fish and Fowl," *Fortune*, vol. 9, no. 2 (February 1934), p. 90; Barbara Szerlip, *The Man Who Designed the Future: Norman Bel Geddes and the Invention of Twentieth-Century America* (New York: Melville House, 2016), pp. 18–21, 101–114, 168–176.

43. Jeffery L. Meikle, *Twentieth Century Limited: Industrial Design in America, 1925-1939*, 2nd ed. (Philadelphia: Temple University Press, 2001), pp. 144, 206–207; Norman Bel Geddes, *Horizons* (Boston: Little, Brown, 1932), pp. 285–288. In 1927, Flagg had proposed a vertical separation scheme for Manhattan with elevated motor expressways running down the centers of avenues, and a network of pedestrian terraces and skybridges one level above them. See Ernest Flagg, "The City of the Future," *Scientific American*, vol. 137, no. 3 (September 1927), pp. 238–241 and Ernest Flagg, "The City of the Future—II," *Scientific American*, vol. 137, no. 4 (October 1927), pp. 334–337.

44. Meikle, *Twentieth Century Limited*, p. 207.

45. Norton, *Fighting Traffic*, p. 249; Meikle, *Twentieth Century Limited*, pp. 206–207; Miller McClintock, "Of Things to Come" in American Planning and Civic Association, *American Planning and Civic Annual* (Washington, DC: American Planning and Civic Association, 1937), p. 384.

46. Sugrue, "Miller McClintock," p. 13; "At the Wheel," *New York Times*, 6 June 1937, p. 12XX; "Making a Motor Market," *Wall Street Journal*, 24 September 1937, p. 4.

47. Paul G. Hoffman, *Highway Safety—A Review and Forecast* (monograph), Society of Automotive Engineers Beecroft Memorial Lecture, 14 October 1947, pp. 9–10; Joel W. Eastman, *Styling vs. Safety: The American Automobile Industry and the Development of Automotive Safety, 1900-1966* (Lanham, MD: University Press of America, 1984), pp. 135–138; Norton, *Fighting Traffic*, p. 246.

48. Eastman, *Styling vs. Safety*, pp. 139–140; Institute of Transportation Engineers, *Pioneers of Transportation*, p. 25; Paul G. Hoffman, *Seven Roads to Safety: A Program to Reduce Automobile Accidents* (New York: Harper & Bros., 1939), pp. 77–83.

49. Eastman, *Styling vs. Safety*, pp. 143–144.

50. Hoffman, *Seven Roads to Safety*, pp. 58–76; Eastman, *Styling vs. Safety*, pp. 141–142.

51. Sugrue, "Miller McClintock," p. 99; "The Traffic Problem," *Life*, vol. 5, no. 1 (4 July 1938), pp. 42–53. Under the ownership of Henry Luce, *Life's* editorial stance on automobiles was opposite to the magazine's stance at the turn of the century. The old *Life* had portrayed automobilists as ravening locusts or killer gladiators. The new *Life* ran unalloyed propaganda for cities to be rebuilt to serve high-speed traffic.

52. Alfred Reeves, "Better Highways Will Multiply Autos," *Popular Science Monthly*, vol. 100, no. 5 (May 1922), p. 26.

53. Paul G. Hoffman, "America Goes to Town," *Saturday Evening Post*, 29 April 1939, pp. 9, 32, 35.

54. National Automobile Chamber of Commerce, *Facts and Figures of the Automobile Industry* (New York: National Automobile Chamber of Commerce, 1921), p. 22.

55. National Safety Council, *Accident Facts*, 1931 ed. (Chicago: National Safety Council, 1931), p. 20; "32,500 Motor Deaths in 1930," *National Safety News*, vol. 23, no. 2 (February 1931), p. 27.

56. Paul G. Hoffman, "Wide Gains Noted in Highway Safety," *New York Times*, 11 November 1936, p. 38; Stève Bernardin, "'Taking the Problem to the People': Traffic Safety from Public Relations to Political Theory, 1937-1954," *Technology and Culture*, vol. 56, no. 2 (April 2015), pp. 424–426; "Money for Safety," *Time*, vol. 32, no. 17 (24 October 1938), p. 39; Paul G. Hoffman, "Winning the War on Traffic Accidents," *Popular Mechanics*, vol. 72, no. 4 (October 1939), p. 568; Hoffman, *Seven Roads to Safety*, pp. 2–3; Hoffman, *Highway Safety*, pp. 11–17.

57. Arthur W. Stevens, *Highway Safety and Automobile Styling* (Boston: Christopher Publishing House, 1941), pp. 144–151; Hoffman, *Highway Safety*, pp. 13–14.

58. Laurence Aurbach, "Functional Classification and Safety Statistics," *Ped Shed* (blog), 3 February 2016, http://pedshed.net/?p=1050.

59. Itai Vardi, "Quantifying Accidents: Cars, Statistics, and Unintended Consequences in the Construction of Social Problems Over Time," *Qualitative Sociology*, vol. 37, no. 3 (September 2014), pp. 352–353.

60. Frank Schipper, *Driving Europe: Building Europe on Roads in the Twentieth Century* (Amsterdam: Aksant, 2008), pp. 173–175, 189–201.

61.   Inger L. Stole, *Advertising at War: Business, Consumers, and Government in the 1940s* (Chicago: University of Illinois Press, 2012), pp. 50, 122; John Bush Jones, *All-out for Victory!: Magazine Advertising and the World War II Home Front* (Lebanon, NH: Brandeis University Press, 2009), pp. 30–32; Marcel Chotkowski LaFollette, *Science on American Television: A History* (Chicago: University of Chicago Press, 2013), pp. 9–10.

62.   Institute of Transportation Engineers, *Pioneers of Transportation*, p. 35.

63.   Robert W. Rydell, *World of Fairs: The Century-of-Progress Expositions* (Chicago: University of Chicago Press, 1993), pp. 9, 113, 150–151; Grover A. Whalen, *Mr. New York: The Autobiography of Grover A. Whalen* (New York: G. P. Putnam's Sons, 1955), p. 176.

64.   Carol A. Hagan, "Visions of the City at the 1939 New York World's Fair," (PhD diss., University of Pennsylvania, 2000), pp. 15–26; New York City Department of Parks, "Progress in the Park Department: 1934–1938" (press release), December 1938, p. 7, in "1938 Parks Department Press Releases" (compilation), from New York City Department of Parks & Recreation, "Historical Reports, Press Releases, and Minutes" (web page), http://www.nycgovparks.org/news/reports/archive.

65.   Meikle, *Twentieth Century Limited*, pp. 189–190; Robert Moses, "From Dump to Glory," *Saturday Evening Post*, 13 January 1938, pp. 72, 74; Robert Moses, "The City of Tomorrow," *New York Times*, 5 March 1939, World Fair section, p. 47.

66.   Hagan, "Visions of the City at the 1939 New York World's Fair," pp. 5, 67–78, 82–85; Szerlip, *The Man Who Designed the Future*, pp. 62, 121.

67.   Meikle, *Twentieth Century Limited*, pp. 190–192, 197–200; R. L. Duffus, "A City of Tomorrow: A New Design of Life," *New York Times Magazine*, 18 December 1938, p. 23.

68.   Geoffrey T. Hellman, "Design for a Living," part 3, *New Yorker*, 22 February 1941, pp. 28–29; Hagan, "Visions of the City at the 1939 New York World's Fair," pp. 95–99; Szerlip, *The Man Who Designed the Future*, pp. 217–230.

69.   Hellman, "Design for a Living," p. 29; Meikle, *Twentieth Century Limited*, p. 202.

70.   Norman Bel Geddes, *Magic Motorways* (New York: Random House, 1940), pp. 196–198.

71.   Bel Geddes, *Magic Motorways*, pp. 219, 238–239.

72.   Bel Geddes, *Magic Motorways*, pp. 212, 213, 239–244.

73.   Handy (Jam) Organization, *Streamlines* (General Motors Corporation, 1936), accessed from Internet Archive, http://archive.org/details/0142_Streamlines_M7960_09_08_44_00; Bel Geddes, *Magic Motorways*, pp. 28–29, 36, 94–95, 191, 234–236.

74.   Lewis Mumford, "Genuine Bootleg," *New Yorker*, 29 July 1939, pp. 39–40.

75.   Rydell, *World of Fairs*, pp. 135, 155.

76.   Christina Cogdell, "Theater of War," in Donald Albrecht, ed., *Norman Bel Geddes Designs America* (New York: Abrams, 2012), pp. 317–318, 326–335.

77.   Nathaniel Robert Walker, "American Crossroads: General Motors' Midcentury Campaign to Promote Modernist Urban Design in Hometown U.S.A.," *Buildings & Landscapes*, vol. 23, no. 2 (Fall 2016), pp. 92–95, 102–105.

78.   "Dr. Conant Tours Fair with Moses," *New York Times*, 27 June 1939, p. 20; "Moses Envisages Future Highways," *New York Times*, 21 January 1940, p. 11.

79.   Robert Moses, untitled essay, in General Motors Corporation, *How to Plan and Pay for Better Highways* (Detroit, MI: General Motors Corporation, 1953), p. 36.

80.   Walker, "American Crossroads," pp. 105–109; Joel Schwartz, *The New York Approach: Robert Moses, Urban Liberals, and the Redevelopment of the Inner City* (Columbus, OH: Ohio State University Press, 1993) pp. 101–103, 216–217.

81.   H. Alker Tripp, *Road Traffic and Its Control* (London: Edward Arnold, 1938), pp. 170, 346, 348; H. Alker Tripp, "The Police and Town Planning," *The Police Journal*, vol. 14, no. 4 (October-December 1941), p. 380.

82.   H. Alker Tripp, "Report by H. Alker Tripp, Assistant Commissioner on Visit to America, October, 1934," December 1934, part I, pp. 1, 13–14, 20–21, from UK National Archives, MEPO 2/5937.

83.   H. Alker Tripp, "The Traffic Problem," *The Police Journal*, vol. 9, no. 1 (January-March 1936), pp. 82–84, 90.

84.   Tripp, *Road Traffic and Its Control*, pp. v, 294–302, 339.

85.   Tripp, *Road Traffic and Its Control*, pp. 304–305, 347–348.

86.   Tripp, *Road Traffic and Its Control*, pp. 291–292, 302.

87.   H. Alker Tripp, *Town Planning and Road Traffic* (London: Edward Arnold, 1942), pp. 25, 71.

88. Tripp, *Town Planning and Road Traffic*, pp. 56, 76–77.

89. Tripp, *Town Planning and Road Traffic*, pp. 31, 42, 71, 79.

90. Tripp, *Town Planning and Road Traffic*, pp. 39–40, 68–69, 82.

91. C. D. Buchanan, "The Road Traffic Problem in Britain," *Town Planning Review*, vol. 26, no. 4 (January 1956), pp. 227–230; Ministry of War Transport, *Design and Layout of Roads in Built-Up Areas* (London: HMSO, 1946).

92. The principle that squabbling factions were an obstacle to effective political action was amply demonstrated by the fight in the US Congress during the 1940s to authorize and fund a national freeway system. See Bruce E. Seely, *Building the American Highway System: Engineers as Policy Makers* (Philadelphia: Temple University Press, 1987), p. 199.

93. US Federal Works Agency, Public Roads Administration, *Public Control of Highway Access and Roadside Development*, by David R. Levin (Washington, DC: USGPO, 1943), pp. 9–11. The BPR had used that rural road classification at least since the 1933 National Industrial Recovery Act had funded rural "secondary or feeder" roads. The concept of secondary roads having a feeder or connecting function was old; MacDonald had used the term *feeder* in a 1912 article. See [William] Lee Mertz, *Origins of the Interstate* (unpublished manuscript), [18 December 1986?], p. 8, http://www.fhwa.dot.gov/infrastructure/origin.pdf.

94. Public Roads Administration, *Public Control*, pp. 39–40.

95. David R. Levin, "The Highway and Land Use," in Jean Labatut and Wheaton J. Lane, eds., *Highways in Our National Life* (Princeton, NJ: Princeton University Press, 1950), pp. 268–276.

96. Chicago Plan Commission, *Building New Neighborhoods: Subdivision Standards and Design*, by H. Evert Kincaid (Chicago: Chicago Plan Commission, 1943), pp. 6–7, 9; "Leaves FHA to Direct Chicago's Master Plan," *Chicago Daily News*, 1 November 1941, p. 23.

97. Chicago Plan Commission, *Building New Neighborhoods*, pp. 36–38. Express highways were not discussed in detail in the booklet, but the commission's 1946 city plan blanketed Chicago with a grid of limited-access highways spaced 2–4 miles (3.2–6.4 km) apart. See Chicago Plan Commission, *Preliminary Comprehensive City Plan of Chicago* (map), 1946, from Newberry Library, *Mapping Movement in American History and Culture*, http://mappingmovement.newberry.org.

98. City of Chicago, *Chicago's Report to the People 1933–1946* (City of Chicago, 1947), pp. 60–61.

99. American Public Works Association, *The Dynamics of Street Layout and Design for Urban Traffic*, bulletin no. 26 (Chicago: American Public Works Association, 1945), forward and pp. 1, 4, 10–17.

100. Marc A. Weiss, *The Rise of the Community Builders: The American Real Estate Industry and Urban Land Planning* (New York: Columbia University Press, 1987), p. 68.

101. Urban Land Institute, *The Community Builders Handbook*, Seward H. Mott and Max S. Wehrly, eds. (Washington, DC: Urban Land Institute, 1947), p. viii.

102. Urban Land Institute, *Community Builders Handbook*, pp. 47–49, 65.

103. Urban Land Institute, *Community Builders Handbook*, pp. 18–19, 25, 39, 58.

104. Jason S. Brody, "Constructing Professional Knowledge: The Neighborhood Unit Concept in the Community Builders Handbook" (PhD diss., University of Illinois at Urbana-Champaign, 2009), pp. 95–108; Urban Land Institute, *The Community Builders Handbook*, 5th revised printing, J. Ross McKeever, ed. (Washington DC: Urban Land Institute, 1960), pp. 131–135.

105. American Public Health Association, *Planning the Neighborhood*, by Anatole A. Solow and Ann Copperman (Chicago: Public Administration Service, 1948), pp. v–vi, xii, 1–3.

106. American Public Health Association, *Planning the Neighborhood*, pp. 55–59.

107. Tridib Banerjee and William C. Baer, *Beyond the Neighborhood Unit: Residential Environments and Public Policy* (New York: Plenum Press, 1984), p. 25.

108. National Committee for Traffic Safety, *Building Traffic Safety into Residential Developments* (Chicago, National Committee for Traffic Safety, [1950]), pp. 2, 38; Burton W. Marsh, "Traffic In Residence Streets," in Harlean James, ed., *American Planning And Civic Annual*, 1950 ed. (Washington, DC: American Planning and Civic Association, 1951), pp. 120–121.

109. National Committee for Traffic Safety, *Building Traffic Safety*, pp. 6–18.

110. Richard F. Weingroff, "A Vast System of Interconnected Highways: Before the Interstates," 9 September 2014, pp. 272–274, from US Department of Transportation, Federal Highway Administration, "Highway History: The Interstate System" (website), http://www.fhwa.dot.gov; US Department of Transportation, Federal Highway Administration, *America's Highways 1776–1976* (Washington, DC: USGPO, 1977), pp. 159–160; American Association of State Highway Officials, "Design Standards for the National System of Interstate Highways," adopted 1 August 1945, in *Policies on Geometric Highway Design*

(Washington, DC: AASHO, 1950), pp. 1–2, 5–6; American Association of State Highway Officials, *A Policy on Arterial Highways in Urban Areas* (Washington, DC: AASHO, 1957), pp. 69–70.

111.   Frederick W. Cron, "Highway Design for Motor Vehicles," part 8, *Public Roads*, vol. 40, no. 3 (December 1976), p. 96.

Chapter 8. Establishment of Functional Classification

1.   Automotive Safety Foundation, *Motorized America in War and Peace* (Washington, DC: Automotive Safety Foundation, 1945), p. 57; Automotive Safety Foundation, *Annual Report 1960* (Washington, DC: Automotive Safety Foundation, 1960).

2.   Carl E. Fritts and C. F. McCormack, "System Classification—Basis for Sound Highway Policy," *ASF Report*, no. 8 (June 1960), p. 8; Institute of Transportation Engineers, *Pioneers of Transportation* (Washington, DC: Institute of Transportation Engineers, 2011), p. 57.

3.   Bruce E. Seely, *Building the American Highway System: Engineers as Policy Makers* (Philadelphia: Temple University Press, 1987), pp. 179, 182.

4.   California Legislature, Joint Fact-Finding Committee on Highways, Streets and Bridges, *Engineering Facts and a Future Program*, by G. Donald Kennedy (Sacramento, CA: California Legislature, 1946), pp. 85, 127–138; "Panel Discussion on Highway Department Public Relations," in American Association of State Highway Officials, *Convention Group Meetings: Papers and Discussions* (Washington, DC: AASHO, 1947), pp. 133–138.

5.   Institute of Transportation Engineers, *Pioneers of Transportation*, pp. 34, 57; "D. Grant Mickle Executive Director of Highway Research Board," *American Highways*, vol. 43, no. 1 (January 1964), p. 49.

6.   Wilfred Owen, *The Metropolitan Transportation Problem* (Washington, DC: Brookings Institution, 1956), pp. 58–61; David R. Levin and Marion G. Markham, "Statutory Authority of State Highway Departments in Municipalities," *Public Roads*, vol. 25, no. 8 (June 1949), p. 161; Automotive Safety Foundation, *Louisiana's Highway Problem*, report to the Louisiana Legislative Council (Washington, DC: Automotive Safety Foundation, 1954), pp. 72–74; Automotive Safety Foundation, *Highway Transportation in Minnesota*, report to the Minnesota Highway Study Commission (Washington, DC: Automotive Safety Foundation, 1954), pp. 42, 60.

7.   Automotive Safety Foundation, *A Plan for Highway Classification in Maine*, report to the State Highway Commission of Maine (Washington, DC: Automotive Safety Foundation, 1952), pp. 4, 20; Owen, *The Metropolitan Transportation Problem*, pp. 54, 61–65.

8.   ASF argued that Depression-era finances were one cause of excessive rural highway mileage. Counties and localities had been unable to pay for their minor roads, so many state highway departments had relieved them of the financial burden by reclassifying minor rural roads as highways. See Carl E. Fritts and C. F. McCormack, "System Classification—Basis for Sound Highway Policy," *ASF Report*, no. 8 (June 1960), p. 3.

9.   Automotive Safety Foundation, *A Plan for Highway Classification in Maine*, pp. 36, 39; Automotive Safety Foundation, *A Highway Program for Kentucky* (Washington, DC: Automotive Safety Foundation, 1955), pp. 55, 66–67; Automotive Safety Foundation, *Facing Up to Cleveland's Traffic Problems* (Washington, DC: Automotive Safety Foundation, 1953), pp. 20, 23–24; Michigan Good Roads Federation, *Highway Needs in Michigan* (Detroit: Michigan Good Roads Federation, 1948), p. 109.

10.   Thomas H. MacDonald, "A Choice of Guides," *American Highways*, vol. 32, no. 1 (January 1953), pp. 34–36. Chief MacDonald retired from BPR in 1953 and joined the recently formed Texas Transportation Institute. MacDonald's assistant, Lawrence S. Tuttle, resigned after 25 years with BPR to take a position with ASF. See "Lawrence S. Tuttle Leaves Bureau of Public Roads," *American Highways*, vol. 32, no. 4 (October 1953), p. 13.

11.   Institute of Transportation Engineers, *Pioneers of Transportation*, p. 35; "Walter Pyke Johnson, 1889–1969," *American Highways*, vol. 48, no. 2 (April 1969), p. 16; President's Advisory Committee on a National Highway Program, transcript of hearings, Washington, DC, 7–8 October 1954, p. 40, accessed from Eno Center for Transportation, http://www.enotrans.org/wp-content/uploads/2017/08/1954-10-7-8-Clay-Committee-hearings-transcript.pdf.

12.   Alan E. Pisarski, "J. Douglas Carroll, Jr.: Pioneer of Urban Transportation Planning," *TR News*, no. 283 (November-December 2012), p. 34.

13.   Roger L. Creighton, *Urban Transportation Planning* (Urbana, IL: University of Illinois Press, 1970), pp. 132–133; Andrew V. Plummer, "The Chicago Area Transportation Study: Creating the First Plan

(1955–1962)" (Chicago: Chicago Area Transportation Study, 2006), pp. 7, 9, http://www.surveyarchive.org/Chicago/cats_1954–62.pdf.

14. Creighton, *Urban Transportation Planning*, p. 131.

15. State of Michigan, State Highway Department, *Report on the Detroit Metropolitan Area Traffic Study*, part 1 (July 1955), p. 30; State of Illinois, Department of Public Works and Buildings, *Chicago Area Transportation Study*, vol. 1 (December 1959), p. 77.

16. Creighton, *Urban Transportation Planning*, p. 94; *Detroit Metropolitan Area Traffic Study*, part 2 (March 1956), p. 45; *Chicago Area Transportation Study*, vol. 3 (April 1962), pp. 27–36.

17. *Chicago Area Transportation Study*, vol. 1, p. 77; vol. 3, pp. 21, 71.

18. Creighton, *Urban Transportation Planning*, p. 204.

19. D. Grant Mickle, "Attacking the Urban Transportation Crisis," *ASF Report*, no. 4 (March 1959), pp. 2–4.

20. Institute of Transportation Engineers, *Pioneers of Transportation*, pp. 51, 57; E. H. Holmes, "Urban Transportation Planning and the National Highway Program," speech given at AASHO annual meeting, 1 December 1960, in *American Highways*, vol. 40, no. 1 (January 1961), p. 10; National Committee on Urban Transportation, *Better Transportation for Your City* (Chicago: Public Administration Service, 1958), pp. iii–x, 2.

21. National Committee on Urban Transportation, *Better Transportation*, pp. 2–3.

22. National Committee on Urban Transportation, *Procedure Manual*, vol. 7A, *Standards for Street Facilities and Services* (Chicago: Public Administration Service, 1958), pp. 2–13.

23. American Association of State Highway Officials, *A Policy on Arterial Highways in Urban Areas* (Washington, DC: AASHO, 1957), pp. 70, 119; National Committee on Urban Transportation, *Better Transportation*, p. 62.

24. National Committee on Urban Transportation, *Standards for Street Facilities and Services*, p. 9; Michael Mehaffy et al., "Urban Nuclei and the Geometry of Streets: The 'Emergent Neighborhoods' Model," *Urban Design International*, vol. 15, no. 1 (Spring 2010), pp. 32–36.

25. American Association Of State Highway Officials, *A Policy on Arterial Highways in Urban Areas*, pp. 67, 86. The Red Book also advised that dead-end local streets were advantageous for residential and industrial areas; see pp. 187–188.

26. National Committee on Urban Transportation, *Better Transportation for Your City*, pp. 6–8; National Committee on Urban Transportation, *Standards for Street Facilities and Services*, pp. 1–2.

27. National Committee on Urban Transportation, *Better Transportation*, pp. 8–10, 73–75.

28. "NCUT Disbands," *ASF Report*, no. 8 (June 1960), p. 10; E. H. Holmes, "The State-Of-The-Art in Urban Transportation Planning or How We Got Here," *Transportation*, vol. 1, no. 4 (March 1973), p. 383.

29. "D. Grant Mickle Named Deputy Federal Highway Administrator," *American Highways*, vol. 40, no. 4 (October 1961), pp. 2, 36; "D. Grant Mickle Executive Director of Highway Research Board," *American Highways*, vol. 43, no. 1 (January 1964), p. 49; "D. Grant Mickle, President of Huffsam, Receives HRB's 1973 Roy W. Crum Award," *Highway Research News*, no. 54 (1974), p. 5.

30. National Association of County Engineers, *First Forty Years of NACE* (Bradenton, FL: National Association of County Engineers, 1996), pp. ii–iii, 4, 12, 15, 21, 106–107, http://www.facers.org/wp-content/uploads/2011/08/NACE-History-First-Forty-Years-of-NACE-1956-through-1995.pdf.

31. Automotive Safety Foundation, *Annual Report 1958* (Washington, DC: Automotive Safety Foundation, 1958), pp. 10, 20; Automotive Safety Foundation, *Annual Report 1963* (Washington, DC: Automotive Safety Foundation, 1963), pp. 17, 40; AASHO-NACO-NACE Joint Subcommittee on Functional Highway Classification, *A Guide for Functional Highway Classification* (Washington, DC: National Association of Counties, 1966), p. 6.

32. AASHO-NACO-NACE, *A Guide for Functional Highway Classification*, pp. 11–12.

33. AASHO-NACO-NACE, *A Guide for Functional Highway Classification*, pp. 12–13; Raymond A. Mohl, "Stop the Road: Freeway Revolts In American Cities," *Journal of Urban History*, vol. 3, no. 5 (July 2004), p. 678.

34. AASHO-NACO-NACE, *A Guide for Functional Highway Classification*, pp. 9, 15.

35. US Congress, Senate Committee on Public Works, *Federal-Aid Highway Act of 1968: Hearings before the Subcommittee on Roads*, 90th Congress, 2nd session, June 1968, p. 201; US Congress, House Committee on Public Works, *Preliminary Report of AASHO on Federal-Aid Highway Needs after 1972: Hearing before the Committee on Public Works*, 90th Congress, 1st session, June 1967, p. 41.

36. Automotive Safety Foundation, *Functional Highway Classification in Urban Areas* (Washington, DC: Automotive Safety Foundation, 1967), p. 32.

37. Automotive Safety Foundation, *Functional Highway Classification in Urban Areas*, pp. 5, 11–16, 28, 30.

38. J. O. Granum, "Functional Highway System Classification," in Automotive Safety Foundation, *ASF Monitor*, no. 1 (Washington, DC: Automotive Safety Foundation, 1969), p. 16.

39. Automotive Safety Foundation, *Functional Highway Classification in Urban Areas*, pp. 10, 16–17, 26.

40. Automotive Safety Foundation, *Functional Highway Classification in Urban Areas*, pp. 28–30.

41. Robert M. Fogelson, *Downtown: Its Rise and Fall, 1880–1950* (New Haven, CT: Yale University Press, 2001), pp. 314–316; Joseph F. C. DiMento and Cliff Ellis, *Changing Lanes: Visions and Histories of Urban Freeways* (Cambridge, MA: MIT Press, 2012), pp. 122–127; A. E. Johnson, "Urbanization, the Automobile and You," *American Highways*, vol. 41, no. 3, July 1962, p. 3; E. H. Holmes, "Urban Transportation Planning and the National Highway Program," for AASHO annual meeting, 1 December 1960, in *American Highways*, vol. 40, no. 1 (January 1961), p. 37; E. H. Holmes, "The State-of-the-Art in Urban Transportation Planning or How We Got Here," *Transportation*, vol. 1, no. 4 (March 1973), pp. 389–390, 395–399.

42. US Department of Transportation, Federal Highway Administration, "President Dwight D. Eisenhower and the Federal Role In Highway Safety" (monograph), by Richard F. Weingroff, September 2003, pp. 139–145, 150–152, 169, http://www.fhwa.dot.gov/infrastructure/safety.pdf.

43. US Department of Transportation, Federal Highway Administration, "Busting the Trust: Unraveling the Highway Trust Fund 1968–1978" (monograph), by Richard F. Weingroff, June 2013, pp. 45–62, http://www.fhwa.dot.gov/highwayhistory/busting_the_trust.pdf.

44. US Congress, House Committee on Public Works, *1968 National Highway Needs Report*, by US Department of Transportation, H.R. report no. 90–22, February 1968, pp. 47–48, 51–52; US Congress, House Committee on Public Works, *Supplement to the 1968 National Highway Needs Report*, by US Department of Transportation, H.R. report no. 90–22A, July 1968, pp. 4–6.

45. US Congress, *1968 National Highway Needs Report*, pp. 1–2, 42, 49–49; US Congress, *Supplement to the 1968 National Highway Needs Report*, pp. 3–4.

46. US Congress, Senate Committee on Public Works, *Federal-Aid Highway Act of 1968: Hearings before the Subcommittee on Roads*, 90th Congress, 2nd session, June 1968, pp. 97–98, 112, 137, 138, 196, 201, 278–279, 287–288, 309–311, 358.

47. US Congress, Senate Committee on Public Works, *Federal-Aid Highway Act of 1968: Hearings*, p. 93; US Congress, House Committee on Public Works, *1968 National Highway Needs Report*, pp. 33–34; "A Preliminary Presentation of the AASHO Special Committee for Planning a Continuing Federal-Aid Highway Program–1967," *American Highways*, vol. 47, no. 4 (October 1968), p. 26. These design techniques drew from BPR's report *Increasing the Traffic-Carrying Capability of Urban Arterial Streets: The Wisconsin Avenue Study* (1962) and paralleled the federal Traffic Operations Program to Increase Capacity and Safety (TOPICS). The latter was merged with the other federal-aid systems after 1973.

48. *Federal-Aid Highway Act of 1968*, Public Law 90–495, 82 Stat. 815 (1968), § 17.

49. US Department of Transportation, Federal Highway Administration, Bureau of Public Roads, *1968 National Highway Functional Classification Study Manual* (Washington, DC: USGPO, April 1969), pp. II-1 to II-6.

50. US Department of Transportation, *1968 National Highway Functional Classification Study Manual*, pp. II-15, III-21.

51. US Department of Transportation, *1968 National Highway Functional Classification Study Manual*, pp. I-2, I-3.

52. US Congress, House Committee on Public Works, *1970 National Highway Needs Report with Supplement*, by US Department of Transportation, H.R. report no. 91–28, September 1970, pp. 26–27, 41, 86–87, 95.

53. *Federal-Aid Highway Act of 1970*, Public Law 91–605, 84 Stat. 1713 (1968), § 106, 121; US Department of Transportation, Federal Highway Administration, Bureau of Public Roads, *National Highway Functional Classification and Needs Study Manual (1970 to 1990)* (Washington, DC: USGPO, February 1970), pp. III-13 to III-16, III-41 to III-45.

54. Federal Highway Administration, *Busting the Trust*, pp. 90–102, 154–155, 195; John Burby, *The Great American Motion Sickness: or Why You Can't Get There from Here* (Boston: Little, Brown, 1971), pp. 311–312.

55. US Congress, Senate Committee on Public Works, *Federal-Aid Highway Act of 1973: Hearings before the Subcommittee on Transportation*, 93rd Congress, 1st session, February 1973, pp. 137, 313–314, 512, 516–517, 526, 708, 809.

56. *Federal-Aid Highway Act of 1973*, Public Law 93–87, 87 Stat. 250 (1973), § 109, 148; US Department of Transportation, Federal Highway Administration, *Highway Statistics 1980* (Washington, DC: USGPO, 1981), pp. 103, 113.

57. Richard Weingroff, "Creating A Landmark: The Intermodal Surface Transportation Act of 1991," *Public Roads*, vol. 65, no. 3 (November/December 2001), p. 16.

58. Herbert S. Levinson, "Street Spacing and Scale," in Transportation Research Board, *Circular E-C019: Urban Street Symposium* (Washington, DC: National Research Council, 1999), section B7, pp. 7–10; Transportation Research Board, "Driveway and Intersection Spacing," *Transportation Research Circular*, no. 456 (Washington, DC: National Research Council, March 1996), pp. 13–15, 27–29.

59. Richard A. Hall, "Walkable Streets: Re-engineering the Suburban DNA," Knight Program in Community Building at University of Miami School of Architecture, 2003, pp. 7–9, http://cbp.arc.miami.edu/publications/ResearchPDFs/Rick%20Hall%20Reportweb2.pdf. The American Association of Highway and Transportation Officials (AASHTO) added "Transportation" to its name in 1973.

60. Michael Southworth and Peter M. Owens, "The Evolving Metropolis: Studies of Community, Neighborhood, and Street Form at the Urban Edge," *Journal of the American Planning Association*, vol. 59, no. 3 (Summer 1993), pp. 271–287.

61. ARTISTS (Arterial Streets Towards Sustainability) Consortium, *A First Theoretical Approach to Classification of Arterial Streets*, document D1.1, by Stephen Marshall, July 2002, pp. 9, 14–20, 52–56, http://home.wmin.ac.uk/transport/download/d1_1.pdf.

Chapter 9. Mid-Twentieth Century to Early Twenty-First

1. Carmen Hass-Klau, *The Pedestrian and City Traffic* (London: Bellhaven, 1990), pp. 158–162; Neil Parkyn, "Sir Colin Buchanan," *The Guardian*, 10 December 2001, p. 20.

2. Great Britain, Ministry of Transport, *Traffic in Towns: A Study of the Long Term Problems of Traffic in Urban Areas* (London: HMSO, 1963), pp. 12, 26–27, 38.

3. Ministry of Transport, *Traffic in Towns*, pp. 16, 39–40.

4. Ministry of Transport, *Traffic in Towns*, pp. 14–23, 50.

5. Ministry of Transport, *Traffic in Towns*, p. 32.

6. Ministry of Transport, *Traffic in Towns*, pp. 32, 44–48.

7. Ministry of Transport, *Traffic in Towns*, pp. 23, 50, 193–195.

8. Ministry of Transport, *Traffic in Towns*, preface, paragraph 22; Hass-Klau, *The Pedestrian and City Traffic*, p. 175.

9. Ministry of Transport, *Traffic in Towns*, p. 196.

10. Hass-Klau, *The Pedestrian and City Traffic*, p. 166–170, 174, 234–237; Malcolm Buchanan, "More or Less Traffic in Towns?" *Proceedings of the Institution of Civil Engineers – Transport*, vol. 157, no. 1 (February 2004), p. 31.

11. Donald Appleyard, *Livable Streets* (Berkeley, CA: University of California Press, 1981), pp. 3, 152.

12. Appleyard, *Livable Streets*, p. 15; San Francisco, Department of City Planning, *Street Livability Study*, by Donald Appleyard (San Francisco: Department of City Planning, 1970), pp. 7, 12.

13. Appleyard, *Livable Streets*, pp. 16–28.

14. US Department of Transportation, Federal Highway Administration, *State of the Art: Residential Traffic Management*, by Daniel T. Smith Jr. and Donald Appleyard et al. (Washington, DC: USGPO, 1980), pp. 3–4, 30; Organisation for Economic Co-operation and Development, *Better Towns with Less Traffic* (Paris: OECD, 1975), pp. 3–6, 258–260; Appleyard, *Livable Streets*, pp. 150–154, 199, 311–317.

15. US Department of Transportation, Federal Highway Administration, *Improving the Residential Street Environment*, by Daniel T. Smith Jr. and Donald Appleyard (Washington, DC: USGPO, 1981), pp. 13–15, 21–34; Appleyard, *Livable Streets*, pp. 310–311.

16. Appleyard, *Livable Streets*, p. 155.

17. Appleyard, *Livable Streets*, pp. 157–165, 179–181; Mayer Hillman and Irwin Henderson, "Towards a Better Kind of Environmental Area," *New Society*, vol. 25, no. 562 (12 July 1973), pp. 75–76.

18. Appleyard, *Livable Streets*, pp. 185–194.

19. Appleyard, *Livable Streets*, pp. 215–236.

20. Federal Highway Administration, *Improving the Residential Street Environment*, pp. 5, 35, 42.

21. Appleyard, *Livable Streets*, pp. 260–261; Hillman and Henderson, "Towards a Better Kind of Environmental Area," p. 77.

22. Appleyard, *Livable Streets*, pp. 253, 291.

23. Peter L. Laurence, *Becoming Jane Jacobs* (Philadelphia: University of Pennsylvania Press, 2016), pp. 19–28, 50–70.

24. Laurence, *Becoming Jane Jacobs*, pp. 70–71, 77–79, 83.

25. Laurence, *Becoming Jane Jacobs*, pp. 94–95, 122–123, 142–144.

26. Laurence, *Becoming Jane Jacobs*, pp. 144–148; [Jane Jacobs], "Philadelphia's Redevelopment: A Progress Report," *Architectural Forum*, vol. 103, no. 1 (July 1955), pp. 126–127.

27. Jacobs, "Philadelphia's Redevelopment," pp. 118, 120.

28. Jane Jacobs, "Washington: 20th Century Capital?" *Architectural Forum*, vol. 104, no. 1 (January 1956), p. 107

29. Jane Jacobs, "Typical Downtown Transformed," *Architectural Forum*, vol. 104, no. 5 (May 1956), pp. 146–155; [Jane Jacobs], "Central City: Concentration vs. Congestion," *Architectural Forum*, vol. 105, no. 3 (September 1956), pp. 115–119.

30. Laurence, *Becoming Jane Jacobs*, pp. 182–183, 188–189, 263–267.

31. Laurence, *Becoming Jane Jacobs*, pp. 162–163, 230–231; Anthony Flint, *Wrestling with Moses: How Jane Jacobs Took On New York's Master Builder and Transformed the American City* (New York: Random House, 2009), p. 62.

32. Jane Jacobs, *The Death and Life of Great American Cities* (New York: Random House, 1961), pp. 360–363; Flint, *Wrestling with Moses*, pp. 85–88; Joseph C. Ingraham, "Moses Says Jack Reneges on Road," *New York Times*, 24 December 1957, p. 16; "Road Test Hailed in Washington Sq." *New York Times*, 25 November 1958, p. 35.

33. Laurence, *Becoming Jane Jacobs*, pp. 238, 240–241, 246–252; Jane Jacobs, "Downtown is for People" *Fortune*, vol. 57, no. 4 (April 1958), pp. 134, 137–138, 236.

34. Jacobs, *Death and Life*, pp. 16, 150–151.

35. Jacobs, *Death and Life*, pp. 8–9, 19–20, 50, 116, 439.

36. Jacobs, *Death and Life*, pp. 47–50, 71–72.

37. Jacobs, *Death and Life*, pp. 87–88, 178–186, 217, 364.

38. Jacobs, *Death and Life*, pp. 338, 349–355.

39. Jacobs, *Death and Life*, pp. 343, 348, 363, 367.

40. Jacobs, *Death and Life*, pp. 364, 367.

41. Jacobs, *Death and Life*, pp. 269, 344–349.

42. Mark Osbaldeston, *Unbuilt Toronto: A History of the City That Might Have Been* (Toronto: Dundurn, 2008), pp. 53–60; Canada, Government of Ontario, "Harbour City" (promotional film), 1970, http://www.youtube.com/watch?v=2jvS6PexWF0.

43. Flint, *Wrestling with Moses*, pp. 124–130; Laurence, *Becoming Jane Jacobs*, pp. 289–293.

44. Christopher Alexander, "A City Is Not a Tree," *Architectural Forum*, vol. 122, no. 1 (April 1965), pp. 58–62 and no. 2 (May 1965), pp. 58–61.

45. Christopher Alexander, *A City is Not a Tree*, 50th anniversary ed., Michael Mehaffy, ed. (Portland, OR: Sustaisis, 2015), pp. 40–42, 154–156, 63, 168–177, 185–195.

46. Richard White, "Jane Jacobs and the Paradigm Shift: Toronto 1968–1978," in Dirk Schubert, ed., *Contemporary Perspectives on Jane Jacobs: Reassessing the Impacts of an Urban Visionary* (London: Routledge, 2016), p. 38–39; John Sewell, *How We Changed Toronto, 1969–1980* (Toronto: James Lorimer, 2015), pp. 39–40.

47. City of Toronto Housing Department, *St. Lawrence: 1974–1979* (Toronto: 1979), p. 7–8; David Gordon and Joseph DeLeo, "Directions for New Urban Neighborhoods: Learning from St. Lawrence," University of Calgary, Centre for Environmental Design Research and Outreach, 1996, p. 5.

48. Sewell, *How We Changed Toronto*, pp. 125–126; Toronto Housing Department, *St. Lawrence: 1974–1979*, p. 18; Richard White, *Planning Toronto: the Planners, the Plans, their Legacies* (Vancouver, BC: University of British Columbia Press, 2016), p. 328.

49. White, "Jane Jacobs and the Paradigm Shift," p. 41; Sewell, *How We Changed Toronto, 1969–1980*, p. 128.

50. Sewell, *How We Changed Toronto*, p. 129; Dave LeBlanc, "35 Years On, St. Lawrence is a Template for Urban Housing," *Globe and Mail*, 8 February 2013, p. G4.

51. White, "Jane Jacobs and the Paradigm Shift," pp. 41–42.

52. Sewell, *How We Changed Toronto*, p. 129.

53. Sewell, *How We Changed Toronto*, pp. 129–130, 286; Toronto Housing Department, *St. Lawrence: 1974–1979*, pp. 19–20, 24, 29; White, "Jane Jacobs and the Paradigm Shift," p. 42.

54. Gordon and DeLeo, "Learning from St. Lawrence," pp. 5–6; J. David Hulchanski, "Planning New Urban Neighbourhoods: Lessons from Toronto's St. Lawrence Neighbourhood," University of British Columbia Planning Papers, Canadian Planning Issues no. 28, September 1990, p. 15, http://www.chs.ubc.ca/archives/?q=node/997.

55. Sewell, *How We Changed Toronto*, p. 132; White, "Jane Jacobs and the Paradigm Shift," p. 42.

56. Léon Krier, *The Architecture of Community* (Washington, DC: Island Press, 2009), p. 327; *Leon Krier: Drawings 1967–1980* (Brussels: Archives d'Architecture Moderne, 1980), p. xviii; Rob Krier, *Architectural Journal 1960–1975* (Berlin: Walter de Gruyter, 2015), pp. 21, 23, http://www.degruyter.com/viewbooktoc/product/457660.

57. Geert Bekaert, "Une mise à nu . . .," in Martin van Schaik and Otakar Máčel, eds., *Exit Utopia: Architectural Provocations, 1956–76* (Munich: Prestel, 2005), p. 301; Léon Krier, personal communication to Laurence Aurbach, 16 May 2016; Krier, *The Architecture of Community*, pp. 327–328.

58. Léon Krier, personal communication to Laurence Aurbach, 15 May 2016; *Leon Krier: Drawings*, pp. xxi–xxii; Léon Krier, "Looking Back without Anger," in van Schaik and Máčel, *Exit Utopia*, pp. 310, 314; Krier, *The Architecture of Community*, p. 328.

59. Léon Krier, personal communication to Laurence Aurbach, 15 May 2016. Note however that Krier was never able to read Jane Jacobs or Christopher Alexander. The similarity of their critiques arose from the similarity of the problems encountered. See Krier, "Looking Back without Anger," p. 314.

60. Richard Economakis, ed., *Leon Krier: Architecture and Urban Design, 1967–1992* (London: Academy Editions, 1992), pp. 41–43; Léon Krier, personal communication to Laurence Aurbach, 15 May 2016.

61. Rob Krier, *Architectural Journal*, pp. 607–609, 637–649, 655–657, 924.

62. Rob Krier, *Urban Space* (London: Academy Editions, 1979), pp. 17, 19, 74–75, 78, 81, 170. First published as *Stadtrum in Theorie und Praxis* (Stuttgart: Karl Kramer, 1975).

63. Léon Krier, personal communication to Laurence Aurbach, 15 May 2016, Léon Krier, "My Kind of Town: Léon Krier on Luxembourg City," *Architecture Today*, no. 223 (November 2011), http://www.architecturetoday.co.uk/?p=20435.

64. Otto Wagner, "The Development of a Great City," *Architectural Record*, vol. 31, no. 5 (May 1912), pp. 492–494; Leon Krier, "The Quartier or City within a City," in *Rational Architecture Rationnelle* (Brussels: Archives d'Architecture Moderne, 1978), pp. 164–165.

65. Kirmo Mikkola, "Eliel Saarinen and Town Planning," in Marika Hausen et al., *Eliel Saarinen: Projects 1896–1923*, trans. Desmond O'Roarke, et. al (Cambridge, MA: MIT Press, 1990), pp. 195, 200–204, 218–219.

66. Mikkola, "Eliel Saarinen and Town Planning," p. 195; Eliel Saarinen, *The City: Its Growth, Its Decay, Its Future* (New York: Reinhold, 1943), pp. 151, 208–212, 251–252, 256–258, 263–264.

67. Léon Krier, "Project for a New Quartier . . .," in van Schaik and Máčel, *Exit Utopia*, p. 278.

68. Leon Krier, "A City within a City: The New Quartier da la Villette Paris 1976," *Architectural Design*, vol. 47, no. 3 (1977), p. 204; Léon Krier, "Project for a New Quartier . . .," pp. 284–285.

69. Krier, "A City within a City," pp. 201, 205; Léon Krier, "The Reconstruction of the City," in *Rational Architecture Rationnelle*, p. 42.

70. Krier, "A City within a City," p. 201; Jaquelin Robertson, "The Empire Strikes Back," in Demetri Porphyrios, ed., *Leon Krier: Houses, Palaces, Cities* (London: Architectural Design, 1984), p. 11.

71. Economakis, *Leon Krier*, pp. 87–101.

72. David Watkin, "Leon Krier," in Economakis, *Leon Krier*, pp. 12–13.

73. Léon Krier, "Urban Components," in Porphyrios, *Leon Krier*, pp. 43–46.

74. Léon Krier, personal communication to Laurence Aurbach, 16 May 2016.

75. Léon Krier, "Definition and Location of the Urban Quarter," in Economakis, *Leon Krier*, p. 30; Léon Krier, personal communication to Laurence Aurbach, 20 May 2016.

76.   Anthony Flint, *Wrestling with Moses* (New York: Random House, 2009), pp. 83, 104, 107, 162–163; Paul Goldberger, "A Design-Conscious Mayor," in Joseph P. Viteritti, ed., *Summer in the City: John Lindsay, New York, and the American Dream* (Baltimore, MD: Johns Hopkins University Press, 2014), p. 144.

77.   Goldberger, "A Design-Conscious Mayor," pp. 139, 143, 146–148.

78.   David L. A. Gordon, *Battery Park City: Politics and Planning on the New York Waterfront* (Amsterdam: Gordon and Breach, 1997), pp. 3–4.

79.   Gordon, *Battery Park City*, pp. 7–21, 29–37.

80.   Battery Park City Authority, *Battery Park City Draft Summary Report and 1979 Master Plan*, by Alexander Cooper Associates, October 1979, pp. 6–9; Gordon, *Battery Park City*, p. 61.

81.   Gordon, *Battery Park City*, pp. 51–60, 107.

82.   Carter B. Horsley, "Young Firm Shaping Future Of Two Areas," *New York Times*, 28 June 1981, p. R1; Battery Park City Authority, *Battery Park City*, pp. 14–15.

83.   Battery Park City Authority, *Battery Park City*, pp. 46–47, 60–62.

84.   Battery Park City Authority, *Battery Park City*, pp. 16, 44–54.

85.   Gordon, *Battery Park City*, p. 77.

86.   Battery Park City Authority, *Annual Report* (2016), p. 2, http://bpca.ny.gov; "Battery Park City Master Plan and Guidelines," *Progressive Architecture*, vol. 65, no. 1 (January 1884), pp. 136–137; Gordon, *Battery Park City*, pp. 107–116; Alexander Cooper, personal communication to Laurence Aurbach, 12 October 2017.

87.   Andrés Duany, "The Road to Seaside," in Dhiru A. Thadani, *Visions of Seaside: Foundation / Evolution / Imagination: Built and Unbuilt Architecture* (New York: Rizzoli, 2013), pp. 61–69; Joanna Lombard, *The Architecture of Duany Plater-Zyberk and Company* (New York: Rizzoli, 2005), pp. 42–46; Vincent Scully, "Back to the Future, With a Detour Through Miami," *New York Times*, 27 January 1991, p. H32.

88.   University of Miami, School of Architecture, Architectural Engineering and Planning, *Architecture for Key West: A Proposal for the Return to Civilian Use of the Former Submarine Base* (Coral Gables, FL: University of Miami, 1977), pp. 2–3.

89.   University of Miami, *Architecture for Key West*, pp. 10–11.

90.   Steven Brooke, *Seaside*, 2nd ed. (Gretna, LA: Pelican, 2005), pp. 13–14; Thadani, *Visions of Seaside*, pp. 31–34, 98, 162–163.

91.   David Mohney and Keller Easterling, eds., *Seaside* (Princeton Architectural Press, 1991), p. 62; "Development Plan Hinges on Road Relocation," *Destin* (Florida) *Log*, 6 March 1980; Thadani, *Visions of Seaside*, pp. 164–169.

92.   Robert A. Davis, personal communications to Laurence Aurbach, 14 December 2016 and 3 January 2017; Andrés Duany, personal communication to Laurence Aurbach, 3 November 2016; Mohney, *Seaside*, pp. 62–63.

93.   Andres Duany and Elizabeth Plater-Zyberk, "The Town of Seaside" (Seaside master plan)(Coconut Grove, FL: Andres Duany and Elizabeth Plater-Zyberk, Architects, 1984).

94.   Thadani, *Visions of Seaside*, pp. 176–181.

95.   Duany and Plater-Zyberk, "The Town of Seaside"; "Building a Down Home Utopia," *Time*, 4 November 1985, p. 81.

96.   "The Town of Seaside," *Progressive Architecture*, vol. 65, no. 1 (January 1884), p. 139; "Building a Down Home Utopia," p. 81; Robert A. Davis, personal communication to Laurence Aurbach, 14 Dec. 2016.

97.   Mohney, *Seaside*, pp. 76, 83–85.

98.   Andres Duany, "Traditional Towns" (based on a 1988 Seaside Symposium lecture), *Architectural Design*, vol. 59, no. 9–10 (1989), p. 61.

99.   Emily Talen, ed., *Charter of the New Urbanism*, 2nd ed. (New York: McGraw-Hill, 2013); Diane Dorney, "Miami Makes Ten," *Town Paper*, vol. 4, no. 2 (Summer 2002), http://www.tndtownpaper.com/Volume4/miami_makes_ten.htm.

100.   Richard A. Hall, personal communication to Laurence Aurbach, 11 February 2016.

101.   Ruth Eckdish Knack, "Repent, Ye Sinners, Repent," *Planning*, vol. 55, no. 8 (August 1989), p. 7; Alex Krieger and William Lennertz, eds., *Andres Duany and Elizabeth Plater-Zyberk: Town and Town Making Principles* (New York: Rizzoli, 1991), p. 103.

102.   Hazel Borys, Emily Talen, and Matthew Lambert, "Codes Study" (web pages), PlaceMakers, February 2017, http://www.placemakers.com/how-we-teach/codes-study/.

103. Frank Spielberg, "The Traditional Neighborhood Development: How Will Traffic Engineers Respond?" *ITE Journal*, vol. 59, no. 9 (September 1989), pp. 17–18; Frank Spielberg, personal communication to Laurence Aurbach, 8 November 2019.

104. ITE Transportation Planning Council Committee 5P-8, *Traditional Neighborhood Development: Street Design Guidelines*, ITE recommended practice, by Chester E. Chellman (Washington, DC: Institute of Transportation Engineers, 1999), pp. iv, 5–7, 10.

105. Walter Kulash, personal communication to Laurence Aurbach, 23 August 2016.

106. Walter Kulash, Joe Anglin, and David Marks, "Traditional Neighborhood Development: Will the Traffic Work?" paper presented at Successful Land Development: Quality and Profits (conference), American Society of Civil Engineers, Orlando, Florida, 5–7 March 1990, pp. 8, 11, 13, 18, 20.

107. Walter Kulash, personal communication to Laurence Aurbach, 23 August 2016.

108. Walter Kulash, *Residential Streets*, 3rd ed. (Washington, DC: Urban Land Institute, 2001), pp. 17–20.

109. Daniel Slone and Doris S. Goldstein, *A Legal Guide to Urban and Sustainable Development for Planners, Developers and Architects* (Hoboken, NJ: John Wiley & Sons, 2008), pp. 219–221, Robert Davis, "The WaterGates," in Thadani, *Visions of Seaside*, pp. 525–527.

110. Seaside Town Council, letter to homeowners, 4 June 2006; Robert A. Davis, personal communication to Laurence Aurbach, 4 January 2017; Jay Liles, "The 30A Mobility Project: A Timeline," *Seaside Times*, July-August 2016, p. 18.

111. Robert W. Burchell, David Listokin, and Catherine C. Galley, "Smart Growth: More Than a Ghost of Urban Policy Past, Less Than a Bold New Horizon," *Housing Policy Debate*, vol. 11, no. 4 (2000), pp. 824–826, 842, 850–852.

112. American Planning Association, "Policy Guide on Smart Growth," April 2002, p. 13, http://planning.org/policyguides; Susan Handy, Robert G. Paterson, and Kent Butler, *Planning for Street Connectivity: Getting from Here to There*, Planning Advisory Service report no. 515 (Chicago: American Planning Association, 2003), pp. 22–58.

113. Smart Growth America and State Smart Transportation Initiative, *The Innovative DOT: A Handbook of Policy and Practice*, 3rd ed., January 2015, pp. 103, 106, 161–162.

114. Norman W. Garrick and Jianhong (Jane) Wang, "New Concepts for Context-Based Design of Streets and Highways," *Transportation Research Record*, no. 1912 (2005), pp. 58–59.

115. Institute of Transportation Engineers and Congress for the New Urbanism, *Designing Walkable Urban Thoroughfares: A Context Sensitive Approach* (Washington, DC: Intitute of Transportation Engineers, 2010), pp. 5–6, 25–32.

116. Congress for the New Urbanism, "CNU/ITE Manual" (web page), July 2015, http://www.cnu.org/our-projects/cnu-ite-manual; US Department of Transportation, Federal Highway Administration, "Bicycle and Pedestrian Facility Design Flexibility" (memorandum), 20 August 2013, http://www.fhwa.dot.gov/environment/bicycle_pedestrian/guidance/design_flexibility.cfm.

117. Don Samdahl (co-chair of ITE committee that produced *Planning Urban Roadway Systems*), personal communication to Laurence Aurbach, 19 December 2017. The original ITE arterial-network guidebook was: Institute of Traffic Engineers, *System Considerations for Urban Arterial Streets* (Washington, DC: Institute of Traffic Engineers, 1969).

118. Institute of Transportation Engineers, *Planning Urban Roadway Systems*, no. RP-105D (Washington, DC: Institute of Transportation Engineers, 2014).

119. US Department of Transportation, Federal Highway Administration, *Highway Functional Classification Concepts, Criteria and Procedures*, no. FHWA-PL-13-026 (2013), pp. 6, 42, 46–48.

120. Christopher Barrington-Leigh and Adam Millard-Ball, "A Century of Sprawl in the United States," *PNAS*, vol. 112, no. 27 (7 July 2015), pp. 8244–8249; David J. Giacomin and David M. Levinson, "Road Network Circuity in Metropolitan Areas," *Environment and Planning B*, vol. 42, no. 6 (November 2015), pp. 1040–1053.

121. Great Britain, Department of the Environment, Transport and the Regions, *Places, Streets and Movement* (London: DETR, 1998); Llewlyn-Davis and Alan Baxter & Associates, *Urban Design Compendium*, prepared for English Partnerships and the Housing Corporation (London: English Partnerships, 2000); Great Britain, Department for Transport, Local Government and the Regions, *Better Places to Live: By Design* (London: Thomas Telford, 2001); Great Britain, Department for Transport, *Manual for Streets* (London: Thomas Telford, 2007); Chartered Institution of Highways & Transportation, *Manual for Streets 2* (London: CHIT, 2010); Scottish Government, *Designing Streets: A Policy Statement for Scotland*

(Edinburgh: Scottish Government, 2010). All these documents were advisory rather than statutory.

122. David Taylor, "Connectivity and Movement," in Peter Neal, ed., *Urban Villages and the Making of Communities* (London: Spon, 2003), pp. x, 103–117.

123. Andrew Cameron, personal communication to Laurence Aurbach, 11 April 2018.

124. Michael W. Mehaffy, Sergio Porta, and Ombretta Romice, "The 'Neighborhood Unit' on Trial: A Case Study in the Impacts of Urban Morphology," *Journal of Urbanism*, vol. 8, no. 2 (2015), pp. 199–217.

125. Chris Webster, Georg Glasze, and Klaus Frantz, "The Global Spread of Gated Communities," *Environment and Planning B: Planning and Design*, vol. 29, no. 3 (June 2002), pp. 316; US Census, American Housing Survey 2015, summary tables and "Appendix A: Subject Definitions and Table Index," p. 39, http://www.census.gov; Georg Glasze, Chris Webster, and Klaus Frantz, eds., *Private Cities: Global and Local Perspectives* (Abingdon, Oxon, UK: Routledge, 2006), pp. 71–72.

126. Glasze, Webster, and Frantz, *Private Cities*, pp. 101–103, 117–118; Samer Bagaeen and Ola Uduku, eds., *Gated Communities: Social Sustainability in Contemporary and Historical Gated Developments* (London: Easthscan, 2010), pp. 29–35, 39–41, 65–68; Jing Xiu, "Origins of China's Enclosed Neighborhoods," *China News*, 25 February 2016, http://fangtan.china.com.cn/2016–02/25/content_37871485.htm.

127. Glasze, Webster, and Frantz, *Private Cities*.

128. Klaus Frantz, "Private Gated Neighbourhoods," in Glasze, Webster, and Frantz, *Private Cities*, p. 68.

129. Setha Low, "Unlocking the Gated Community," in Glasze, Webster, and Frantz, *Private Cities*, pp. 54–63.

130. Har Ye Kan, Ann Forsyth, and Peter Rowe, "Redesigning China's Superblock Neighbourhoods: Policies, Opportunities and Challenges," *Journal of Urban Design*, vol. 22, no. 6 (2017), pp. 757–777.

131. UN Human Settlements Programme (UN-Habitat), *Planning and Design for Sustainable Urban Mobility: Global Report on Human Settlements 2013*, revised version (Abingdon, Oxon, UK: Routledge, 2014), pp. 45, 49; UITP, "Light Rail in Figures: Statistics Brief," October 2015, p. 2, http://www.uitp.org; Institute for Transportation and Development Policy, "Rapid Transit Trends Show Record Growth in 2016, with Huge Increases in China, Brazil," 17 February 2017, http://www.itdp.org/rapid-transit-trends/.

132. John Schumann, "World Context: And North American Systems," in Gloria Ohland and Shelley Poticha, eds., *Street Smart: Streetcars and Cities in the Twenty-First Century* (Oakland, CA: Reconnecting America, 2009), pp. 10–11; UITP, "Light Rail in Figures," p. 2

133. UITP, "Light Rail in Figures," pp. 1–3; Mohamed Mezghani, "Light Rail Projects Booming in North Africa & the Middle East," *PTI - Public Transport International*, September-October 2008, p. 14.

134. Jeffrey Kenworthy, "An International Comparative Perspective on Fast Rising Motorization and Automobile Dependence," in Harry T. Dimitriou and Ralph Gakenheimer, eds., *Urban Transport in the Developing World* (Cheltenham, UK: Edward Elgar, 2011), pp. 83–84.

135. Herbert S. Levinson et al., *Bus Use of Highways: State of the Art*, NCHRP research report no. 143 (Washington, DC: Highway Research Board, 1973), p. 41; Asha Weinstein Agrawal et al., *Shared-Use Bus Priority Lanes on City Streets*, MTI report no. 11–10 (San Jose, CA: Mineta Transportation Institute, 2012), pp. 7–9.

136. Organisation for Economic Co-operation and Development, *Bus Lanes and Busway Systems* (Paris: OECD, 1977).

137. Jonas Rabinovitch and John Hoehn, "A Sustainable Urban Transportation System: The 'Surface Metro' in Curitiba, Brazil," USAID Environmental and Natural Resources Policy and Training Project, working paper no. 19, May 1995.

138. BRT+ Centre of Excellence and EMBARQ, *Global BRTData* (online database), version 3.33, 7 March 2018, http://www.brtdata.org.

139. Hass-Klau, *The Pedestrian and City Traffic*, pp. 22–24.

140. Melia et al. presented a shorter, simpler typology of carfree schemes. See Steve Melia et al., "Carfree, Low-Car—What's the Difference?" *World Transport Policy & Practice*, vol. 16, no. 2 (August 2010), pp. 24–28, http://worldtransportjournal.com.

141. Simon Field, "Vauban," in Institute for Transportation & Development Policy, *Europe's Vibrant New Low Car(bon) Communities*, by Nicole Foletta and Simon Field (New York: IDTP, 2011), pp. 95–106, http://www.itdp.org; Gregory M. Rowangould, "A Census of the US Near-Roadway Population: Public Health and Environmental Justice Considerations," *Transportation Research Part D*, vol. 25 (December 2013), pp. 59–67.

142. France, Agence de l'Environnement et de la Maîtrise de l'Énergie, *Les zones à faibles émissions (Low Emission Zones) à travers l'Europe*, by Marie Pouponneau et al. (Angers, France: ADEME, 2018), p. 8, www.ademe.fr; Lucas W. Davis, "The Effect of Driving Restrictions on Air Quality in Mexico City," *Journal of Political Economy*, vol. 116, no. 1 (February 2008), pp. 38–81; Wei Zhang et al., "The Effects of License Plate-Based Driving Restrictions on Air Quality," *Journal of Environmental Economics and Management*, vol. 82 (March 2017), pp. 181–220.

143. "How Many Access Regulations?" *Urban Access Regulations in Europe* (website), Sadler Consultants, November 2017, http://urbanaccessregulations.eu; Michelle DeRobertis and Maurizio Tira, "Traffic-Restricted Zones in Italy," *ITE Journal*, vol. 86, no. 12 (December 2016), pp. 44–49.

144. Hass-Klau, *The Pedestrian and City Traffic*, pp. 22–24, 86–89, 156, 195, 197, 204–205, 253.

145. Luigi Tomba, "Gating Urban Spaces in China," in Bagaeen and Uduku, *Gated Communities*, p. 29.

Chapter 10. Conclusion: Evaluating Traffic Separation

1. James Winter, *London's Teeming Streets 1830–1914* (London: Routledge, 1993), pp. 3–8; Asha Elizabeth Weinstein, "The Congestion Evil: Perceptions of Traffic Congestion in Boston in the 1890s and 1920s" (PhD diss., University of California Berkeley, 2002), pp. 462–468.

2. William Haywood, *Report . . . in Relation to the Traffic of the City, and the Improvements Needed in the Public Ways* (London: London Common Council, 1867), p. 38; John Wolfe Barry, "Address on the Streets & Traffic of London," presented to Royal Society of Arts, 15 November 1899 (London: 1899), pp. 10–15.

3. J. Richard Kuzmyak, *Land Use and Traffic Congestion*, Arizona Department of Transportation report no. 618 (Phoenix, AZ: Arizona DOT, 2012), pp. 108–148, http://www.azdot.gov; Brian Bern and Wesley Earl Marshall, "Capacity Analysis of Pedestrian Treatments at Large Arterial Intersections and Comparison with a Lane-Equivalent, Small Intersection Gridded Network," *Journal of Urban Planning and Development*, vol. 139, no. 4 (December 2013), pp. 241–249; Milan Zlatkovic, "Traffic Modeling" in *Utah Street Connectivity Guide* (Orem, UT: Mountainland Association of Governments, 2017), pp. 38–61 and appendix, http://mountainland.org.

4. Pavithra Parthasarathi, "Network Structure and Metropolitan Mobility," *Journal of Transport and Land Use*, vol. 7, no. 2 (2014), pp. 162, 164.

5. Anthony Downs, *Still Stuck in Traffic: Coping With Peak-Hour Traffic Congestion* (Washington, DC: Brookings Institution, 2004), pp. 8–9, 26–28.

6. Australia, Bureau of Infrastructure, Transport and Regional Development, *Traffic and Congestion Cost Trends for Australian Capital Cities*, information sheet no. 74 (Canberra: BITRE, 2015), http://bitre.gov.au; Joe Cortright, *Measuring Urban Transportation Performance: A Critique of Mobility Measures and a Synthesis*, prepared for Rockefeller Foundation (Chicago: CEOs for Cities, 2010), pp. 37–39, http://cityobservatory.org; Prottoy Akbar and Gilles Duranton, "Measuring the Cost of Congestion in Highly Congested City: Bogotá," first draft (2017), pp. 41–42, http://faculty.wharton.upenn.edu.

7. Andrew Mondschein, et al., *Congested Development: A Study of Traffic Delays, Access, and Economic Activity in Metropolitan Los Angeles* (Los Angeles: UCLA Luskin School of Public Affairs, 2015), pp. 30–38.

8. Wesley E. Marshall and Eric Dumbaugh, "Revisiting the Relationship between Traffic Congestion and the Economy: A Longitudinal Examination of US Metropolitan Areas," *Transportation* (23 May 2018), http://doi.org/10.1007/s11116-018-9884-5; Patricia C. Melo, et al., "Agglomeration, Accessibility and Productivity: Evidence for Large Metropolitan Areas in the US," *Urban Studies*, vol. 54, no. 1 (January 2017), pp. 179–195. Researchers have found mixed and inconsistent evidence about congestion's effect on income growth and job growth. One US study found that higher traffic congestion was associated with lower income growth in the 1990s, while in the 2000s it had no significant effect. Job growth may not necessarily be associated with prosperity; for example, in the United States in the 2000s, job growth was associated with income decline. One possible explanation is that new jobs were low-paying, and decreased the nation's average income. See Jangik Jin and Peter Rafferty, "Does Congestion Negatively Affect Income Growth and Employment Growth? Empirical Evidence from US Metropolitan Regions," *Transport Policy*, vol. 55 (April 2017), p. 5.

9. Reid Ewing et al., "Does Urban Sprawl Hold Down Upward Mobility?" *Landscape and Urban Planning*, vol. 148 (April 2016), pp. 80–88.

10. Camillo Sitte, *City Planning According to Artistic Principles*, trans. George R. Collins and Christiane Crasemann Collins (New York: Random House, 1965), pp. 93–96, originally published as *Der Städte-Bau* (Wien: Carl Graeser, 1889).

11. Radburn and 4-way intersections: Fritz Malcher, "The Economic Value of Laying Out Roadways for Steadyflow Traffic," in American Society of Municipal Engineers, *Proceedings of the Thirty-Sixth Annual Convention* (St. Louis, MO: American Society of Municipal Engineers, 1931), pp. 42–45.

12. Harold Marks, "Subdividing for Traffic Safety," *Traffic Quarterly*, vol. 11, no. 3 (July 1957), pp. 308–325.

13. Eric Dumbaugh and Robert Rae, "Safe Urban Form: Revisiting the Relationship Between Community Design and Traffic Safety," *Journal of the American Planning Association*, vol. 75, no. 3 (Summer 2009), pp. 315–317; Wesley Earl Marshall and Norman W. Garrick, "Does Street Network Design Affect Traffic Safety?" *Accident Analysis and Prevention*, vol. 43, no. 3 (May 2011), pp. 769–771.

14. Reid Ewing and Eric Dumbaugh, "The Built Environment and Traffic Safety: A Review of Empirical Evidence," *Journal of Planning Literature*, vol. 23, no. 4 (May 2009), pp. 347–367; Marshall and Garrick, "Does Street Network Design Affect Traffic Safety?" pp. 778–780; Dumbaugh and Rae, "Safe Urban Form," pp. 319–321; Eric Dumbaugh & Wenhao Li, "Designing for the Safety of Pedestrians, Cyclists, and Motorists in Urban Environments," *Journal of the American Planning Association*, vol. 77, no. 1 (Winter 2011), 69–88.

15. Reid Ewing et al., "Urban Sprawl as a Risk Factor in Motor Vehicle Crashes," *Urban Studies*, vol. 53, no. 2 (February 2016), pp. 247–266; Reid Ewing and Shima Hamidi, "Urban Sprawl as a Risk Factor in Motor Vehicle Occupant and Pedestrian Fatalities: Update and Refinement," *Transportation Research Record*, no. 2513 (2015), pp. 40–47; Jiho Yeo et al., "Effects of Urban Sprawl and Vehicle Miles Traveled on Traffic Fatalities," *Traffic Injury Prevention*, vol. 16, no. 4 (2015), pp. 397–403; Pooya Najaf et al., "City-Level Urban Form and Traffic Safety: A Structural Equation Modeling Analysis of Direct and Indirect Effects," *Journal of Transport Geography*, vol. 69 (May 2018), pp. 257–270; Matthew J. Trowbridge et al., "Urban Sprawl and Delayed Ambulance Arrival in the US," *American Journal of Preventive Medicine*, vol. 37, no. 5 (November 2009), pp. 428–432; KC Kiran and Jonathan Corcoran, "Modelling Residential Fire Incident Response Times: A Spatial Analytic Approach," *Applied Geography*, vol. 84 (July 2017), pp. 64–74.

16. Dinesh Mohan et al., "Urban Street Structure and Traffic Safety," *Journal of Safety Research*, vol. 62 (September 2017), pp. 67–69; Wesley Marshall et al., "Street Networks," in Robin Hickman, et al., eds., *International Handbook on Transport and Development* (Cheltenham, UK: Edward Elgar, 2015), p. 220; Wesley E. Marshall and Norman W. Garrick, "Evidence on Why Bike-Friendly Cities Are Safer for All Road Users," *Environmental Practice*, vol. 13, no. 1 (2011), pp. 16–27; Joachim Scheiner and Christian Holz-Rau, "A Residential Location Approach to Traffic Safety: Two Case Studies from Germany," *Accident Analysis and Prevention*, vol. 43, no. 1 (January 2011), pp. 307–322.

17. Yuanyuan Zhang, et al., "Investigating the Associations between Road Network Structure and Non-Motorist Accidents," *Journal of Transport Geography*, vol. 42 (January 2015), pp. 34–47.

18. Yeo et al., "Effects of Urban Sprawl and Vehicle Miles Traveled on Traffic Fatalities," pp. 401–402.

19. International Organization of Motor Vehicle Manufacturers, "World Vehicles in Use - All Vehicles" (spreadsheet), 20 June 2017, http://www.oica.net/category/vehicles-in-use.

20. TNS Sofres, *Global Image of the Auto Industry*, produced for International Organization of Motor Vehicle Manufacturers (Paris: OICA, 2015), http://www.oica.net.

21. UK Department for Environment, Food and Rural Affairs, Air Quality Expert Group, *Non-Exhaust Emissions from Road Traffic* (Defra, 2019), http://uk-air.defra.gov.uk; US Federal Highway Administration, *The Little Book of Quieter Pave*ments, publication no. FHWA-IF-08-004, by The Transtec Group (Washington, DC: Federal Highway Administration, 2007), pp. 10–13, https://www.thetranstec-group.com/LittleBookQuieterPavements.pdf.

22. National Cooperative Highway Research Program, "Connected Road Classification System (CRCS) Development" (web page), NCHRP 20-24(112), 20 March 2017, https://apps.trb.org/cmsfeed/TRBNetProjectDisplay.asp?ProjectID=4224; National Cooperative Highway Research Program, *Dedicating Lanes for Priority or Exclusive Use by Connected and Automated Vehicles*, research report 891 (Washington, DC: National Academies Press, 2018), pp. 132–134.

23. Eric A. Taub, "Make Way for Self-Driving Cars," *New York Times*, 1 August 2019, p. B7.

24. UK Department for Transport, *Pedestrian Guardrailing*, local transport note no. 2/09 (Norwich: The Stationery Office, 2009), pp. 7–15; Transport for London, *Guidance on the Assessment of Pedestrian Guardrail*, document no. SQA-00234, by Sam Wright (London: Transport for London, 2012),

https://tfl.gov.uk; Transport for London, *Collisions Before and After the Removal of Pedestrian Railings . . .*, report no. SB257, by Street Behaviour (London: Transport for London, July 2017), http://foi.tfl.gov.uk.

25.   Caroline Rodier, *Travel Effects and Associated Greenhouse Gas Emissions of Automated Vehicles*, National Center for Sustainable Transportation (Davis, CA: University of California, 2018), https://escholarship.org/uc/item/9g12v6r0; Tom Cohen and Clémence Cavoli, "Automated Vehicles: Exploring Possible Consequences of Government (Non)Intervention for Congestion and Accessibility," *Transport Reviews*, vol. 39, no. 1 (2019), pp. 129–151; Michael Levin et al., *Non-Linear Spacing Policy and Network Analysis for Shared-Road Platooning*, Center for Transportation Studies report no. CTS 19-27 (Minneapolis, MN: University of Minnesota, 2019), pp. 49–53, http://www.cts.umn.edu; Adam Millard-Ball, "The Autonomous Vehicle Parking Problem," *Transport Policy*, vol. 75 (March 2019), pp. 99–108.

26.   National Association of City Transportation Officials, *Blueprint for Autonomous Urbanism*, 2nd ed. (New York: NACTO, 2019).

27.   Wheelchairs and other disability-assist devices are generally not included in this category. They typically operate at walking speeds.

28.   Sébastian Compagnon, "Trottinettes électriques à Paris: le stationnement sera interdit sur les trottoirs," *Le Parisien*, 6 June 2019, http://www.leparisien.fr.

29.   K. M. Hunter-Zaworski, "Impacts of Low-Speed Vehicles on Transportation Infrastructure and Safety," *Journal of Transport and Land Use*, vol. 5, no. 2 (2012), pp. 68–76; David Levinson, "The (Re-) Allocation of Roadspace," *Transportist* (blog), 24 January 2012, https://transportist.org; Mark Delucchi and Kenneth S. Kurani, "How to Have Sustainable Transportation without Making People Drive Less or Give Up Suburban Living," *Journal of Urban Planning and Development*, vol. 140, no. 4 (December 2014).

30.   Peter D. Norton, *Fighting Traffic: The Dawn of the Motor Age in the American City* (Cambridge, MA: MIT Press, 2008), pp. 257–260.

Image Sources

Some images have been retouched to remove damage such as marks, stains, and tears. Also, some images have been processed to improve tone and contrast. The overall intent was to present the original images as clearly as possible. The few that have content alterations (such as tinted water bodies) are labeled as such in the captions.

Chapter 1

1.1, 1.2: Leonardo da Vinci, Paris Manuscripts, Manuscript B, p. 16r, p. 37r. Reprinted in Jean Paul Richter, ed., *The Literary Works of Leonardo da Vinci*, vol. 2 (London: Sampson Low, Marston, Serle & Rivington, 1883), p. 30 facing, p. 29 facing.

1.3: *The* [London] *Mirror of Literature, Amusement, and Instruction*, vol. 28, no. 810 (17 December 1836), front cover.

1.4: Carl August Noback, ed., *Bilder-Atlas für Kaufleute und Fabrikanten* (Leipzig: Georg Wigand, 1840–1841).

1.5: Fl. de Kerizouet, *Projet d'etablissement d'un chemin de fer dans l'interieur de la ville de Paris* (Paris, 1845), figure 4.

1.6: *London Improvements*, drawn by G. E. Madely, ca. 1845, London Metropolitan Archives, Wakefield Collection catalog no. p7502101, COLLAGE record no. 27437.

1.7: James Clephan, *London Improvements*, 1844, London Metropolitan Archives, Wakefield Collection catalog no. p7503365, COLLAGE record no. 27154.

1.8: *View of Broadway in the City of New York with the Proposed Elevated Rail-Way Invented by John Randel . . .*, 1848, New York Public Library Digital Collections, image ID 54834.

1.9: Joseph Paxton, *Design for The Great Victorian Way*, 1855, Victoria & Albert Museum, Prints, Drawings & Paintings Collection, museum no. E.2425-1983.

1.10: Great Britain, Parliament, House of Commons, Sessional Papers, 1854–1855, *Reports from Committees*, vol. 4, "Report from the Select Committee on Metropolitan Communications," 23 July 1855, plate 6.

1.11: City of London, Holborn Valley Improvement Committee, *Report of Proceedings in Connection with the Holborn Valley Improvements* (London: City of London, 1872).

1.12: Edward Walford, *Old and New London*, vol. 5, revised ed. (London: Cassell, 1887), p. 235.

1.13: City of London, Holborn Valley Improvement Committee, *Report of Proceedings in Connection with the Holborn Valley Improvements* (London: City of London, 1872).

1.14: *Illustrated London News*, vol. 50, no. 1431 (15 June 1867), p. 596.

1.15: Ferd. Mayer & Sons, *Proposed Arcade Railway--Under Broadway, View near Wall Street*, ca. 1868. From Library of Congress, Prints & Photographs Online Collection, reproduction no. LC-USZC4-2342.

1.16: *Evidence Submitted to the Senate Railroad Committee of New York, as to the Practicability of the Arcade Plan, in Rebuttal* (n.p., 1868). New York Public Library, Rare Book Collection, Astor, Lenox, Tilden Foundations, call no. VDCP p.v. 52.

1.17: Alfred Speer, *Treatise on City Travel with a True Solution of Rapid Transit* (Passaic, NJ: 1875). From American Antiquarian Society (Worcester, MA), catalog record no. 480307.

1.18, 1.19, 1.20: King C. Gillette, *The Human Drift* (Boston: New Era, 1894), p. 102, plate 5; p. 104, plate 6; p. 96, plate 2.

1.21: Alfred H. Thorp, "A Scheme for Rapid Transit for New York City," *Architecture and Building*, 28 February 1891, p. 103.

1.22: *American Architect and Building News*, vol. 49, no. 1047 (31 August 1895).

1.23: "A Suggested Improvement of the Water Front of New York," *Engineering News Record*, vol. 49, 23 April 1904, p. 525.

Chapter 2

2.1: John Wolfe Barry, "Address on the Streets & Traffic of London," presented to the Society of Arts, 16 November 1898 (London: 1899).

2.2, 2.3: Charles Scott Meik and Walter Beer, "The Improvement of London Traffic," in Society of Engineers, *Transactions for 1905* (London: E. & F. N. Spon, 1906), figure 5, figure 3.

2.4: "New York City as It Will Be in 1999," *New York World* (supplement), 30 December 1900.

2.5: "Yesterday's Futurama," *Famous Fantastic Mysteries*, vol. 2, no. 2 (May-June 1940), pp. 114-115.

2.6: Charles Clifton, "Miracles Made to Order," *Collier's Magazine*, vol. 69, no. 1 (7 January 1922), p. 7.

2.7: *Scientific American*, vol. 89, no. 3 (18 July 1903), front cover.

2.8: *Scientific American*, vol. 95, no. 26 (29 December 1906), front cover.

2.9: *Scientific American*, vol. 96, no. 25 (22 June 1907), front cover.

2.10: "Plans for Improving and Beautifying New York," *Harper's Weekly*, vol. 49, no. 2543 (16 September 1905), p. 1343.

2.11: *King's Views of New York, 1908 1909* (New York: Moses King, 1908), p. 1.

2.12: *Scientific American*, vol. 59, no. 4, 26 July 1913, front cover.

2.13: Letter from William J. Wilgus to W. H.

Newman, 22 December 1902. From New York Public Library Digital Collections, image ID 5513098.

2.14: *Inception and Creation of the Grand Central Terminal* (New York: Stem and Fellheimer Architects, 1913).

2.15: "Grand Central Development Seen As Great Civic Center," *Engineering News-Record*, vol. 85, no. 11 (9 September 1920), p. 498.

2.16: *Park Avenue - 46th Street*, ca. 1925. From New York Public Library Digital Collections, image ID 1508151.

2.17: Laurence Aurbach.

2.18: "Chicago Freight Subway," *Electric Railway Journal*, vol. 40, no 14 (5 October 1912), p. 589.

2.19, 2.20, 2.21: William Wilgus, *Proposed New Railway System for the Transportation and Distribution of Freight by Improved Methods . . .* (New York: The Amsterdam Co., 1908), p. 24, p. 27, p. 28.

2.22: Walter D. Mooney, *Wacker's Manual of the Plan of Chicago*, 3rd ed. (Chicago: Chicago Plan Commission, 1920), p. 121.

2.23: Chicago Plan Commission, *South Water Street Facts: Why the Improvement Should Go Forward without Delay* (Chicago: Chicago Plan Commission, 1922), front cover.

2.24: "Building Double-Decked Highway in Trap Rock Cut," *Engineering News-Record*, vol. 97, no. 11 (9 September 1926), p. 415.

2.25: F. Lavis and S. Johannesson, "New Jersey Extension of Holland Tunnel Highway," *Engineering News-Record*, vol. 100, no. 1 (5 January 1928), p. 6.

2.26: *West Side Elevated Express Highway, New York City*, 1938. From New York State Archives Digital Collections, identifier no. NYSA_A3045-78_Dn_NC67.

2.27, 2.28: Benjamin W. Levitan, "A Unique Institutional Building," *The American Architect*, vol. 67, no. 2310 (31 March 1920), p. 421, p. 422.

2.29: *Scientific American*, vol. 124, no. 26 (25 June 1921), p. 508.

2.30: Chester Higgins, *Approach to the George Washington Bridge*, May 1973. From US National Archives via Wikimedia Commons, National Archives identifier no. 553846.

2.31, 2.32: Thomas Adams, *Regional Plan of New York and Its Environs*, vol. 2, *The Building of the City* (New York: Committee on Regional Plan of New York and its Environs, 1931), p. 310, p. 307.

2.33: Jean Ferriss Leich, *Architectural Visions* (New York: Whitney Library of Design, 1980), p. 69.

2.34: Le Corbusier and Saugnier, "Trois rappels a MM. LES ARCHITECTS," *L'esprit nouveau*, no. 4 (January 1921), p. 468.

2.35: Le Corbusier, *Oeuvre complète de 1910-1929*, nouvelle ed. (Zürich: H. Girsberger, 1937), p. 39.

2.36: Raymond Francis Yates, "Underground Roads and Elevated Speedways May Solve the World's Worst Traffic Tangle," *Popular Science*, vol. 99, no. 2 (August 1921), p. 43.

2.37: "Dr. John A. Harriss Proposes Six-Deck Streets," *The American City*, vol. 36, no. 6 (June 1927), p. 804.

Chapter 3

3.1: Jan van Call, *Het Lange Voorhout . . .*, ca. 1690. From Haags Gemeentearchief, identifier no. kl. A 426.

3.2: Joseph Lauthier, *New Rules for the Game of Mail*, trans. James Cunningham (1910), p. 4 facing. Originally published as *Nouvelles regles pour le jeu de mail* (Paris: Charles Huguier, 1717).

3.3: Henry René d'Allemagne, *Sports et jeux d'adresse* (Paris: Librairie Hachette, 1903), p. 200.

3.4: Laurence Aurbach.

3.5: Adolphe Alphand, *Les promenades de Paris*, vol. 2, *Planches* (Paris: J. Rothschild, 1873).

3.6: *Album du Bois de Boulogne: photographs par Charles Marville*, ca. 1858–1860. From Bibliothèque Nationale de France, identifier no. ark:/12148/btv1b52501564v.

3.7: Frederick Law Olmsted and Calvert Vaux, *Description of a Plan for the Improvement of Central Park "Greensward,"* revised ed. (New York: Aldine, 1868), p. 36 facing.

3.8: John Dower, *Plan of the Gardens of the Zoological Society in the Regent's Park*, in D. W. Mitchell, *A Popular Guide to the Gardens of the Zoological Society of London* (London: 1852).

3.9: *Plan of a Portion of Park Way . . .*, in William Bishop, *Manual of the Common Council of the City of Brooklyn* (1868). From Wikimedia Commons.

3.10: "The Riverside Boulevard," *The Land Owner*, vol 1, no. 3 (September 1869), p. 60 facing.

3.11: West Chicago Park Commissioners, "System of Parks and Boulevards of the City of Chicago" (Chicago: 1880). From Boston Public Library, Norman B. Leventhal Map Center, identifier no. 06_01_011138.

3.12: Frederick Law Olmsted and John C. Olmsted, "Study of Plan for the Extension of Commonwealth Avenue on the Line of Beacon Street," illustrated by Aspinwall & Lincoln (Boston: 1886). From Boston Public Library, Norman B. Leventhal Map Center, identifier no. 06_01_005099.

Chapter 4

4.1, 4.2: James Elmes, *Metropolitan Improvements; or, London in the Nineteenth Century. . .* (London: James, 1827), p. 22 facing, p. 18 facing.

4.3, 4.4: John Britton, *Descriptive Sketches of Tunbridge Wells and the Calverley Estate* (London: 1832), p. 98, frontispiece.

4.5: Olmsted, Vaux & Co. Landscape Architects, *General Plan of Riverside*, 1869. From Riverside Historical Museum, Riverside, IL.

4.6: Richard J. Compton and Camille N. Dry, *Pictorial St. Louis* . . . (St. Louis: Compton, 1876), plate 39. From Library of Congress Geography and Map Division, control no. rc01001392.

4.7: *Bird's Eye View Looking Over Vandeventer Place from Grand Avenue*, ca. 1902. From Missouri Historical Society, identifier no. N40429.

4.8: Emil Boehl, *Westmoreland Place, East Entrance at Kingshighway Looking West*, ca. 1900. From Missouri Historical Society, identifier no. N15000.

4.9: H. M. Meinell, "Center Walks Supplemented by Back Alleys in Place of Roadways and Sidewalks in Venice, Cal.," *Engineering News*, vol. 62, no. 23 (2 December 1909), p. 605.

4.10: Barry Parker and Raymond Unwin, *The Art of Building a Home* (London: Longmans, Green & Co., 1901), plate 11.

4.11: Barry Parker and Raymond Unwin, *1st Garden City* (Letchworth Garden City masterplan), 1903. From Garden City Collection, Letchworth, no. 2008.80.

4.12: Laurence Aurbach. Based on Raymond Unwin, *Town Planning in Practice* (London: T Fisher Unwin, 1909), fold map 6.

4.13: Raymond Unwin, *Town Planning in Practice* (London: T Fisher Unwin, 1909), p. 330.

4.14: Raymond Unwin, "Roads and Streets," *Town Planning Review*, vol. 5, no. 1 (April 1914), p. 33.

4.15: Laurence Aurbach.

4.16: Alfred B. Yeomans, ed., *City Residential Land Development* (Chicago: University of Chicago Press, 1916), pp. 82, 88.

Chapter 5

5.1: Martin Wagner, *Das sanitäre Grün der Städte* (PhD. diss., Royal Technical College of Berlin, 1915), figure 8.

5.2: "Un exemple d'organisation moderne Francfort-sur-Mail," *La cité*, vol. 9, no. 6 (January 1931), p. 78.

5.3: Ernst Hopmann, "Städtebau in der U.d.S.S.R." *Die Form*, vol. 7, no. 5 (15 May 1932), p. 153.

5.4: Ernst May, *Fotografie des Stadtplans Avtostroj*, 1931. From Nürnberg, Germanisches Nationalmuseum, Deutsches Kunstarchiv, no. I, B-25 (0017).

5.5: Ludwig Hilberseimer, *The New City* (Chicago: P. Theobald, 1944), p. 120, illustration 91.

5.6: Ludwig Hilberseimer, *Dessau, Regional Site Plan of Industrial City*, c.1932. From The Art Institute of Chicago, Ryerson and Burnham Archives, Ludwig Karl Hilberseimer Papers, digital file no. 070383_181129-001.

5.7, 5.8: Ludwig Hilberseimer, *Entfaltung einer Planungsidee* (Berlin: Ullstein, 1963), p. 52, p. 55.

5.9, 5.10: Walter Gropius and Martin Wagner, "A Program for City Reconstruction," *Architectural Forum*, vol. 79, no. 1 (July 1943), p. 81, p. 81.

5.11: Photograph of town model from 1946 Townlets and Towns studio. From Harvard University Graduate School of Design, Frances Loeb Library, Papers of Martin Wagner, folder 57, "Illustrations: Housing Types and Sites," DES-1971-0001-000603299 57.

5.12: Clarence Arthur Perry, "The Neighborhood Unit," in *Regional Survey of New York and Its Environs*, vol. 7, *Neighborhood and Community Planning* (New York: Regional Plan of New York and Its Environs, 1929), p. 88.

5.13: Henry Wright, "The Autobiography of Another Idea," *Western Architect*, vol. 39, no. 9 (September 1930), plate 130.

5.14: Laurence Aurbach. Based on Henry N. Wright, "Radburn Revisited," *Architectural Forum*, vol. 135, no. 1 (July-August 1971), p. 56.

5.15: Henry Wright, "The Place of the Apartment in the Modern Community," *Architectural Record*, vol. 67, no. 3 (March 1930), p. 235.

5.16: Robert Whitten and Thomas Adams, *Neighborhoods of Small Homes* (Cambridge, MA: Harvard University Press, 1931), p. 69.

5.17: Edmund B. Gilchrist, *Housing Project (Low Cost Housing Corporation of Philadelphia)*, 1933. From University of Pennsylvania School of Design, Architectural Archives, ID no. 007.332

5.18: Walter H. Blucher, "Planning a Housing Project," *City Planning*, vol. 10, no. 3 (July 1934), p. 121.

5.19: Carol Aronovici et al., "Realistic Replanning," *Architectural Forum*, vol. 61, no. 1 (July 1934), p. 53.

5.20: US Federal Housing Administration, *Planning Profitable Neighborhoods*, technical bulletin no. 7 (Washington, DC: USGPO, 1938), p. 29.

Chapter 6

6.1: Currier & Ives, *Fast Trotters on Harlem Lane, N.Y.*, by John Cameron, ca. 1870. From Library of Congress, Prints & Photographs Online Catalog, no. LC-DIG-pga-00705.

6.2: *Harper's Weekly*, vol 44, no. 2272 (7 July 1900), front cover.

6.3: Charles Chapin Sargent Jr., "A Horseman's Paradise," *Munsey's Magazine*, vol. 20, no. 2 (November 1898), p. 196.

6.4, 6.5: North Side Board of Trade, *The Great North Side or Borough of the Bronx* (New York: North Side Board of Trade, 1897), p. 167, p. 171.

6.6: "Our Leisure Class Must Be Amused," *Life*, vol. 40, no. 1036 (4 September 1902), pp. 196-197.

6.7: "Where They Belong," *Life*, vol. 42, no. 1083 (30 July 1903), p. 130.

6.8: "Field Completed for Fairmount Park Race," *Motor Age*, vol. 16, no. 15 (7 Oct 1909), p. 9.

6.9: Westchester County Park Commission, *Report* . . . (Bronxville, NY: 1926), p. 9. From Westchester County Archives, Annual Reports Digital Collection.

6.10: C. L. Grant, ed., *New York State Parks and Highways* (Albany, NY: State Council of Parks, 1928), p. 14.

6.11: "Plans for Improving and Beautifying New York," *Harper's Weekly*, vol. 49, no. 2543 (16 September 1905), p. 1342.

6.12: US Congress, House Committee on Roads, *Toll Roads and Free Roads*, House document no. 272, 76th Congress, 1st session, 1939, p. 95.

Chapter 7

7.1: *Saturday Evening Post*, 13 September 1924, p. 116.

7.2: Eugene S. Taylor, "Chicago's Superhighway Plan," *National Municipal Review*, vol. 18, no. 6 (June 1929), p. 373.

7.3: "City 1960: Norman Bel Geddes, Designer," *Architectural Forum*, vol. 67, no. 1 (July 1937), p. 60.

7.4, 7.5: Laurence Aurbach.

7.6: New York World's Fair, *Theme Center - Democracity - Model of City*, ca. 1939. From New York Public Library, Manuscripts and Archives Collection, identifier no. 1684003.

7.7: Richard Garrison, ca. 1939. From University of Texas at Austin, Harry Ransom Center, Norman Bel Geddes Collection, photo box 9, folder 381.4.

7.8: Richard Garrison, ca. 1939. From University of Texas at Austin, Harry Ransom Center, Norman Bel Geddes Collection, photo box 10a, folder 381.19.

7.9: Handy (Jam) Organization, *Streamlines* (film), created for General Motors, 1936. From Internet Archive, Prelinger Archives, identifier no. 0142_Streamlines_M7960_09_08_44_00.

7.10: H. Alker Tripp, *Road Traffic and Its Control* (London: Edward Arnold, 1938), p. 347.

7.11: H. Alker Tripp, *Town Planning and Road Traffic* (London: Edward Arnold, 1942), p. 84.

7.12: "Planned Neighborhoods for 194X," *Architectural Forum*, vol. 10, no. 4 (October 1943), p. 112.

7.13: Urban Land Institute, *Community Builder's Handbook* (Washington, DC: ULI, 1947), p. 40.

Chapter 8

8.1: California Legislature, Joint Fact-Finding Committee on Highways, Streets and Bridges, *Engineering Facts and a Future Program*, by G. Donald Kennedy (Sacramento, CA: California Legislature, 1946), pp. 88-89.

8.2: National Committee on Urban Transportation, *Standards for Street Facilities and Services*, procedure manual 7A (Chicago: Public Administration Service, 1958), p. 11, table 2.

8.3, 8.4: Automotive Safety Foundation, *Functional Highway Classification in Urban Areas* (Washington, DC: Automotive Safety Foundation, 1967), p. 6, p. 32.

8.5: US Department of Transportation, Federal Highway Administration, Bureau of Public Roads, *1968 National Highway Functional Classification Study Manual* (Washington, DC: USGPO, 1969), p. II-6.

8.6, 8.7, 8.8, 8.9: Laurence Aurbach.

8.10: Michael Southworth and Peter M. Owens, "The Evolving Metropolis: Studies of Community, Neighborhood, and Street Form at the Urban Edge," *Journal of the American Planning Association*, vol. 59, no. 3 (Summer 1993), p. 280.

Chapter 9

9.1: Great Britain, Ministry of Transport, *Traffic in Towns* (London: HMSO, 1963), p. 44.

9.2: US Federal Highway Administration, *State of the Art: Residential Traffic Management*, by Daniel T. Smith Jr. and Donald Appleyard et al. (Washington, DC: USGPO, 1980), p. 80.

9.3: US Federal Highway Administration, *Improving the Residential Street Environment*, by Daniel T. Smith Jr. and Donald Appleyard (Washington, DC: USGPO, 1981), p. 25.

9.4: City of Toronto Planning Board, *St. Lawrence Site Plan*, St. Lawrence plan, report no. 14, 1976. From City of Toronto Archives, fonds 388, series 1653, file 249.

9.5: City of Toronto Planning Board, *St. Lawrence: Built Form* (poster accompanying final site plan report), by Barbara Dewhirst and Jurgen Henze, May 1976. From City of Toronto Archives, fonds 2, series 236, file 133.

9.6: Laurence Aurbach, using OpenStreetMap and "Toner-Background" map theme by Stamen Design.

9.7, 9.8: Léon Krier, quartier plan and traffic plan, created for La Villette competition, 1976.

9.9: Léon Krier, *Nouvelle division de quartier*, 1978.

9.10: Léon Krier. From *A.D.* (Architectural Design), vol. 49, no. 1 (1979), front cover.

9.11, 9.12: Léon Krier, *Network of High Streets . . .* and traffic plan, created for Poundbury project, 1988.

9.13, 9.14: Alexander Cooper Associates, *Vehicular Circulation* and *Rector Place*, created for Battery Park City master plan, 1979.

9.15 University of Miami School of Architecture, *Architecture for Key West: A Proposal for the Return to Civilian Use of the Former Submarine Base* (Miami, FL: 1977), pp. 12, 13.

9.16, 9.17: Andrés Duany and Elizabeth Plater-Zyberk, *Existing Conditions* and *Walkways*, created for Seaside, FL, master plan, ca. 1984.

9.18: Ruth Eckdish Knack, "Repent, Ye Sinners, Repent," *Planning*, vol. 55, no. 8 (August 1989), p. 4.

9.19: US Department of Transportation, Federal Highway Administration, *Highway Functional Classification Concepts, Criteria and Procedures*, no. FHWA-PL-13-026 (Washington, DC: USGPO, 2013), p. 6.

Acknowledgements

Many people helped make this book possible. Above all, my heartfelt thanks goes to my family and friends for their patience, encouragement, and continuing interest throughout the lengthy process of writing this book.

Designers, Professors, and Others

My gratitude to Richard A. Hall (Hall Planning & Engineering), Professor Peter Norton (University of Virginia), Professor Emily Talen (University of Chicago), and Professor Norman Garrick (University of Connecticut) for their exceptionally generous support and advice. Without Mr. Hall's initial encouragement, this book would not have been written.

As well, numerous other people have been very helpful and considerate: Hannah Abdullah (Goethe-Institut), Professor Carol Atkinson-Palombo (University of Connecticut), Professor Daniel Bluestone (Boston University), Professor Jeffry Diefendorf (University of New Hampshire), Diane Dorney, Andrés Duany (DPZ CoDesign), Douglas Farr (Farr Associates), Lucy Gibson (Toole Design), F. Xavier Iglesias (DPZ CoDesign), Léon Krier, Philip Langdon, Professor Stephen Marshall (University College London), Professor Wesley Marshall (University of Colorado Denver), Michael Mehaffy (Structura Naturalis), Alan Pisarski, Niko Pfund (Oxford University Press), Michael Ronkin (Designing Streets for People), Robert Rozycki (US Federal Highway Administration), Professor Kurt C. Schlichting (Fairfield University), Dhiru Thadani, Nancy Voorhees, and Richard Wynne (Lodestar Books).

Librarians and Archivists

My thanks to the hardworking staff members at the University of Maryland College Park libraries, the US Library of Congress, and the New York Public Library. My gratitude also extends to HathiTrust, the Internet Archive, and Google Books for creating unparalleled collections of digitized, searchable materials. Those and similar online collections have, without a doubt, revolutionized historical research.

I wish to thank certain librarians and archivists individually for their valuable assistance: Vicky Axell (Garden City Collection), Kevin M. Bailey (Dwight D. Eisenhower Presidential Library), Lori Hanna Boyer (Art Institute of Chicago), Trenton Carls (Chicago History Research Center), Christo Datini (GM Heritage Center), Edwin Deegan (University of Pennsylvania), Cindy Frank (University of Maryland College Park), Eric Frazier (Library of Congress), Jackie Graziano (Westchester County Archives), Sarah Huggins (Library of Virginia), Marilyn Ibach (Library of Congress), David Jones (US Department of Transportation Library), Cristina I. Meisner (University of Texas Austin), Eisha Neely (Cornell University), Allison Rose Olsen (University of Pennsylvania), Nathaniel Parks (Art Institute of Chicago), Jason D. Stratman (Missouri History Museum), Michel Wendt (Washington State Department of Transportation Library), and Christine Windheuser (Smithsonian National Museum of American History).

Copyright Holders

My thanks to the many image-copyright holders who granted permission for their intellectual properties to be included in this book. Your permission allows this book to be far more engaging and instructive than it would be otherwise.

Interviewees

Finally, my thanks go to the individuals who granted interviews or provided information about their historical roles: Andrew Cameron (Andrew Cameron Associates), Alexander Cooper, Robert A. Davis, Andrés Duany (DPZ CoDesign), Richard A. Hall (Hall Planning & Engineering), Léon Krier, Walter Kulash, John Massengale (Massengale Architecture), Don Samdahl (Fehr & Peers), and Frank Spielberg.

Index

access, limited
American Association of State Highway Officials recommendations (1940s–1950s), 261
legalization in US, 217–218, 221, 225
and vertical traffic separation, 79–82, 98, 217, 236–238
See also classifications of roadways based on access; fast roadways: and limited access
Adams, Thomas, 145, 150, 177, 182–183, 229–230, 252, 366
Alexander, Christopher, 295
alternating-assignment traffic limitation, 329
American Association of State Highway Officials, 218, 219, 224, 225, 261, 263–264, 268, 271–272, 274–281
American Automobile Association, 37, 203–204, 242, 260, 275, 277
American Public Health Association, 260
Appleyard, Donald, 287–290
Astor, John Jacob, IV, 36–37, 352
Automobile Club of America, 37, 96, 201, 203, 206
Automobile Manufacturers Association. *See* National Automobile Chamber of Commerce
automobiles
commercialization, early, 35
electric, autonomous, connected, and micro, 343–345
growth rates in early 21st cen. and beyond, 343–344
opposition to, 200–204, 234, 274, 284, 293
as panacea for urban ills, 199
and road racing, 201–206
and speed, psychological attraction of, 226–227
and suburbanization, 199, 242
Automotive Safety Foundation
and *Building Traffic Safety*, 260
criticism of, 244, 274
formation and early activities, 223, 240–245
and functional-classification guidebooks (1960s), 270–274
and National Committee on Urban Transportation, 268
state and city plans, 263–266

Barry, John Wolfe, 47–49, 338
Bartholomew, Harland, 138, 216–217, 224, 235, 365
Bassett, Edward, 140, 217–218
Bel Geddes, Norman, 239–240, 246, 247–251
Berlin, 43, 100, 109, 114, 158, 159–160, 163, 164, 166–167
bicycling, 48, 49, 118–119, 194, 248, 352
blight removal. *See* demolition and population displacement

blocks, small, 293–294, 297, 301, 302, 305, 309–311, 312, 317, 320, 322, 340–341. *See also* neotraditional roadway layouts
Buchanan, Colin, 284–288
Bureau for Street Traffic Research, 236, 241, 242, 265
Bureau of Public Roads, 218–226, 242, 256, 260, 263, 268, 271, 272, 274–277. *See also* Federal Highway Administration
Burnham, Daniel, 35, 75–77, 152–153
bus rapid transit, 327

carfree
districts, carfree and car-limited, 328–330, 345
Jacobs, Jane, 294
La Villette, passages, 302
Tripp, H. Alker, minor roads, 253
typology of schemes, 328
Carroll, J. Douglas, 266–268
cellular roadway layouts
Appleyard, Donald, and London and Berkeley, CA, retrofits, 288–290
Building New Neighborhoods (1943), 382
and congestion, 183, 302, 338, 341
in Detroit and Chicago studies (1950s–1960s), 267
and ethics, 289–290, 328
and guidebooks for roadway planning, 141, 189, 252–262
and health, 260
justified by fallacious assumptions, 341–342
Le Corbusier, 93, 344
National Committee on Urban Transportation, 270
as neighborhood units, 155, 160, 174–176, 178–180, 182–184, 184–186, 189, 252, 260, 369
and neotraditionalism. *See* neotraditional roadway layouts: and cellularity
Perry, Clarence, 174–176
as precincts, 254–255, 285, 291, 294, 344
recommendations by the author, 346–347
Riverside, IL, 133–134
spacing of arterials, 182, 267, 269–270, 273, 276, 279
spacing of intersections on arterials, 183, 260, 261, 269–270, 279, 302
and speed, 167, 169–170, 175, 176, 179
Traffic in Towns (1963), 285
and traffic safety, 340–342
trend in US, 1990–2010 increase, 321
Unwin, Raymond, 149
US city planning policy, 187–190, 225, 321–322
See also cul-de-sacs; dendritic roadway layouts; insular roadways; superblocks; traffic restraint
Chellman, Chester, 317–318

Chicago
    Burnham, Daniel, 35, 75–77, 152–153
    Chicago Area Transportation Study, 266–268
    Chicago Plan Commission, 76–77, 237, 256–258,
        382
    Delano, Frederic. *See* Delano, Frederic
    Drexel Boulevard, 194
    Drummond, William, 155, 174
    freight tunnels, 68–70
    Grand Boulevard, 193
    Hilberseimer, Ludwig. *See* Hilberseimer, Ludwig
    Illinois Institute of Technology, 166–167, 169
    Kincaid, Harry Evert, 256–258
    McClintock, Miller, 237–238
    Michigan Avenue, 75–76, 86
    Norton, Charles. *See* Norton, Charles
    park-boulevard system, 116–118, 148, 193
    Plan of Chicago (1909), 74–76, 152–153, 155
    Quarter Section Competition, 153–155, 174, 367
    Riverside, 133–134
    Riverside parkway, 115–116
    superhighway vision of 1927, 237
    Wacker Drive, 76–77
    Wright, Frank Lloyd, 155
Chinese city planning, 99, 122, 227, 324–325, 331
City Beautiful movement, 90, 140, 152–153
Clarke, Gilmore, 208–213, 215, 220, 246
classifications of roadways based on access
    *1968 National Highway Functional Classification
        Manual* (1969), 272, 275–276, 278
    A Guide for Functional Highway Classification
        (1966), 271–272
    A Policy on Arterial Highways in Urban Areas
        (1957), 256, 261, 269–270, 384
    Automotive Safety Foundation, city and state plans
        (1940s–1960s), 265
    Building New Neighborhoods (1943), 256–258, 382
    Building Traffic Safety (1950), 260
    Detroit and Chicago studies (1950s–1960s), 267
    Functional Highway Classification in Urban Areas
        (1967), 272–274
    National Committee on Urban Transportation
        (1958), 268–269
    Public Control of Highway Access (1943), 256
    Tripp, H. Alker (1938), 253
    US nationwide functional classification studies
        (1970s), 276–280
    See also functional classification; guidebooks for
        roadway planning
commercial traffic
    and carfree zones, 329
    and early boulevards, 102–103, 362
    and fast roadways, 150, 194–199, 204, 207, 216–218
    and hyperurbanism, 12, 17, 18, 27, 36, 38, 43, 49,
        68–77, 91

commercial traffic (*continued*)
    and insular roadways, 122, 126, 135, 138, 139, 141–
        142, 152
    Loudon, John Claudius, 104
    McClintock, Miller, 237–238
    and neotraditional roadways, 292–293, 312, 321
    and parkways (motor), 215
    and parkways (Olmsted style), 114–119, 196
    Travels in Icaria, 104
    and vertical traffic separation, 42, 77–87, 96,
        196–197
community-center movement, 155, 173
congestion, 221, 229–230, 292–294
    and fast roadways, 209, 217, 220, 225, 238, 242
    and cellular roadway layouts, 183, 302, 338, 341
    costs of, 16, 267, 337–339
    and dendritic roadway layouts, 168, 338, 341
    and divided roadways, 95, 106–107
    and hyperurbanism, 17, 18, 27, 43–44, 63, 65, 72–74,
        75, 87, 88, 96, 164
    and neotraditional roadway layouts, 293, 302, 318,
        321, 322
    and suburban sprawl, 338
    and superblocks, 183, 338
    and traffic control, 233–234
    and vertical traffic separation, 42, 238
congestion-charge zones, 328
Cooper, Alexander, 308–312, 319
Corbett, Harvey Wiley, 61, 86–88, 94, 230, 239, 248,
    358
crashes. *See* traffic fatalities; traffic safety
cul-de-sacs, 273
    American Association of State Highway Officials
        recommendations, 384
    Benton Place, St. Louis, MO, 135
    and British bye-laws, 143–144
    British guidance in 2000s, 323
    economics of, 182–183, 189
    Federal Housing Administration, 189
    and Forest Hills Gardens, 152
    Futurama, 1939 World's Fair, 248
    German modernist architects, 157–172
    Islamic cities, 122, 123
    and neotraditional development, 317–318
    Pennypack Creek Homes, 184–185
    Perry, Clarence, 175
    Radburn, NJ, 177–180
    Sturr, Albert, Quarter Section Competition, 153
    trend in US, 1970s–1980s increase, 281
    trend in US, 1990s–2010s decrease, 321
    Unwin, Raymond, 145–150
    Urban Land Institute recommendations, 259–260
Curitiba, Brazil, 327

Davis, Robert, 312–316, 319

dead ends. *See* cul-de-sacs

Delano, Frederic, 74, 80, 182, 224, 229

demolition and population displacement, 14, 18, 27, 50, 91–94, 106, 141–142, 150, 184–186, 216, 222–225, 227, 231, 240, 242, 274, 286, 287, 291–295, 308

dendritic roadway layouts, 149
 British guidance in 2000s, 323
 and congestion, 168, 338, 341
 criticism of, 295, 317–318
 and gated developments, 325
 Hilberseimer, Ludwig, 164–169, 368
 justified by fallacious assumptions, 341–342
 Kincaid, Harry Evert, 258
 May, Ernst, 162–164
 and social space, lack of, 168, 317
 and traffic safety, 168, 340–342
 trend in US, 1970s–1980s increase, 281
 trend in US, 1990–2010 increase, 321
 Wagner, Martin, 169–172

Der Ring, 159

Detroit, MI, 119, 138, 169, 184–186, 265, 266–268

divided roadways, 334, 337
 ancient and medieval examples, 99
 as response to traffic diversity, 118–119, 194
 Beacon Street, Brookline, MA, 118, 362
 boulevard antecedents and origins, 100–103
 Brooklyn parkways, 113–115, 118, 193, 198, 353, 372
 Burnham, Daniel. *See* Burnham, Daniel
 bus lanes, global increase after 1950, 327
 Chicago park boulevards, 116–118, 148, 193
 and congestion, 95, 106–107
 Detroit, MI, super-highway proposal, 119
 and elitism, 100–103, 107–108, 118, 119
 European boulevards, influence of in America, 110, 116, 135
 inflexibility of, 50
 light rail, global increase after 1980, 326
 Loudon, John Claudius, 103
 Olmsted and Vaux, roadway evolution model, 114
 Olmsted, Frederick Law, San Francisco proposal, 113–114
 revival after 1950s, 120, 326–327
 Riverside, IL, parkway, 115–116
 and speed, 36, 118–120
 Travels in Icaria, 103–106
 Unter den Linden, 100, 114
 and urban development, 114–115, 116, 196
 See also commercial traffic

Downer, Jay, 207–215, 220, 246, 249

Duany, Andrés, 312–318

fast roadways, 334, 336
 and bigotry, 207, 223, 226
 as solution to downtown decline, 238
 definition of, 192, 372

fast roadways (*continued*)
 divisive effects of, 209, 224–226, 286
 and ecosystems, 209, 211, 217, 224, 226
 and elitism, 194, 204, 222
 freeways, 216–226, 267
 and health, 205–207, 267
 and limited access, 198–199, 204, 208, 212, 215–218, 230, 237–238, 248, 252–255, 267
 Olmsted, Frederick Law, and Calvert Vaux, 193–195, 206, 353
 psychological attraction of, 226–227
 and residential frontages, 175
 and traffic safety, 208–209, 267
 and speeding, 201–204, 209
 speedways and trotting, 192–199
 and suburbanization, 204, 207–208, 210, 215, 226
 Tripp, H. Alker, 253–255
 See also commercial traffic

fast roadway schemes
 Boston thoroughfares, 194, 206
 Bronx River Parkway, NY, 205–214, 224, 249
 Buffalo, NY, parkways, 115, 194
 Century Speedway, Washington, DC, 198
 Chicago park boulevards, 193
 Chrysler Freeway, Detroit, 185
 Fairmount Park drives, Philadelphia, 206
 Grand Concourse, Bronx, 196–197
 Harlem River Speedway, Manhattan, 195–196, 373
 Long Island Motor Parkway, NY, 201–206, 208, 215, 249, 374
 Long Island, NY, parkways, 215, 218
 Mount Vernon Memorial Highway, VA, 213, 220–221
 New York City motor parkways and expressways, 215–217, 221, 353
 Ocean Parkway, Brooklyn, 193, 198
 Route 1 Extension, NJ, 78–80, 230, 336
 Taconic State Parkway, NY, 211–212
 Wagner, Martin, 169–171
 Westchester County, NY, parkways, 210–215, 220–221, 223, 230, 375

Federal Highway Administration, 274, 321

Federal Housing Administration, 187–191, 260, 371

Flagg, Ernest, 239, 249, 380

Forest Hills Gardens, Queens, NY, 141, 150–153, 175–176, 190, 229, 366

Frankfurt, Germany, 161

freight. *See* commercial traffic

functional classification, 336
 disadvantages of, 283
 guidebooks of 1960s, 271–273
 international spread of, 282
 introduction to, 263
 National Committee on Urban Transportation, 268–269
 Robinson, Charles Mulford, 141

functional classification (*continued*)
  and US city planning policy, 274–282, 321
functional traffic separation, 1–3
  and fallacious assumptions, 341–342
  historical knowledge and traffic-planning progress,
    5, 347
  justifications of, 333–337
  recommendations by the author, 346–347
  trends, consolidation after 1910s–1920s, 335–337
  trends, future, 342–345
Futurists, Italian, 61

garden cities and suburbs, 141, 152, 161, 252
  Adams, Thomas, 145, 229–230
  Forest Hills Gardens (1909). *See* Forest Hills Gar-
    dens, Queens, NY
  in Germany, 157
  Hampstead Garden Suburb (1905). *See* Hampstead
    Garden Suburb, London
  Howard, Ebenezer, 144–145, 178, 293
  Le Corbusier, 91, 358
  Letchworth (1903), 145–146
  May, Ernst, 160–161
  New Earswick (1903), 145
  Quarter Section Competition, 153
  Queensbridge Dwellings (1934), 185–187
  Radburn, NJ (1929). *See* Radburn, NJ
  Regional Planning Association of America, 177–179
  Regional Plan of New York, 229–230
  Wagner, Martin, 158
  Wright, Henry, 176, 177–179
gated developments
  American Planning Association, 319
  Calverley Park (1828), 127
  and Chinese policy (mid 20th–early 21st cen.),
    324–325, 331
  Davis, Robert, 312–314
  global increase after 1980, 324
  Llewellyn Park (1857), 130–131, 363
  London's street barriers (18th–19th cen.), 126, 135
  Olmsted, Frederick Law, Berkeley, CA, proposal
    (1866), 132–133
  Parc de Montretout (1832), 128
  Prince's Park (1843), 130, 131
  private places, St. Louis, MO (late 19th–early 20th
    cen.), 135–137, 141
  Regent's Park (1811). *See* Regent's Park, London
  retrofitting of, 325
  Rock Park (1837), 129
  Victorial Park (1837), 129, 131
  Villa Montmorency (1853), 129
General Motors
  and Automotive Safety Foundation, 241
  and Futurama, 247–248
  Parade of Progress tours, 251–252
  Streamlines (film), 248–249

German city planning, 138–140, 144, 152, 157–166,
    287, 329
Gilchrist, Edmund, 184–185
Gillette, King Camp, 38–40, 92, 352
Goodrich, Ernest, 79, 87–86, 230, 238, 365
grids, traditional. *See* traditional roadway layouts
Gropius, Walter, 159–160, 167, 169–172, 266
guidebooks for roadway planning, 141, 189, 222–224,
    235, 252–262, 268–280, 319–323

Hampstead Garden Suburb, London, 91, 141, 145–148,
    160, 175, 178
Harriss, John, 53–55, 94–97, 249
Hilberseimer, Ludwig, 159, 164–169, 295, 368
Hoffman, Paul, 223, 231–236, 240–245, 270
Hoover, Herbert, 179, 181
Howard, Ebenezer, 144–145, 178, 293
hyperurbanism
  as cultural movement, 98, 351, 354
  and class stratification, 12–14, 46
  and congestion, 17, 18, 27, 43–44, 63, 65, 72–74, 75,
    87, 88, 96, 164
  decline of, 83, 337
  definition of, 11–12
  disadvantages of, 337
  and inhabited space, 16, 17, 29–27, 31–32, 43, 95–96
  inventions that promoted, 34–35, 350
  and skyscraper-bridge urbanism, 83–86
  skywalk and tunnelwalk networks, 336
  and social space, 21, 33, 43–44
  and speed, 18, 36, 49, 88, 286
  and traffic safety, 49
  and urban development, 17, 29, 31–32, 50, 62–63,
    70, 76, 98
  See also commercial traffic
hyperurban schemes
  Arcade Railway (1866), 31–32, 230, 347
  Astor, John Jacob, IV (1894), 36
  Barry, John Wolfe (1898), 47–49
  Borie, Henri-Jules (1865), 91
  Burnham, Daniel (early 1900s), 75–77
  Chicago freight tunnels (1904), 68–70
  Clephan, James, and William Curtis (1846), 18–20
  Corbett, Harvey Wiley (1923, 1925), 86–88
  Crystal Way (1855), 25
  Ferriss, Hugh (1929, 1930), 88–91
  Flagg, Ernest (1927), 239, 249, 380
  Futurama (1939), 247–251, 293
  Grand Central Terminal (1913), 61–67
  Great Victorian Way (1855), 23
  Harriss, John (1920s), 53–55, 94–97
  The Human Drift (1894), 38–40, 92
  Kérizouët, Fl. de (1845), 16–18
  Lafferty, Robert (1923), 83
  Lamb, Charles (1904), 44
  Le Corbusier (1920s–1930s). *See* Le Corbusier

hyperurban schemes (*continued*)
 Leonardo da Vinci (ca. 1487), 12–14, 56, 86
 Meik, Charles, and Walter Beer, Main Avenues
  (1905), 49–51
 Michigan Avenue (1920), 75–76, 86
 Randel, John (1847), 21
 Speer, Alfred, Endless Sidewalk (1871), 33–34, 347
 Thorp, Alfred (1891), 42–45
 Traffic in Towns (1963), 284–287
 Wacker Drive (1926), 76–77
 Wilgus, William, freight system (1908), 70–74

illustrators and illustration
 Biedermann, Louis, 51–55, 95
 comic and sober styles, 53
 Ferriss, Hugh, 88–91, 94, 230, 239, 246, 248
 governmental authority suggested by, 61, 90, 94
 Pettit, Harry, 57–61, 354
 shift in urban settings circa 1900, 51
 Smith, Charles McKnight, 55–57, 92, 230, 354
Institute of Traffic Engineers, 252, 275
 formation of, 238–239
 Mickle, D. Grant, 265
 See also Institute of Transportation Engineers
Institute of Transportation Engineers
 Designing Walkable Urban Thoroughfares (2010),
  320–321
 Planning Urban Roadway Systems (2014), 320–321
 Traditional Neighborhood Development (1999), 318
insular roadways, 334
 ancient and medieval examples, 122–123
 and business discouragement, 116, 132, 134, 135–
  138, 140–141, 152, 184
 definitions of, 121
 and elitism, 116, 124–125, 126, 128, 129, 131, 134–
  138, 155, 189, 325
 Federal Housing Administration, 188–189
 German planning (late 19th–early 20th cen.),
  138–140
 and health, 123, 127, 130–134, 143, 158–160, 168,
  184, 351
 local and through roadway distinction, 137–142, 149,
  152–155, 175–176, 179, 189, 248, 253–255
 and security, 122–123, 129, 131, 153, 324–325
 and segregation, racial, 134, 189–191
 and segregation, social, 122, 124–125, 126, 129, 134,
  141, 190, 290, 325
 and traffic harms, 126, 137–138, 140, 142, 148, 152–
  155, 176, 184, 186–187, 281, 285, 289–290
 and traffic safety, 142, 155, 159, 175, 179, 184,
  340–342
 See also cellular roadway layouts; commercial traffic;
  cul-de-sacs; dendritic roadway layouts; gated
  developments; superblocks
Islamic city planning, 122, 123

Jacobs, Jane, 291–296, 308, 314
Jansen, Hermann, 159
Johnson, Pyke, 245, 266

Kahn, Louis, 184, 291
Kennedy, G. Donald, 224, 264–265
Kohn, Robert, 177, 181, 184, 246
Krier, Léon, 299–308, 315, 317, 388
Krier, Rob, 299–301
Kulash, Walter, 318–319

Le Corbusier, 56, 91–94, 230, 239, 293, 295, 300, 344,
 358
Levin, David, 256, 268
Life magazine, 200–202, 242, 380
Lindsay, John, 308–309
livability of roadways, 1, 254, 267, 279, 284–290, 293,
 311, 312, 320–321, 328–329, 333, 342, 346
Liverpool & Manchester Railway, England, 14
London
 Barry, John Wolfe, 47–49, 338
 Bedford estate, 126–127
 Cabet, Etienne, 103, 106
 Clephan, James, and William Curtis, 18–20
 Crystal Way, 25
 estates, leasehold, 125–127, 135, 141
 Great Victorian Way, 23–25
 Hampstead Garden Suburb. *See* Hampstead Garden
  Suburb, London
 Haywood, William, 27–29, 338
 Holborn Viaduct, 27–29, 48, 50, 351
 London & Greenwich Railway, 15–16
 Meik, Charles, and Walter Beer, 49–51
 Metropolitan Railway Commission of 1846, 18–20
 Napoléon III, 106
 Nash, John, 106, 123–125
 Paxton, Joseph, 23–25, 112–113, 130
 Regent's Park, 110, 123–125, 127, 129, 130, 362
 Select Committee on Metropolitan Communications
  of 1855, 23–27
 traffic-restraint schemes of 1970s, 289–290
 Tripp, H. Alker, 176, 252–255, 285
Los Angeles, 142, 232, 235, 286, 340
Louisville, KY, pedestrian courts, 141
low-emission zones, 328

MacDonald, Thomas, 176, 218–226, 242, 247, 266,
 268, 333, 382, 383
Marsh, Burton, 238, 258, 260, 268
May, Ernst, 159–164, 169
McClintock, Miller, 234–240, 242, 245, 248
Mickle, D. Grant, 265, 268, 271, 277
micromobility. *See* personal transporters
Mies van der Rohe, Ludwig, 159, 166, 301, 367
modernist planning and architecture, 184, 186, 252,
 317

modernist planning and architecture (*continued*)
and Battery Park City, 308–309
criticism of, 293, 295, 300–301
Germany, rise in, 159–160
Hilberseimer, Ludwig, 164–169
Le Corbusier, 93–94
May, Ernst, 160–164
and St. Lawrence neighborhood, 296
Wagner, Martin, 158–160, 169–173
Moses, Robert, 58, 187, 198, 205, 213–218, 223, 246, 249, 251, 292, 308, 333, 353
Mumford, Lewis, 150, 155, 177, 249–251

National Association of City Transportation Officials, autonomous-vehicle recommendations, 344
National Association of County Engineers, 271, 276
National Automobile Chamber of Commerce, 53, 234, 241, 245
as Automobile Manufacturers Association, 241, 245
National Committee on Urban Transportation, 268–271, 273
neighborhood unit. *See* cellular roadway layouts
neotraditional roadway layouts
"A City is Not a Tree" (1965), 295
and American Planning Association, 319
and cellularity, 294, 297–299, 301–302, 304, 306–308, 309, 318, 323–324
and congestion, 293, 302, 318, 321, 322
Cooper, Alexander, 308–312, 319
Davis, Robert, 312–316, 319
Death and Life of Great American Cities, The (1961), 292–294, 296, 308
Duany, Andrés, 312–318
Eckstut, Stanton, 308–312
introduction and definition, 290
Jacobs, Jane, 291–296, 308, 314
Krier, Léon, 299–308, 315, 317, 388
Krier, Rob, 299–301
Lindsay, John, 308–309
opposition to, 319
Planning Urban Roadway Systems (2014), 320–321
Plater-Zyberk, Elizabeth, 312–317
Residential Streets (2001), 319
and smart growth, 294, 319, 321
spacing of arterials, 320
spacing of intersections on arterials, 317, 320, 323
subnetworks optimized for travel modes, 321
Traditional Neighborhood Development (1999), 318
and traffic safety, 312, 321, 340–341
See also new urbanism
neotraditional schemes
Battery Park City (1979), 308–312, 316
Key West Naval Station redevelopment (1977), 312–313
La Villette (1976), 304–306
Luxembourg City (1978), 304–306

neotraditional schemes (*continued*)
Poundbury (1988), 305–308, 323
Seaside (1980–1983), 312–317, 319
St. Lawrence neighborhood (1975), 295–299
new urbanism, 294, 317–322
and British street-design manuals, 323
Chellman, Chester, 317–318
Congress for the New Urbanism, 317, 320–321
Designing Walkable Urban Thoroughfares (2010), 320–321
Duany, Andrés, and Elizabeth Plater-Zyberk, 317
Hall, Richard, 317
Kulash, Walter, 318–319
SmartCode (2003), 318
Spielberg, Frank, 318
New York, 47, 97, 375
Adams, Thomas. *See* Adams, Thomas
Arcade Railway, 31–32, 230, 347
Astor, John Jacob, IV. *See* Astor, John Jacob, IV
Automobile Club of America, 37, 96, 201, 203, 206
Bassett, Edward. *See* Bassett, Edward
Battery Park City, 308–312
Bel Geddes, Norman. *See* Bel Geddes, Norman
Biedermann, Louis, 51–55, 95
Bing, Alexander, 177–178, 182, 191, 230, 378
Bronx River Parkway, 205–214, 224, 249
Brooklyn parkways, 113–115, 118, 193, 198, 353, 372
Central Park, 109–113, 194, 208, 249
Clarke, Gilmore. *See* Clarke, Gilmore
Cooper, Alexander. *See* Cooper, Alexander
Corbett, Harvey Wiley. *See* Corbett, Harvey Wiley
Delano, Frederic. *See* Delano, Frederic
Downer, Jay. *See* Downer, Jay
Eckstut, Stanton, 308–312
elevated railway visions, 30
Elevator Storehouse, 83–84, 357
Ferriss, Hugh. *See* illustrators and illustration
Flagg, Ernest, 239, 249, 380
Forest Hills Gardens. *See* Forest Hills Gardens, Queens, NY
Goodrich, Ernest, 79, 87–86, 230, 238, 365
Grand Central Terminal & Terminal City, 61–68, 252
Grand Concourse, 196–197
Grant, Madison, 205–207, 212–214
Harlem River Speedway, 195–196, 373
Harriss, John, 53–55, 94–97, 249
Holland Tunnel, 77–78, 236
Improvement Commission (1904–1907), 44–45, 353
Jacobs, Jane. *See* Jacobs, Jane
Kohn, Robert. *See* Kohn, Robert
Lamb, Charles, 44, 86
Lindenthal, Gustav, 83–86, 354
Lindsay, John, 308–309
Llewellyn Park, 130–131, 363
Long Island Motor Parkway, 201–206, 208, 215, 249, 374

New York (*continued*)
Moses, Robert. *See* Moses, Robert
New York Central Railroad, 61–67, 80–81
Norton, Charles. *See* Norton, Charles
Olmsted, Frederick Law. *See* Olmsted, Frederick Law
Olmsted, Frederick Law, Jr. *See* Olmsted, Frederick Law, Jr.
Perry, Clarence. *See* Perry, Clarence
Pettit, Harry, 57–61, 354
Port of New York Authority, 74, 78, 81, 86
Queensbridge Dwellings, 185–187
Radburn. *See* Radburn, NJ
rail tunnels under Hudson River, 356
Randel, John, 21–22
Regional Plan of New York. *See* Regional Plan of New York
Roosevelt, Eleanor. *See* Roosevelt, Eleanor
Roosevelt, Franklin. *See* Roosevelt, Franklin
Route 1 Extension, 78–80, 230, 336
skyscrapers and lack of height limit, 35
Smith, Charles McKnight, 55–57, 92, 230, 354
speedways in New Jersey suburbs, 198
Speer, Alfred, 33–34, 347, 351
Stein, Clarence, 150, 177–181, 184, 246, 370
Stevens, John, 21
Thorp, Alfred, 42–45
Tripp, H. Alker, 252
Vanderbilt, William, Jr., 201–205, 206
Vaux, Calvert, 109–110, 113–118, 131, 193–195
Viele, Egbert, 31, 351
Westchester County parkways, 210–215, 220–221, 223, 230, 375
West Side Elevated Highway, 80–83, 223, 249, 252, 309–311
West Street (late 19th–early 20th cen.), 41–42, 77, 353
Wilgus, William, 61–67, 70–74, 78
World's Fair of 1939, 61, 245–251
Wright, Henry. *See* Wright, Henry
Norton, Charles, 74–75, 228–229

Olmsted, Frederick Law, 109–119, 131–133, 140, 151, 158, 193–194, 206, 333, 364
Olmsted, Frederick Law, Jr., 140, 150–152, 177, 235

Paris
Alphand, Jean Charles Adolphe, 108, 113
arcades, 25, 350
Avenue de l'Imperatrice, 106–109, 114, 360
Bonaparte, Charles-Louis Napoléon (Napoléon III), 106–108
Burnham, Daniel, 76
Cabet, Etienne, 103–106
cours la Reine, 101–102
Grands Boulevards, 102–103

Paris (*continued*)
Haussmann, Georges-Eugène (Baron Haussmann), 106–108
Hittorff, Jacques-Ignace, 107
Kérizouët, Fl. de, 16–17
La Villette competition, 304–306
Le Corbusier. *See* Le Corbusier
palemail, 101
Parc de Montretout, 128
Villa Montmorency, 129
Parker, Barry, 143–145
Paxton, Joseph, 23–25, 112–113, 130
pedestrian barriers, 235, 252–253, 343–344
pedestrian networks that traverse block interiors, 104, 130, 141–142, 148, 153, 158–172, 179–180, 259, 315
Perry, Clarence, 173–176, 178, 333
personal transporters, 345
Philadelphia, PA, 17, 184–185, 206, 291–292
Pitzman, Julius, 135–138
Plater-Zyberk, Elizabeth, 312–317
precinct. *See* cellular roadway layouts
President's Conference on Home Building and Home Ownership. *See* US city planning policy

Radburn, NJ, 148, 150, 158, 175, 176–181, 184, 186, 189, 191, 230, 248, 252, 291, 340, 370
Regent's Park, London, 110, 123–125, 127, 129, 130, 362
Regional Plan Association. *See* Regional Plan of New York
Regional Planning Association of America, 177–181, 184, 246–247, 293, 333, 370
Regional Plan of New York, 80–82, 86–88, 150, 174, 176, 182, 215, 217–218, 223, 228–231, 252, 333, 353, 370
as Regional Plan Association, 218, 246, 378
Robinson, Charles Mulford, 118, 140–142, 177
Roosevelt, Eleanor, 177, 185
Roosevelt, Franklin, 179–180, 184, 188, 212, 215–216, 222–224, 231, 246, 352

Saarinen, Eliel, 90, 172, 301–302, 304, 308
safety. *See* insular roadways: and security; traffic fatalities; traffic safety
San Francisco Bay area, CA, 113–114, 287–290
Sitte, Camillo, 91, 139–140, 152, 153, 300, 340
slum clearance. *See* demolition and population displacement
smart growth, 294, 319, 321
Stein, Clarence, 150, 177–181, 184, 246, 370
St. Louis, MO, 134–138, 177, 364
Stübben, Josef, 138
suburban sprawl, 164, 169, 172, 176, 189, 252, 270, 276
and auto industry, 242
and congestion, 338

suburban sprawl (*continued*)
 criticism of, 93, 143, 317
 Futurama, 1939 World's Fair, 248–249
 Long Island, NY (1910s–1920s), 204–205, 215
 and traffic danger, 341
 trends in US since 1990s, 321
superblocks, 344
 and Battery Park City, 308–309
 and congestion, 183, 338
 economics of, 182–183, 259
 German modernist architects, 158–172
 and guidebooks for roadway planning, 257, 259, 262
 Hampstead Garden Suburb, London, 147
 Hastings Street, Detroit, 184–186
 introduction and definition, 121
 and Jacobs, Jane, 293
 and Le Corbusier, 91–94
 Letchworth, England, 145
 Pennypack Creek Homes, Philadelphia, 184–185
 and Quarter Section Competition, 153–155
 Queensbridge Dwellings, Queens, 185–187
 Radburn, NJ, 178–180
 Regent's Park, London, 123

Toronto, Ontario, 294, 295–299
traditional neighborhood development. *See* neotraditional roadway layouts
traditional roadway layouts, 21, 62, 79, 117, 121, 133,
 142, 157, 183
 Appleyard, Donald, San Francisco study, 287–288
 corridor street, definition of, 359
 German planning (19th cen.), 138
 as inspiration for neotraditionalism, 296, 299–300,
 308, 312, 314–315
 local and through distinction, ancient to medieval,
 122–123
 opposition to, 139–140, 143–144, 152, 168, 222, 259,
 273, 352
 spacing of arterials, 270
 and traffic control in US (1910s–1920s), 232–235
 and traffic safety, 340
traffic control
 philosophy of, 232–234, 293
 replacement by market-supply philosophy, 234–235
traffic fatalities
 public anger in 1900s, 200–204
 public anger in 1920s, 234
 public anger in 1930s, 241
 public anger in 1960s, 274
 publicity about, and auto sales, 241
 and roadway-layout connectivity, 339–340
 statistics and metrics, 242–245
traffic-limited zones (in Italy), 329
traffic restraint
 and ethics, 289–290, 328
 and traffic safety, 341

traffic restraint (*continued*)
 Appleyard, Donald, 288–290
 Berkeley, CA, retrofit scheme (1975), 289–290
 Jacobs, Jane, 293
 London, retrofit schemes (1970s), 289–290
traffic safety
 and insular roadways, 142, 155, 159, 175–176, 179,
 184, 340–342
 and fast roadways, 208
 Hilberseimer, Ludwig, dendritic layouts, 168
 and hyperurbanism, 49
 and neotraditional roadway layouts, 312, 321
 and traditional and neotraditional layouts, 340–341
 and traffic restraint, 341
 See also traffic fatalities
traffic volume
 and land-use conflicts, 267, 293, 339
 and car-limited districts, 328–330
 health and social impacts of, 287–288
 Planning the Neighborhood, 260
 and roadway classification, 141, 272, 275
Tripp, H. Alker, 176, 252–255, 285, 344

UK city planning policy
 bye-laws, 143–144
 Hampstead Garden Suburb Act (1906), 145–146
 London, street barriers (late 19th cen.), 127
 park access (mid-19th cen.), 130
 precinct planning, 255
 Restriction of Ribbon Development Act (1935), 221
 street design manuals (1990s–2000s), 322–323
 superblock layouts (1919–1933), 149
 Traffic in Towns (1963), 284–287
Unwin, Raymond, 143–153, 160, 164, 169, 177, 178–
 179, 229, 252, 333, 365, 366
Urban Land Institute, 258–260, 319, 371
urban renewal. *See* demolition and population
 displacement
US city planning policy
 *1968 National Highway Functional Classification
 Manual* (1969), 272, 275–276, 278
 arterials, design of, 275, 279, 385
 Automotive Safety Foundation, city and state plans,
 263–266
 Bureau of Public Roads. *See* Bureau of Public Roads
 and cellular roadway layouts, 187–190, 225, 321–322
 Detroit and Chicago studies (1950s–1960s), 267
 Federal-Aid Highway Act of 1956, 225, 252, 266
 Federal Housing Administration, 187–191, 260, 371
 functional classification, 272, 276–280
 Interregional Highways (1944), 224–225, 336
 National Committee on Urban Transportation,
 269–271
 neotraditional roadway layouts, 318, 320–323
 parkways, federal, 213, 220–221

US city planning policy (*continued*)
  President's Conference on Home Building and Home Ownership, 181–184, 188, 371
  Public Works Administration, Housing Division, 184–186
  and Regional Plan of New York, 231
  roadway classification, 255–256, 262, 382, 383
  and Shell Oil campaign for urban freeways, 239–240
  Toll Roads and Free Roads (1939), 222–224
  urban federal-aid system, growth of, 277–279
  urban freeways, 217, 221–226, 336, 382
  urban freeways, opposition to, 225, 227, 271, 274
  urban highways, 219, 220, 377
  and vertical traffic separation, 223, 224
  and World's Fair of 1939, 246
USSR city planning, 161–164
utopianism, 25, 104–106, 230
  Arts and Crafts movement, 143, 365
  Howard, Ebenezer, 144–145, 178, 293
  Robinson, Charles Mulford, 140–141
  technological utopianism, 37–38, 40–41

Vaux, Calvert, 109–110, 113–118, 131, 193–195
Venice, CA, center walks, 142
vertical traffic separation, 334, 336
  Bronx River Parkway, 208
  change in perceived feasiblity in US (1920s–1930s), 236–237
  and congestion, 42, 238
  and cost, 230, 286
  Democracity, 1939 World's Fair, 246–247
  Grand Concourse, Bronx, 196
  and health, 12, 86, 87–88, 93, 110, 112
  impacts on surroundings, 224, 238
  and limited access, 79–82, 98, 217, 236–238
  McClintock, Miller, 235–238
  and railways, early British, 14–16
  Regional Plan of New York, 230
  Route 1 Extension, NJ, 78–80, 230, 336
  skywalk and tunnelwalk networks, 336
  and social space, 93
  as solution to downtown decline, 238
  and speed, 37–38, 79
  Stevens, John, schemes of, 21
  Streamlines (film), 248–249
  Tripp, H. Alker, 254–255
  See also commercial traffic; hyperurbanism; US city planning policy

Wagner, Martin, 158–161, 163, 167, 169–172
Washington, DC, 109, 198, 220–221, 291
Whitten, Robert, 182–183
Wilgus, William, 61–67, 70–74, 78
Wright, Henry, 137–138, 150, 169, 176–187, 288, 333, 371

zona traffico limitato (in Italy), 329

CPSIA information can be obtained
at www.ICGtesting.com
Printed in the USA
BVHW050927160220
572479BV00008B/419